FISHES OF THE GREAT BARRIER REEF

and coastal waters of Queensland

Fishes of the Great Barrier Reef

and coastal waters of Queensland

Tom C. Marshall

Government Ichthyologist 1943-1962,
Department of Harbours and Marine,
Queensland

Angus and Robertson

First published in August 1964 by

ANGUS & ROBERTSON LTD

89 Castlereagh Street, Sydney
54 Bartholomew Close, London
107 Elizabeth Street, Melbourne

Reprinted 1966

LIBRARY OF CONGRESS CATALOGUE CARD NO. 64-25698

Registered in Australia for transmission by post as a book
PRINTED IN AUSTRALIA BY HALSTEAD PRESS, SYDNEY

To my friend
GEORGE COATES
of Townsville, Queensland

This book owes its existence largely to his keen interest in collecting thousands of specimens of fishes and in painting many beautiful water-colours from the living fishes over the years.

ACKNOWLEDGMENTS

My thanks are due to the many authors from whose works illustrations have been reproduced. Their names are given in the appropriate places in the text.

I am also indebted to the Director of the Queensland Museum, Mr G. Mack, M.Sc., for his kindness in placing the Museum collections and library at my disposal for the many problems which arose during my studies.

To my friend Professor W. Stephenson, Professor of Zoology, University of Queensland, go my sincere thanks for his helpful advice at all times and for writing the foreword.

Mr G. P. Whitley, Curator of Fishes, Australian Museum, Sydney, has also been of great assistance over the long period of time taken in the preparation of this book, and my thanks are due to him and to Dr J. W. Evans, Director of the Museum, who made available certain illustrations in early works.

Dr G. F. Humphrey, Chief of the Division of Fisheries, C.S.I.R.O., very kindly prepared the many reproductions from Bleeker's Atlas.

I am deeply indebted to my friend Mr George Coates of Townsville for the beautiful water-colour illustrations in my book, which is dedicated to him. His keen interest in collecting and forwarding some thousands of specimens of fishes and in executing hundreds of water-colour drawings from the living fishes over many years has enabled me to illustrate some of the most colourful of the Queensland fishes as they appear in life, though I could include only a comparative few of the drawings that he did for me.

Lastly, I am really grateful to the many other kind persons—too numerous to mention but none the less important—who helped to make possible the production of this book.

TOM C. MARSHALL

FOREWORD

To a marine biologist who is interested in fish and who has been born and bred near the cold waters of Britain, the fish of Queensland are fascinating. During the years I have been in Queensland my main relaxations—as well as my more serious scientific research—have been near, on, or in the cool blue waters of Queensland. I have angled for fish, netted fish, speared fish, and observed fish under water.

At first all the species were new to me, and there was as much novelty in a tarwhine or a flathead as there was in anything else. That phase passed and soon I was asking "What fish is that?" Neighbouring anglers seemed as ignorant as I was, which is not surprising, for not only is there a bewildering variety of fish in Queensland waters, but there is always the possibility of the next capture being something odd.

Through the years I have frequently been a nuisance to my good friend Mr Tom Marshall in calling for his assistance when naming my captures. With a lifetime of experience and an excellent museum collection behind him, he has been able to give this assistance in a most accurate and immediate fashion.

There have been occasions, especially when one has been distant from Brisbane, when it has been impossible to call upon Mr Marshall for help, and one then had two alternatives: the first was to carry round a small library of books and attempt the identification oneself. The second was to destroy the evidence by either eating it or returning it to the sea. The appearance of Mr Marshall's book alters all this. By referring to a single volume one ought to be able to identify all but an extremely small number of the marine fish of Queensland. To the layman this will be an important boon. No longer will the self-appointed authority invent a name on the spot and carry the day: he should be able to give the correct name, and if he does not he can be put right.

To the scientist the book will be equally invaluable. The time-consuming checking of literature and extraction of relevant data has been done, and the way is clear for further studies on food, movements, behaviour, and other aspects of the subject. Having done this type of work upon marine organisms I can appreciate better than most how much solid and scholarly work has gone between the covers of this book. It is a credit not only to Mr Marshall himself but also to his Department and to the State.

No piece of scientific work is ever complete. Mr Marshall knows better than anyone that his book on the Queensland fishes will remain incomplete until every species in Queensland waters has been accounted for. Many have never yet been collected. But now that we know what to expect, we can more readily appreciate the novelty of our catches, and can build upon sure foundations.

W. STEPHENSON

Professor of Zoology, University of Queensland

13th November 1962

PREFACE

ABOUT 1,500 species of fishes are known from the marine and the numerous fresh waters of Queensland. Among them are rare fish that have not been seen since they were first described, but many of the species are commonly seen not only in these waters but in other parts of Australia, in countries as far away as Africa, the Philippines, India, and Japan, and in numerous other localities. Identification is difficult without access to an extensive library, for the literature is scattered throughout hundreds of volumes and is in several languages. The main purpose of this book is to bring together the essential information in such a way that anyone will be able to study and to identify any fish of the Great Barrier Reef or the coastal waters of Queensland.

Because of space limitations it has not been possible to fully describe and illustrate every species, but complete keys have been provided, one or more of each genus has been written up and illustrated, and descriptions sufficient for identification have been provided for the remaining species. The classification adopted is mainly that of Dr C. Tate Regan, F.R.S., who gives a full diagnosis of the orders and sub-orders in his articles on Selacians, Fishes, etc., in the fourteenth edition of the *Encyclopaedia Britannica* (1929).

The fishes of Queensland, especially those of the northern parts of the State, are typical of the fishes inhabiting the great area known to zoologists as the Indo-Pacific or Oriental Zone. A number of these species extend their range southward along the Queensland coastline as stragglers as far south as Caloundra, there to meet and mingle with southern stragglers ranging northwards from the cooler waters of New South Wales; others frequent the sandy shallow bays and beaches or muddy areas in the mangrove-lined rivers along the coast; but by far the greater number of the Queensland species live among the coral reefs bordering the coast or inhabit the clear blue pelagic waters outside the reefs.

The Great Barrier Reef extends along almost the entire coastline of Queensland and is the largest coral formation in the world. From a point about 250 miles from the Queensland-New South Wales border it runs north almost to the shores of New Guinea, a distance of about 1,260 statute miles. Although it does not present an unbroken barrier to the rollers from the south Pacific Ocean (despite its name it is not one continuous reef but a vast collection of coral reefs, outcrops, and islands) it forms an effective breakwater that protects the inside coastal waters. The coral islands of the reefs are typical coral cays, there being no atolls within the Great Barrier Reef.

It is only to be expected that such a mass of reefs, with their rich coral growths, molluscs, and thousands of other marine animals, should be the happy hunting grounds of teeming millions of little fishes which in their turn attract millions of larger fishes. In fact we have in the Great Barrier Reef, which stretches from the temperate regions far into the tropics, a richness of marine fauna greater than that contained in any other area of a similar size in the world.

TOM C. MARSHALL

HOW TO USE THIS BOOK

To assist the reader in separating the many families, genera, and species of fishes contained in the text, artificial keys have been inserted. Suppose that identification of a shark is required; as an example, take the order Selachii (Sharks) and turn to the Key to families on page 5. Look at the first letter of the alphabet and its similar double. Here there are two alternatives:

A.   Dorsal fins with fixed spines.

AA.   No dorsal spines.

Suppose the shark that is to be identified is without dorsal spines: the lack of them means that for the purposes of identification the item lettered A, leading to the family Heterodontidae, is eliminated. We now proceed to the next single and double letters of the alphabet:

b.   Eyes with nictitating membranes.

bb.   Eyes without nictitating membranes.

Having made ourselves familiar with the term "nictitating membrane" in the Glossary on page 519 as meaning an inner eyelid, we examine the shark and find that the eyes have such membranes. We can now proceed to the next letter and its double:

c.   Head normally formed.

cc.   Head hammer- or kidney-shaped.

The head of our shark being normally formed, the letters cc are ignored, together with the family Sphyrnidae to which they lead, and we now come to:

d.   Functional teeth upstanding, triangular, and compressed, or tricuspid.

dd.   Teeth flattened, in bands or pavements.

The shark to be identified may have the teeth described under d, in which case we would know that it belongs to the family Galeidae, which comprises the true sharks. We now turn to page 7 and there we see a key to the genera contained within that family. The same method of elimination is followed until the genus the creature belongs to has been established, then we follow to the final key, namely that to the species in that genus.

The species are then described. First comes the species number, then the common or vernacular name, the scientific name, and the author's name. Sometimes the name of the author is in parentheses, e.g., *Heterodontus portus-*

jacksoni (Meyer). In this case the original author of the species *portusjacksoni* was Meyer but he placed it in a different genus from that which is now accepted, and the brackets are put round his name to indicate this. (Meyer actually described this fish as *Squalis portusjacksoni*.) The plate on which the species is illustrated in this book is then indicated in square brackets. In the next line is the reference to the author's original description, with the publication where it was described, and following is either an acknowledgment to the publication from which the illustration was copied or an indication of the new illustrator's name. Other common names given to the species are listed, then a rough description and colour notes, and finally notes on habits, distribution, size, and other features. The sizes given in the legends are of the actual specimens illustrated, not the lengths to which the fish grow. Many fishes exhibit great colour variation though their patterns may remain fairly constant. In most of the colour notes I have referred to the colours exhibited in life or at least soon after death.

A glossary of technical terms is included at the end of the book, but there are certain words and phrases used in the descriptions of fish which require amplification here. Unless otherwise specified, "length" applies to the total length of the fish—that is, it is measured from the extreme tip of the snout to the extreme tip of the tail fin. Abbreviations for fin-ray and scale counts are frequently used; taking the Common Bream, *Mylio australis*, as an example, we shall now explain these abbreviations:

D. 10-12/10-13   The *dorsal fin* consists of ten to twelve spines, and from ten to thirteen soft rays.

A. 3/8-10   The *anal fin* consists of three spines and from eight to ten soft rays.

L. 1. 47-58   The number of scales along the length of the *lateral line* varies forty-seven to fifty-eight.

L. tr. 4-6/11-15   The *transverse scale count* is from four to six above the lateral line, and from eleven to fifteen below it.

In some formulae certain other terms are used, as, for instance, C, P, and V for the caudal, pectoral, and ventral fin counts respectively. D1 signifies the first dorsal fin, and D2 the second.

CONTENTS

ILLUSTRATIONS

COLOUR PLATES

BLACK-AND-WHITE PLATES

Class **ELASMOBRANCHII: SHARKS, RAYS,** and **GHOST SHARKS**

Class ELASMOBRANCHII: SHARKS, RAYS, and GHOST SHARKS

THE sharks and rays differ greatly from the teliosts or true bony fishes in many features, the most outstanding being their lack of a bony skeleton. The differences are as follows:

A. Skeleton cartilaginous. Skull without sutures and membrane bones (opercles, suborbital ring, etc.). Males with paired appendages or claspers.　　SHARKS and RAYS

AA. Skeleton bony. Skull with sutures and membrane bones. Males without paired appendages or claspers.　　BONY FISHES

Sub-class PLAGIOSTOMI: SHARKS and RAYS
(CARTILAGINOUS FISHES)

Because of their general structure the sharks and rays are classed together, though the rays are so unlike sharks in general that their affinities are not usually recognized. They agree in that they have no bones, the skeleton being composed entirely of cartilage, the surface of which, although usually calcified, does not exhibit the character of true bone. They lack typical scales, the skin being covered with tooth-like structures, closely set to form a hard armour. This sandpaper-like surface, known as shagreen, is extremely tough and difficult to penetrate. There are no gill-covers, and, with few exceptions, five gill-slits open on each side of the body. Many of the sharks and rays have, in addition to the gill-slits, a hole situated near the eye. This orifice, known as a spiracle, enables the animal to breathe whilst feeding, or, as in the case of the rays, when the mouth, which is situated on the under-surface, is covered in sand or mud.

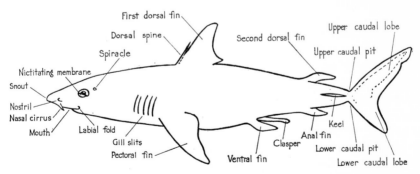

FIG. 1. The principal features of an imaginary shark. No one species exhibits all the characters illustrated. F. OLSEN.

Unlike ordinary fishes the sharks and rays produce large ova or egg-cells which are fertilized by copulation. In some species these undergo development within the body of the parent until hatched, so that the young are born alive, or they are deposited in a horny egg-case and attached by tendrils to sub-merged objects until hatched. The following key serves to separate the sharks from the rays:

A.   Gill-openings on sides. Pectoral fins free from head.   SELACHII

AA.   Gill-openings on under-surface. Pectoral fins attached
     to head. No anal fin.   BATOIDEI

Order SELACHII: SHARKS

The sharks represent the most primitive known type of jaw-bearing vertebrate. They are the aristocrats of the fish world, their lineage dating back to the Upper Devonian or Lower Carboniferous periods. Their remains, in the form of teeth and fin-spines, are found in the deposits of those periods down to the present day. Teeth almost 6 inches long which have been dredged from the ocean's depths belonged to one of these recently extinct sharks, the length of which has been estimated at not less than 90 feet (see Plate 1). The White Pointer, *Carcharodon carcharias*, a descendant of this giant of the past, lives in Australian seas today. It attains a length of over 40 feet and is a fierce and dangerous species.

Although found in their greatest numbers in tropical and subtropical seas, sharks also frequent temperate regions, while certain species are known even from the Arctic and Antarctic regions.

Most of the sharks are large, powerful, active, and fast-swimming, catching their prey, which consists mainly of fishes, by their great strength and activity. Some, however, are feeble swimmers, small and toothless. The active types, such as the blue pointer or mackerel shark, pursue and catch fast-swimming fishes, while the sluggish wobbegongs lie in wait for passing fishes or forage for offal. Others with blunt pavement-like teeth seek out shellfish which they crush and feed upon. The mighty basking and whale sharks, which grow to 40 and 60 feet respectively, feed like whales on the minute organisms known as cope-pods. There is little doubt that the sense of smell is highly developed in the sharks, and flesh, blood or putrefying carcasses will always attract them.

The teeth of a shark are not fixed into sockets but are attached to a band which is continually growing forward: the teeth at the rear, which are in a recumbent position, moving forward and becoming upright and functional as those in front are shed.

The sharks and rays will some day lay the foundation of an important industry in Queensland. They frequent our seas in countless numbers, cost nothing to bring to maturity, and only await an enterprising company to convert them from pests and menaces to valuable articles of commerce. There is a ready market for sharks' fins in the East, where they are valued and used in soup-making. The livers yield great quantities of good oil which is used for many purposes; a 13-foot tiger shark has a liver weighing no less than 275 pounds. Valuable high-grade leather may be made from the hides; and from the intestines a soft leather, the equivalent of chamois, is obtained. The flesh makes excellent meal for fattening pigs, calves, etc., or for use in fertilizer manufacture, while marine glue and various other by-products are obtained from the residue.

Eight families of sharks occur in Queensland waters. They may be readily separated.

KEY TO FAMILIES REPRESENTED IN QUEENSLAND

A.   Dorsal fins with fixed spines.   HETERODONTIDAE

AA. No dorsal spines.

    b. Eyes with nictitating membranes.
      c. Head normally formed.
        d. Functional teeth upstanding, triangular and compressed, or tricuspid.   GALEIDAE
        dd. Teeth flattened, in bands or pavements.   MUSTELIDAE
      cc. Head hammer- or kidney-shaped.   SPHYRNIDAE
    bb. Eyes without nictitating membranes.
      e. First dorsal over or behind ventrals.   ORECTOLOBIDAE
      ee. First dorsal more or less in advance of ventrals.
        f. Caudal peduncle without lateral keels.
          g. Tail very long, more than half total length.   ALOPIIDAE
          gg. Tail normal, less than half total length.   CARCHARIIDAE
        ff. Caudal peduncle with lateral keels.   ISURIDAE

Family **Heterodontidae: Port Jackson Sharks**

The Port Jackson sharks are small species, commonly found in the shallow waters of the southern half of Australia. The fixed spine set in front of each dorsal fin is sufficient to identify them by, apart from their peculiar teeth. The anterior teeth are pointed and conical, whilst the posterior ones are flattened and almost molar-like, a few rows being very large, but finally becoming small posteriorly.

These sharks grow to a length of only 4 feet and are harmless to man. Their food consists of shellfish, sea-urchins, and crabs, which they seize with their front teeth and pass back to the rear crushing-teeth. In Tasmanian waters they are pests on the oyster-banks, where they destroy many of those valuable shellfish. The females deposit curious egg-cases encircled with a double spiral flange.

Two species belonging to different genera are found in Australian waters, but others inhabit the seas of Japan and America.

KEY TO GENERA IN QUEENSLAND

A. Supraorbital ridges gradually decreasing in height posteriorly. Enlarged lateral teeth without distinct keels. *Heterodontus*

AA. Supraorbital ridges ending abruptly posteriorly. Enlarged lateral teeth with distinct keels. *Gyropleurodus*

1. PORT JACKSON SHARK *Heterodontus portusjacksoni* (Meyer) [Plate 2]

Squalis portusjacksoni Meyer, Zool. Entdeck., 1793. (Based on Port Jackson Shark figured in Phillip's Voyage, 1789, p. 166, pl. 42.)
Heterodontus portusjacksoni Whitley, Mem. Qld Mus., 10, pt 4, 1934, p. 181, pl. 27, fig. A.
Heterodontus philippi Waite, Fish. Sth Austr., 1923, p. 25 (teeth only).

Bulldog Shark, Bullhead (New South Wales); Tabigaw (New South Wales aborigines); Pigfish (Victoria); Oyster-crusher (Tasmania).

Anterior teeth pointed, often cusped for seizing prey, those posteriorly with rounded surfaces without keels. Colour light brownish or greyish, with blackish harness-like stripes on body and broad blackish bar below eye; dark blotch on snout.

Included as a Queensland species on the record of Saville Kent, who noted it from Moreton Bay. Not seen alive, though its egg-cases are occasionally washed up on the beaches of southern Queensland. Inhabits the waters of South Queensland, New South Wales, Victoria, and South Australia, being most common in the southernmost States. Grows to 4½ feet. Harmless. Feeds upon molluscs, crustaceans, etc.

2. CRESTED PORT JACKSON SHARK *Gyropleurodus galeatus* (Günther) [Plate 2]

Cestracion galeatus Günther, Cat. Fish. Brit. Mus., 8, 1870, p. 416.
Molochophrys galeatus Whitley, Mem. Qld Mus., 10, pt. 4, 1934, p. 182, pl. 27, fig. B.

Teeth cuspidate anteriorly, hinder ones attenuated and keeled. Colour: "Light brownish. Interorbital region and back in front of dorsal fin blackish; a broad blackish bar below the eye; back with some dark transverse bars, one at base of each dorsal fin most prominent, but not joining to form a 'harness'. Sometimes becomes stained a reddish colour on teeth or skin apparently through eating the large Purple Sea Urchins, *Centrostephanus rodgersii*, of our harbours." (Whitley.)

The record of this shark in Queensland waters has been based mainly on its cast-up egg-cases, the adults being seldom seen. The curious spiral-flanged egg-cases are provided with long tendrils, and according to Whitley the period of incubation is at least five months. Found in littoral waters of New South Wales to 50 fathoms. Grows to 4 feet. Harmless.

Family **Galeidae: True Sharks**

This family constitutes the largest group of the existing sharks and is represented in almost all seas. Many of the members attain a large size and are dangerous to man. One exotic species is unique in that it is confined to fresh water.

In these sharks the body is elongate, the head depressed, of normal shape, the snout depressed and rounded to pointed when viewed from above, projecting beyond the crescent-shaped mouth. Spiracle small or obsolete. The eyes are provided with a nictitating membrane or third eyelid which can be drawn over the eye from below. There are two dorsal fins, the first short, elevated, and entirely before the ventrals; the second is small, opposite the anal. The caudal peduncle is without keels.

The teeth are the principal character in determining the many species which are brought forth alive and in large numbers (as many as 57 have been taken from a female Tiger Shark).

The family is represented in Queensland waters by ten genera, comprising at least fifteen species, among them being the tiger shark and the blue sharks, which latter include the well-known whalers.

KEY TO GENERA IN QUEENSLAND

A. Spiracles present, though minute.

    b. A conspicuous pit above root of tail.

       c. Teeth serrated and oblique in both jaws. Body with tiger-like stripes, especially in the young.   *Galeocerdo*

       cc. Teeth serrated and oblique in upper jaw only, lower erect. Coloration uniform.   *Hemigaleus*

    bb. No pit at root of tail.   *Galeorhinus*

AA. Spiracles absent.

    d. Teeth serrated on cusps or bases, or both and in one or both jaws.

       e. Teeth tricuspid in both jaws. Dorsal and caudal lobes white-tipped.   *Triaenodon*

       ee. No tricuspid teeth. Dorsal and caudal lobes not white-tipped.

     f. Teeth in upper jaw oblique, serrated on one base
       more strongly than on the other, in lower jaw
       curved, slender, not serrated.   *Platypodon*

    ff. Teeth serrated on both cusps and bases, their
      form variable.   *Eulamia*

   fff. Teeth serrated at bases only, in one or both
      jaws, cusps smooth.   *Rhizoprionodon*

  dd. Teeth everywhere smooth, both base and cusp.

    g. Teeth erect or nearly so.   *Aprionodon*

    gg. Teeth oblique, bases swollen; upper jaw with a
       median, unpaired tooth.   *Physodon*

    ggg. Teeth oblique, bases not swollen; lower jaw
       with a median unpaired tooth.   *Scoliodon*

Galeocerdo

Body robust, rather elongate, deepening with age. Head depressed. Snout short, wide, rounded. Mouth crescentic, large. Teeth alike in both jaws, oblique, more or less triangular, compressed, edges strongly serrated and edges of denticles serrated, outer edge deeply notched. Small spiracle present. Nictitating membrane present. Caudal with notch at its base, both above and below. Second dorsal and anal small.

    Large and fierce sharks of tropical seas, the young being barred and striped, becoming uniform with age. Species few, one in Queensland.

3. TIGER SHARK *Galeocerdo cuvier* (Peron and Lesueur)   [Plate 3]

Squalus cuvier Peron and Lesueur, Journ. Acad. Nat. Sci. Philad., 2, 1822, p. 351.
Illustration by G. Coates.

    The Tiger Shark is a fierce and dangerous species which attains a length of over 20 feet. It is widely distributed in tropical and temperate seas. In Queensland it is commonly caught in the rivers and bays. When young it is whitish in colour, with very conspicuous dark-blue tiger-like stripes. These fade out in the adults, which become bluish-grey or greenish above and exhibit only the faintest trace of dark spots and bars, seen more clearly whilst the creature is in the water.

    This shark may be readily recognized by its blunt head and by the serrated oblique teeth in many rows in both jaws. Spiracles are present, though minute, and there is a conspicuous pit above the root of the tail.

Hemigaleus

Body slender. Head depressed, flattened below. Snout tapering. Mouth with distinct labial folds. Upper teeth oblique, with denticles on their bases at outer edges; lower teeth erect, the cusps narrow, on wide bases and without denticles.

Small sharks frequenting the western Pacific and tropical parts of the Indian Ocean. Species few, one in Queensland.

4. WEASEL SHARK *Hemigaleus microstoma* Bleeker [Plate 3]

Hemigaleus microstoma Bleeker, Verh. Bat. Gen., 24, 1852, p. 46, pl. 2, fig. 9.
Illustration by F. Olsen after Whitley.

Teeth in upper jaw oblique, strongly serrated on their outer margins; those in lower jaw much smaller, narrow, erect, and not serrated, their bases broad; symphysial teeth smaller than lateral ones. Colour silvery-grey, white below.

An East Indian species now recorded from North Queensland, where it was first captured by G. Coates at Salamander Rocks, off Townsville. Grows to at least 28 inches. Harmless.

Galeorhinus

Body slender, elongate. Head depressed. Snout obtuse, depressed. Mouth crescentic, wide, with short labial fold on each jaw. Teeth alike in jaws, oblique, compressed, subtriangular, notched, outwardly inclined, with coarse serrations between notch and base. Spiracle small. Nictitating membrane present.

Smooth sharks of large to small size found in most warm seas. The genus includes the American Soup-fin Shark, *G. zyopterus*. The livers of these sharks are rich in vitamins. One species in Queensland.

5. SCHOOL SHARK *Galeorhinus australis* (Macleay) [Plate 4]

Galeus australis Macleay, Proc. Linn. Soc. N.S.Wales, 6, pt 2, 1881, p. 354.
Galeorhinus australis McCulloch, Proc. Linn. Soc. N.S.Wales, 46, 1921, p. 459, pl. 37, figs 5-7.
Galeus australis Waite, Fish Sth Austr., 1923, p. 29 (teeth).
Illustration of embryo by F. Olsen after Whitley.

Tope (New South Wales); Snapper Shark (Victoria).

Teeth acute, depressed, and coarsely serrated. Colour slaty-purplish, light bluish-grey or brownish above, much lighter below; fins without dark marks.

Not known to be dangerous to man. Allied American species are known as oil sharks or soup-fin sharks and are valued for their fins, which are used for soups, and for the livers, which yield oil. The School Shark grows to over 6 feet. It is viviparous. It occasionally straggles northwards to Moreton Bay from southern waters. The species is also found in New South Wales, Victoria, Tasmania, South Australia, and New Zealand.

Triaenodon

Body slender, tapering to head and tail. Head wide, blunt, depressed. Mouth wide, greatly arched, labial folds rudimentary. Nictitating membrane present. Teeth small, even, and numerous, with a strong central cusp and 1 to 2 small lateral cusps. Caudal with a pit at root above. One species in Queensland.

6. WHITE-TIP SHARK *Triaenodon apicalis* Whitley   [Plate 4]

Triaenodon apicalis Whitley, Austr. Zool., 9, pt 3, 1939, p. 236, fig. **9.**
Illustration by F. Olsen after Whitley.

Teeth of moderate size and similar in both jaws, backwardly directed, each with 3 entire, acute cusps, the central one longest. Colour: "Greyish to brownish-grey, tinged pinkish on parts of head and body; the darkest grey is on the back, and the belly is a whitish-grey. Eye blue. All dorsal and caudal lobes with conspicuous milky-white tips; anterior edges of fins dusky. Some irregular dusky blotches on and near ventral fins." (Whitley.)

A small tropical species known by its tricuspid teeth and the white fin-tips. The largest examples known are 44 inches, but an unidentified species over 6 feet in length with white fin-tips has been seen and is perhaps this shark. The White-tip Shark is known from North Queensland and the Northern Territory.

Platypodon

7. COATES' SHARK *Platypodon coatesi* Whitley   [Plate 4]

Platypodon coatesi Whitley, Austr. Zool., 9, pt 3, 1939, p. 234. fig. 7.
Illustration by G. Coates.

Teeth in upper jaw more strongly serrated on one base than on the other, but the cusp may be minutely serrate or entire; teeth in lower jaw slender, curved, entire, end sloping outwards. Colour: "Satiny grey above with a violaceous tinge on fins. A dark brown blotch on anterior half of second dorsal fin. Whitish below." (Whitley.)

A handsome shark first known from examples captured by G. Coates at Cape Cleveland, North Queensland. Length 31 inches.

Eulamia: Blue Sharks

Body somewhat robust, shapely. Head depressed, normal shape. Mouth inferior, curved forward, labial folds rudimentary or short. Teeth somewhat triangular, with large, erect cusps, strongly serrated, more so in the adults. Nictitating membrane present. Spiracles absent. A notch at base of tail above. First dorsal large, not far behind pectorals. Second dorsal small.

Many species of blue sharks are known from the warm seas of the world, one of them, the Great Blue Shark, *Glyphis glaucus*, attaining to 25 feet. Many others reach a length of 10 and 15 feet, and all are fierce and voracious, with insatiable appetites. Although these sharks are denizens of the open seas, the juveniles frequently penetrate to the upper reaches of the rivers, far beyond the brackish water.

On the reefs the blue sharks are pests to the line fishermen, for they take up a position under the boat and methodically snap off each fish as it is being hauled up, leaving the heads only.

In many species correct identification is very difficult without the aid of full and complete descriptions.

KEY TO SPECIES IN QUEENSLAND

A. Snout moderate, rather pointed; second dorsal smaller than anal, the origins of both fins opposite; preoral length greater than width of mouth, which is wider than long; tail as long as head and trunk. Colour greyish. *macrura*

B. Snout moderately rounded, more flattened above and below, not acute. (Probably only a form of *E. macrura.*) Colour bright bronze. *ahenea*

C. Snout pointed; second dorsal somewhat smaller than anal, the origins opposite; preoral length less than width of mouth, which is more than twice as wide as long; tail shorter than head and trunk. *amblyrhynchoides*

D. Snout short, bluntly rounded; second dorsal origin opposite to or varying before or after anal origin, the two fins equal in size. Colour fawnish or brownish; fins black-tipped. *spallanzani*

E. Snout broad, rounded; second dorsal slightly smaller than anal, its origin slightly in advance of anal origin; preoral length only half width of mouth, which is wider than long. Colour grey to bluish above, lighter below. *lamia*

8. WHALER SHARK *Eulamia macrura* (Ramsay and Ogilby) [Plate 5]

Carcharias macrurus Ramsay and Ogilby, Proc. Linn. Soc. N.S.Wales (2), 2, 1887, p. 163, 1024.
Carcharhinus macrurus McCulloch, Proc. Linn. Soc. N.S.Wales, 46, 1921, p. 457, pl. 37, figs 1-4.

Common Whaler, Black Whaler, Cocktail (New South Wales).

Teeth serrated in both jaws, those in upper jaw being triangular, oblique laterally, broad based, and notched on outer edges; teeth in lower jaw erect and smaller; nostrils nearer to mouth than to end of snout. Mouth one-third longer than wide; a very short groove extends forward on each side near the posterior angle. Colour sandy to dark grey above, whitish below; sometimes with a trace of a narrow, darker longitudinal stripe along each side; tips of fins often dusky.

A large and dangerous shark which attains a length of 12 feet and a weight of at least 890 pounds. It frequents rivers, harbours, and also outside waters of Queensland and New South Wales. The young are born alive, and as many as forty have been taken from one female. The common name was apparently bestowed in the early days of New South Wales by the men of the whaling industry at Twofold Bay, where these sharks were always noticed in the vicinity of the whales.

9. BRONZE WHALER *Eulamia ahenea* Stead

Eulamia ahenea Stead, Austr. Nat., 10, pt 2, 1938, p. 98.
Galeolamna ahenea Whitley, Fish. Austr., pt 1, Sharks, 1940, p. 100, fig. 93.

Teeth in both jaws with broad bases, those in lower jaw with the cusps very narrow; much broader in upper jaw but considerably narrower than in the true Whaler, *E. macrura*.

According to Whitley this shark has the "Body rather more rounded than in the ordinary Whaler and snout rather more flattened above and below." Probably only a form of *E. macrura*. In life the colour of this shark is a bright bronze or the colour of a new penny.

The Bronze Whaler inhabits the open sea off the coasts of South Queensland and New South Wales. A popular shark with the big-game clubs, whose members capture it on light tackle, it is an active and strong fighter when hooked. Grows to at least 9 feet in length and over 700 pounds in weight.

10. GRACEFUL SHARK *Eulamia amblyrhynchoides* (Whitley) [Plate 5]

Gillisqualis amblyrhynchoides Whitley, Mem. Qld Mus., 10, pt 4, 1934, p. 189, text-fig. 4.
Illustration by F. Olsen after Whitley.

Teeth compressed, erect, and serrated in both jaws, those in the lower more minutely so. Colour coppery, with a bluish tinge above and on fins; white below; under-surface of pectorals white, the apex blackish; ventral and caudal edged blackish.

A common shark in the waters of North Queensland. Grows to at least 24 inches, probably much more.

11. BLACK-TIP SHARK *Eulamia spallanzani* (Le Sueur) [Plate 5]

Squalis spallanzani Le Sueur, Journ. Acad. Nat. Sci. Philad., 2, Nov. 1822, p. 351.
Mapolamia spallanzani Whitley, Fish. Austr. pt 1, Sharks, 1940, p. 94, fig. 89.

Jervis Bay Shark (Townsville).

Teeth finely serrated with age, edges nearly or quite smooth in the young; bases broad, upper cusps broadly triangular, with tips somewhat attenuated;

inner edges almost straight, outer edges deeply notched; lower cusps narrower and more erect.

One of the commonest sharks on the reefs, and a pest to line fishermen on the Great Barrier Reef. Often seen swimming along with its black-tipped fins out of the water. It ranges from Queensland to the Northern Territory and north-western Australia and is also found in New Guinea. It is wide-ranging outside Australia. Grows to at least 10 feet.

12. ESTUARY SHARK *Eulamia lamia* (Blainville)   [Plate 5]

Squalis lamia Blainville, Faune Française, Poissons, 1820, p. 88, pl. 22, fig. C.
Carcharias gangeticus Day, Fish. India, 1878, p. 715, pl. 187, fig. 1.

Blue Shark (Brisbane and Rockhampton districts).

Teeth triangular, serrated, those in upper jaw broad, slightly inclined in front, but more so towards angles of mouth and outer ones with their outer edges more indented; teeth in lower jaw erect, narrower, the bases wide, edges serrated and deeply indented above bases; symphysial teeth small; origin of first dorsal opposite posterior edge of pectoral base; anal origin slightly behind second dorsal origin. Colour greyish to bluish above, lighter below. Usually the tips of the second dorsal, caudal and pectorals are darker.

This ferocious shark is found along the coasts and in the estuaries of south and middle Queensland. It commonly enters the rivers, chasing schools of fishes well beyond the tideway. Grows to at least 7 feet. Wide-ranging. In India it is known to attack bathers; in instances of shark attacks in Queensland rivers no doubt the blame could more often be attributed to this species if identification were made.

Rhizoprionodon

Spiracles absent. Teeth serrated at bases only, in one or both jaws, cusps smooth. One species in Queensland.

13. LITTLE BLUE SHARK *Rhizoprionodon palasorrah* (Cuvier)   [Plate 5]

Carcharias palasorrah Cuvier, Règne Animal., 2nd ed., vol. 2, 1829, p. 388.
Carcharias acutus Day, Fish. India, 1878, p. 712, pl. 184, fig. 3.

Dog Shark, Lesser Blue Shark (South Africa).

Teeth in jaws similar, in 25-26 rows, oblique, with smooth median cusps, their outer bases finely serrated, the cusps smooth; second dorsal origin above middle of anal base or its posterior end. Colour bluish-grey or grey-brown above, with light hind margin to pectoral fins; belly whitish.

The most common of small sharks on the Queensland coast. Found also in New South Wales, where it has been trawled down to 73 fathoms. In northern areas it ranges into the waters of the Northern Territory and the Indo-Pacific region. Wide-ranging. Harmless. Grows to 4 feet.

Aprionodon

Small sharks of tropical and temperate seas, with broad-based, compressed teeth, the edges of which are smooth and the cusps narrow and erect. Two species are found in Queensland.

KEY TO SPECIES IN QUEENSLAND

A. Snout elongate, acute; second dorsal smaller than anal.   *brevipinna*

AA. Snout short and broad; second dorsal larger than anal.   *acutidens*

14. SMOOTH-FANGED SHARK *Aprionodon brevipinna* (Müller and Henle)
[Plate 6]

Carcharias (Aprion) brevipinna Müller and Henle, Plagiost., 1841, p. 31, pl. 9.
Illustration by F. Olsen after Müller and Henle.

Teeth nearly erect in upper jaw, their bases broad, not notched and without serrations on base or cusp; teeth in lower jaw smaller, more narrow, erect, with broad bases, wider spaced, acute and without serrations; second dorsal fin originating somewhat behind anal origin, smaller than anal; gill-slits wide.

Colour greyish-blue or greyish-brown above, white below; an indistinct band along the side near middle of body; eye bluish.

A small East Indian shark which frequents the waters of North Queensland. Also found in Japan and Arabia. Grows to at least 32 inches.

15. SHARP-TOOTHED SHARK *Aprionodon acutidens* (Rüppell)   [Plate 6]

Carcharias acutidens Rüppell, Neue Wirbelth., Abyssin., Fische, 1837, p. 65.
Illustration by F. Olsen after Whitley.

Teeth entire, bases broad, smooth on both base and cusp; the cusps erect, narrow, and lanceolate; second dorsal fin a little longer than anal, its origin a little before that of anal. Colour greyish-brown above, whitish below.

A species which grows to over 6 feet, the smaller ones moving about in schools. It is readily recognized by its smooth, erect teeth and by the features of the second dorsal as described above. Found in Queensland, North Australia, and Micronesia, through the East Indies to India, the Red Sea, and Arabia.

Physodon

Small sharks with slender, elongate, and compressed bodies and with long depressed heads and long snouts. The teeth are oblique, notched and without serrations, small in the mandible medianally, becoming larger laterally, their bases swollen and rounded. There is a small median unpaired tooth in the upper jaw. Found in the seas of India, China, and Australia. Two species, one in Queensland.

16. TAYLOR'S SHARK *Physodon taylori* Ogilby [Plate 6]

Physodon taylori Ogilby, Mem. Qld Mus., 3, 1915, p. 117.
Illustration by F. Olsen after Whitley.

Teeth stout; oblique, notched, with swollen, rounded bases, those in upper jaw with tips straight, in lower jaw with tips bent slightly inwards; lower jaw without, upper jaw with, a median unpaired tooth; snout short; small labial folds in upper jaw and grooves in lower; second dorsal and anal fins low and with long points; origin of anal in advance of second dorsal, the length of its base being almost twice that of second dorsal. Colour bluish-grey or fawnish-grey above, paler below, the two colours fairly sharply defined; fins tinged vinous and blue.

A common shark of small size found in the coastal waters of Queensland and the Northern Territory. It is commonly taken in mackerel nets set by the fishermen at Deception Bay in South Queensland during the winter months. As many as eight hundred have been taken from the nets of a single fisherman in the one night, but the average is about three hundred per night. Grows to about 33 inches.

Scoliodon

A genus of small sharks inhabiting temperate and tropical seas. They have the form of *Eulamia* but are distinguished from them mainly by the teeth, which are without serrations on both base and cusp. One species in Queensland.

17. JORDAN'S BLUE DOG SHARK *Scoliodon jordani* Ogilby [Plate 6]

Scoliodon jordani Ogilby, Proc. Roy. Soc. Qld, 21, 1908, p. 88.
Illustration by G. Coates.

Teeth quite smooth on both base and cusp, none enlarged, their bases narrow and with the points deflected outwards; lower jaw with a single median tooth; outer labial fold very short and directed outwards at a right angle to jaw; no inner groove; first dorsal nearer to ventral than to pectoral; second dorsal inserted wholly behind anal. Colour dark bluish-grey above, grey below; pectoral and ventral fins with their outer edges ashy-grey; iris white.

Another small and fairly common Queensland shark which ranges from inshore waters down to 25 fathoms. Grows to 36 inches.

Family **Mustelidae: Gummy Sharks**

Slender sharks, with head and body nearly as long as tail. Head wide, short and depressed, tapering in front to long, depressed snout. Eye large, with nictitating membrane. Mouth crescentic, labial folds well developed. Teeth alike in both jaws, small, numerous, flattened, and arranged pavement-like.

Spiracle small, close behind eye. Dorsals large, almost alike in shape and size, the second dorsal above or slightly in advance of the smaller anal.

Small sharks of temperate to cool seas, characterized by the small pavement-like teeth. One species in Queensland.

18. GUMMY SHARK *Mustelus antarcticus* Günther [Plate 6]

Mustelus antarcticus Günther, Cat. Fish. Brit. Mus., 8, 1870, p. 387.
Mustelus antarcticus McCulloch, Rec. Austr. Mus., 7, 1909, p. 315, pl. 90, fig. 3.
Mustelus antarcticus Waite, Fish. Sth Austr., 1923, p. 31 (teeth).

Smooth Hound, Sweet William (South Australia); Manga (Maori).

Teeth in 60 rows in jaws, smooth, broader than long, blunt, flattened, and each with an obscure flattened ridge, in pavement-like formation. Colour ashy-grey above, passing into white below, the two colours fairly sharply demarcated posteriorly; all fins edged whitish posteriorly; light spots irregularly placed over head and body, more numerous on head and anterior part of body, are more or less present in young examples.

The name "Gummy" has been bestowed upon this harmless shark on account of its smooth pavement-like teeth, which are without sharp points. The young develop within the body of the parent, receiving their nourishment whilst encased in a placenta-like structure similar to that which is found in the mammals. This shark grows to 42 inches and feeds upon crustaceans and shell-fish. Its flesh is excellent eating. Oil from the livers has a high medicinal value and is now used extensively in Australia in place of cod-liver oil.

The Gummy Shark ranges from South Queensland through the southern States to Western Australia.

Family **Sphyrnidae: Hammer-head Sharks**

The curious hammer-head sharks are readily recognized by the greatly expanded and flattened lobes on each side of the head, the eyes being situated at the extreme tips of the lobes. It has been suggested by some authorities that the function of such a curious-shaped head is to act as a "bow-rudder", enabling the shark to rise, dive, or turn quickly. The young are produced alive and may number as many as thirty-seven.

Several species of hammer-heads have been described from the warm seas of the world, but it is doubtful whether more than one or two are valid. One species in Queensland.

19. HAMMER-HEAD SHARK *Sphyrna lewini* (Griffith) [Plate 7]

Zygaena lewini Griffith, Anim. Kingd. Cuvier, 10, 1834, p. 640.
Sphyrna lewini Whitley, Mem. Qld Mus., 10, pt 4, 1934, p. 192, pl. 28.

Kidney-headed Shark (Queensland); Mangopare (Maori); Cornuda (West Africa).

Teeth oblique, outer edges nearly straight, notched, serrated only in the juveniles. Colour pale grey above, passing into pale yellowish below; eye bluish, orbit and part of nictitating membrane brown.

A common shark which frequents the open seas and coastal bays of Queensland, the young ascending the rivers to the end of the tidal influence. It is a dangerous species and grows to a length of at least 20 feet, with the "hammer" 6 feet in width. Young examples are frequently caught along the beaches by line fishermen.

The Hammer-head Shark ranges from Queensland and New South Wales to Tasmania, New Zealand, and Western Australia.

Family **Orectolobidae: Wobbegongs and Cat Sharks**

Body short, somewhat cylindrical to depressed, the tail long. Spiracles present. Head narrow. Eyes small. No nictitating membrane. Snout short to wide. Mouth with labial folds round angles of both jaws. Teeth compressed. Gill-openings small to moderate.

A large family of oviparous or viviparous sharks, mostly of small size, in the Indo-Pacific region. A few are found in the Atlantic. Some of the species reach a length of 12 feet or more. With the exception of one or two species they are harmless to man. The pelagic forms are usually of uniform coloration, whilst the bottom-dwellers, such as the wobbegongs or carpet sharks, are mottled and patterned to resemble the weeds and rocks among which they live. Others are strongly contrasted in colour when young, becoming more uniform with age.

The skinny fringes or lobes which adorn the sides of the head in some species serve as feelers when these sharks are groping among weeds in search of the various bottom-dwelling animals upon which they feed, or when they are lying dormant awaiting prey. Five genera are found in Queensland.

KEY TO GENERA IN QUEENSLAND

A.   Anal fin quite distinct from caudal, nearly opposite second dorsal. Spiracles very small.   *Nebrius*

AA. Anal fin either continuous with caudal or terminating directly in front, inserted wholly behind second dorsal. Spiracles large.

    b. Spiracles below level of eye. Caudal short, not more than one-third total length.

       c. Teeth dissimilar. Sides of head and snout more or less fringed with dermal lobes. Spiracles wide oblique slits.   *Orectolobus*

      cc. Teeth all similar, small and tricuspid. Sides of head and snout without dermal lobes.

B

        d. Tail short, not more than one-third longer than
           head and trunk.   *Brachaelurus*

        dd. Tail longer, not less than half longer than head
           and trunk.   *Hemiscyllium*

     bb. Spiracle behind eye. Caudal long, half total length
        or even greater. The young banded, the adults
        spotted.   *Stegostoma*

Nebrius

Body moderate, depressed anteriorly, compressed posteriorly. Head broad, the snout short and obtuse. Eyes small. Spiracle minute, behind eye. Mouth wide, inferior and slightly curved. Teeth small, in 3 series, compressed, with 3 to 5 or more cusps. Nostrils near end of snout. Front nasal valves reaching mouth. Fourth and fifth gill-slits close together. Dorsals rather large, origin of second before that of anal.

    Sharks of medium or large size found in tropical seas. One species in Queensland.

20. TAWNY SHARK *Nebrius concolor* Rüppell   [Plates 7, 9]

Nebrius concolor Rüppell, Neue Wirbelth, Fische, 1837, p. 62.
Illustration by F. Olsen after Whitley.

Teeth in three series and multicuspid. Skin covered with coarse denticles, spiracles minute. Origin of second dorsal before that of anal. Colour sandy-brown or tawny.

    This common and harmless shark has been reported from various points along the coast of Queensland. Curious stories were told by fishermen of a shark that "coughed and spat water" at them, but no specimens were forwarded for classification, and it remained unidentified for some time. It was given the name of "Madame X" by Norman Caldwell.[1] He later secured a specimen and forwarded it for examination. "I got the shark near the surface, hauled rapidly, then dodged back. From the oval mouth gushed a solid stream of water two feet high. After each 'exhaust' the shark gave a coughing grunt. It was number two of a species, which, up to that date, was unidentified. Since then Tom Marshall of the Queensland Museum, and Gilbert Whitley of the Australian Museum, Sydney, have identified it as *Nebrodes concolor ogilbyi*. It was a female, a foot smaller than the one mentioned in my book 'Fangs of the Sea' and, like its predecessor, a splendid fighter. The post mortem revealed that the strange creature was not viviparous, but laid eggs; over three hundred were in the body. They were not unlike the ray's but longer and lighter in colour."[2]

---

[1] In *Fangs of the Sea*, 1936, pp. 109-10.
[2] *Titans of the Barrier Reef*, 1938, pp. 109-10.

The largest known example was caught by Norman Caldwell off Armit Island, North Queensland. The length was 10 feet 4 inches and the girth measurement 7 feet. The Tawny Shark is found from Queensland through the East Indies and the Indian Ocean to the Red Sea.

Orectolobus

The members of this genus, the Wobbegongs, are slow, sluggish, bottom-dwelling sharks which lie in wait for their prey on weed-covered grounds, their carpet-like patterns harmonizing with their surroundings. The skinny fringes or lobes on the sides of their heads and the handsome patterns on their bodies serve to distinguish them from all other sharks. Their teeth are very sharp, and though these sharks are considered harmless they will not hesitate to seize an arm or leg of an unsuspecting bather should the opportunity arise. The young are born alive.

The distribution of the genus is through the eastern Pacific and Australia. Four species occur in Queensland waters.

KEY TO SPECIES IN QUEENSLAND

A. Nasal cirrus with a short branch at about the middle of its length.

    b. Sides of head with a nearly continuous row of branched lobes.   *ogilbyi*

    bb. Sides of head with only a few widely spaced lobes.

      c. Branch of nasal cirrus bifid; body with large light ocelli.   *maculatus*

      cc. Branch of nasal cirrus simple; body marbled, with distinct cross-bands.   *ornatus*

AA. Nasal cirrus simple.   *wardi*

21. TASSELLED WOBBEGONG *Orectolobus ogilbyi* Regan   [Plate 7]

Orectolobus ogilbyi Regan, Ann. Mag. Nat. Hist., ser. 8, vol. 3, 1909, p. 529.
Orectolobus dasypogon Ogilby and McCulloch, Journ. Proc. Roy. Soc. N.S.Wales, 42, 1909, p. 272, pl. 43, fig. 1 (not of Bleeker).

Six more or less branched dermal lobes on upper lip; at least 14 branched lobes between angle of mouth and first gill-opening, in 3 groups, of which the first is the longest; chin with a similar row, the median being longest.

Colour light sandy, covered with a network of dark-brown rings, small on head and larger on sides and tail; each ring with more or less distinct darker centre, which is plainest on tail; large dark-brown blotches break uniformity of network at regular intervals; about 5 inconspicuous darker cross-bands on body and 4 more distinct ones on tail; fins like body, except network is finer on hind borders. (Ogilby and McCulloch.)

A handsome wobbegong found in North Queensland from Torres Strait down to about Port Douglas. It is said to attain a length of 12 feet. Probably dangerous to man.

22. SPOTTED WOBBEGONG *Orectolobus maculatus* (Bonnaterre) [Plate 7]

Squalis maculatus Bonnaterre, Tabl. Encyclop. Ichth., 1788, p. 8.
Orectolobus maculatus Ogilby and McCulloch, Journ. Proc. Roy. Soc. N.S.Wales, 42, 1909, p. 273, pl. 42, fig. 2.

Carpet Shark (Queensland).

Teeth fang-like, entire, in 19 or 20 rows above, 16 or 17 rows below; lobe of nasal cirrus branched. Colour brown above, paler to whitish below; head, back, and fins spotted and marked with pale-brown and creamy rings, arcs, or blotches; about 10 dark, underlaid bands on back and tail.

This species, with its long and fang-like teeth, is probably dangerous. It is sometimes caught in South Queensland, but is much more commonly found in New South Wales. According to Whitley thirty-seven young have been taken from one female. This wobbegong is also found in Victoria, South Australia, Tasmania, and Western Australia. Grows to at least 10 feet. Feeds upon small fishes, octopuses, shellfish, etc.

23. BANDED WOBBEGONG *Orectolobus ornatus* (De Vis)   [Plate 7]

Crossorhinus ornatus De Vis, Proc. Linn. Soc. N.S.Wales, 7, 1883, p. 289.
Orectolobus ornatus Ogilby and McCulloch, Journ. Proc. Roy. Soc. N.S.Wales, 42, 1909, p. 276, pl. 42, fig. 1.
Orectolobus devisi Waite, Fish. Sth Austr. 1923, p. 33 (teeth).

Carpet Shark (Queensland).

Teeth dissimilar; long lower labial folds not crossing mandibular symphysis; nasal cirrus short, simple lobe with shorter outer one each side; spiracle almost twice the eye diameter. Colour brown, marbled darker and lighter to form somewhat obscure dark-brown cross-bars and with scattered creamy ocelli, mostly imperfect; fins with large dark spots.

This well-marked wobbegong, with its rich colour pattern of brown and cream, is common among weed-covered rocks and coral. It ranges from the coast of Papua southward along the Queensland coast to New South Wales, Victoria, and South Australia. Grows to 7 feet.

24. NORTHERN WOBBEGONG *Orectolobus wardi* Whitley [Plate 8]

Orectolobus wardi Whitley, Rec. Austr. Mus., 20, no. 4, 1939, p. 264.
Orectolobus tentaculatus Regan, Proc. Zool. Soc. Lond., 2, 1908, p. 357, pl. 12, fig. 2 (not of Peters).

Nasal cirrus and dermal lobes simple; no tubercles on back. Ground colour yellowish, back greyish; on the back, before first dorsal fin, 3 large dark spots edged with white, subcontinuous with dark vertical bars on sides; tail encircled by 3 dark bands corresponding to the 2 dorsal and the anal fins; fins with large dark spots.

A rare species recorded only from the Northern Territory and North Queensland. Little is known about it. Grows to at least 18 inches.

Brachaelurus

Body elongate, depressed anteriorly, somewhat cylindrical posteriorly. Head broad, snout wide, short, and blunt. Eyes small. Spiracles moderate, behind and partly below eye. Mouth with labial folds on both jaws, around angles and with symphysial fold, but not extending across chin. Teeth small, tricuspid. Nostrils with nasoral grooves and long, slender cirri.

Small harmless sharks inhabiting the coasts of southern Queensland and New South Wales. Only two species are known.

KEY TO SPECIES

A. Anal fin entirely behind second dorsal. Colour dark brown; young banded. *waddi*

AA. Anal fin slightly behind second dorsal. Colour ashy-grey. *colcloughi*

25. BLIND SHARK *Brachaelurus waddi* (Bloch and Schneider) [Plate 8]

Squalis waddi Bloch and Schneider, Syst. Ichth., 1801, p. 130.
Chiloscyllium modestum Günther, Proc. Zool. Soc. Lond., 1871, p. 654, pl. 54.

Dusky Dog-fish, Brown Cat Shark (Queensland).

Teeth in jaws in 18 to 20 rows, entire, cusps narrow, triangular, with small cusps each side at base. Colour dark brown to blackish, sometimes with small white spots and flecks; fins greyish; underparts yellowish; juveniles with dark transverse bands.

Like the wobbegongs, this harmless shark is very sluggish in habit. It is a lover of rocky situations, feeding upon crabs, squid, small fishes, and seaweed, etc. The name "Blind Shark" is really a misnomer, the fish having received its name from its habit of closing its eyelids when it is taken from the water. It is able to live for a considerable time out of water. This shark is found in South Queensland and New South Wales and reaches 36 inches in length. The young are born alive.

26. BLUE-GREY CAT SHARK *Brachaelurus colcloughi* Ogilby [Plate 8]

Brachaelurus colcloughi Ogilby, Proc. Roy. Soc. Qld, 21, 1908, p. 4.
Illustration by F. Olsen after Whitley.

Colour ashy-grey above, white below.

A rare shark known only from a single example (in the collection of the Queensland Museum) captured at Mud Island, Moreton Bay, South Queensland, in 1908. Length 18 inches.

Hemiscyllium

Body elongate, shorter than tail. Head moderate to short. Snout short, obtuse. Eyes small. Mouth with labial folds around angles, with or without continuous fold across chin. Nostrils with nasoral grooves; front nasal valves reaching mouth, each with long, pointed cirrus. Teeth small, compressed, median cusp triangular, smaller lateral cusps sometimes present at base. Gill-openings narrow, last two wider, and close together. Spiracle small. First dorsal behind front of ventral. Anal far behind second dorsal, close to caudal.

Small oviparous ground-sharks inhabiting the Indo-Pacific region. They differ from the wobbegongs in that they are devoid of fringes or lobes adorning the head. The egg-cases are frequently picked up on the beaches, and if one is held to the light the embryo within may be seen wriggling about attached to its large yolk-sac.

KEY TO SPECIES IN QUEENSLAND

A.   A large black ocellus above each pectoral fin; body spotted.

    b. Body with large dark scattered spots.   *ocellatum*
    bb. Body with numerous small dark spots, closely set.   *trispeculare*

AA. No ocellus above pectoral fin; body banded in young.   *punctatum*

27. EPAULETTE SHARK *Hemiscyllium ocellatum* (Bonnaterre) [Plate 8]

Squalis ocellatus Bonnaterre, Tabl. Encycl. Meth. Ichth., 1788, p. 8.
Hemiscyllium ocellatum Whitley, Rec. Austr. Mus., 18, no. 6, 1932, p. 321, pl. 36, fig. 1.

Teeth small, tricuspid, in 38 rows above and 30 rows below. Colour rich brown above, with denticles of the skin highly polished; under-surface brownish-white; back, sides, and fins with large and irregular blackish-brown spots; a much larger round eye-like spot or blotch, with narrow whitish edge, situated above each depressed pectoral.

A very common shark among the coral growths on the Great Barrier Reef, where it is always to be seen nosing about in the shallows. It is a harmless little shark and if picked up by the tail makes little effort to break free. In Australian waters it is known from North and north-western Australia and Queensland. In Queensland it is not commonly found south of the Capricorns. Occurs also in the East Indies and India. Grows to 36 inches.

28. SPECKLED CAT SHARK *Hemiscyllium trispeculare* Richardson [Plate 8]

Hemiscyllium trispeculare Richardson, Icon. Piscium, 1843, p. 5, pl. 1, fig. 2.
Hemiscyllium trispeculare Whitley, Rec. Austr. Mus., 18, no. 6, 1932, p. 321, pl. 36, fig. 2.

Colour similar to *H. ocellatum* but covered with small brownish dots which are absent only on the under-surface and between the cross-bands on the tail; 2 imperfect ocelli or dark markings, sometimes confluent, behind the large blackish ocellus.

A small and harmless shark which is occasionally met with on the reefs of North Queensland. It is found also in North and north-western Australia, though nowhere does it seem to be common. Grows to 24 inches.

29. BROWN-BANDED CAT SHARK *Hemiscyllium punctatum* (Müller and Henle) [Plate 9]

Chiloscyllium punctatum Müller and Henle, Plagiost., 1, 1838, p. 18, pl. 3 (ex Kuhl and Van Hasselt MS.).
Illustrations by G. Coates.

Spotted Cat Shark (Queensland).

Teeth in upper jaw in 30 rows, 28 in lower, small cusps, somewhat triangular; fourth and fifth gill-slits close together. Colour of adults uniform reddish-brown or greyish-fawn, darkest on sides and tail; some examples are more or less spotted with small dark-brown spots; the young are brownish, with 10 or more broad dark bands as wide as, or wider than, the interspaces.

This harmless shark is well known to the net fishermen of Moreton Bay, where it is commonly taken in the seine nets on the banks and in the shallows. It is also captured by line, taking almost any kind of fish bait, but showing a decided preference for squid. Its flesh is excellent eating, being of short texture, firm, and having a very faint sub-acid flavour resembling the few drops of lemon juice one usually adds to a fish dinner.

The species is very tenacious of life. One that I captured late one afternoon was still alive the following morning. The egg-cases and banded embryos are frequently cast up on the beaches after heavy weather. The Brown-banded Cat Shark ranges from Moreton Bay in South Queensland to Torres Strait in the far north. It also occurs in the Northern Territory of Australia, the East Indies, the Philippines, and China. Grows to at least 41 inches.

Stegostoma

Sharks of the Indian Ocean and western Pacific, with slim bodies and with tails which are long, slender, and compressed and more than half the total length of the fish. Head short and wide. Snout short, thick, and obtuse. Teeth, in about 28 rows, small and tricuspid. The young are banded and quite unlike the spotted adults. A single species.

30. ZEBRA SHARK *Stegostoma tigrinum* (Pennant) [Plate 9]

Squalis tigrinus Pennant, Ind. Zool., 1769, p. 24 (*fide* Sherborn).
Illustrations by G. Coates.

Monkey-mouthed Shark (India); Leopard Shark (South Africa).

Colour: Juveniles are dark brown or black above, with creamy-white stripes or bands on head, back, and tail, looped and paired anteriorly; adults are tawny or creamy-yellowish, covered over head, body, and tail with dark-brown spots of different sizes, the largest about the size of the eye.

A species not commonly met with. It feeds upon shellfish and crustaceans and is quite harmless to man. Its large horny purplish-black egg-cases, measuring 7 by 4 inches, are occasionally picked up on the beaches. The Zebra Shark ranges along the Queensland coast from north to south, rarely straying into New South Wales. Found also from western and northern Australia through the Indo-Australian Archipelago to the Indian Ocean and the Red Sea, China, and Japan. Grows to 11 feet.

Family **Alopiidae: Thresher Sharks**

Sharks from the Pacific and Atlantic oceans, with very long and slender tails, arched and of greater length than the rest of the body and with large pectoral fins. One genus, *Alopias*, and probably only one species.

31. THRESHER SHARK *Alopias vulpinus* (Bonnaterre) [Plate 10]

Squalis vulpinus Bonnaterre, Tabl. Encycl. Meth. Ichth., 1788, p. 9, pl. 85.
Alopecias vulpes McCoy, Prodr. Zool. Vict., dec. 9, 1884, p. 27, pl. 88.

Fox Shark, Whiptail Shark (South Africa).

Teeth triangular, edges smooth, sharp-edged, in 28 to 42 rows. Colour grey or bluish-grey above, white below, the junction of the two colours sometimes with greyish blotches.

A widely distributed species found in all warm seas. Known by the great length of the tail, which it uses to round up and frighten schools of fishes upon which it feeds. That this shark attacks whales is a common fallacy. Not considered harmful to man. Grows to 18 feet and a weight of at least 922 pounds.

Family **Carchariidae: Sand Sharks**

Body rather elongate. Head depressed, snout pointed. Spiracles small. No nictitating membrane. Mouth wide, large, curve almost pointed in front. Teeth long, slender, awl-like, with a small point each side at base. Caudal elongate, with notch at tip.

Voracious sharks of large or moderate size found in the Pacific and Atlantic oceans. One genus, *Carcharias*, with a single species in Australia.

32. GREY NURSE *Carcharias taurus* Rafinesque [Plate 10]

Carcharias taurus Rafinesque, Caratteri animali plante Scicilia, 1810, p. 10, pl. 14, fig. 1 (*fide* Fowler).
Odontaspis taurus McCoy, Prodr. Zool. Vict., dec. 7, 1882, pl. 64, fig. 1.

Sand Shark, Long-toothed Shark, Shovel-nose Shark (Victoria); Yellow Shark, Ragged-tooth Shark, Brown Shark (South Africa).

Colour varies from light grey to pale brownish above, dirty white below.

A dangerous shark which grows to a length of 15 feet. Found in Queensland, New South Wales, Victoria, Tasmania, and South Australia but not commonly met with on the Queensland coast. Wide-ranging outside Australia.

Family **Isuridae: Porbeagles or Mackerel Sharks**

Large surface-swimming sharks found in almost all seas. Bodies torpedo-shaped and stoutly built, tapering to a slender, depressed caudal peduncle, usually with a strong keel on each side of the large tail. Head subconic, snout sharply pointed. Gill-openings wide, before pectoral. Spiracles small. No nictitating membrane. First dorsal large. Second dorsal and anal small. Caudal with pits.

These sharks, which are active and fast-swimming, are fierce and voracious creatures. The family is represented in Queensland waters by two genera, each with one species.

KEY TO GENERA IN QUEENSLAND

A. Teeth slender and awl-like, smooth. Colour dark blue above. *Isurus*

AA. Teeth triangular, edges serrated. Colour very light ashy-grey. *Carcharodon*

Isurus

Body fusiform or mackerel-like, snout pointed. Teeth long, awl-like, lanceolate, the edges sharp and entire, a small point each side at base. Spiracle present or absent. First dorsal large. Second dorsal and anal small. Caudal with notch and well-produced lower lobe. A keel on each side of peduncle. Pectorals large.

33. BLUE POINTER or MAKO *Isurus glaucus* (Müller and Henle) [Plate 10]

Oxyrhina glauca Müller and Henle, Plagiost., 1838, p. 69, pl. 29.
Isurus glaucus Waite, Rec. Sth Austr. Mus., 2, no. 1, 1921, p. 21, fig. 27.

Snapper Shark (South Australia); Blue Porpoise Shark (South Africa).

Colour dark blue above, white below, the two colours sharply contrasted.

The Blue Pointer of Australian seas, called Mako by New Zealand game-fishermen, is a savage and dangerous shark which grows to a length of 15 feet and a weight of almost 800 pounds. When hooked on a line it has proved to be the world's gamest and most spectacular fighter, often repeatedly charging a boat when failing to break free. According to game-fishermen this is the only shark that will take a fast-moving bait. It is a wide-ranging, pelagic species not commonly found in Queensland waters.

Carcharodon

Body fusiform. Head conic, snout pointed. Mouth large. Teeth large, erect, regularly triangular, serrated, broader in upper jaw; third tooth on each side small. Upper lobe of lunate caudal fin but little larger than lower.

One large pelagic species widely distributed in all warm seas. This is one of the most dangerous of all the sharks.

34. WHITE POINTER *Carcharodon carcharias* (Linnaeus) [Plate 11]

Squalis carcharias Linnaeus, Syst. Nat., 10th ed., 1758, p. 235 (ex Artedi). Illustration by G. Coates.

White Death, Great White Shark (Australia).

Colour pale grey or slaty-brown above, shading to white on sides and below; a black spot usually present in pectoral axil; fins posteriorly dark, except the ventrals which are tinged pale olive anteriorly and white posteriorly.

This powerful and dangerous shark is found in most warm seas. It reaches a length of 40 feet and a weight of at least 2 tons and has jaws which are armed with large triangular serrated teeth 3 inches in length. From the evidence of fossil teeth which have been dredged from the depths of the Atlantic and Pacific oceans, the White Pointer of today is but a pygmy when compared with its supposedly recently extinct ancestors. The teeth of those monsters of the past were almost 6 inches in length and are estimated to have belonged to a shark not less than 90 feet long (see Plate 1).

Order **BATOIDEI: RAYS**

This second big group of cartilaginous fishes contains many diverse types of rays, ranging from the thick-tailed shark-like guitar-fishes (Rhinobatidae), known in Australia as shovel-nose sharks, through many intermediate forms to the more specialized whip-tailed stingrays.

The rays are a comparatively recent offshoot from the sharks, their bodies having become specially modified to suit their life on the sea-bottom. They are simply flattened sharks. The most distinctive character is the position of the gill-openings, which are situated beneath the disc and not at the sides of the head as in the sharks. The spiracles, which are placed close behind the eyes, are very large and enable the rays to breathe while lying on the sand or mud. The pectorals have become enlarged and joined to the head and body. The dorsal fins are placed well back on the tail or may be wanting altogether. The tail in many species is reduced to a whip-like appendage with one or more serrated spines at its base. There is no anal fin. Many species have the skin on their backs armoured with numerous dermal denticles or spines. The teeth being flat and pavement-like, are admirably suited for crushing the crabs and shellfish upon which the creatures feed. Many species frequent fairly shallow water, though some have been found at considerable depths.

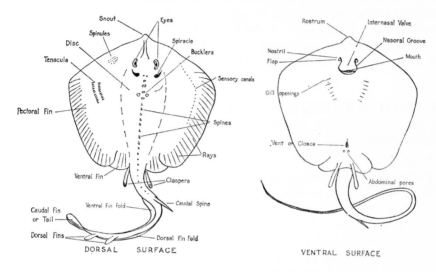

DORSAL SURFACE   VENTRAL SURFACE

FIG. 2. The dorsal and ventral surfaces of an imaginary ray, com-bining the features found in many species. F. OLSEN.

Many of the rays are splendid edible species, the most popular being the skates. Some day greater use will be made of the so-called useless stingarees, many of which are as finely flavoured as any of our food-fishes. Seven families of rays are represented in Queensland waters.

KEY TO FAMILIES IN QUEENSLAND

A. Snout produced into a long saw-like blade. PRISTIDAE

AA. Snout not saw-like.

   b. Head without horn-like fleshy fins.

    c. Tail stout, dorsal surface with 2 fins, no spines. Caudal fin large.

d. Body scaly, without electric organs. Tail stout and long. Dorsal fins well separated, entirely behind disc.   RHINOBATIDAE

dd. Body soft and naked, electric organs present. Dorsal fins bunched, not entirely behind disc.   TORPEDINIDAE

cc. Tail more slender. Caudal fin small or absent.

e. Tail without serrated spine.   RAJIDAE

ee. Tail usually with a serrated spine.

f. Teeth small and numerous. Pectoral fins rounded.   DASYATIDAE

ff. Teeth large and flat, tessellated, few in number. Pectorals acute.   MYLIOBATIDAE

bb. Head with horn-like fleshy fins.   MOBULIDAE

Family **Pristidae: Saw-fishes**

In this family of shark-like rays the snout is prolonged into a heavy, flattened, saw-like weapon which is armed with numerous enamelled "teeth" set in sockets on either side. In large examples the "saw" may be as long as 6 feet, with a width of 12 inches at its base. Armed with this formidable weapon, the fish swims through shoals of small fishes, lashing to right and left, maiming many and returning at leisure to devour them. It usually frequents the estuaries and river-mouths, living mainly in shallow waters, but is known to penetrate far up the rivers beyond tidal influence and into fresh water. One species on Cape York Peninsula lives and breeds in the fresh water. L. C. Ball, one-time Government Geologist, saw and photographed saw-fishes 150 miles up the Walsh River on Cape York, North Queensland.

When first born the young have a gristly covering over the sharp teeth on the saw, the purpose of which is to protect and prevent injury to the mother before and during birth.

Saw-fishes are found in nearly all warm seas, and some exotic species grow to a length of over 30 feet and a weight of 5,700 pounds. Two species belonging to the one genus, *Pristis*, are found in Queensland waters.

35. NARROW-SNOUTED SAW-FISH *Pristis zijsron* Bleeker   [Plate 12]

Pristis zijsron Bleeker, Nat. Tijdschr. Ned. Ind., 2, 1851, p. 442.
Pristis zysron Day, Fish. India, 1878, p. 729, pl. 191, fig. 2.
Section of rostral saw: Photograph from Public Relations Bureau.

Dindagubba (North Queensland aborigines).

Rostrum long, the teeth in 25 to 32 pairs, usually about 26. Colour greenish-grey, becoming yellowish on sides, whitish below; eye greyish and silvery, the pupil black; dorsal fins dirty yellowish-grey.

These weird creatures feed mainly upon various species of marine animals, including fishes, living on or below the bottom of the sea and which they obtain by ploughing up the sand with their long, toothed rostra. They are not regarded as dangerous to man unless he is confined in close proximity to them—during netting operations, for instance. Terrible injuries may be inflicted by a sideways strike with their saws. Day stated that one has been known to cut a bather entirely in halves. The species ranges from Queensland and New South Wales to the East Indies, India, and Ceylon. Grows to 24 feet. Common.

OTHER SPECIES

Queensland Saw-fish, *P. clavata*. Found only on the Queensland coast. It is apparently rare and little is known about it. In length it does not appear to exceed 4 feet 6 inches. The rostral teeth, which are strong, are in 18 to 21 pairs. The second dorsal fin is smaller than the first.

Family **Rhinobatidae: Shark Rays, Shovel-nose Rays and Fiddler Rays**

The members of this family, known in Australia as shovel-nose sharks, are long-bodied shark-like rays with powerful depressed tails on which 2 dorsals and a caudal fin are well developed. The depressed body usually passes forward into a tapering snout. The large spiracles are close to the eye, which has a fold below and a projecting shield above the pupil. The 5 gill-slits are on the lower surface. The teeth are small and numerous, set in pavement-like bands, and admirably suited for crushing the crabs and shellfish upon which these rays feed. Their bodies are covered with denticles or shagreen, similar to the sharks and saw-fishes, and there are usually some larger denticles on the middle of the back.

These creatures are ovoviviparous, the young being born alive from the egg hatched within the mother. Several young are produced at a time. Numerous species abound in all warm seas, usually frequenting shallow water. Five genera occur in Queensland waters.

KEY TO GENERA IN QUEENSLAND

A. Anterior dorsal fin above ventrals. A subcaudal lobe present.

    b. Snout broad, semicircular in shape. Mouth deeply undulated.   *Rhina*

    bb. Snout long, narrow, and pointed. Mouth not deeply undulated.   *Rhynchobatus*

AA. Anterior dorsal fin well behind ventrals. No sub-caudal lobe.

    c. Snout long, shovel-shaped, and pointed. Body plain-coloured.

      d. Nostrils oblique.   *Rhinobatos*

      dd. Nostrils nearly transverse.   *Aptychotrema*

    cc. Snout more obtuse. Body ornate.   *Trygonorrhina*

SHARK RAYS
Rhina

Snout broad, blunt, rounded. Mouth deeply undulated. Teeth larger on the prominences.

An Indo-Pacific genus recognized by its peculiar-shaped mouth and teeth. One species in Queensland.

36. SHARK RAY *Rhina ancylostomus* Bloch and Schneider   [Plate 12]

Rhina ancylostomus Bloch and Schneider, Syst. Ichth., 1801, p. 352, pl. 72.
Rhynchobatus ancylostomus Day, Fish. India, 1878, p. 730, pl. 193, fig. 3.
Rhina ancylostomus Whitley, Fish. Austr., pt 1, Sharks, 1940, p. 179, fig. 206 (jaws and teeth).

Bow-mouthed Angel-fish, Short-nosed Mud Skate (Queensland).

Colour dull brown, lighter below; sometimes with whitish dots and spots; twisting black lines on body and fins may also be present.

This weird fish is widely distributed in the Indian and Pacific oceans. It grows to at least 9 feet with a weight of 275 pounds. The head and shoulders are armed with stout bony bucklers or tubercles.

Apparently not a common fish on the Queensland coast, but it has been recorded at long intervals from various points along the whole Queensland coastline. It feeds upon crabs and shellfish. Wide-ranging outside Australia.

Rhynchobatus

Body depressed, tapering to caudal. Snout elongate, narrow, pointed. Teeth obtuse, pavement-like, dental surfaces undulated. Large spiracles close to eye. First dorsal opposite ventrals. Back with fairly large tubercles.

Large rays inhabiting the shallow waters of the Indo-Pacific and African coast. Species few, one in Queensland.

37. WHITE-SPOTTED RAY *Rhynchobatus djiddensis* (Forskål)   [Plate 12]

Raja djiddensis Forskål, Descr. Anim., 1775, p. 18.
Illustration by G. Coates.

Shovel-nose, Sand Shark (South Africa).

Colour greyish, olive, or brownish above, with scattered white spots or ocelli on sides and pectorals; a black spot as large as the spiracles is usually present on the scapular region, though sometimes absent in the adults.

A common ray frequently caught by big-game fisherman at the mouth of the Brisbane and other rivers, the bait usually being squid or mullet. It is also found in New South Wales and is wide-ranging in the seas outside Australia.

Feeds upon crustaceans and offal. Grows to a weight of 500 pounds and a length of 10 feet. The flesh of this ray is excellent to eat—tasting, when cooked, very like prawns.

SHOVEL-NOSE RAYS

Harmless shark-like rays, common and numerous in the shallow waters of most warm seas. Two genera, *Rhinobatos* and *Aptychotrema*, are found in Queensland. The species vary greatly in the form of the snout and nostrils. Species numerous, few in Queensland.

Rhinobatos

Teeth obtuse, with indistinct transverse ridge. Nostrils oblique, wide, front valve not confluent and not reaching mouth. Species numerous in warm seas, one in Queensland.

38. COMMON SHOVEL-NOSE RAY *Rhinobatos armatus* (Gray) [Plate 13]

Rhinobatis [*sic*] *armatus* Gray, Illust. Ind. Zool., 2, 1832-4, pts 13-14, pl. 99.
Rhinobatus armatus Ogilby, Mem. Qld Mus., 5, 1916, p. 85, text-fig. 1.
Illustration by G. Coates.

Shovel-nose Shark (Queensland and New South Wales).

Mouth almost straight, width 3 or almost 3 in the preoral length; preorbital length 4 times the distance between spiracles; nostrils very oblique and long slits, nearly equal to mouth width. Colour light brownish or olive, whitish below; pectorals and ventrals yellowish.

Although found along the whole coastline of Queensland, this ray is more common in the northern waters of the State. It is a littoral species which freely enters and breeds in the fresh water. It grows to 7 feet, though the average ones met with are from 3 to 4 feet. In its young stages it is an excellent food-fish and good quantities are sold in the markets. It ranges across North Australia from Shark's Bay in Western Australia to Queensland, also through the East Indies to India.

Aptychotrema

Distinguished from *Rhinobatos* mainly in the nostrils being almost transverse, the inner extension of the front nasal valve crossing the inner angle of the nostril and absence of folds on the hind edge of the spiracles. Two species are found in Queensland.

KEY TO SPECIES IN QUEENSLAND

A.   Mouth only slightly curved; length of snout almost 4 times the width between spiracles.   *banksii*

AA. Mouth strongly curved, bow-shaped; length of snout nearly 3 times width between spiracles.   *bougainvillii*

39. BANKS' SHOVEL-NOSE RAY *Aptychotrema banksii* (Müller and Henle)
[Plate 13]

Rhinobatus banksii Müller and Henle, Plagiost., 1841, p. 123.
Rhinobatus banksii Waite, Mem. Austr. Mus., 4, 1899, p. 38, pl. 3.
Rhinobatus banksii Ogilby, Mem. Qld Mus., 5, 1916, p. 85, text-fig. 1.

Mouth-width $3\frac{1}{2}$ in the preoral length; snout $1\frac{1}{3}$ to $1\frac{2}{5}$ in head measured to first gill-opening. Colour yellowish or olive, lighter on the fins; under-surface white.

The common Shovel-nose Shark of the Moreton Bay fishermen. It is found in the waters of southern Queensland and New South Wales, also in South Australia and New Zealand. It frequents the sandy beaches and is also taken by trawl down to 30 fathoms. Ovoviviparous. Grows to 4 feet. Its flesh makes excellent eating.

39a. BOUGAINVILLE'S SHOVEL-NOSE RAY *Aptychotrema bougainvillii*
   (Müller and Henle) [Plate 13]

Rhinobatus (Syrrhina) bougainvillii Müller and Henle, Plagiost., 1841, p. 117.
Illustration by F. Olsen after Norman.

A little-known species which has the nostrils more transverse than oblique. The mouth is strongly curved. Colour brownish with a few marks on the fins. This ray is occasionally taken in the waters of South Queensland and New South Wales. It grows to about 33 inches.

Trygonorrhina

Disc wide, shorter than tail. Snout rounded, obtusely pointed. Anterior nasal valves united to form a wide quadrangular flap. Spiracle large, close to eye, with fold. One species in Australia.

40. FIDDLER RAY *Trygonorrhina fasciata* Müller and Henle   [Plate 13]

Trygonorhina fasciata Müller and Henle, Plagiost., 1841, p. 124.
Trygonorhina fasciata McCulloch, Proc. Linn. Soc. N.S.Wales, 46, 1921, p. 460, pl. 38, figs 1-2.

Banjo Shark (New South Wales).

Colour light brown, with a bluish-grey pattern bordered with dark brown or black and in shape somewhat similar to the scroll-like holes in a violin, hence the name of Fiddler Ray.

A common ray, but very rare in Moreton Bay. Whitley states: "Common on sand-flats, in estuaries, and around wharves where it swims by swaying laterally or else lies partially buried by sand or stones; it has been trawled down to 60 fathoms." He further states: "Ovoviviparous; the egg is bolster or pillow-shaped, of a beautiful golden colour; it contains two or three embryos and hatches within the mother's body, in which it may be found rolled up."

The Fiddler Ray ranges from southern Queensland through New South Wales, Victoria, South Australia, and south-western Australia. Grows to 4 feet.

Family **Torpedinidae: Electric Rays**

Rays with an almost circular disc, the head and body smooth, depressed, the skin soft and naked, characterized by 2 large electric organs, one on each side of the head.

The numb-fishes or electric rays have the power of generating electric energy and imparting a severe shock to anything which may come into contact with them. Situated on each side of the head, between the upper and lower surfaces of the skin, are a series of hexagonal cells filled with a clear jelly-like substance. Here the electric current is generated, and the discharge is of sufficient strength to render a grown man prostrate for an hour or so. The fish is capable of giving forty to fifty consecutive shocks, each one becoming weaker. A period of rest is then required for the fish to recover normality again.

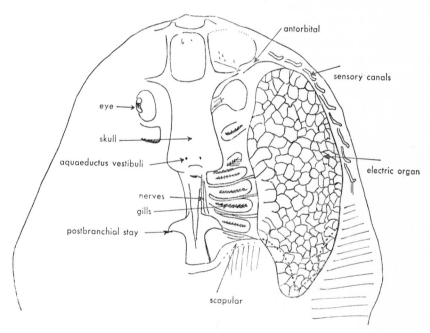

FIG. 3. Head of a Tasmanian numb-fish dissected from the dorsal surface, showing the position of the electric organs. AFTER WHITLEY.

Some of these electric rays, which are known by the names of torpedoes, cramp-fishes or numb-fishes, grow to a large size, and exotic species 5 feet in length and weighing 200 pounds are known. Some of the species live in inshore waters, whilst others, certain of them being quite blind, live in the oceans at great depths. One genus, with its single species, is found in Australian waters.

Hypnarce

Disc broader than long. Tail short. Fringed spiracles large, close behind eyes. Eyes small. Numerous small tricuspid teeth in rather wide bands. Electric organs large, between head and each pectoral. Two small dorsal fins above ventrals. Caudal small. Ventrals large, united.

41. NUMB-FISH *Hypnarce subnigra* (Duméril) [Plate 13]

Hypnos subnigrum Duméril, Rev. Mag. Zool. (2), 4, 1852, p. 279.
Hypnos subnigrum McCulloch, Proc. Linn. Soc. N.S.Wales, 46, 1921, p. 467, pl. 38, figs 3-4.

Cramp-fish is another common name applied to this fish.
Colour dark brown above, white below.
This is a common species in the waters of Moreton Bay, but it does not appear to be found in the northern parts of Queensland. Whitley gives the following notes on this interesting fish: "The numb-fish leads a lazy life, lying at the bottom of the sea half buried in mud or sand. It can afford to do this because of its power of giving off electric shocks from hexagonal muscle cells in its head and body. Any animal touching the numb-fish is immediately paralysed, and, if small enough, doubtless eaten. Any little crabs, worms and fishes which come its way are relished by the numb-fish. Cramp-fish, numbie, electric ray and torpedo are among the politer names applied to this fish which often bestows shocks upon unsuspecting fishermen when they are handling or standing upon their catches. The numb-fish looks rather like a shapeless mass of raw beef in life, though its body is white underneath.

"This numb-fish is not uncommon around Sydney. I have touched one as it lay buried in the sand and received a shock through my arm as I swam in shallow water at Shelly Beach in February 1939. Then on 23rd February 1933, whilst wading at Gunnamatta Bay, I trod on an electric ray and it was as if a large hand clutched my foot and ankle. I netted the specimen and put it on a sandbank. Here I noticed a black leech between its eyes, and in trying to knock this off with my net, got a more severe shock which so suddenly contracted the muscles of my arms and legs that I leapt a foot in the air. The fish lived a long time out of water and was doubtless saved when the tide returned. The leech was apparently insulated in some way against electricity."

Whitley further states: "Though this species lies on sandflats and is even stranded by the tide for hours, it is also trawled down to about 60 fathoms in New South Wales."

Numb-fish are evidently relished by sharks for they are frequently found in their stomachs. The Numb-fish grows to over 24 inches and ranges from South Queensland through New South Wales to South Australia and Western Australia.

Family **Rajidae: Skates**

Body and head flat, depressed, united with pectorals to form a rhomboid or circular disc. Tail distinct, fairly slender, depressed, but not whip-like. Two small dorsal fins. Teeth small, numerous, in pavement-like formation. Gill-openings small, inferior. Spiracles large. Males often with large claspers.

The skates differ from the other rays by the presence of a blunt-tipped tail, without a tail-fin, and armed with rows of "prickles", and also by the absence of a serrated spine or "sting" on the tail as in the stingarees. They further differ in that they deposit eggs which are laid in horny cases, roughly wheel-barrow-shaped. Being sticky when deposited, the eggs become attached to shells, sticks, etc., and are thus anchored until hatched. Apart from the clasper of the males, many differences are exhibited between the sexes. The females, which are usually about one-third larger than the males, lack the thorns or spines on the back and pectoral fins which are often present in the males.

The large family of skates mainly inhabit the cooler waters of the Northern Hemisphere. There are, however, several species that live in the cool waters along the southern coastline of Australia, and two species belonging to a single genus frequent the waters of South Queensland.

Skates are valued as food in many parts of the world. Some species attain a width of 8 feet and a weight of 200 pounds or more.

Raja

Disc rhomboid or almost circular. Tail with fold along each side. Snout more or less produced and pointed. Teeth small, tessellate, usually flattened and pavement-like, usually more pointed in the males. Gill-openings small. Spiracles close to eye. Skin more or less spiny. Two rayed dorsals on tail above. Caudal rudimentary or absent.

This is a large genus containing many species inhabiting the cooler seas of the world. Only two of the species are found in Queensland.

KEY TO SPECIES IN QUEENSLAND

A. Colour uniform brown or with obscure light spots; size moderate.   *australis*

AA. Colour light grey or pale brown, with patches of small white-edged black spots; size small.   *polyommata*

42. COMMON SKATE *Raja australis* (Macleay) [Plate 14]

Raia australis Macleay, Proc. Linn. Soc. N.S.Wales, 8, 1884, p. 461.
Raja australis Waite, Mem. Austr. Mus., 4, 1899, p. 40, pl. 4.

Smooth-backed Skate, Pommy Skate, Thorn-back Skate (New South Wales).

Colour olive-brownish or dark greyish above, with edges of fins lighter or flesh-coloured; light spots or indistinct dusky markings are sometimes present towards bases of fins; blackish pores below head; tip of snout and point of tail blackish.

A deep-water skate which enters southern Queensland waters from the south, where it is known as Pommy Skate on account of its resemblance to the English skates. A valued food-fish, common at from 10 to 85 fathoms. Grows to 4 feet.

OTHER SPECIES

Argus Skate, *R. polyommata*. Discovered by the trawler *Endeavour* at Cape Moreton and North Reef, Queensland, during trawling investigations in 1910. Specimens were taken at depths of 70 to 75 fathoms on a bottom of shell and mud. Grows to 13 inches.

Family **Dasyatidae: Stingrays**

Head, body, and pectorals depressed, forming a flat, wide disc. Tail long, narrow, tapering, distinct from disc, with usually a serrated spine well behind base. Teeth small, in pavement-like formation. Spiracles large, close behind eye.

In the stingrays the tails are mostly very slender and whip-like and usually armed with poisonous serrated spines, sometimes to the number of three. There are often folds or keels on the upper and lower surfaces and a single dorsal and caudal fin may be present. It is in this group that the caudal spines are most developed, and they may be all lengths up to 15 inches. These spines are shed from time to time, being replaced by new ones growing from beneath. The spine is provided with a groove on each side, along which a virulent venom flows from cells at its base. The jagged wounds made by these spines cause intense agony, followed usually by blood-poisoning. It may take months to heal, and in the case of children death has been known to result within a few hours.

This large family of rays contains many species found living in tropical and subtropical countries. Some inhabit the coral reefs whilst others prefer the shallow bays or muddy mangrove-lined rivers. In various parts of Queensland they are to be commonly seen entering the shallow bays in great numbers on the rising tide, spreading out and feeding on such animals as prawns, mantis-prawns, shellfish, worms, etc.

They conceal their bodies in the sand or mud by rapid movements of the large pectoral fins, settling down and leaving only the eyes and spiracles free and uncovered. Their favourite feeding grounds can always be recognized by the numerous pot-holes made by their bodies and left exposed by the falling tide.

The aborigines, having captured a stingaree, break off the spine and use it like a surgeon's knife, cutting a D-shaped flap in the belly over the liver to enable them to extract that "dainty morsel", which is relished as a special treat. The pectoral fins or flaps of most of the stingarees are excellent eating, being rich, glutinous, and of good flavour.

Apart from the claspers there are no great differences between the sexes, such as are exhibited in the skates. The name stingaree is a corruption of stingray. Seven genera are found in Queensland waters.

KEY TO GENERA IN QUEENSLAND

A.   Tail usually with at least one serrated spine.

    b. Tail long and whip-like. No caudal fin.

      c. Tail with keels or cutaneous folds.

        d. Dental surface of jaws straight or undulous. Back more or less smooth. Narrow tail-folds.   *Dasyatis*

        dd. Dental surface of upper jaw angular. Back rough. Broad fold below tail.   *Pastinachus*

      cc. Tail without keels or folds.   *Himantura*

    bb. Tail moderate or short.

      e. Disc subcircular. Tail stout. No caudal fin. Body spotted blue.   *Taeniura*

      ee. Disc subcircular. Tail stout. Caudal fin present. Colour uniform.   *Urolophus*

      eee. Disc very wide, angular. Tail short, slender. Caudal fin vestigial, and also spine when present.   *Gymnura*

AA. No serrated spine on tail. Head, body, and tail with bony and thorny cusps.   *Urogymnus*

Dasyatis

Disc partly quadrangular to partly circular. Tail moderate to very long and whip-like, fairly thick at base, with 1 or 2 serrated spines and with or without dermal folds of skin above and below tail. No dorsal fin. Species numerous, two in Queensland.

KEY TO SPECIES IN QUEENSLAND

A. Scapular region smooth or with median spines only.
Body blue-spotted. *kuhlii*

AA. Scapular region with a broad patch of tubercles. Colour
uniform olive-brown. *fluviorum*

43. BLUE-SPOTTED STINGAREE *Dasyatis kuhlii* (Müller and Henle)
[Colour-plate 1]

Trygon kuhlii Müller and Henle, Plagiost., 1841, p. 164.
Illustration by G. Coates.

Disc broader than long; a low median cutaneous fold behind spine and a
long ventral fold along tail; tail about as long as disc; scapular region smooth
or with only a few spines.

The young are pale grey or brown, spotted with black or rusty-red and white,
the markings varying; lower surface white with pinkish or pale-brown edges;
ventral fins fawn with some black spots; tail-tip black, preceded by two obscure
blackish cross-bands. (Whitley.)

The adults are light pinkish-brown, with numerous large bluish ocelli having
indefinite darker margins; the black spots exhibited in the juveniles have become
lost, the blue spots being the most striking feature.

The Blue-spotted Stingaree is an Indo-Pacific species found on the reefs
of North Queensland. It is a small ray which is commonly seen lying partially
buried in the sand on the coral reefs, usually in shallow water. When disturbed
it glides away swiftly, throwing up a puff of sand as it departs. It is excellent
eating when roasted over an open fire. It has been trawled on the Queensland
coast down to 20 fathoms. Grows to a width of 10 inches.

44. ESTUARY STINGAREE *Dasyatis fluviorum* Ogilby
[Plate 14]

Dasyatis fluviorum Ogilby, Proc. Roy. Soc. Qld, 21, 1908, p. 6.
Dasyatis fluviorum McCulloch, Biol. Res. Endeavour, 3, pt 3, 1915, p. 103, pl. 16, fig. 1.

Brown Stingaree (Queensland and New South Wales).

Small groups of blunt tubercles and tubular pores on back; above each
spiracle are other blunt tubercles which also extend along superciliary edge;
a series of spines along dorsal ridge, extending almost to base of caudal spine
on tail; tail more than twice length of disc. Colour olive-brown or blackish-
brown above, with margins of disc and ventral fins lighter; bluish-white below,
with margins pale brownish; tail blackish; spine and tubercles whitish.

An extremely common species found in the bays and estuaries of southern
Queensland and New South Wales, where it ascends rivers to beyond the tidal
limits. In the male the teeth are triangular and acute, the outer surface of each

being deeply grooved. In the female they are tubular and their surface is broken up into many small facets. Grows to a width of 4 feet across the disc.

Pastinachus

Tail with a cutaneous fold below, none above. Disc broader than long, rough. Tubercles rounded, stellate. One species in Queensland.

45. COW-TAIL or FANTAIL RAY *Pastinachus sephen* (Forskål) [Plate 14]

Raja sephen, Forskål, Descr. Animal., 1775, p. 18.
Illustration by G. Coates.

Tail long, with spine, but without a dorsal or caudal fin; a broad cutaneous fold below tail but not extending more than half-way to its slender tip; disc smooth in the young but with age finely and closely roughened; dental surface of upper jaw angular. Lead-coloured or blackish above, becoming black towards tail; white below; the young are reddish-brown.

A very common ray seen in numbers on the shallow flats when the tide is rising. The black feather-like fold on the under-side of the tail is a distinctive feature.

Most fishermen handle rays by gripping them in the spiracles with the thumb and first finger, a method which renders them harmless and unable to use their poison-barb, but in this species such a method is unsafe. With great speed they are able to curve the tail over the back and drive the spine into the hand which holds them, thereby inflicting very severe injury.

The Cow-tail Ray ranges from Queensland and New South Wales to New Guinea, through the Indo-Australian Archipelago to the Indian Ocean and the Red Sea. It grows to a width of 6 feet across the disc.

Himantura

Disc broader than long. Tail without keels or folds; at least one serrated spine. No caudal fin. Tubercles granular, pavement-like formation. Two species occur in Queensland.

KEY TO SPECIES IN QUEENSLAND

A. Entire disc covered with granules. Colour olive-brown, a few scattered creamy spots on dorsal surface. *granulata*

AA. Granules in mostly 2-3 widely separated rows on head, vertebral tubercles not extending upon tail. Colour brown, with darker spots; tail with black and white rings. *uarnak*

46. MANGROVE RAY *Himantura granulata* (Macleay) [Plate 14]

Trygon granulatus Macleay, Proc. Linn. Soc. N.S.Wales, 7, 1883, pt 4, p. 598.
Illustration by F. Olsen after Whitley.

Rough-back Coach-whip Ray (Queensland).

Disc about as broad as long; tail without cutaneous folds, slender, its length about one and a half times the length of the disc; head and back covered with minute thorny granules which extend along ridge of tail to spine. Colour usually uniform brown, but sometimes dark olive-greyish with a few scattered white spots.

A very common ray in North Queensland where there are many mangroves. It may often be seen lying motionless in the shallow water. It feeds upon small crabs and prawns. Found also in New Guinea and in the Santa Cruz Islands. Grows to a width of at least 13 inches.

47. COACH-WHIP RAY *Himantura uarnak* (Forskål)
[Plate 14; Colour-plate 2]

Raja uarnak Forskål, Descr. Animal., 1775, p. 18.
Himantura toshi Whitley, Austr. Zool., 9, pt 3, 1939, p. 258; and Fish. Austr. pt 1, Sharks, 1940, p. 212, fig. 240.
Colour illustration by G. Coates.

Disc little wider than long; skin largely smooth in the young, but in the adults with a few tubercles or a solitary one on middle of back. Colour sandy to dark brown, with a few scattered dark spots or with numerous closely set dark spots which sometimes coalesce to form a reticulating pattern in dark brown; tail ringed alternately with blue-black and white.

A common ray on the tidal sand- and mud-flats of Queensland, New South Wales, and North Australia. Found also in the Arafura Sea. Wide-ranging. Grows to a width of at least 5 feet and a weight of 200 pounds. Feeds upon small fish, crabs, and shellfish. It can inflict dangerous wounds with its large spine. Viviparous. Known by its long black and white tail.

Taeniura

Disc oval. Tail longer than body, compressed and ribbon-like, with one or two spines. Mouth small; teeth small, in pavement, grooved transversely. No dorsal fin. Two Indo-Pacific species, one in Queensland.

48. BLUE-SPOTTED LAGOON RAY *Taeniura lymma* (Forskål)
[Colour-plate 2]

Raja lymma Forskal, Descr. Animal., 1775, p. 9.
Illustration by G. Coates.

Ribbon-tail Ray, Fantail (South Africa).

Disc smooth, except for a few flattened spines along middle of back; tail longer than body; eyes large, nearly equal to spiracles. Colour tan-brown above, with large bright-blue spots over disc; a broad blue stripe runs along each side of tail from back to behind spines.

A handsome ray which is very common in North Queensland. It inhabits the lagoons of the many reefs and feeds upon prawns, mantis-prawns, worms, etc. Somewhat rare south of the Whitsunday Passage, Queensland. Found also in North Australia and in New Guinea. Wide-ranging outside Australia. Queensland examples reach a width of about 15 inches, though larger ones are known from South Africa.

Urolophus

Disc somewhat quadrangular, more narrow posteriorly, angled bluntly in front. Tail short, stout, and muscular, terminating in a well-developed caudal fin. A small fin present or absent. Several species in Australian seas, one in Queensland.

49. COMMON STINGAREE *Urolophus testaceus* (Müller and Henle)
[Plate 15]

Raja testacea Müller and Henle, Plagiost., 1841, p. 174.
Urolophus testaceus McCulloch, Biol. Res. Endeavour, 4, pt 4, 1916, p. 174, pl. 50.

Teeth pavement-like, each with a horizontal ridge in the female but elevated into an obtuse spine in the male; nostrils with broad lobes posteriorly; a small dorsal fin usually present just in advance of the spine. Colour reddish or brownish, with extreme edges white; lower surface white with broad pale-brown margins to the "flaps"; large examples are a darker brown with blackish on tail.

A common ray on the sandy flats in shallow water, but it also enters deep water down to 60 fathoms or more. It grows to about 13 inches across the disc. Ranges from Queensland to New South Wales, Victoria, and South Australia.

Gymnura

Disc wider than long, becoming more so with age. Tail short, thin, with or without narrow dermal folds behind serrated spine. Usually no dorsal fin. Eyes small. Spiracles large, close behind eyes. Teeth minute, numerous, in a broad band in each jaw, each tooth with a wide base and 1 to 3 sharp cusps.

Large rays of temperate and tropical seas. One species in Queensland.

50. RAT-TAILED RAY *Gymnura australis* (Ramsay and Ogilby)

[Plate 15]

Pteroplatea australis Ramsay and Ogilby, Proc. Linn. Soc. N.S.Wales, 10, 1886, p. 575.
Illustration by G. Coates.

Skate (South Queensland); Butterfly Ray (New South Wales).

Tail usually less than half as long as disc in the adult; serrated spine minute or absent. Colour brown or greenish-grey, variegated with lighter and darker areas, or speckled with small black spots; tail black above, white below, forming incomplete annuli on its sides.

A fairly common ray on the coasts of Queensland and New South Wales. In the Brisbane Fish Market it is sold under the name of skate. The species is readily recognized by the great width of the disc in proportion to its length and by the very short tail. Grows to a width of at least 40 inches.

Urogymnus

Body disciform, partly circular. Body covered with osseous tubercles with broad rounded to polygonal bases, varying in size, shape, and numbers with age. Tail long, without spine or dorsal or caudal fins. Mouth undulate. Teeth tessellated, flattened. Spiracles large, close behind eyes. A single genus and species. Wide-ranging.

51. THORNY RAY *Urogymnus africanus* (Schneider)

[Plate 15]

Raja africana Schneider, Syst. Ichth. Bloch, 1801, p. 367.
Urogymnus asperrimus Day, Fish. India, 1878, p. 736, pl. 195, fig. 1.

Body covered with tubercular scales with broad rounded to polygonal bases, varying in shape according to age and with numerous erect thorns. Colour greenish or brownish above, yellowish to whitish on tubercles.

A wide-ranging species but one that is rarely seen in Australian waters. It has been recorded from North Queensland. Grows to a width of at least 24 inches.

Family **Myliobatidae: Eagle Rays**

Disc rather wide, the pectorals terminating with more or less falcate tips. Eyes prominent, lateral. Spiracles large, behind eyes, opening laterally. Lower front of head expanded as a thick fleshy flap (in one genus divided into 2 separate lobes). Teeth angular, broad, flat, tessellated, the median series usually wider than laterals, if present. Tail long, often with small dorsal basally and usually with one or more serrated spines.

The eagle rays are closely related to the stingrays, differing mainly in their much more acutely pointed pectoral fins and their large pavement-like teeth. Like the stingrays, their tails have serrated spines. The family contains many species, all of which are large, some growing to a length of 15 feet and a weight of 800 pounds.

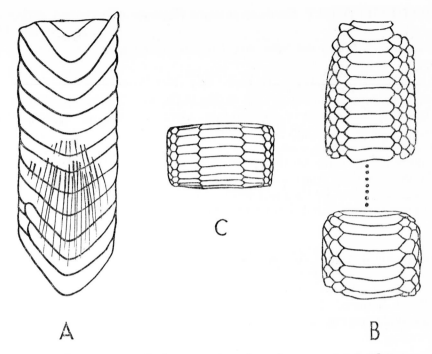

Fɪɢ. 4. Dentition of three species of eagle rays. A, *Aetobatus narinari*; B, *Myliobatus australis*; C, *Rhinoptera neglecta*.   ꜰ. ᴏʟsᴇɴ.

Eagle rays inhabit the warm seas of the world but do not dwell on the bottom to the same extent as do the stingrays—preferring, when not feeding, to swim at or just below the surface with a flying or soaring motion. They feed upon shellfish and crabs, which they crush with their powerful teeth. The young are born alive and number several at a birth. Eagle rays take their name from the eagle-like appearance of the head. Three genera occur in Queensland waters.

ᴋᴇʏ ᴛᴏ ɢᴇɴᴇʀᴀ ɪɴ ǫᴜᴇᴇɴsʟᴀɴᴅ

A. Snout in a single lobe.
    b. Teeth in one row in each jaw.   *Aetobatus*
    bb. Teeth in more than 3 rows in each jaw.   *Myliobatus*

AA. Snout in 2 separate lobes.   *Rhinoptera*

Aetobatus

Head prominent, narrowing downward and forward on sides. Snout narrower, produced. Rostral fins distinct from pectorals and set at a lower level on side of head. Pectorals slightly falciform, not continued forward to snout. Probably only a single species, widely distributed in shallow water of all warm seas.

52. SPOTTED EAGLE RAY *Aetobatus narinari* (Euphrasen) [Plate 15]

Raia narinari Euphrasen, Kon. Vet. Acad. Nya Handl., 11, 1790, p. 217 (*fide* Sherborn).
Aetobatus punctatus Whitley, Fish. Austr., pt 1, Sharks, 1940, p. 225, fig. 257.

Spotted Eagle Ray, Jumping Ray (Queensland and South Africa), Duckbill Ray, Bonnet Skate (South Africa).

Teeth in a single row, wide, flat, chevron-shaped and pavement-like above; in the lower jaw they are sometimes angularly bent or may be nearly straight. Colour greyish to greenish-olive or leaden colour above, with bluish-white diffused-edged spots; tail black; eye golden-yellow, the pupil black.

This large ray feeds upon oysters and clams and is a destructive fish where those bivalves are farmed. It is viviparous, and when the young are about to be born it is said that the female leaps high from the water, the curled-up embryos being thrown from her body one at a time.

The species is wide-ranging, being found from Queensland, Melanesia, Micronesia, and Polynesia through the East Indies to the Indian Ocean and the Red Sea. It grows to a width of 11 feet and a weight of at least 200 pounds.

Myliobatus

Head prominent, snout narrower forward. Spiracles open upward. Teeth in the median row very wide, each side with 3 very narrow rows. Tail long, slender, with serrated spine behind dorsal.

Bottom-dwelling rays of all warm seas. Species few, one in Queensland.

53. EAGLE RAY *Myliobatus australis* Macleay [Plate 15]

Myliobatus australis Macleay, Proc. Linn. Soc. N.S.Wales, 6, pt. 2, 1881, p. 380.
Myliobatus tenuicaudatus (not of Hector) Waite, Fish. Sth Austr., 1923, p. 54.

"Colour greenish, olive or sandy, with indistinct blue blotches, but sometimes bright orange-yellow (xanthistic) specimens with dull blue blotches come to light." (Whitley.)

This large ray is a pest on the oyster-banks, where it is sometimes seen in small schools feeding upon those valuable molluscs, which it crushes with its powerful grinding teeth.

The Eagle Ray grows to a width of at least 4 feet. It is found in the waters of South Queensland, New South Wales, Victoria, South Australia, Western Australia, and Tasmania.

Rhinoptera

Disc lozenge-shaped, wider than long. Head prominent. Eyes prominent, lateral. Spiracles large, behind eyes, the openings lateral. Teeth wide, angular, and flat, in pavement-like formation, the median row widest. Tail long, slender, with serrated spine and dorsal fin at its base. A pair of rostral fins separated from front of head and not continued with pectorals.

Rays of moderate size inhabiting mainly the waters of the Indo-Pacific region. Species few, one in Queensland.

54. COW-NOSE RAY *Rhinoptera javanica* Müller and Henle   [Plate 15]

Rhinoptera javanica Müller and Henle, Plagiost., 1841, p. 182, pl. 58.

Teeth pavement-like, 9 series in each jaw, those of middle upper series 8 times as wide as long and $1\frac{2}{3}$ times as wide as the adjacent series; middle lower teeth a little wider than upper. Disc more than twice as broad as long. Colour uniform brown above, white below.

This species, which ranges from India and Ceylon to China and the East Indies, is apparently not commonly met with in Australian waters (the only examples which have come under notice to date were one taken in Moreton Bay, South Queensland, in 1885, and two, male and female, taken in a net off the mouth of the Elliott River, near Bundaberg, in December 1946, by R. B. May). Grows to a width of at least 36 inches.

Family **Mobulidae: Devil Rays or Sea Devils**

These gigantic but harmless rays are closely related to the eagle rays. The most noticeable feature is the two cephalic "horns" or head-fins which project forward on each side of the head. The mouth is wide but the teeth are small and numerous, set in many rows, and take the form of a flat, blunt rasp (Plate 16). The tail is somewhat short and there is usually no serrated spine, or if so it is very rudimentary. The skin is more or less rough.

These rays are favourite hosts of the sucking-fishes and when attended by too many of those hitch-hikers they have the habit of leaping high from the water to rid themselves of the pests. The sound made by their great bodies striking the water on descent has been likened to a thunderclap and can be heard many miles at sea.

These monsters inhabit most warm seas and are the largest of all the rays. Two genera are known, a single species of each being found in Queensland waters.

KEY TO GENERA

A.   Mouth anterior, wide. Teeth minute, in a band (covered with skin) usually on lower jaw only, sometimes in both jaws. Cephalic fins not curled outwards.   *Manta*

AA.   Mouth inferior, well beneath head, less extensive. Minute teeth in bands on both jaws or at least on upper jaw. Cephalic fins curled outwards.   *Mobula*

Manta: Mantas or Giant Devil Rays

Head greatly depressed, broad, flat. Mouth terminal, between cephalic fins, very wide, straight. Teeth very small, numerous, not functional, covered over by skin, usually present in lower jaw only. Tail slender, whip-like, without serrated spine. Small dorsal fin present.

Several species of these huge bat-like rays are said to be known, but further study may show them to be referred to only one or two species. Some attain a width of 24 feet and a weight of 4 tons.

Unlike most other rays, mantas spend most of their time swimming on or just below the surface, usually in the vicinity of rocky headlands or around islands. Unless frightened, they cruise slowly along, usually in pairs, with one or both pectoral fin-tips showing above the water—in a similar way to a shark.

The food of the mantas consists of the tiny crustaceans, etc., known as plankton, which they obtain by swimming open-mouthed, the cephalic fins serving to guide the food into the mouth. The young are born alive; an American species 15 feet in width had an embryo taken from it which measured 5 feet across and weighed 20 pounds.

Most native races fear the devil rays, and pearl-divers believe that they will fold their huge "wings" around them and sink into the depths or squeeze them to death. Such stories are of course without foundation, for in spite of their great bulk they are harmless. One species in Australia.

55. AUSTRALIAN DEVIL RAY *Manta alfredi* (Macleay)   [Plate 16]

Ceratoptera alfredi Macleay, Proc. Linn. Soc. N.S.Wales, 6, 1881, p. 381.
Daemomanta alfredi Whitley, Fish. Austr., pt 1, Sharks, 1940, p. 226 *et seq.*, figs 265, 266.

Devil-fish, Devil Ray (Queensland and New South Wales).

In these large rays the teeth, which are usually on the lower jaw only—though sometimes on both jaws—are very small and numerous and are function-less, being completely covered by the skin of the jaw. According to Whitley[3] they number between 1,500 and 2,000. Colour dark bluish-black or slaty-grey above, white below with dull blue-black blotches.

These rays are to be commonly seen on the Queensland coast, especially around islands with rocky headlands. They are more frequently seen during the winter months. Occasionally found in the waters of New South Wales. They grow to a width of at least 15 feet and are closely related to, if not identical with, *M. birostris*, a large devil ray which attains a width of 24 feet and a weight of at least 4 tons, and is found in the Indian Ocean and the Atlantic.

---

[3] In an excellent paper on the species, with remarks on the family generally, in *Austr. Zool.*, 8 pt 3, 1936, pp. 164-88.

Mobula

These devil rays differ from the genus *Manta* in the position of the mouth, the arrangement of the teeth, and the outward curl of the cephalic fins. The mouth is smaller and is placed farther beneath the head. Minute teeth present in both jaws or at least in upper jaw. Several species have been described, but further study will no doubt prove them to be not all distinct.

According to some authorities these rays are said to feed upon shoals of small fishes. They may even at times feed upon large fishes, as the following statement seems to suggest. I relate an observation of E. G. Ogg, of Gladstone, Queensland: "In 1933 when trolling for mackerel between North West and Tryon Islands, my attention was taken by the antics of a mackerel of about 40 pounds weight, some little distance from my boat. It appeared to be held by the tail on the surface of the sea and kept making frantic flops out of the water with its body, the tail remaining fast to some unseen object. On taking my launch alongside, I was surprised to see the mackerel was held firmly by the tail in the mouth of a large devil ray, which appeared to be about 10 or 12 feet across. In a short space of time the devil ray succeeded in swallowing the fish and disappeared below."

Norman and Fraser state:[4] "Dr Coles has observed them feeding off the coast of Carolina, and states that they carry the cephalic fins tightly curled to a sharp point until a school of small 'Minnows' are sighted; then the group swings round in a semicircle and rushes them to the beach, and at that instant these fins flash open, and, meeting below the mouth, form a tunnel through which the minnows are carried to the mouth."

One species in Queensland.

56. PYGMY DEVIL RAY *Mobula diabolus* (Shaw)   [Plate 16]

Raja diabolus Shaw, Gen. Zool., 5, pt 2, 1804, p. 291 (based on the "Eregoodootenkee" of Russell, Vizagapatam, 5, 1803, pl. 9).
Dicerobatis eregoodoo Day, Fish. India, 1878, p. 744, pl. 193, fig. 1.

Ox-ray, Smaller Devil Ray, Devil-fish, Diamond-fish (Queensland).

Teeth in many rows, usually in both jaws; skin quite smooth; no caudal spine; spiracle small. Colour greyish or grey-brown above, lighter below, with pectorals brownish or blackish terminally.

A common species on the Great Barrier Reef and its many islands. These rays approach the shallow waters in small schools of three to five or so, and swim and play about in water about 6 feet deep or shallower, and quite close to the beach. An extremely timid and difficult species to approach. Found on the coast of Queensland from north to south, also through the East Indies to the Indian Ocean, Africa, and the Red Sea. Grows to a width of about 8 feet.

---

[4] *Giant Fishes, Whales and Dolphins*, 1937, p. 85.

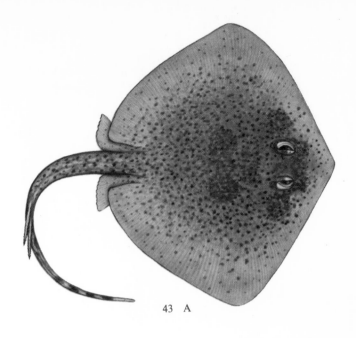

43   A

COLOUR-PLATE 1
43.   Blue-spotted   Stingaree,
Dasyatis kuhlii. A, Width 9 in.;
B, width 7 in.

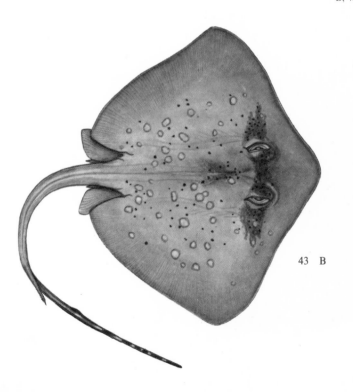

43   B

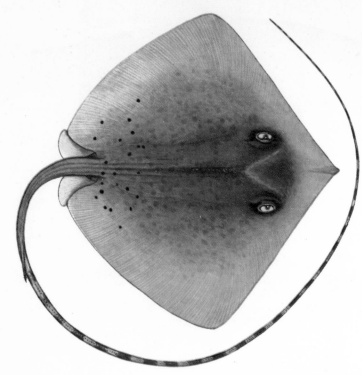

47

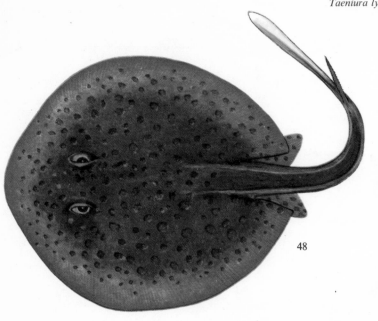

48

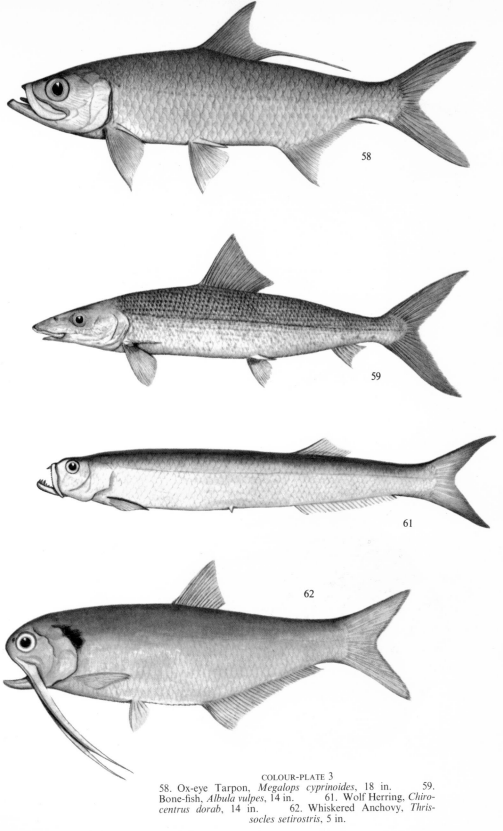

COLOUR-PLATE 3
58. Ox-eye Tarpon, *Megalops cyprinoides*, 18 in.   59.
Bone-fish, *Albula vulpes*, 14 in.   61. Wolf Herring, *Chiro-
centrus dorab*, 14 in.   62. Whiskered Anchovy, *Thrissocles setirostris*, 5 in.

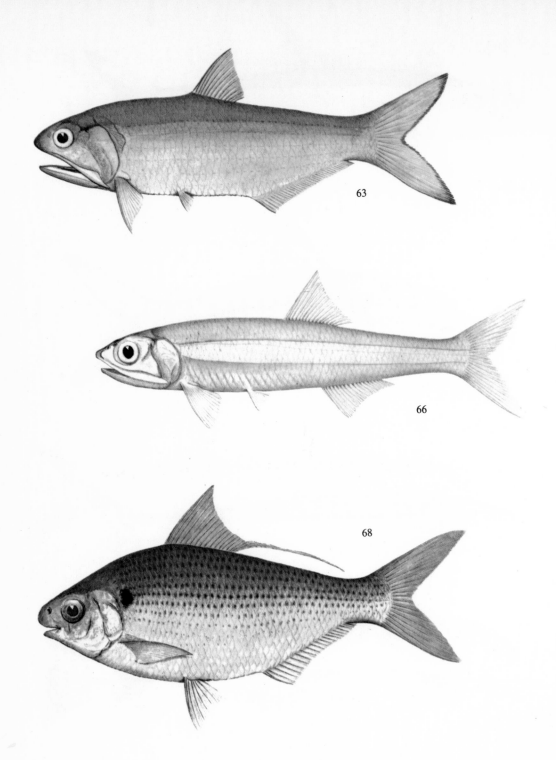

63. Hamilton's Anchovy, *Thrissocles hamiltoni*, $4\frac{1}{2}$ in.
66. De Vis' Anchovy, *Amentum devisi*, $3\frac{1}{2}$ in.
68. Hairback Herring, *Nematalosa come*, $4\frac{3}{4}$ in.

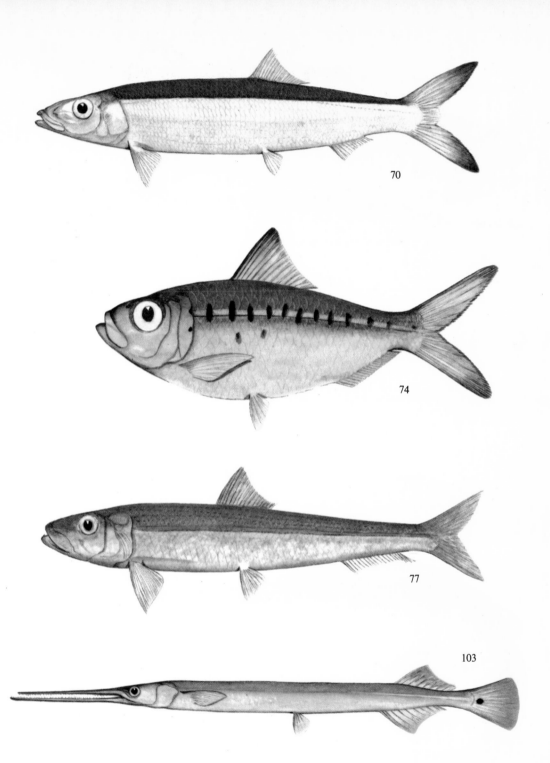

COLOUR-PLATE 5
70. Hasselt's Sprat, *Dussumieria hasseltii*, 7 in.
74. Spotted Herring, *Harengula koningsbergeri*, 6½ in.
77. Australian Pilchard, *Arengus neopilchardus*, 8 in.
103. Black-spot Long Tom, *Tylosurus strongylurus*, 17 in.

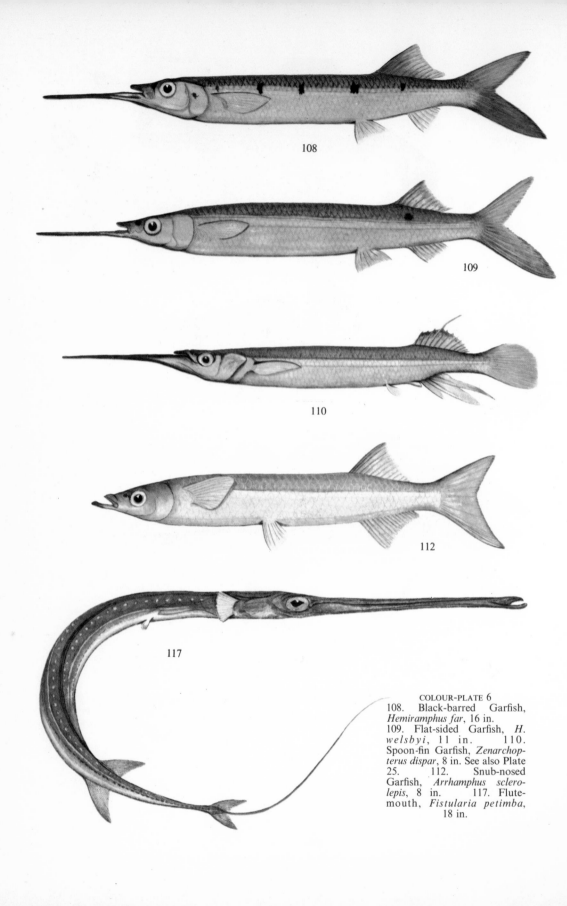

142

143

COLOUR-PLATE 7.
142. Scarlet-fin Soldier-fish, *Holocentrum spiniferum*, 14 in.
143. Crowned Soldier-fish, *H. diadema*, 6 in.

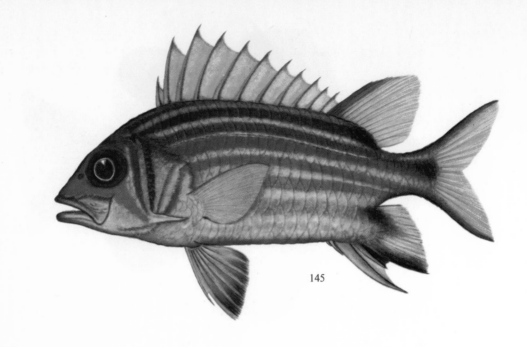

145

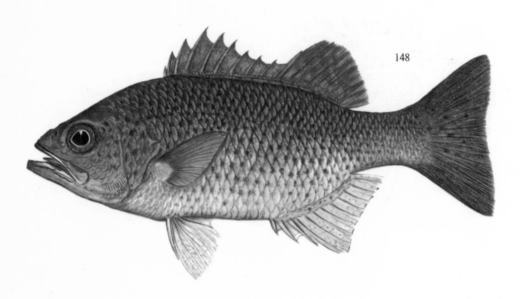

148

COLOUR-PLATE 8
145. Red Soldier-fish, *Holocentrum rubrum*, 9 in.
148. Rock Flag-tail, *Kuhlia rupestris*, 10 in.

149

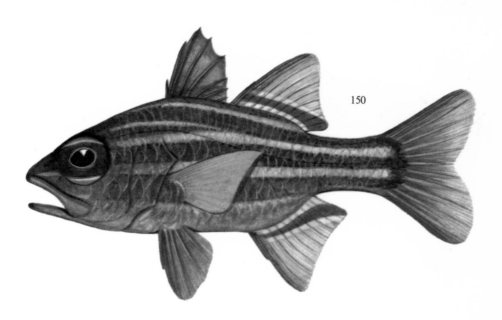

150

COLOUR-PLATE 9
149. Black-finned Cardinal-fish, *Apogon atripes*, 4¼ inches.
150. Cardinal-fish, *A. fasciatus fasciatus*, 2½ in.

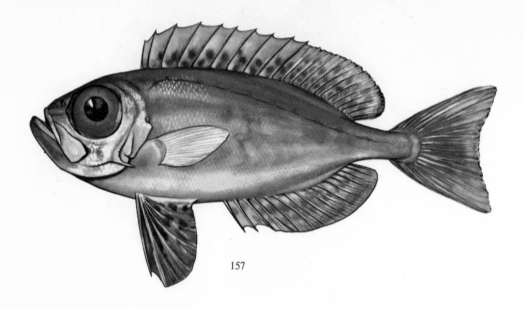

157

158

COLOUR-PLATE 10
157. Red Bulls-eye, *Priacanthus macracanthus*, 6 in.
158. Rifle-fish or Archer-fish, *Toxotes chatareus*, 7 in.

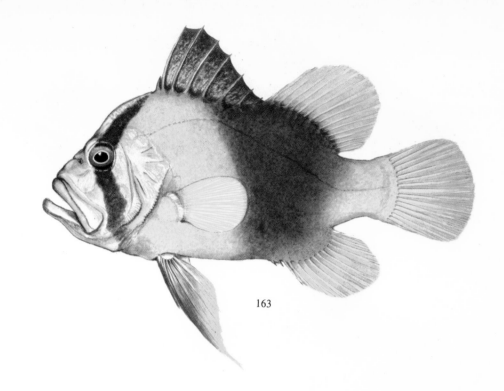

163

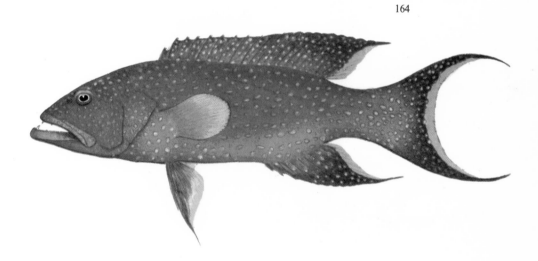

164

COLOUR-PLATE 11
163. Yellow Emperor, *Diploprion bifasciatum*, 8 in.
164. Lunar-tailed Rock Cod, *Variola louti*, 14 in.

COLOUR-PLATE 12
165. Blue-spotted Rock Cod, *Cephalopholis cyanostigma*,
11 in.   166. Freckled Rock Cod, *C. coatesi*, 11½ in.
167. Coral Trout, *C. miniatus*, 10 in.

COLOUR-PLATE 13
168. Yellow-spotted Rock Cod, *Epinephelus areolatus*, 12 in.
170. Black-tipped Rock Cod, *E. fasciatus*, 10 in.
171. Estuary Rock Cod, *E. tauvina*, 19 in.

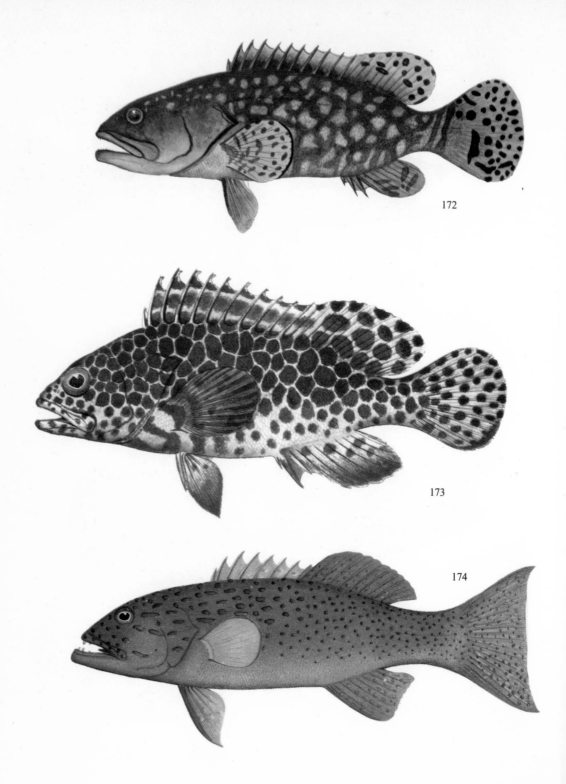

172

173

174

COLOUR-PLATE 14

172. Groper, *Epinephelus lanceolatus*, 21 in.   173. Honeycomb Rock Cod, *E. merra*, 12 in.   174. Coral Cod or
Leopard-fish, *Plectropomus maculatus*, 22 in.

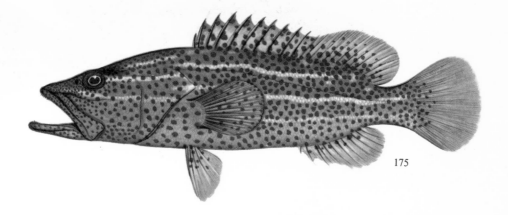

175

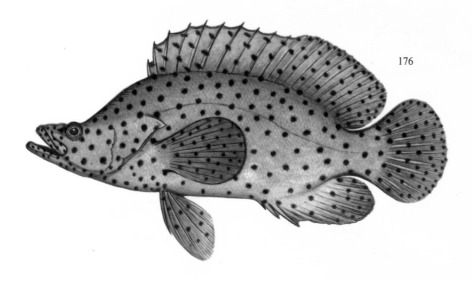

176

COLOUR-PLATE 15
175. White-lined Rock Cod,
Anyperodon leucogrammicus,
$10\frac{1}{2}$ in. 176. Hump-
backed Rock Cod, *Cromileptes
altivelis*, 20 in.

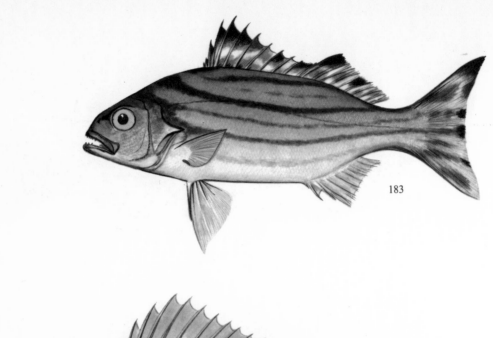

183

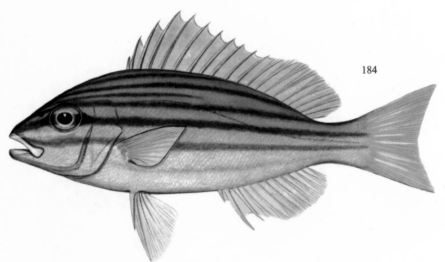

184

188

Class PISCES: FISHES

Class **PISCES: FISHES**

Sub-class NEOPTERYGII: BONY FISHES

FISHES with a firm skeleton of true bone, not cartilaginous as in the sharks and rays. The skull is with membrane bones and the males are without sexual claspers. Scales of rounded design normally present.

Extremely complicated combinations of external and internal characters distinguish the major divisions or orders of the fishes, but since any of these may approach close to and in some instances overlap other divisions, no simple key can be devised which will serve to clearly distinguish the orders. However, little difficulty should be experienced in placing any fish under its correct order, because the chief characteristic features of each are given.

The great majority of living fishes, freshwater and marine, are of the sub-class Neopterygii.

Order **ISOSPONDYLI: HERRINGS and TROUT-LIKE FISHES**

Soft-rayed fishes with the dorsal and anal fins without spines. Ventrals abdominal, sometimes absent. Scales usually cycloid.

A large group of fishes, mostly marine but some entering estuaries and fresh water, others permanently living there. Some of the forms, such as Elopsidae and Albulidae, exhibit the primitive characters of the higher ganoids or bowfins, suggesting possible lines of descent of the Isospondylii from that group.

Sub-order CLUPEOIDEA

The members of this sub-order are characterized by having only one true dorsal fin, which is without spines. They are distinguished from the trout-like forms (sub-order Salmonoidea) by the absence of an adipose (fatty) fin. The trout-like forms are excluded from this book, since the few which enter Queensland waters are mainly freshwater species. Four families in Queensland.

KEY TO FAMILIES REPRESENTED IN QUEENSLAND

A. Lateral line present.

    b. An elongate bony plate on throat, between the
        branches of the lower jaw.   ELOPSIDAE

    bb. No elongate bony plate on throat.

        c. Teeth present.   ALBULIDAE

        cc. No teeth.   CHANIDAE

AA. No lateral line.   CLUPEIDAE

52

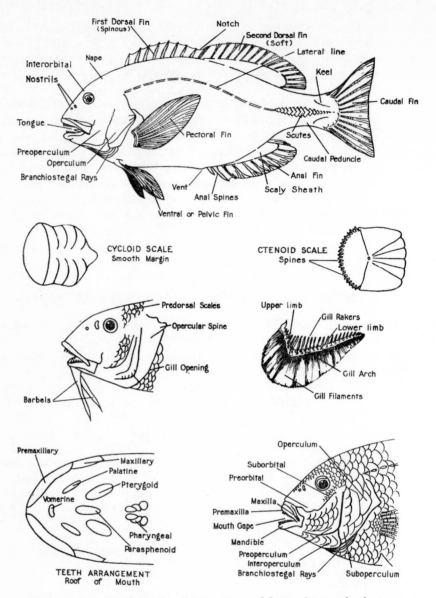

FIG. 5. Anatomical details of an imaginary fish, combining the features found in many species. F. OLSEN, AFTER MUNRO.

Family **Elopsidae: Tarpons**

Body elongate, more or less compressed. Scales silvery, cycloid, not extending on head. Mouth broad, terminal, lower jaw prominent; premaxillaries not protractile, short, the maxillaries forming the lateral margins of upper jaw;

maxillary extending beyond eye. An elongate bony plate between the branches of the lower jaw. Teeth in a villiform band in each jaw and on vomer, palatines, pterygoids, tongue, and base of skull. Eye large, with an adipose eyelid. Dorsal fin situated over or slightly behind ventrals. Caudal fin forked. Pectorals and ventrals each with a long axillary scale. Lateral line present.

A small family containing few species and inhabiting tropical seas. Included in the family is the famous Tarpon, a large and well-known sporting fish of America, which grows to a length of 6 feet or more. Two genera, each with a single species, occur in Australian waters.

KEY TO GENERA IN QUEENSLAND

A. Dorsal and anal fins with their bases encased in a scaly sheath. Dorsal base longer than anal, its last ray not produced. *Elops*

AA. Dorsal and anal fins without scaly sheaths. Anal base longer than dorsal, which has the last ray produced. *Megalops*

Elops

Fishes of large size found in tropical and subtropical seas, frequently entering tidal rivers and ascending almost to the fresh water. Like *Megalops* and *Albula*, the young undergoes a metamorphosis, commencing life as a transparent band-like creature and changing with age. Probably only one species.

57. GIANT HERRING *Elops saurus* Linnaeus [Plate 17]

Elops saurus Linnaeus, Syst. Nat., 12th ed., vol. 1, 1766, p. 518.
Elops (Gularus) australis Whitley, Austr. Zool., 9, pt 4, 1940, p. 398, fig. 1.

Banana-fish (Queensland); Springer, Cape Salmon (South Africa); Ten-pounder, Bony-fish (America).

Colour brilliant silvery, bluish on back; head blackish; dorsal and caudal obscure yellowish, tinged blackish terminally; anal and ventrals tinged yellowish; pectorals black, inner parts white.

A large fish found in most warm seas of the world. Not valued as a food-fish, the flesh being tasteless and full of fine bones. Grows to at least 4 feet.

Megalops

Body oblong, compressed. Abdomen flat. Scales large, tough, silvery. Eyes large, with adipose lids. Mouth large, oblique. Lateral line distinct, with branched tubes. Last dorsal ray much elongated.

Large fishes, widely distributed in tropical and subtropical seas, also entering rivers. Two species: *M. cyprinoides* belonging to the Indo-Pacific region, and *M. thrissoides* to the Atlantic.

58. OX-EYE TARPON *Megalops cyprinoides* (Broussonet) [Colour-plate 3]

Clupea cyprinoides Broussonet, Ichth., 1782, no pagination, pl. 9.
Illustration by G. Coates.

Ox-eye Herring, Big-eyed Herring (New South Wales); Bony Mullet (Thursday Island); Lady-fish, Bastard Mullet (Natal).

Colour bluish-green above, sides silvery, white below; head dark olive; dorsal greenish-yellow, the margin dusky; caudal yellowish; anal, ventrals, and pectorals greenish, tinged with yellow.

A widely distributed tropical species, the young of which freely enter fresh water. Grows to 5 feet and may be termed the Eastern representative of the famous American Tarpon. In Java these fishes are farmed in tanks or ponds, the fry being obtained from the coast. To Europeans the flesh is of poor quality and bony.

Family **Albulidae**

Body elongate, covered with brilliant silvery cycloid scales. Belly flattened. Snout conic, conspicuous. Mouth inferior. Villiform teeth on jaws, vomer, and palatines. Coarse, blunt teeth on pterygoids, sphenoid, and tongue. No gular plate on lower jaw. Gill-membranes widely separated, free. Paired fins each with a long scaly basal flap. Dorsal in advance of ventrals. Anal fin very small, far behind vent, near caudal. Ventrals small. Caudal deeply forked.

A single genus and species, widely distributed in all tropical and subtropical seas, freely entering estuaries.

59. BONE-FISH *Albula vulpes* (Linnaeus) [Colour-plate 3]

Esox vulpes Linnaeus, Syst. Nat., 10th ed., 1758, p. 313.
Illustration by G. Coates.

Lady-fish (Queensland); Tarpon, Lady-fish (Natal).

Depth 4-5¾; interorbital equal to or greater than eye; only a narrow vertical aperture in adipose lid; D. 15-17; A. 8; L. 1. 65-77; L. tr. 8/12. Colour silvery, margins of dorsal and caudal dusky, all the other fins clear; some examples have dusky lines running longitudinally along the back, or have dusky cross-bars.

A very active and beautiful fish, widely distributed in all warm seas. In America it is highly esteemed as a game-fish. It grows to over 36 inches but is of no value as a food-fish. Jordan and Evermann[1] note: "In this, and probably in related families, the young pass through a metamorphosis analogous to that seen in the conger eels; they are for a time elongate, band-shaped, with very small head and loose, transparent tissues; from this condition they become gradually shorter and more compact, shrinking from 3 to 3.5 inches in length

---

[1] *Bull. U.S. Fish. Comm.*, 23, pt 1, 1903 (1905), p. 55.

to 2 inches. According to Dr Gilbert, this process, like that seen in various eels, is a normal one, through which all individuals pass. In the Gulf of California, where these fishes abound, these band-shaped young are often thrown by the waves on the beach in great masses."

Family **Chanidae**

Body oblong, compressed. Abdomen flat. Scales small, cycloid, adherent. Lateral line distinct. Snout depressed. Mouth small, anterior, lower jaw with small symphysial tubercle. Maxillary short, wide, excluded from gape of mouth, without supplemental bone. Lower jaw overlapped by upper. No teeth. Eye completely covered with broad adipose lids. Dorsal opposite ventrals, larger than anal. Caudal long, deeply forked.

Large fishes of the Indo-Pacific region, popular with game-fishermen. A single genus and species.

60. SALMON HERRING *Chanos chanos* (Forskål) [Plate 17]

Mugil chanos Forskål, Descr. Animal., 1775, p. 74.
Lutodeira salmonea Richardson, Ichth. Voy. Erebus and Terror, 1846, p. 58, pl. 36, figs 1-2.

Moreton Bay Salmon (South Queensland); Bony Salmon, Milk-fish, Giant Herring (North Queensland); White Mullet (Western Australia); Bangos (Philippines); Bandang (East Indies).

Depth $3\frac{1}{2}$-$4\frac{3}{4}$; D. 14-16; A. 8-10; scales with numerous horizontal parallel striae, ending in slender points; L. 1. 78-90; L. tr. 12-13 above, 9-11 below lateral line. Colour: black and head bluish above, body silvery, fins and tail with dusky tips.

A large, brilliantly silver fish, swift in the water. Grows to 6 feet and is a delicious food-fish. Widely ranging and freely entering fresh water. This species is farmed by the natives of the Philippine Islands in tide-ponds. According to Professor Dakin farming is also practised by the natives of Nauru. He states that the Milk-fish is farmed in practically freshwater lakes. The natives obtain the newly hatched fry from pools in the fringing reefs and after keeping them for two or three weeks in large shells and other receptacles transfer them to the lakes, where they flourish until a couple of feet in length.[2]

This fish takes one of its common names, that of Bony Salmon, from its many bones and its pink flesh.

Family **Clupeidae: Herring-like Fishes**

This large and important family contains the herrings and their allies, of which there are over two hundred species. Although mainly distributed throughout the Northern Hemisphere, many species of herrings frequent the Southern

---

[2] See *Proc. Linn. Soc. N.S.Wales*, 59, pts 5-6, 1936 (Abs.).

Hemisphere, and along the vast coastline of Australia dense shoals in teeming millions exist, visiting our inshore waters at certain seasons for the purpose of breeding. Most species are marine, though some enter rivers to breed or are found living in fresh water. They feed upon the minute marine crustaceans, etc., known as plankton.

The numerous species occurring in Queensland waters are divided into six sub-families.

KEY TO SUB-FAMILIES REPRESENTED IN QUEENSLAND

A. Dorsal fin posterior.   CHIROCENTRINAE

AA. Dorsal fin median.

    b. Maxilla very large, greatly produced backward.   ENGRAULINAE

    bb. Maxilla small or moderate, not produced unusually
       far backward.

    c. Mouth small, inferior, transverse. No teeth. Pos-
       terior dorsal ray produced.   DOROSOMATINAE

    cc. Mouth lateral, jaws equal. Posterior dorsal ray
       not produced.

    d. Belly rounded, no serrated edge of spiniform
       scales.   STOLEPHORINAE

    dd. Belly usually compressed and with a serrated
       edge of spiniform scales.

    e. Anterior dorsal profile with a serrated edge of
       spiniform scales, similar to belly.   HYPERLOPHINAE

    ee. Anterior dorsal profile not serrated.   CLUPEINAE

Sub-family CHIROCENTRINAE

Body very elongated and strongly compressed. Scales small, thin, and very deciduous. Mouth large, superior, greatly inclined. Lower jaw prominent. Canine teeth in front of premaxillaries and mandibular bones, others long and pointed. Teeth in narrow bands on palatines, pterygoids, and tongue. Pectoral fins with long axillary scales. Ventrals with similar scales and 2 long scales at caudal base. Dorsal origin opposite that of long anal. Ventrals very small. Caudal deeply forked.

A single genus and probably only one species. Wide-ranging.

61. WOLF HERRING *Chirocentrus dorab* (Forskål)   [Colour-plate 3]

Clupea dorab Forskål, Descr. Animal., 1775, p. 72.
Illustration by G. Coates.

Leaping Silver-bar (North Queensland); Ribbon-fish (South Queensland); Knife-fish (Malay States); Dorab (India).

Colour deep bluish-green above, intense silvery on sides and abdomen; a golden stripe along the side separating the two colours; dorsal fin pale yellow, narrowly edged black; pectorals dusky; anal hyaline; caudal yellowish, becoming black on lobes terminally.

The leaping powers of this giant herring are remarkable. George Coates, of Townsville, writes of the fish: "I have seen a small one jump clear over a travelling launch."

The mouth of the Wolf Herring is armed with very long fang-like teeth, and when caught the fish will snap at anything within reach. As a food-fish it is of little value, the flesh being so full of small bones as to render it useless. The name Silver-bar is bestowed on account of its gleaming silver colour, and the name Knife-fish from its very compressed body. Grows to 12 feet. Circumtropical.

Sub-family ENGRAULINAE: ANCHOVIES

Body oblong or elongate, more or less compressed. No lateral line. Belly sharp or rounded, with more or less numerous keeled abdominal scutes. Snout rounded and usually overlaps mouth, which is large, with maxilla long and narrow, sometimes greatly extended. Teeth small or absent. Eye moderate or enlarged, covered by skin.

The anchovies are small gregarious fishes, mostly translucent and readily distinguished from all other allied species by the enormous gape of the mouth. They are found in abundance along most warm and tropical coasts. At certain seasons of the year great numbers rove the Queensland coastline and enter the estuaries, feeding upon plankton and moving in shoals. Four genera are found in Queensland.

KEY TO GENERA IN QUEENSLAND

A. Belly compressed, with a serrated edge of projecting spiniform scutes.

    b. Dorsal fin preceded by a short free spine.

        c. Abdominal scutes well developed, extending from gill-opening to vent.   *Thrissocles*

        cc. Ventral scutes weak, almost hidden by scales.   *Thrissina*

    bb. No free spine before dorsal fin.   *Amentum*

AA. Belly scarcely compressed, without projecting spiniform scutes.   *Engraulis*

Thrissocles

Body oblong or elongate, compressed, with well-developed scutes along sharp edge of abdomen, from gill-opening to vent. Dorsal origin usually in advance of anal, with tiny spine in front. Snout prominent or short, maxilla produced, sometimes reaching anal. Minute teeth, in jaws, on palate and tongue. No silvery lateral stripe.

Small fishes of the warm waters of the Indo-Pacific, living usually in large schools, some species entering estuaries. Two species in Queensland.

KEY TO SPECIES IN QUEENSLAND

A. Maxillary greatly produced, reaching far beyond pectorals. *setirostris*

AA. Maxillary not so greatly produced, reaching only to gill-opening. *hamiltoni*

62. WHISKERED ANCHOVY *Thrissocles setirostris* Broussonet

[Colour-plate 3]

Thrissocles setirostris Broussonet, Ichthyol., 1, 1782, no pagination, pl. 2.
Illustration by G. Coates.

Glass-nose (South Africa).

Colour dirty greenish above, silvery below; black venules on shoulders; pectorals and caudal ochre-yellow, the latter narrowly edged black posteriorly; other fins colourless.

The remarkable prolongation of the maxillary readily distinguishes this species. It was first made known from Queensland by George Coates, who obtained it from Townsville. He remarks, "Apparently rare in local waters as it is many years since I last saw them." The range of the species is North Queensland and the Indo-Pacific region. Grows to 8 inches.

63. HAMILTON'S ANCHOVY *Thrissocles hamiltoni* (Gray)

[Colour-plate 4]

Engraulis hamiltoni Gray, Illust. Ind. Zool. Hardwicke, 2, 1832-4, pl. 92, fig. 3.
Illustration by G. Coates.

Anal origin below or slightly behind end of dorsal; maxillary reaches gill-opening; lower gill-rakers about 13. Colour greenish-grey above, silvery on sides and below, black venules on shoulders; dorsal light greyish; pectorals yellowish; ventrals and anal whitish; caudal pale yellow, with narrow black margin posteriorly.

An Indo-Australian species found along the shores and in the estuaries of Queensland in great shoals. Grows to 8 inches.

Thrissina

Maxillary not extending to gill-opening. Lower jaw included. Teeth even, no canines. Ventral scutes weak, almost hidden by scales. Dorsal fin preceded by a short free spine. Anal base behind level of dorsal. Anal rays 31 to 34. Scales firm. No silvery lateral band. One species in Queensland.

64. ESTUARY ANCHOVY *Thrissina aestuaria* (Ogilby)   [Plate 17]

Anchovia aestuaria Ogilby, Proc. Roy. Soc. Qld, 23, Nov. 1910, p. 4.
Thrissina aestuaria Whitley, Austr. Zool., 10, pt 1, 1941, p. 2, fig. 2.

Anal rays 31-34; maxillary reaches slightly beyond mandibular articulation; lower gill-rakers about 24. Colour cinnamon-buff on back and upper sides down to a line from eye to tail; lower sides and belly silvery, with pale-pink reflections; usually a dusky shoulder-spot; dorsal and caudal cinnamon-buff, the longer dorsal rays and caudal lobes narrowly tipped with blackish; pectorals, ventrals, and anal white.

A common little fish in Queensland, especially southwards, where it is frequently caught by prawners when they are netting in the rivers. Apparently present on the coast at all times of the year and in the rivers during the colder months. Grows to 6 inches.

Amentum

Thorax compressed, bearing 2 to 7 sharp-pointed scutes between pectoral and ventral fins. Maxillary not extending farther back than just behind gill-openings. Teeth small. Anal fin behind or below level of middle of dorsal or slightly in advance of same. Scales thin, deciduous. Body very translucent, with silvery lateral band.

Tropical Indo-Australian anchovies of small size, living in large schools and feeding on plankton. Two species in Queensland.

KEY TO SPECIES IN QUEENSLAND

A.   Origin of anal fin slightly behind that of dorsal; snout
     shorter than eye.   *carpentariae*

AA. Origin of anal fin below last dorsal ray; snout as long
     as eye.   *devisi*

65. GULF ANCHOVY *Amentum carpentariae* (De Vis)   [Plate 17]

Engraulis carpentariae De Vis, Proc. Linn. Soc. N.S.Wales, 7, 28th Oct. 1882, p. 320.
Illustration by F. Olsen after Whitley.

D. 1/15 or 2/14; A. 2/21; P. 12. Colour orange, with a rather broad silvery stripe; head pale, silvery; a large dark spot on each side of occiput with a few black dots around it; black dots along spine and on each interneural joint of dorsal and anal; caudal punctated with black, other fins white, immaculate. (De Vis.)

This little fish probably occurs along the whole coastline of Queensland. For many years it was known only from the Gulf of Carpentaria, where it was taken when first described in 1882. It was unknown elsewhere until I secured several close inshore at Peel Island, Moreton Bay, in October 1946. No doubt a closer search will reveal its presence between the two localities mentioned. Grows to at least 2 inches, probably much more.

66. DE VIS' ANCHOVY *Amentum devisi* Whitley   [Colour-plate 4]

Amentum devisi Whitley, Austr. Zool., 9, pt 4, 1940, p. 404, fig. 11.
Illustration by G. Coates.

Colour greyish-white, with a broad silvery longitudinal lateral band from opercle edge to caudal base; fins hyaline, the caudal with a pale tinge of orange.

This anchovy is found from the Gulf of Carpentaria down the coast of Queensland as far south as Moreton Bay. Grows to about 5¼ inches.

Engraulis

Body but little compressed, belly rounded. No abdominal scutes. Maxillary not extending to gill-opening. No silvery lateral stripe.

Small fishes of cool or temperate waters of most seas. One species in Australia.

67. AUSTRALIAN ANCHOVY *Engraulis australis* (White)   [Plate 17]

Atherina australis White, Voy. N.S.Wales, 1790, p. 296 and opposite plate.
Engraulis australis McCulloch, Rec. Austr. Mus., 13, pt 2, 1920, p. 43, pl. 12, fig. 1.

Pilchard (South Queensland).

D. 15; A. 17; P. 16. Colour greenish above, silvery below, a broad stripe along middle of side.

Large shoals of this anchovy frequent the southern Australian seaboard and also the coast of New South Wales, visiting the shores of southern Queensland during the winter months. Stragglers have been found in Queensland as far north as the Capricorns. They frequent the deeper waters of the bays and estuaries as well as the open outside waters.

This anchovy, which also occurs in Tasmania and New Zealand, is closely allied to the well-known European Anchovy. Grows to 5 inches.

Sub-family DOROSOMATINAE: GIZZARD SHADS

Body short, deep, well compressed, with scutes on edge of the compressed belly. Head short, rather small. Eyes with adipose lids. Mouth small, inferior. No teeth. Stomach short, muscular, gizzard-like. No lateral line. Scales thin, cycloid, deciduous. Head naked. Dorsal median, usually behind ventrals, the last ray often produced into a filament. Anal low, very long. Caudal forked. Genera few, one in Queensland.

Deep-bodied compressed herrings found in most warm regions. None of the species are valued as food on account of their numerous bones. They take the name of Gizzard Shad from their muscular and short gizzard-like stomach. Their food consists largely of mud.

Nematalosa

Mouth subterminal or inferior, transverse, cleft forming an angle. No teeth. Scales 40 to 50 in lateral series, 14 to 21 transversely. Dorsal with 13 to 18 rays, set in a scaly basal sheath, the last ray prolonged. Anal with 18 to 24 rays.

Members of this genus range from Arabia to Japan and to Australia. Probably only one species in Queensland.

68. HAIRBACK HERRING *Nematalosa come* (Richardson) [Colour-plate 4]

Chatoessus come Richardson, Ichth. Voy. Erebus and Terror, 1846, p. 62, pl. 38, figs 7-9.
Illustration by G. Coates.

Stinker (South Queensland); Bony Bream (Queensland and New South Wales).

D. 4/10; A. 2/16-18. Colour greenish-grey above, silvery below; 6 to 7 longitudinal lines along centres of scales on back from head to tail; a black shoulder-spot is usually present.

A common mud-eating fish, readily recognized by the lengthened posterior dorsal ray. It inhabits coastal waters, estuaries, and freshwater streams in Queensland from south to north, also in New South Wales and Western Australia. It is also found far into the interior of the continent. Grows to at least 10 inches.

Sub-family STOLEPHORINAE: DWARF ROUND HERRINGS or SPRATS

Body elongate, belly rounded below. No scutes. Jaws equal or almost so. Mouth terminal, rather small. Teeth small, in jaws, on vomer, palatines, and tongue, deciduous, or may be absent. Scales moderate or large, thin, easily shed. Fins small, anal short. No lateral line.

Small herring-like fishes of tropical and temperate seas, recognized by their rounded bellies which are without scutes or spines. Three genera are known, two being found in Queensland.

KEY TO GENERA IN QUEENSLAND

A. Origin of dorsal fin nearer to tip of snout than to caudal base. Anal rays 9-13. *Stolephorus*

AA. Origin of dorsal fin nearer to caudal base than to tip of snout. Anal rays 15-17. *Dussumieria*

Stolephorus

Body elongate, belly rounded below. Mouth terminal, smallish, premaxillary small, maxillary long, broad and rounded behind. Teeth mostly absent. Fins small; anal short.

Small silvery fishes of the tropical Indo-Pacific region, readily recognized by their rounded bellies without scutes. One species in Queensland.

69. BLUE SPRAT *Stolephorus delicatulus* (Bennett)   [Plate 17]

Clupea delicatula Bennett, Proc. Zool. Soc. Lond., 1831, p. 168.
Stolephorus robustus McCulloch, Rec. Austr. Mus., 13, pt 2, 1920, p. 42, pl. 11, fig. 1.

D. 12; A. 11; P. 13; V. 8; C. 17. Colour intense dark blue above, with silver sides cleanly contrasted; eye silver.

This wide-ranging little fish visits the shores of Queensland in vast shoals during the winter months for the purpose of spawning. Its red flesh is of fine flavour. This fish, with many other species of Australian herrings, is destined some day to be of great economic importance. Grows to 4 inches.

Dussumieria

Form elongate, more or less compressed. Snout pointed, jaws equal. Maxillary and premaxillary very small. Small teeth in jaws; villiform patches of teeth on palatines, pterygoids, and tongue. Eyes with very thin, wide adipose lids. Dorsal opposite ventrals, its origin nearer to caudal than to end of snout. Anal small, far behind dorsal. Scales of medium or small size, very deciduous.

Small fishes of the Indo-Pacific region. Species few, one in Queensland.

70. HASSELT'S SPRAT *Dussumieria hasseltii* Bleeker   [Colour-plate 5]

Dussumieria hasseltii Bleeker, Nat. Tijdschr. Ned. Ind., 1, 1851, p. 422.
Illustration by G. Coates.

D. 18-19; A. 16; P. 14-15; L. 1. 52-56; L. tr. 12-13; gill-rakers 12 + 26. Colour a beautiful dark green, shot with blue above, silvery below; upper margin of opercle and along the back light blue, with a bronze line below and a silvery one beneath that one again; upper surface of head and eye emerald green; caudal shot with blue, green, and gold; pectorals, ventrals, and anal white.

This large sprat is found in the northern waters of Queensland. Wide-ranging outside Australia. Grows to 8 inches.

Sub-family HYPERLOPHINAE: ROUGH-BACKED SPRATS

A small family of sprats inhabiting Australian waters. They are characterized by the presence of a median row of predorsal scutes as well as the median row on the abdomen, Two genera, species few.

A. Ventrals inserted beneath anterior third of dorsal. Fluviatile.   *Potamalosa*

AA. Ventrals inserted in advance of dorsal. Marine.   *Hyperlophus*

Potamalosa

Body oblong, strongly compressed. Maxillaries narrow, $3\frac{1}{2}$ to 4 in eye diameter. Jaws, palatines, and tongue toothed, vomer and pterygoids toothless. Eight branchiostegals. Dorsal inserted well in front of middle of body. Anal moderate, its base as long as its distance from caudal. Ventrals inserted beneath anterior third or fourth of dorsal. Predorsal scutes prominent, but not so strong as those of abdomen. Scales with smooth posterior border.

Freshwater herrings, represented by a single species.

71. FRESHWATER HERRING *Potamalosa richmondia* (Macleay)
[Plate 18]

Clupea richmondia Macleay, Proc. Linn. Soc. N.S.Wales, 4, pt 3, 1st Dec. 1879, p. 380.
Potamalosa novae-hollandiae McCulloch, Rec. Austr. Mus., 11, no. 7, 1917, p. 166, pl. 29, fig. 4.

D. 16; A. 16; L. 1. 48; L. tr. 11. Colour dark green above, sides silvery, white below; an indistinct blackish band may be present, extending from above pectoral fin to origin of anal; opercles golden, tinged red; dorsal and caudal dark greenish-grey; anal and ventrals hyaline, as is the extremity of the pectorals, the bases of which are greenish.

Although recorded from Queensland, there is no definite evidence of this species having been captured in the State. However, it is so common in the coastal rivers of northern New South Wales, and so close to the Queensland border that it is surprising it has not been commonly taken here. Roughley[3] states that "during the greater part of the year this fish confines its wanderings to the freshwater at the heads of the streams, but during the colder months it migrates to the mouths of the rivers, where the water is quite salt, for the purpose of spawning". Grows to 10 inches.

Hyperlophus

Body oblong or elongate, more or less compressed. Maxillaries broad, $2\frac{1}{3}$ to $2\frac{1}{2}$ in eye diameter. Teeth absent. Four branchiostegals. Dorsal inserted behind middle of body. Anal rather long, its base much more than its distance from caudal. Ventrals inserted in advance of dorsal. Predorsal scutes weak, less developed than those of abdomen. Scales pectinated.

Marine herrings, the genus represented in Australia by two species.

---

[3] *Fishes of Australia and their Technology*, 1916, p. 17.

A.   Origin of anal fin behind end of depressed dorsal; scales adherent.   *vittatus*

AA.   Origin of anal fin close behind base of last dorsal ray; scales deciduous.   *translucidus*

72. SANDY SPRAT *Hyperlophus vittatus* (Castelnau)   [Plate 18]

Meletta vittata Castelnau, Res. Fish. Austr. (Vic. Offic. Phil. Exhib.), 1875, p. 46.
Hyperlophus vittatus McCulloch, Rec. Austr. Mus., 11, no. 7, 1917, p. 163, pl. 29, figs 1-2.

Smelt (Melbourne Fish Market).

D. 15-17; A. 19-20; L. 1. 48-51; L. tr. 11-13; depth $4\frac{1}{4}$-$4\frac{2}{3}$; abdominal scutes 20 + 12-13. Colour light green, with a broad, well-defined silvery longitudinal stripe on each side; belly white; operculum and throat silvery and iridescent; dorsal and caudal yellow, other fins translucent; eye silvery; above the silvery band the scales are margined with a series of blackish dots; similar dots are present on mouth-parts; snout and interorbital regions with more or less scattered dots; occiput deep blue; dorsal and caudal fins with a series of fine dots along each ray.

A sprat which visits the waters of southern Australia in vast shoals during the autumn and winter months. A valuable food-fish, so far little used. It is found in the shallow bays, estuaries, and beach waters of Queensland, New South Wales, Victoria, South Australia and, Western Australia. In Queensland it is frequently captured by prawners. Grows to 5 inches.

73. GLASSY SPRAT *Hyperlophus translucidus* McCulloch   [Plate 18]

Hyperlophus translucidus McCulloch, Rec. Austr. Mus., 11, no. 7, 1917, p. 165, pl. 29, fig. 3.

D. 15-16; A. 19-22; P. 10-13; V. 7; C. 19; depth almost 4; abdominal scutes 17 + 9. Colour: The body is translucent in life, with a broad silvery band extending from head to tail; back with scattered black dots and a dark spot at base of each anal ray; lips and chin also dotted.

A small New South Wales species, rarely seen in Queensland waters. It has been recorded only as far north as Caloundra, South Queensland. Grows to 2 inches.

Sub-family CLUPEINAE: TRUE HERRINGS and PILCHARDS

The members of this sub-family are characterized mainly by their compressed bellies, on the sharp edges of which are bony, keeled scales with or without spines. They are a large group of important fishes found in all warm seas. Their numbers are legion, beyond anything we can imagine. It is estimated that of the world's annual catch of fishes more than 50 per cent is comprised of herrings.

Their great abundance comes not so much from their fecundity as from their ability to change from one layer of water to another, thus following a rich food-supply and readily adapting themselves to depths from the surface down to 100 fathoms. They are principally coastal fishes which school at the surface during the breeding season, after which they descend into the deeper waters. Three genera are found in Queensland waters.

KEY TO GENERA IN QUEENSLAND

A.   Ventral fins well developed. Anal fin moderate, with 15-25 rays.

    b. Belly compressed, with serrated edge of keeled, spiniform scales.   *Harengula*

    bb. Belly not markedly compressed, not serrated; keeled scutes not prominent or spiniform.   *Arengus*

AA. Ventral fins very small. Anal fin long, with 33-37 rays.   *Pellona*

Harengula

Body compressed and with scutes on lower edge of sharp belly. Jaws with fine teeth. Gill-rakers fine, long, and numerous. Dorsal with low scaly basal sheath.

Small fishes inhabiting the coastal and estuarine waters of the Indo-Pacific region. Six species occur in Queensland.

KEY TO SPECIES IN QUEENSLAND

A.   Height less than 3 in the length.

    b. Bases of anal and dorsal fins about equal.

      c. Upper sides with 8-13 dark vertical spots; dorsal tipped with black.   *koningsbergeri*

      cc. No dark vertical spots; caudal tips sometimes black.   *macrolepis*

    bb. Base of anal fin much shorter than that of dorsal; dorsal and caudal tipped with black.   *castelnaui*

AA. Height more than 3 in the length.

    d. Bases of anal and dorsal fins equal; scales perforated.

      e. Gill-rakers 40. Caudal fin with deep black tips.   *atricauda*

      ee. Gill-rakers 50-52. Caudal fin uniform, no black tips.   *fimbriata*

    dd. Base of anal fin shorter than that of dorsal; no perforations in scales.   *ovalis*

74. SPOTTED HERRING *Harengula koningsbergeri* Weber and de Beaufort
[Colour-plate 5]

Clupea (Harengula) koningsbergeri Weber and de Beaufort, Verh. Akad. Wet. Amster., 17, no. 3, 1912, p. 14.
Illustration by G. Coates.

D. 18-19; A. 20-21; P. 15; V. 8; L. 1. 43-44; L. tr. 12; depth $2\frac{2}{3}$; head $3\frac{2}{3}$; eye $2\frac{3}{4}$ in head; lower gill-rakers 33; ventrals below or little in advance of middle of dorsal; ventral scutes 17-18 + 11-12. Colour greyish-green above, silvery below; 3 to 4 longitudinal dark lines along each side of back, below which is a longitudinal salmon-coloured stripe on upper sides, overlaid with a row of 8 to 13 vertical dusky spots or bars and sometimes another row of 3 or so on the flanks; tip of snout, dorsal and caudal lobes dusky, other fins hyaline.

This herring is common along the coastline of North Queensland. It also occurs in north-western Australia, the Aru Islands, and New Guinea. Grows to 7 inches.

75. SOUTHERN HERRING *Harengula castelnaui* (Ogilby)   [Plate 18]

Kowala castelnaui Ogilby, Proc. Linn. Soc. N.S.Wales, 22, 1897, p. 66.
Sardinella castelnaui Stead, Edib. Fish. N.S.Wales, 1908, p. 26, pl. 5.

D. 17-19; A. 19-21; Sc. 44-45/12; depth $2\frac{3}{4}$-$2\frac{7}{8}$; head $3\frac{3}{5}$-$3\frac{4}{5}$; eye $2\frac{7}{8}$-3 in head; gill-rakers 18 + 52, finely lanceolate; ventral scutes 17 + 11. Colour blue above, sides and below silvery, the back with 1 to 3 more or less distinct golden, dark-edged bands; dorsal and caudal tinged yellow and tipped with black.

A common herring on the coasts and in the estuaries and inlets of Queensland and New South Wales. In Queensland it has been recorded from as far north as the Burdekin River and at times is seen in great shoals. Grows to 9 inches.

OTHER SPECIES

The Deep Herring, *H. macrolepis*, inhabits the waters of North Queensland, growing to a length of about 6 inches. The Black-tailed Herring, *H. atricauda*, also frequents the northern waters. The Fringe-scaled Herring, *H. fimbriata*, and the Torres Strait Herring, *H. ovalis*, are two more northern herrings, the latter occurring in vast shoals and forming a valuable food-supply for the natives of Murray and other islands (it is the *H. punctata* of earlier authors). Both the Fringe-scaled Herring and the Torres Strait Herring grow to about 7 inches.

Arengus

Body elongate, robust, moderately compressed, belly not sharp-edged, scutes feeble. Eye with well-developed adipose lids. Teeth usually absent. Opercle with radiating grooves. Caudal base with enlarged scales. Anal rays 16 to 20.

Small fishes of economic importance, widely distributed, mainly in cool and temperate waters, though one Queensland species inhabits tropical waters, the other entering the cooler southern waters.

A. About 37 gill-rakers on lower limb of first branchial arch. Colour dark blue above, silvery below; about 11 large distinct dark spots along upper sides.   *dakini*

AA. About 75 gill-rakers on lower limb of first arch (60 in young). Colour dark blue above, silvery below, each scale of back with a small black basal spot; a row of distinct blackish spots along sides.   *neopilchardus*

76. DAKIN'S PILCHARD *Arengus dakini* (Whitley)   [Plate 18]

Sardinops dakini Whitley, Mem. Qld Mus., 11, pt 2, 1937, p. 114.
Illustration by F. Olsen after Whitley.

D. 18; A. 18 + 2; depth, $\frac{1}{5}$, head $\frac{1}{4}$, of standard length; eye $3\frac{1}{4}$ to nearly 4 in head, partly concealed by adipose lids; abdominal scutes 17-18 + 12-14; gill-rakers 37 on lower limb of first arch; form robust, fusiform, belly not markedly compressed; scales deciduous. Colour blue-grey above, yellowish or silvery below; about 11 more or less distinct dark spots along upper sides; fins whitish; a dusky brown blotch on snout.

A common Torres Strait pilchard found in shoals in the region of Thursday Island, North Queensland. It evidently visits these northern waters for the purpose of spawning. Grows to $7\frac{1}{2}$ inches.

77. AUSTRALIAN PILCHARD *Arengus neopilchardus* (Steindachner)
[Colour-plate 5]

Clupea neopilchardus Steindachner, Denkschr. Akad. Wiss. Wien, 41, pt 1, 1879, p. 12.
Illustration by G. Coates.

D. 4 + 14-15; A. 3 + 13-14; depth 4.9, head 3.9, in the length; eye 4.05 in head; body moderately elongate, compressed, ventral profile more curved than back; ventrals inserted below or a little behind middle of dorsal fin; ventral scutes 19 + 15, keeled, but not prominent; gill-rakers fine and closely set, 75 on lower limb of first arch; scales deciduous. Colour dark blue above, changing abruptly into silver on sides, each scale on back with a small black basal spot and a row of round blackish spots along junction of the blue and silver; eye silvery; tips of jaws blackish; dorsal and caudal with dusky tips.

This is one of the commonest Australian herrings and destined one day to be of commercial importance. It occurs in shoals during the winter months

68

and ranges northwards to Hervey Bay in Queensland, its place being taken in the far north by Dakin's Pilchard. It is more commonly met with in the waters of the southern portion of the continent, where it ranges across to Western Australia. Tasmania and New Zealand are also included in its extended range. Grows to 11 inches.

Pellona

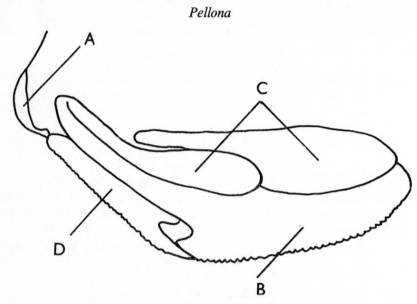

Fig. 6. *Pellona hoevenii.* A, Intermaxillary; B, maxillary; C, supplemental bones; D, ossified ligament between the intermaxillary and maxillary.   F. OLSEN, AFTER WEBER AND DE BEAUFORT.

Body compressed. Belly with sharp scutes. Dorsal origin before anal. Edge of upper jaw with a ligament, or in some species, a small supplemental bone, armed with teeth, extending from lateral end of premaxillary to middle of maxillary. There are also 2 dorsal supplemental bones, larger of which reaches almost to posterior border of maxillary.

Small fishes of the Indo-Pacific, one from the shores of Queensland.

78. DITCHELEE HERRING *Pellona ditchela* Cuvier and Valenciennes

[Plate 18]

Pellona ditchela Cuvier and Valenciennes, Hist. Nat. Poiss., 20, 1847, p. 314.
Ilisha hoevenii Bleeker, Atlas Ichth., 6, 1870-2, p. 117, pl. 269, fig. 2.

D. 17-18; A. 33-37; depth 2¾-3; head 3-3¼; origin of dorsal midway between snout and caudal, or a little nearer the latter; origin of anal below or a little in advance of last dorsal ray; scales deciduous, margins slightly crenulated;

gill-rakers 20-23; ventral scutes 23-27, of which 9 are post-ventral. Colour silvery, with burnished lateral band; dorsal and caudal fins with dark margins, other fins hyaline; a dark, ill-defined shoulder-spot may be present.

This Indo-Australian herring has been trawled on the Queensland coast between Cairns and Townsville and has been found also in the Gulf of Carpentaria. It is apparently not a common species in Queensland. Grows to 8 inches.

Sub-order GONORHYNCHOIDEA

Family **Gonorhynchidae**

This family contains a single genus and species, found in the cooler regions of the Indo-Pacific. It is a primitive elongate fish with a small mouth and a barbel below the end of the snout, and with elongate fine ctenoid scales over its head and body. Fossil genera and species now extinct are known from the Tertiary and Cretaceous periods.

Gonorhynchus

Body anguilliform, compressed posteriorly. Scales subquadrangular, with free border feebly rounded. Lateral line complete, nearly straight. Eyes large. Head scaly. Teeth present on pterygoid and hyoid bones. Dorsal inserted near commencement of posterior third of body.

79. RATFISH *Gonorhynchus gonorhynchus* (Linnaeus)   [Plate 19]

Cyprinus gonorhynchus Linnaeus, Syst. Nat., 12th ed., vol. 1, 1766, p. 528.
Rhynchana greyi Richardson, Ichth. Voy. Erebus and Terror, 1845, p. 44, pl. 29, figs 1-6.

Beaked Salmon (New South Wales); Mouse-fish (South Queensland and New South Wales); Sand Eel (New Zealand); Ratfish (Western Australia).

D. 11-13; A. 9-10. Colour greyish or brownish above, silvery below; a pink lateral stripe from head to tail; fin-tips black; caudal with a median black patch on each lobe and the tips pink.

This fish frequents sandy bottoms, usually in shallow water, though sometimes at considerable depths. It feeds upon small shellfish, crustaceans, etc., which it obtains by burrowing into the sand. It grows to at least 18 inches and its flesh is said to be excellent eating. It is found on the coasts of temperate Australia, New Zealand, Japan, and South Africa, but is not commonly seen in Queensland waters.

Order **INIOMI**

Sub-order MYCTOPHOIDEA: SERGEANT BAKER, LIZARD-FISHES, and "BOMBAY DUCK"

Three families of the order are found in Queensland waters.

70

A.   Body totally scaly, flesh firm. Teeth simple.

  b. Maxillary expanded posteriorly.   AULOPIDAE
  bb. Maxillary not expanded posteriorly.   SYNODONTIDAE

AA. Body not scaly, scales only well developed in lateral
     line. Flesh flabby. Canine teeth in lower jaw barbed.   HARPADONTIDAE

Family **Aulopidae**

A small family represented in Australian waters by a single genus and species.

Aulopus

Head and body rather elongate, slightly compressed. Scales of moderate size. Cleft of mouth very wide. Teeth small, cardiform, in bands in jaws, on vomer, palatines, pterygoid, and tongue. Maxillary well developed, expanded posteriorly. Eye moderate. Pectorals and ventrals well developed, the latter inserted behind the former and below the anterior dorsal rays. Dorsal fin elongate, with 15 or more rays, inserted in middle of body length. Adipose fin small. Anal of moderate length. Caudal forked.

80. SERGEANT BAKER *Aulopus purpurissatus* Richardson   [Plate 19]

Aulopus purpurissatus Richardson, Icones Piscium, 1843, p. 6, pl. 2, fig. 3.
Aulopus purpurissatus McCoy, Prodr. Zool. Vict., dec. 6, 1881, p. 19, pls 54-5 (male and female).

  D. 19-22; A. 12-14; V. 9; L. 1. 49-51; L. tr. 5-6/7-9; depth 6, head 4, times in the total length; eye $5\frac{1}{3}$ in head; second and third dorsal rays produced into a long filament in the males. Colour mottled purplish or pinkish-red, edges of scales crimson and crimson blotches on back and sides; belly creamy-white; dorsal and caudal fins yellow with crimson spots in oblique bands, other fins yellow with orange-red bands and spots.

  This handsome southern species is occasionally taken on the reefs in South Queensland. It is a lover of rocks and reefs, frequenting grounds over which snapper are usually caught and feeding upon similar food to that fish. It is most common along the coast of New South Wales, but is also found in Victoria and in Western Australia. Principally taken by hook and line. Grows to 24 inches.

Family **Synodontidae**: Grinners or Lizard-fishes

Fishes of small or moderate size with almost cylindrical bodies, frequenting temperate and tropical seas, some at great depths. Many of them are adorned with bright colours which render them inconspicuous on the particular backgrounds on which they lie. The names of "Grinners" and "Lizard-fishes" are bestowed on them on account of their lizard-like heads and large mouths which are armed with bands of sharp and long depressible teeth, visible when the mouth is closed. Four genera are found in Queensland waters.

KEY TO GENERA IN QUEENSLAND

A. A single band of teeth on each side of palate. Inner rays of ventral fins much longer than outer ones.

  b. A small adipose fin above anal fin.
    c. Snout very blunt, shorter than eye.   *Trachinocephalus*
    cc. Snout more acute, as long as, or longer than, eye.   *Synodus*
  bb. No adipose fin (except in post-larval examples).   *Xystodus*

AA. Two bands of teeth on each side of palate, the inner row much shorter than the outer. Inner rays of ventral fins not or but little longer than outer ones.   *Saurida*

Trachinocephalus

Ventrals with 8 rays, the inner ones being at least twice as long as the outer. Snout short, less than eye diameter. Mouth large, teeth small, close-set, a single band on each side on palate. A small adipose dorsal fin present. A single tropical species.

81. PAINTED GRINNER *Trachinocephalus myops* (Bloch and Schneider)
[Plate 19]

Salmo myops Bloch and Schneider, Syst. Ichth., 1801, p. 421 (after MS. of Forster).
Salmo myops Bleeker, Atlas Ichth., 6, 1875, p. 153, pl. 278, fig. 3.

D. 12-13; A. 14-15; P. 12; V. 8; L. 1. 55-58; L. tr. $3\frac{1}{2}$/6-7; depth $4\frac{1}{3}$-$5\frac{1}{2}$, head $3\frac{1}{2}$-4, in the length; eye $4\frac{1}{2}$-$6\frac{1}{2}$ in head; form elongate, gradually tapering; head and body compressed. Colour golden-brown above, yellowish below, back with 10 more or less distinct dark cross-bands; sides with faint blue-grey longitudinal stripes, edged with dark brown; an oblique black blotch on shoulder; fins pale yellowish, dorsal and caudal dusky terminally.

A tropical species found on the coast of Queensland and rarely in New South Wales. It occurs also in the Indo-Pacific region and in the Atlantic Ocean. Grows to 13 inches.

Synodus

Ventrals with 8 rays, the inner ones being about twice the length of the outer. Head depressed. Snout triangular, rather pointed. Mouth large, teeth compressed, knife-shaped. Palatine teeth similar, smaller, in a single band on each side, also teeth on tongue. A small adipose dorsal fin present.

Fishes of moderate size inhabiting warm seas on sandy bottoms, usually at no great depths. Species numerous, two in Queensland waters.

72

A. 4½ scales between lateral line and middle of dorsal fin. No dark marking on upper part of gill-membranes.   *houlti*

AA. 3½ scales between lateral line and middle of dorsal fin. Gill-membranes with 2 large black spots on each side above operculum.   *similis*

82. HOULT'S GRINNER *Synodus houlti* McCulloch   [Plate 19]

Synodus houlti McCulloch, Mem. Qld Mus., 7, 1921, p. 165, pl. 8, fig. 1.

D. 12; A. 9; P. 13; L. 1. 59; L. tr. 4½/7; depth less than breadth, and 6.5 in the length to hypural joint; head 3.3 in same; eye 1.8 in snout and 8.1 in head. Colour greyish, sides and belly white; back with some ill-defined cross-bars, most prominent at caudal base, and some darker markings above lateral line; vermiculating grey lines on upper surface of head extend on to lips near end of snout; fins without markings.

A handsome grinner first known from the Capricorns, Queensland, where it was trawled in 25 to 30 fathoms. Not met with by the casual collector. Grows to at least 8 inches.

OTHER SPECIES

Black-spot Grinner, *S. similis*. Has been trawled off the coast at Cape Capricorn in 25 to 30 fathoms and has also been taken in the Arafura Sea and in southern Japan. Grows to 7 inches.

Xystodus

Ventrals 8-rayed, the inner ones much longer than the outer. Body depressed. Snout longer than eye. Jaws with large spear-shaped teeth. Palatine teeth in a single long and narrow band. Eye small, adipose lid rudimentary. A pit, fringed with papillae, behind and below eye. Lateral line present. Pectorals small. About 14 anal rays. No adipose dorsal fin (except in young).

Lizard-fishes from Australian seas. One species.

83. SPEAR-TOOTHED GRINNER *Xystodus sageneus* (Waite)   [Plate 19]

Synodus sageneus Waite, Rec. Austr. Mus., 6, no. 2, 15th Sept. 1905, p. 58, pl. 8, fig. 1.

D. 12; A. 15; V. 8; P. 13; L. 1. 52; L. tr. 4/7; depth 7, head 3.66, in the total length; eye 7.8, snout 4.8, in head; interorbital space equal to eye. Colour lilac, with about 9 narrow longitudinal pencil lines above; a purplish lateral band, about half a scale in width, runs from head to tail, dividing the lilac from the yellowish-white under-surface; above pectoral the band is black and from its lower edge it throws off 12 short bars to encroach on the lighter colour below; head spotted with violet and with dark-edged bands between eyes; base and middle rays of caudal and base of pectorals yellow.

A rare fish, first known from an example trawled between Fremantle and Houtman's Abrolhos, Western Australia, but since discovered on the east coast of Queensland and also in the Gulf of Carpentaria. Whitley[4] states: "Small examples have a minute adipose dorsal fin, but this is lost and its site covered by scales in larger fish." Grows to $10\frac{1}{2}$ inches.

Saurida

Ventrals with 9 rays, the inner ones not or but little longer than the outer ones. Head depressed. Snout shorter than in *Synodus*. Palatine teeth in 2 bands, the inner short and broad; tongue toothed. Adipose eyelids and adipose dorsal fin present.

Fishes of moderate size inhabiting warm seas. Species numerous, four in Queensland waters.

KEY TO SPECIES IN QUEENSLAND

A. Second ray of dorsal fin greatly produced, much longer than head.   *filamentosa*

AA. Second ray of dorsal fin not produced, not longer than head.

   b. Snout rounded; pectoral fin $1\frac{1}{3}$-$1\frac{2}{3}$ in head; upper edge of caudal fin usually with a row of dark dots.   *undosquamis*

   bb. Snout obtusely pointed; pectoral fin $1\frac{4}{5}$-$2\frac{1}{10}$ in head; no dark dots on upper edge of caudal fin.

     c. Pectoral fin with 12-13 rays; longest ray of dorsal fin $2\frac{1}{4}$-$2\frac{2}{5}$ times as long as the last ray.   *gracilis*

     cc. Pectoral fin with 14-16 rays; longest ray of dorsal fin at least 3 times as long as the last ray.   *tumbil*

84. YELLOW-BANDED GRINNER *Saurida tumbil* (Bloch)   [Plate 19]

Salmo tumbil Bloch, Nat. ausl. Fische, 9, 1795, p. 112.
Illustration by G. Coates.

Sand Smelt (Townsville); Saury (New South Wales).

D. 11-13; A. 10-11; P. 14-15; L. 1. 50-53; depth $5\frac{2}{3}$-7, head 4-$4\frac{1}{4}$, in the length; snout obtuse, broader than long, somewhat longer than eye, which is $4\frac{1}{5}$-6 in head. Colour: Head and body pale reddish-brown, mottled darker; silvery below; fins dusky creamy-yellowish, dotted with black, the dorsal and caudal more dusky-blackish.

---

[4] *Austr. Zool.*, 10, pt 2, 30th April 1943, p. 174.

A common fish in Queensland waters from south to north, and also in New South Wales, Western Australia, and the Indo-Pacific. Grows to 18 inches.

OTHER SPECIES

Thread-fin Grinner, *S. filamentosa*. Trawled by the *Endeavour* in 1910, on fine sand and mud, off Cape Moreton, South Queensland. Apparently a deep-water species. Attains $10\frac{1}{2}$ inches in length.

Spotted-tailed Grinner, *S. undosquamis*. Grows to 20 inches. A species from East Africa and the Red Sea, which ranges through the Indian Ocean to Japan, Australia, and the Pacific.

Clouded Grinner, *S. gracilis*. Wide-ranging outside Australia, it is found inshore and on the coral reefs in South Queensland and but rarely in the waters of New South Wales. Grows to 12 inches.

The voracity of these fishes may be gauged from a specimen in the Queensland Museum which measures 11 inches in total length and has a $4\frac{1}{2}$-inch whiting, *Sillago*, in its stomach.

Family **Harpadontidae: Bummalows, "Bombay Ducks"**

Small or moderate-sized flabby fishes with elongate compressed bodies covered with thin cycloid deciduous scales. Eyes small, situated far forward near the short snout.

Fishes inhabiting the waters of the Indo-Pacific region. A single genus.

Harpadon

Body elongate, compressed. Snout short, cleft of mouth deep. Teeth cardiform, recurved, of unequal size, barbed, the largest on the mandibles; teeth on pre-maxillaries, mandibles, palatines, and tongue. Eyes small, situated far forward. Scales thin and deciduous, developed only on posterior half of body. Dorsal fin in middle of the length of the body. Adipose fin small. Caudal trilobed. Species few, one in Queensland.

85. GLASSY BOMBAY DUCK *Harpadon translucens* Saville Kent
[Plate 20]

Harpodon translucens Saville Kent, Proc. Roy. Soc. Qld, 6, 1889, pp. 222-34, pl. 13, fig. 2.
Harpadon translucens Marshall, Ichth. Notes, no. 1, Jan. 1951 (Dept Har. and Marine, Qld), p. 1, pl. 1, fig. 1.

Ghost Grinner (Bundaberg and Gladstone districts).

D. 14; A. 15; elongate, somewhat compressed; head $4\frac{1}{2}$ in the length. The young are transparent in life, with minute black specklings along the dorsal surface; iris of eye is peacock-blue. Adults are tinged greenish above and are opalescent-pink below; fins dusky terminally; everywhere with minute blackish specklings.

A flabby and transparent fish with remarkable bristle-like barbed teeth, many of which are on the outside of the oral cavity. Saville Kent in his interesting description of the species states: "One of its most remarkable features . . . is the abnormal development of the teeth of the lower jaw; several of these at the symphysis lie entirely outside the oral cavity, and to the unassisted eye, present the aspect of curved projecting bristles. Examined with a lens, these projecting teeth are found to be minutely barbed like a fish-hook . . . this species of *Harpodon* was captured in the Cambridge Gulf in some quantity, with the aid of a prawn trawl fastened overboard in the tideway, while the 'Myrmidon' was at anchor. On being hauled on deck, the little fish clung so tenaciously to the meshes of the net with their barbed teeth that it was difficult to detach them without injury."

This interesting fish is commonly taken in the Mary River at Maryborough, in the stripe-nets of the prawners. Elsewhere in Queensland it has so far been rarely met with. A closely related species, *H. nehereus*, is famed in India and the East, where it is known in the form of a relish called Bombay Duck. The species grows to at least 16 inches; and I am informed that specimens over 4 pounds in weight have been taken at Maryborough.

Order **NEMATOGNATHI: CATFISHES**

The large group of whisker-jawed fishes known as catfishes is represented in most temperate and tropical regions. Over a thousand species are known, and though the majority of them are freshwater fishes, some enter salt water temporarily, whilst others permanently reside there. The Queensland species are readily recognized by their naked and smooth bodies and by the fleshy feelers surrounding their mouths, a feature which has earned them the name of catfishes. They are lovers of turbid waters in the estuaries of rivers, dams, and billabongs, and those species which are found in the salt water are usually seldom far from the coast.

In these fishes the dorsal and pectoral fins are armed anteriorly with a strong serrated spine which is capable of inflicting a very severe and painful wound.

The two secondary marine families, Plotosidae and Tachysuridae, are represented in Queensland waters.

KEY TO FAMILIES REPRESENTED IN QUEENSLAND

A. Caudal fin pointed, united with second dorsal and anal fins. PLOTOSIDAE

AA. Caudal fin forked, not united with dorsal and anal fins. TACHYSURIDAE

Family **Plotosidae**

No scales. Body elongate, eel-like, tapering to pointed tail. Head depressed. Mouth subterminal. Conical teeth in jaws, sometimes lacking in upper jaw or mixed with molars below. Four pairs of barbels. A serrated spine at front of dorsal and also pectoral fins. No adipose dorsal fin. Second dorsal and anal long, with numerous rays, both being joined with the pointed caudal.

The members of this family are found in the tropical and subtropical regions of the Indo-Pacific. Some of them grow to a large size. A few species inhabit the sea, but most of them are to be found in the brackish and freshwater streams, only occasionally entering the sea outside the rivers.

The freshwater species, some of which are to be found far in the interior of Australia, construct nests of pebbles and gravel on the beds of the streams, depositing their ova therein and keeping guard over them until hatched. A curious dendritic or arborescent appendage is usually present behind the vent. The use of this peculiar organ is apparently unknown.

The saltwater forms of catfish are the only ones dealt with here. Five genera occur in Queensland waters.

KEY TO GENERA IN QUEENSLAND

A. Gill-membranes meeting across, and narrowly united with isthmus.

   b. Premaxillary teeth numerous.

     c. Anterior nostril at front border of upper lip, directed upward or forward. Axillary pore minute.   *Plotosus*

     cc. Anterior nostril at front border of upper lip directed downward.   *Paraplotosus*

   bb. Premaxillary teeth few. Anterior nostril on front border of upper lip, looking upward.   *Cnidoglanis*

AA. Gill-membranes not united across isthmus.

   d. Occipital region osseous, not covered with loose skin.   *Exilichthys*

   dd. Occipital region not osseous, covered with loose skin.   *Euristhmus*

Plotosus

Form elongate, tail tapering, head depressed. Head and fin-spines covered with soft skin. Eye with free borders. Lips thick, with papillae or small laminated folds. Premaxillary teeth numerous. Gill-membranes very narrowly united with isthmus. A conspicuous dendritic organ behind vent present. A single species in Queensland.

86. STRIPED CATFISH *Plotosus anguillaris* (Bloch) [Plate 20]

Platysiacus anguillaris Bloch, Nat. ausl. Fische, 8, 1794, p. 61 (*fide* Sherborn).
Illustration by G. Coates.

Barbel Eel, Barber (South Africa).

D. 1/4-5; spine strong, serrated on both edges; second dorsal + C. + A. about 110-180; gill-rakers 22-24 on entire first branchial arch, the first ones minute; nasal barbels reaching to front or hind margin of eye; teeth conical in upper jaw, molar-like on vomer, mixed in lower jaw; easily shed; depth of body 6-8, head 4½-5, times in the length. Colour brown above, lighter below; fins dark; second dorsal, anal, and caudal with a dark edge; the young are olive-greenish, lighter below and with 2 or 3 longitudinal yellowish stripes along the sides, which disappear in the adult.

A very common fish which frequents the sea, estuaries, and rivers of the Queensland coastline. Sometimes a dark object like a ball several feet in diameter is seen slowly revolving along in the water. It is a school of these catfishes, packed so closely together as to form a compact and wriggling mass.

The pectoral spines inflict very painful and dangerous wounds. The Striped Catfish is a wide-ranging species, being found from the Red Sea and the east coast of Africa to India, Japan, the Indo-Australian Archipelago, and the Pacific. In Queensland it grows to only about 12 inches, but according to Professor J. L. B. Smith of South Africa it reaches 30 inches in that country.

Paraplotosus

Form elongate, tail tapering, head depressed, mouth transverse, rounded in front. Lips thick, with papillae and folds. Upper lip prominent. Eye not covered by skin. Gill-membranes confluent in the middle, only the anterior confluent portion united with the isthmus. A conspicuous preanal dendritic organ present. One species in Queensland.

87. WHITE-LIPPED EEL CATFISH *Paraplotosus albilabris* (Cuvier and Valenciennes) [Plate 20]

Plotosus albilabris Cuvier and Valenciennes, Hist. Nat. Poiss., 15, 1840, p. 427.
Plotosus microceps Richardson, Zool. Voy. Erebus and Terror, Fish., 1845, p. 31, pl. 21, figs 4-7.

(1) D. 1/4-5; (2) D. + C. + A. 160-216. Depth of body 7-8; head 6, in the total length; eye 4-6 in head, more than twice in snout; nasal barbels reach to or beyond hind border of operculum; mandibular barbels sometimes reach base of pectorals; first dorsal fin almost as high as body; second dorsal and anal rather high. Colour uniform blackish, under-surface of head and abdomen greyish; lips white. In spirits, light brownish or yellowish-grey, mottled with spots and blotches of pale lead-grey.

A common fish in the coastal waters of Queensland. Found also in North Australia, Western Australia, and the East Indies. Grows to 14 inches.

Cnidoglanis

Form elongate, tail tapering, head depressed. Mouth transverse, rounded in front. Lips thick, with papillae. Upper lip prominent. Teeth in upper jaw conical, on the vomer molar-like, in the lower jaw mixed. Anterior nostril on front border of upper lip directed upward or forward. Posterior nostril behind nasal barbel. Eight barbels. Eyes covered by skin. Gill-membranes united below throat and attached to the isthmus along the median line. Origin of second dorsal before or above origin of ventrals. A conspicuous preanal dendritic organ present. One species in Queensland.

88. ESTUARY CATFISH *Cnidoglanis macrocephalus* (Cuvier and Valenciennes) [Plate 20]

Plotosus macrocephalus Cuvier and Valenciennes, Hist. Nat. Poiss., 15, 1840, p. 317.
Plotosus megastomus Richardson, Ichth. Voy. Erebus and Terror, 1845, p. 31, pl. 21, figs 1-3.

Head very broad, depressed, its length 1.5 of the total length; barbels not very long, those of nostril and maxillary extending somewhat beyond eye; lower lip broad, pendant, with lobes, the outer of which is situated below maxillary barbel, and has the appearance of a short barbel; intermaxillary teeth small, conical, in 2 small patches; those of lower jaw in a broad band, tapering on side, the outer ones conical, the others molar-like; vomerine teeth in a large triangular patch; eye small, covered with skin. Colour uniform blackish-brown above, whitish on belly; under-surface of head fawn, faintly freckled with darker; pectorals and ventrals dusky above, lighter below.

A common species inhabiting muddy bottoms along the whole Australian coastline but apparently rare in Queensland. Grows to a length of 36 inches.

Exilichthys

Form elongate, tail tapering. Head small, depressed, with gill-membranes not united across isthmus. Occipital region osseous, not covered with loose skin. One species in Queensland.

89. NETTLE-FISH *Exilichthys nudiceps* (Günther) [Plate 20]

Cnidoglanis nudiceps Günther, Rept Voy. Challenger, Zool., 16, 1880, p. 49.
Illustration by G. Coates.

Depth about 11, head about 7, times in the total length; eye nearly 3 in postorbital part of head; nasal and maxillary barbels not extending to end of head; occipital region osseous, not covered with loose skin. Colour light brown or fawn, the fins with black edges.

This well-known species from the Arafura Sea is fairly common on the coast of North Queensland, where it has been recorded as far south as the Whitsunday Passage. Grows to at least 12 inches.

Euristhmus

Body elongate. Tail more than twice as long as head and trunk. Skin smooth. Head much wider than long. Eyes small, without free lids. Gill-membranes separate, broadly attached to isthmus. Axillary pore present. A single species.

90. LONG-TAILED CATFISH *Euristhmus lepturus* (Günther) [Plate 20]

Cnidoglanis lepturus Günther, Cat. Fish. Brit. Mus., 5, 1864, p. 28.
Euristhmus lepturus McCulloch, Rec. Austr. Mus., 13, no. 4, 1921, p. 123, pl. 21, fig. 1.

D. 1/4; P. 1/11; V. 12; depth 1.3 in head and 8.5 in the length to hypural joint, head 6.3 in the same; head and body 2.1 in the length of the tail; form slender, the tail elongate; gill-openings wide, but separated by a broad interspace on isthmus. Colour brownish or dark greyish-brown above, lighter below, and obscurely mottled with lighter areas on tail; soft dorsal and anal fins with darker borders; some examples have numerous small creamy-white spots over body and tail.

A very common South Queensland and New South Wales species which frequents the coastal rivers and muddy bays. Grows to about 14 inches.

Family **Tachysuridae**: Sea Catfishes

Body elongate, without scales. Caudal forked. Head conic or depressed, with prominent bony plates above, more or less granular or with rugose shields, usually covered with skin. Barbels present. Teeth in jaws conic, villiform or incisor-like, in single or more rows or in bands. Palate with villiform, conic, or granular-like teeth, in 1 to 3 groups on each side. Dorsal fin short, with long sharp spine. Adipose fin shorter than dorsal, situated above anal. Pectoral with strong spine.

A large group of catfishes living in the sea and about the mouths of rivers and even ascending the streams far beyond tidal influence into fresh water. The sea or salmon catfishes are bottom-feeding fishes with carnivorous tendencies. The females lay large eggs about the size of peas. These are incubated by the males, who carry them about in their capacious mouths until hatched. No food is partaken of by the males during the nursing period.

The skulls of these catfishes exhibit on their under-surfaces a fairly good representation of a crucifix; and in some parts of the world are looked upon by superstitious people with veneration, the fishes being known as "crucifix fish".

The numerous species have been grouped by various authors under many genera, but the earlier name of *Tachysurus* is here used, in preference to the better-known *Arius*, for all Queensland species.

Tachysurus

Form elongate, compressed posteriorly. No scales. Upper surface of head with more or less granular or rugose bony shields. Three pairs of barbels. Eye with free orbital margin. A serrated spine in front of first dorsal and in each pectoral. Adipose dorsal fin present. Caudal forked.

Species numerous in tropical seas, along sandy and muddy shores, in bays and rivers; five in Queensland waters.

KEY TO SPECIES IN QUEENSLAND

A.   Teeth on palate granular.   *broadbenti*

AA. Teeth on palate villiform.

    b. Teeth in 3 groups on each side, forming a large triangular patch, the hinder group extending backward.   *thalassinus*

    bb. Teeth in 2 transverse groups on each side; no third group extending backward.

    c. Maxillary barbels long, reaching to below posterior dorsal rays.   *berneyi*

    cc. Maxillary barbels short, reaching gill-openings at opercular flap or not quite to base of pectoral fin.

    d. Palatine patches subcircular, their inner edges parallel. Anal with 15 rays.   *proximus*

    dd. Palatine patches elongate, transverse, widely divergent and almost parallel with maxillary teeth. Anal with 16-17 rays.   *australis*

91. GIANT SALMON CATFISH *Tachysurus thalassinus* (Rüppell)
[Plate 20]

Bagrus thalassinus Rüppell, Neue Wirbelth., Abyssin. Fische, 1837-8, p. 75, pl. 20, fig. 2.
Illustration by G. Coates.

D. 1/7; A. 15-18; depth of body $4-5\frac{2}{5}$, head $3\frac{3}{4}-4$, in the length to caudal base; villiform teeth in upper jaw in a broad band, in lower jaw in a divided, but somewhat narrower band, more curved; palatine teeth villiform or conical, in 2 large triangular separate patches, the base of each triangle being formed by 2 more or less square patches, the outer of which is larger. Colour reddish-brown above, whitish below; fins almost hyaline; distal parts of dorsal, adipose, anal, and caudal fins dusky.

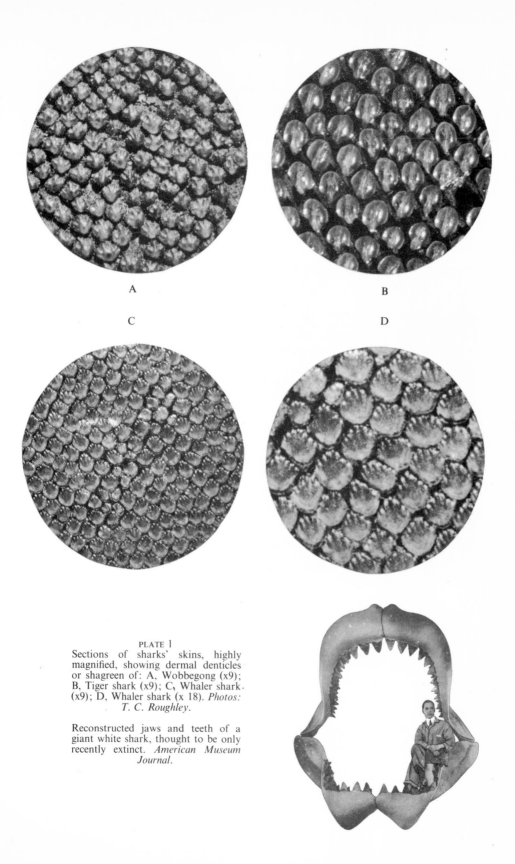

Sections of sharks' skins, highly magnified, showing dermal denticles or shagreen of: A, Wobbegong (x9); B, Tiger shark (x9); C, Whaler shark (x9); D, Whaler shark (x 18). *Photos: T. C. Roughley.*

Reconstructed jaws and teeth of a giant white shark, thought to be only recently extinct. *American Museum Journal.*

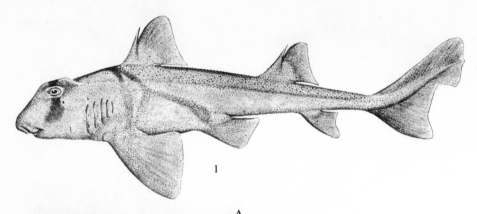

1

A

PLATE 2

1. Port Jackson Shark, *Heterodontus portusjacksoni*, female, 22 in. A, Jaw showing enlarged lateral teeth without keels.   2. Crested Port Jackson Shark, *Gyropleurodus galeatus*, with detail of mouthparts.

2

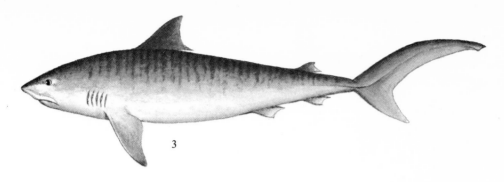

3

4

3. Tiger Shark, *Galeocerdo cuvier*, about 8 ft. Also (centre) a portion of the dried jaws with flesh removed, showing the rows of unerupted teeth lying against the jaw, and (bottom) front row of functional teeth.　　4. Weasel Shark, *Hemigaleus microstoma*, about $28\frac{1}{2}$ in.

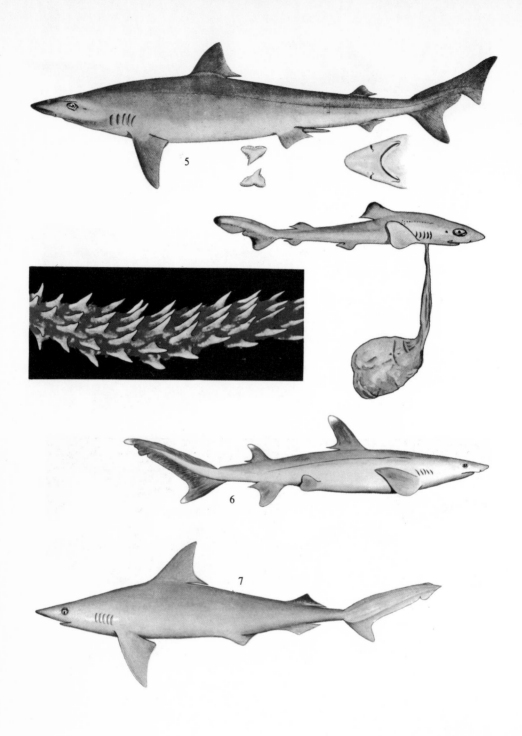

PLATE 4
5. School Shark, *Galeorhinus australis*, 5 ft. Also section of jaw (with teeth), and the embryo.   6. White-tip Shark, *Triaenodon apicalis*, young female, 28 in.
7. Coates' Shark, *Platypodon coatesi*, male, $37\frac{1}{2}$ in.

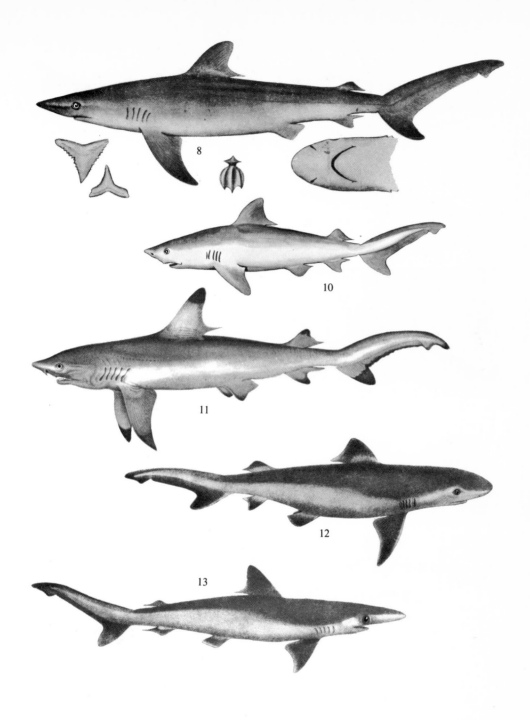

PLATE 5

8. Whaler Shark, *Eulamia macrura*, female, 35 in. Also (from left) upper and lower tooth of same species, scale from shoulder, and undersurface view of head.   10. Graceful Shark, *E. amblyrhynchoides*, female, 24 in.   11. Black-tip Shark, *E. spallanzani*.   12. Estuary Shark, *E. lamia*, 18 in.   13. Little Blue Shark, *Rhizoprionodon palasorrah*, 11 in.

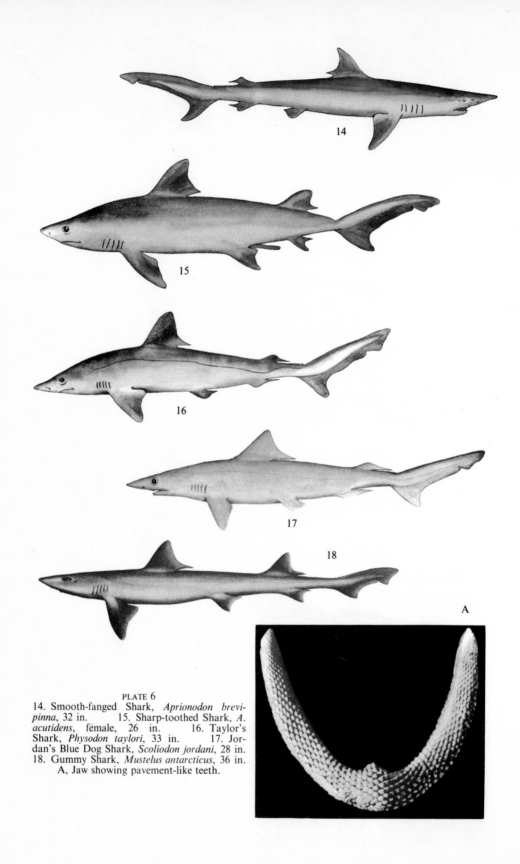

PLATE 6
14. Smooth-fanged Shark, *Aprionodon brevipinna*, 32 in.   15. Sharp-toothed Shark, *A. acutidens*, female, 26 in.   16. Taylor's Shark, *Physodon taylori*, 33 in.   17. Jordan's Blue Dog Shark, *Scoliodon jordani*, 28 in. 18. Gummy Shark, *Mustelus antarcticus*, 36 in.
A, Jaw showing pavement-like teeth.

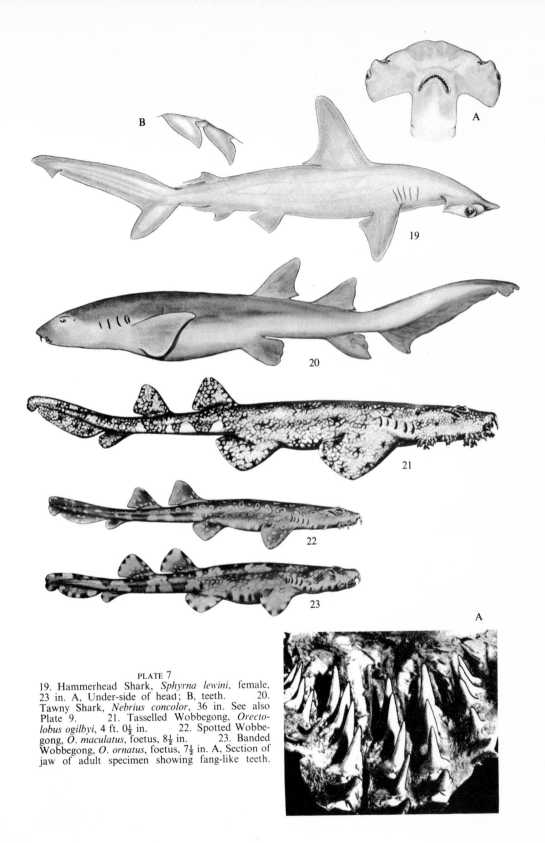

19. Hammerhead Shark, *Sphyrna lewini*, female, 23 in. A, Under-side of head; B, teeth.　　20. Tawny Shark, *Nebrius concolor*, 36 in. See also Plate 9.　　21. Tasselled Wobbegong, *Orectolobus ogilbyi*, 4 ft. 0½ in.　　22. Spotted Wobbegong, *O. maculatus*, foetus, 8½ in.　　23. Banded Wobbegong, *O. ornatus*, foetus, 7½ in. A, Section of jaw of adult specimen showing fang-like teeth.

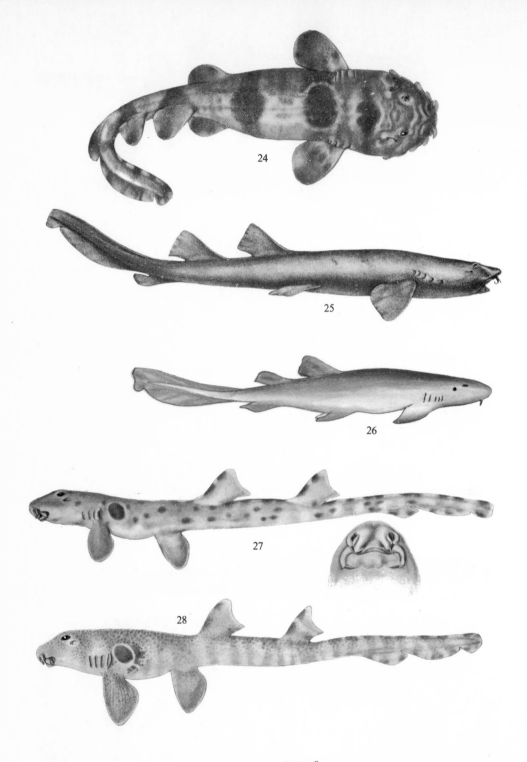

PLATE 8

24. Northern Wobbegong, *Orectolobus wardi*.   25. Blind Shark, *Brachaelurus waddi*, 20½ in.   26. Blue-grey Cat Shark, *B. colcloughi*, 18 in.   27. Epaulette Shark, *Hemiscyllium ocellatum*, 16 in., and detail of mouthparts.   28. Speckled Cat Shark, *H. trispeculare*, 22 in.

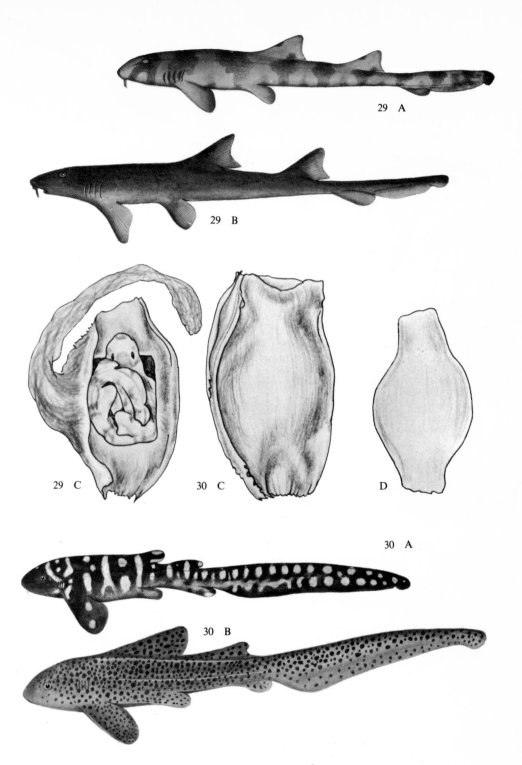

PLATE 9

29. Brown-banded Cat Shark, *Hemiscyllium punctatum*. A, Juv., 15 in.; B, adult, 21 in.; C, egg.　　30. Zebra Shark, *Stegostoma tigrinum*. A, Juv., 14 in.; B, adult, 7 ft. 3 in.; C, egg. At D the egg of the Tawny Shark, *Nebrius concolor* (species 20, see Plate 7) is shown.

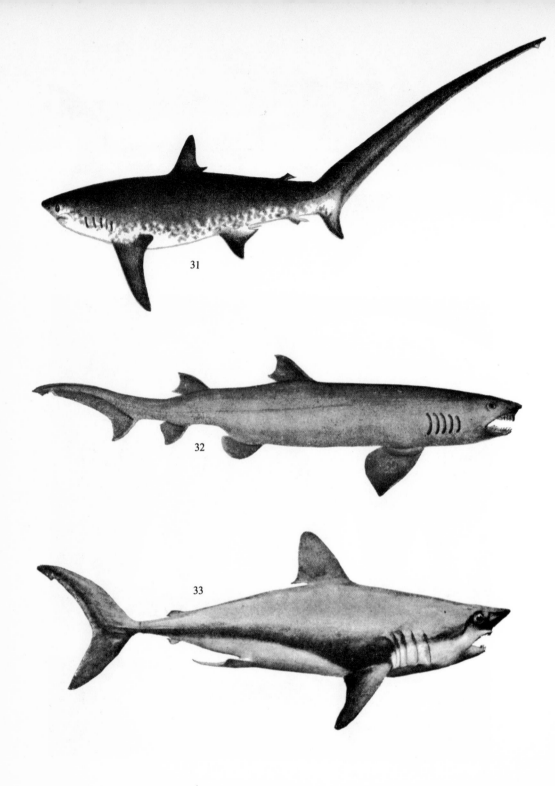

PLATE 10
31. Thresher Shark, *Alopias vulpinus*, 10 ft. 2 in.   32. Grey Nurse, *Carcharias taurus*, 9 ft. 11 in.   33. Blue Pointer or Mako, *Isurus glaucus*.

34

PLATE 11
34. White Pointer, *Carcharodon carcharias*, about 13 ft. Section of jaws shows
large upright serrated teeth complete as in a live specimen.

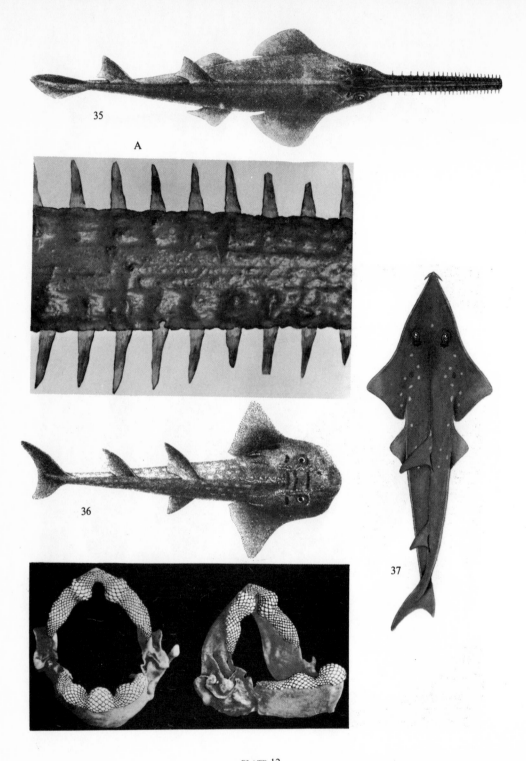

PLATE 12

35. Narrow-snouted Saw-fish, *Pristis zijsron*, 34 in. A, Section of snout or rostral saw of a much larger specimen, probably 15 to 18 feet long (full length of this saw was 4 ft. 7 in.).   36. Shark Ray, *Rhina ancylostomus*, 6 ft. 10 in. Two views of teeth and jaws are also shown. Each tooth has a rippled surface.   37. White-spotted Ray, *Rhynchobatus djiddensis*, 46 in.

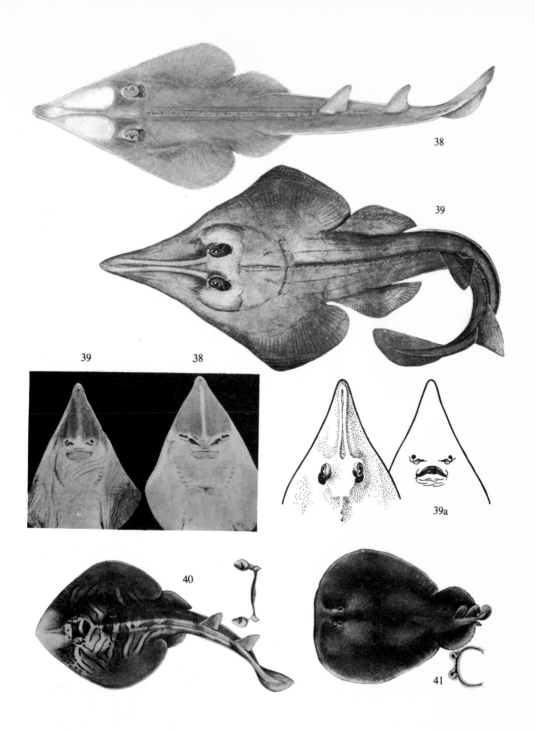

PLATE 13

Common Shovel-nose Ray, *Rhinobatos armatus*, 19 in. (38) and Banks' Shovel-nose
Ray, *Aptychotrema banksii*, 22 in. (39), also undersurface of heads. 39a.
Bougainville's Shovel-nose Ray, *A. bougainvillii*, upper and lower surfaces of head
of a 32½-in. male. 40. Fiddler Ray, *Trygonorrhina fasciata*, 15 in. 41.
Numb-fish, *Hypnarce subnigra*, 14 in.

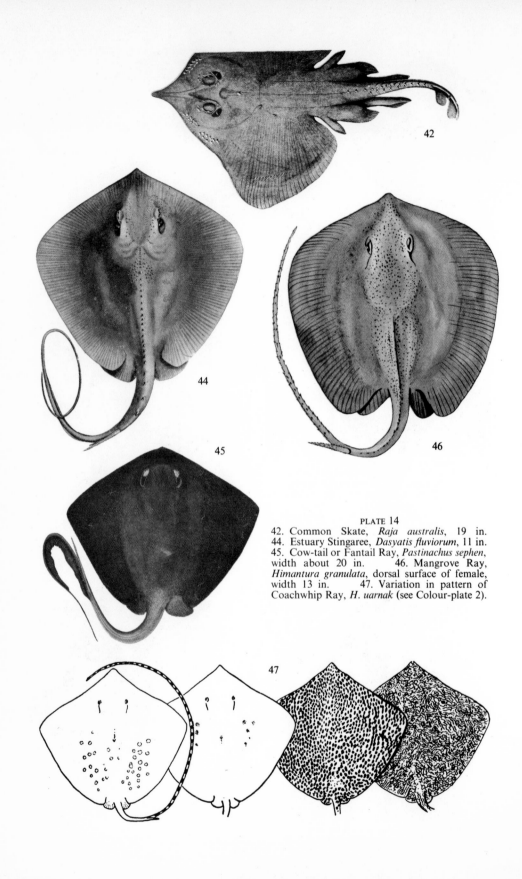

PLATE 14
42. Common Skate, *Raja australis*, 19 in.
44. Estuary Stingaree, *Dasyatis fluviorum*, 11 in.
45. Cow-tail or Fantail Ray, *Pastinachus sephen*,
width about 20 in.   46. Mangrove Ray,
Himantura granulata, dorsal surface of female,
width 13 in.   47. Variation in pattern of
Coachwhip Ray, *H. uarnak* (see Colour-plate 2).

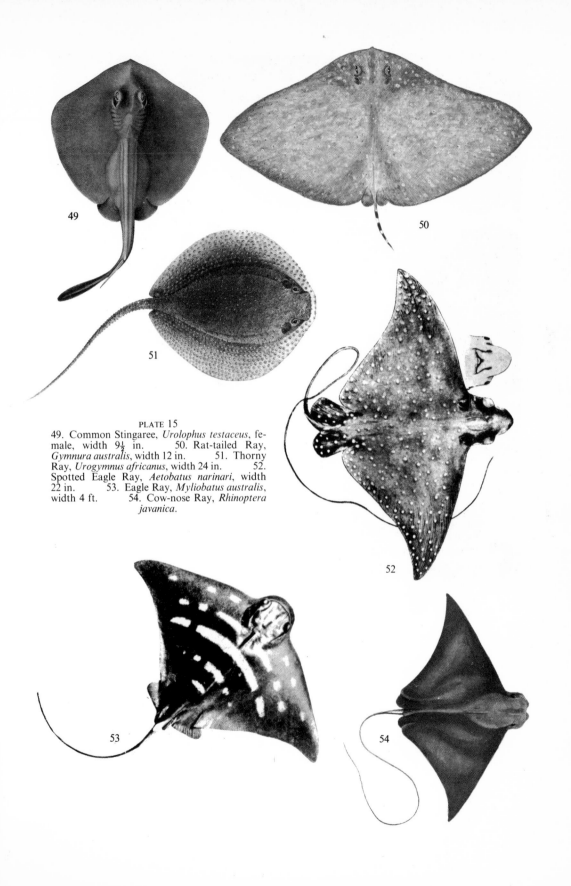

49. Common Stingaree, *Urolophus testaceus*, female, width 9½ in.   50. Rat-tailed Ray, *Gymnura australis*, width 12 in.   51. Thorny Ray, *Urogymnus africanus*, width 24 in.   52. Spotted Eagle Ray, *Aetobatus narinari*, width 22 in.   53. Eagle Ray, *Myliobatus australis*, width 4 ft.   54. Cow-nose Ray, *Rhinoptera javanica*.

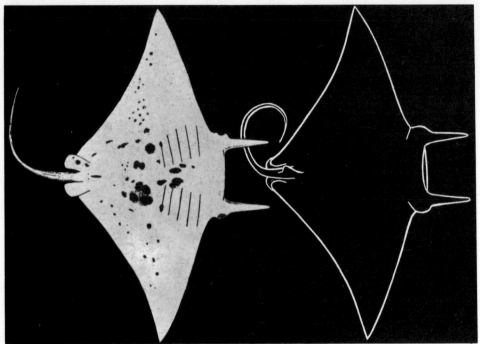

55

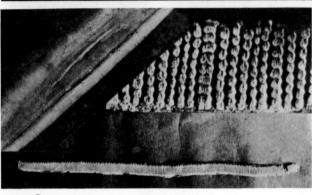

A

B

C

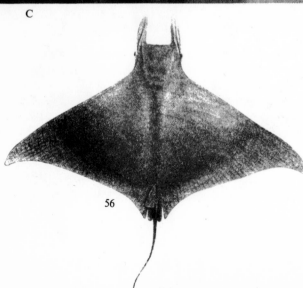

56

PLATE 16

55. Australian Devil Ray, *Manta alfredi*, scale diagram one-fiftieth natural size, showing horns, eyes, and form of fins and tail. Dorsal view (55, right) shows slit-like spiracles behind eyes, also small dorsal fin near root of spineless tail. Ventral surface (55, left) is white with irregular dark blotches, and the five pairs of gill-slits are plainly seen. The photographs (A-C) show teeth of one of this species. A, Skin of lower lip reflected to expose some of teeth; B, some of teeth enlarged; C, entire dental strip, less than one-quarter natural size, removed from lower jaw (there are 1,500 to 2,000 teeth in this strip).

56. Pygmy Devil Ray, *Mobula diabolus*, width 34 in.

A giant catfish which is found more frequently in our northern waters, where it lives in the estuaries and is often captured with its mouth full of eggs. It ranges from the northern rivers of New South Wales along the coast of Queensland to North Australia and New Guinea, through the Indo-Australian Archipelago to India and the Red Sea. Grows to 40 inches.

OTHER SPECIES

Broadbent's Catfish, *T. broadbenti*. A little-known species, mainly inhabiting North Queensland waters. Grows to at least 15 inches.

Berney's Catfish, *T. berneyi*. Inhabits the estuaries of the streams of Cape York Peninsula, North Queensland. Grows to at least 7 inches.

Allied Catfish, *T. proximus*. A species from North Queensland which resembles the common Blue Catfish of Moreton Bay, *T. australis*. It is also found in the Northern Territory and in Western Australia. Grows to at least 16 inches.

Blue Catfish, *T. australis*. The very common coastal and estuarine catfish of the Moreton Bay district. Though despised as a food-fish in Queensland, this fish has quite edible flesh of very good flavour. It is sometimes sold in the fish-shops under the name of "New Zealand Blue Cod", after first being carefully filleted. The species grows to 20 inches and is found on the coasts of South Queensland and New South Wales.

All four species are equally good as food fishes.

Order **SYMBRANCHII: PYGMY EELS**

Form eel-like. Body naked, or covered with minute scales. Only one gill-opening, which is on the ventral surface. Caudal fin very small, 8- to 10-rayed, and continuous with dorsal and anal, which are rayless folds of the skin.

Sub-order ALABETOIDEA: SINGLE-SLIT EELS

Vent in anterior half of the length. Dorsal and anal fins well developed. Pelvic fins present, very small, 2-rayed, just behind gill-opening. Mouth small. Palate toothless.

A group of small eel-like fishes of widely diversified structure, inhabiting mainly the Australian zone and India. Although they are probably related to the true eels, *Apodes*, the structure of the head of the single-slit eels suggests that they are nearer to the true fishes. Two families are found in Queensland waters, one of which we are not concerned with here, for it inhabits fresh water and is not a coastal species.

D

Family **Alabetidae**

Body elongate, naked or with minute scales; no barbels; snout blunt, eyes placed far forward; mouth small, terminal; teeth blunt, compressed, in a single series in the jaws; paired fins none.

The family contains the single genus *Alabes*, small fishes of the coasts of Australia.

92. RED-BANDED PYGMY EEL or SHORE EEL *Alabes rufus* (Macleay)
[Plate 21]

Cheilobranchus rufus Macleay, Proc. Linn. Soc. N.S.Wales, 6, 1881, p. 266.
Cheilobranchus rufus Waite, Rec. Austr. Mus., 6, 1906, p. 195, pl. 36, fig. 1.

Head $\frac{1}{8}$ of the total length, and about 2-2.3 times in the distance between gill-openings and vent; distance between end of snout and vent is 1.5 in the remaining portion; depth of body 8.6 in the total length. Colour green, with darker spots when alive, but when placed in preservative it sometimes changes to red, hence the specific name of *rufus*.

A common species in the southern waters of Australia, this pygmy eel is to be found just below tide-mark. Apparently it is not so common on the coast of Queensland and is known only from a few examples taken in South Queensland. Grows to 4 inches.

Order **APODES: EELS**

The members of this large group are characterized mainly by their snake-like forms. The species are many and varied and some have been mistaken at times for gaudy-coloured snakes. The group contains such diverse types as the tiny worm-eels and the mighty Long-tailed Eel, *Evenchelys macrurus*, which attains to over 12 feet. Most of the species are marine and are distributed in temperate and tropical seas, whilst a few species are found living in fresh water. Six families are represented in Queensland waters.

Almost all eels are extremely vicious, not waiting until molested before attacking, and the larger reef-eels, whose jaws are armed with powerful teeth, are considered dangerous.

Most eels, perhaps all, undergo a larval stage of growth when first hatched from the egg, during which they are flat and glass-like in appearance and quite unlike their parents. The freshwater eels, like the marine species, breed in the ocean's depths, and chapters have been written on their remarkable life-history.[5] Whilst most of the species are more or less edible, it is the freshwater eels, Anguillidae, and the congers, Congridae, which are esteemed throughout the world as food-fishes.

---

[5] It is to the late Professor J. Schmidt of Copenhagen that the scientific world owes a debt of gratitude for his valuable discoveries and contributions on the breeding habits of the freshwater eels of the Atlantic and Pacific oceans.

KEY TO FAMILIES REPRESENTED IN QUEENSLAND

Adapted from McCulloch[6]

A. Body covered with minute scales. (Freshwater eels.)	ANGUILLIDAE
AA. Body naked. (Saltwater eels.)	
b. Tip of tail surrounded by fin-membranes.	
c. Posterior nostril superior or lateral.	
d. Pectoral fin present.	
e. Jaws and vomer with large conspicuous canines. Tongue narrow, not free.	MURAENESOCIDAE
ee. No canines on jaws and vomer. Tongue broad, free anteriorly.	CONGRIDAE
dd. No pectoral fins.	MURAENIDAE
cc. Posterior nostril in upper lip near eye.	MYRIDAE
bb. Tip of tail free, without fin-membranes. Dorsal and anal fins not confluent.	OPHICHTHYIDAE

Family **Anguillidae: Freshwater Eels**

Body covered with minute scales, embedded in the skin. Anus in anterior half of the length. Dorsal, anal, and caudal confluent. Pectorals well developed. Anterior nostrils tubular, situated near anterior margin of snout. Posterior nostrils in front of eye. Teeth conical, small, in cardiform bands on jaws and vomer. Wide-ranging, but not extending into the Arctic and Antarctic regions. One genus, *Anguilla*.

Everyone in Queensland is more or less familiar with common freshwater eels, though few people are aware of their interesting life-history or habits.

Although spending the greater part of their lives in fresh water, they descend to the sea to breed, the salt water being necessary for the stimulating of the generative organs and the ripening of the resultant ova.

Having remained far up in the fresh water, feeding and growing, and more or less undisturbed, the eels attain maturity, which is at the age of five or six years, and, with the restless urge to breed now upon them, they commence the long journey down to the sea. In the big migration the males usually precede the females. Isolated water-holes are vacated under cover of night, the eels travelling over the dewy grass until a main stream is reached, which will lead them down to the sea. On entering the salt water they travel out many miles and penetrate down to great depths, where, having deposited their now ripe ova, they die. The adults never return to the fresh water after having spawned.

The eggs float about in the ocean's depths until the tiny larval eels hatch out. At this stage of their lives they are so unlike their parents that for many years they were not associated with our common eels, but were known as

---

[6] *The Fishes and Fish-like Animals of New South Wales*, 1927, p. 23.

Leptocephali or glass-eels. They are quite flat in shape, as transparent and colourless as a piece of glass, and measure about three-fifths of an inch in length. See Plate 22.

These baby eels or elvers now commence to journey to the land with as great an urge as did their parents to the sea, the journey occupying about two or three years. By this time they have undergone a great change, their length has decreased and their tape-like flatness has given place to a cylindrical body which is a replica of the parent.

Arriving at the shore, the tiny elvers continue to push onward and inland as far as possible, there to feed and to grow to maturity as have countless generations of eels before them, and finally to make their second and last long journey back to the sea from whence they were born. Plate 22 shows stages in the development of the young freshwater eels.

In certain parts of England and Europe, during the periodical migrations of the little eels or elvers they are captured and used as food. They arrive in the rivers in such numbers that they may be scooped up by the thousands. Such runs are termed eel-fares, which means a journey or passage of eels. After capture the little eels are pounded or pressed into a kind of paste which when fried in butter makes delicious cakes. In these same countries the adult eels are marketed in great numbers, their sale realizing many thousands of pounds.

Anguilla

Members of this genus inhabit the freshwater streams of most tropical and subtropical countries. Of the three species found in the streams and billabongs of Queensland one is extremely common; the other two are not so frequently met with.

KEY TO SPECIES IN QUEENSLAND

A. Dorsal fin extending well forward beyond vent. Body
    and tail spotted.   *reinhardtii*

AA. Dorsal fin not extending forward much beyond vent.
    Coloration uniform.

    b. Angle of mouth extending approximately to below
       hind margin of eye.   *australis*

    bb. Angle of mouth extending considerably beyond eye. *obscura*

93. LONG-FINNED FRESHWATER EEL *Anguilla reinhardtii* Steindachner
[Plate 21]

Anguilla reinhardtii Steindachner, Sitzb. Akad. Wiss. Wien, 55, pt 1, 1867, p. 15, figs A-B.
Anguilla reinhardtii Waite, Fish. Sth Austr., 1923, p. 70.

Dorsal fin long, extending far forward, beyond origin of anal; mouth comparatively small, extending to hind margin of eye or a little farther. Colour: Body olive-greenish above, sides golden-yellowish, more or less spotted and streaked with blackish; white below; fins darker.

This is the common freshwater eel of Queensland. It is found in most of the coastal streams and is readily recognized by its long dorsal fin and spotted body. It is valued as a food-fish, its flesh being rich and wholesome and of good flavour. It inhabits the rivers of eastern Australia, Lord Howe Island, and Norfolk Island. Grows to 4 feet and a weight of at least 15 pounds.

OTHER SPECIES

Short-finned Freshwater Eel, *A. australis*. Rarely met with in Queensland, its place being taken by the preceding species. It is commonly taken in the coastal rivers of New South Wales, Victoria, South Australia, and in Tasmania. So far its northernmost limit is the Brisbane River. Grows to at least 24 inches and is a good food-fish.

Pacific Short-finned Freshwater Eel, *A. obscura*. Found on the Queensland coast from the Burdekin River northwards. It is a South Pacific species that ranges from North Queensland and southern New Guinea to Tahiti. It is, however, rare in Queensland waters.

Family **Muraenesocidae: Pike Eels**

Body elongate, subcylindrical, only tail compressed. Snout elongate. Mouth large, extending far behind eye. Upper jaw prominent, conical, rounded at tip, broadened and with somewhat of a notch. Tongue not free. Teeth large, caniniform in front of jaws and on vomer. Pectorals well developed.

Large eels found in most seas, in estuaries and sometimes even in fresh water. A single genus with one species in Queensland waters.

The pike eels are closely related to the congers, being distinguished from them mainly by the presence of the canine teeth in the front of the jaws and on the vomer, also by their much more attenuated snouts.

94. PIKE EEL *Muraenesox arabicus* Bloch and Schneider   [Plate 21]

Muraenesox arabicus Bloch and Schneider, Syst. Ichth., 1801, p. 488 (based on *M. cinerea* Forskål).
Muraenesox bagio Bleeker, Atlas Ichth., 4, 1864, p. 24, pl. 170, fig. 2.

Silver Eel (New South Wales); Conger Pike (South Africa).

Height about 20, head 6-7, in total length; origin of dorsal fin above gill-opening, its height about half depth of body. Colour greyish above, sides silvery; median fins with a broad black margin.

A very vicious eel found in the sea and also in brackish and freshwater streams. Wide-ranging from the Red Sea to India, China, Japan to Australia. Grows to about 5 feet.

Family **Congridae: Conger Eels**

Body moderately compressed, robust. Scales absent. Snout conical. Mouth large, but not extending far behind eye. Teeth strong, conical or granular, but no large canines in the jaws. Gill-openings wide. Pectorals well developed or absent.

Powerful, large, uniformly coloured marine eels found living at moderate depths in most temperate and tropical seas. The well-known conger of Europe is one of the largest species and is said to grow to 9 feet with a weight of 160 pounds. Genera few. Two species of the one genus enter Queensland waters, one being closely related to the European conger.

Conger

Pectorals well developed. Dorsal origin behind pectoral base. Head flattened above. Tongue free. Lips thick. Outer teeth close together, forming a strong cutting edge. Inner series minute or obsolete. Vomerine teeth in a short band. No canines. Anterior nostril tubular.

Large eels found in most seas, excepting the eastern Pacific. Species few, two in Queensland waters.

KEY TO SPECIES IN QUEENSLAND

A. Dorsal fin commencing above or slightly behind middle
    of pectorals.   *cinereus*

AA. Dorsal fin commencing above or slightly behind posterior
    of pectorals.   *labiatus*

95. AUSTRALIAN CONGER EEL *Conger labiatus* Castelnau   [Plate 21]

Conger labiatus Castelnau, Proc. Linn. Soc. N.S.Wales, 1879, p. 396.
Conger labiatus Phillipps, New Zeal. Journ. Sci. Tech., 13, pt 4, 1932, p. 229, fig. 3.

Cleft of mouth extending back a little beyond middle of eye, which is rather shorter than snout; origin of dorsal fin above or slightly behind end of pectorals. Colour brownish-yellow, with purple tinges; white or yellow below; edges of vertical fins darker.

A large and powerful eel which is but rarely found in Queensland waters. It occurs in New South Wales and is well known in New Zealand. Grows to at least 5 feet and a weight of 37 pounds.

OTHER SPECIES

Grey Conger Eel, *C. cinereus*. Only very occasionally found on the Queensland coast. Ranges to New Guinea, Hawaii, Samoa, and the East Indies. Grows to about 40 inches.

Family **Muraenidae: Morays or Reef Eels**

These large and powerful eels, whose bodies are adorned with brightly coloured patterns, are mainly coastal fishes living in shallow water among crevices of the reefs. They lie in wait for their prey with only their heads exposed, striking in serpent-like manner at anything they can overpower. Of an extremely pugnacious disposition and with jaws armed with knife-like teeth, they are creatures to be avoided. Large reef eels are dangerous, and after being driven off will repeatedly return to the attack.

Over one hundred species are known from tropical and subtropical seas, many attaining 6 or 7 feet in length. The world's largest species is a Queensland eel which grows to at least 12 feet. There are five genera in Queensland, three of which will be treated in detail. The other two can be recognized from the descriptions given in the following key.

Reef eels are not esteemed as food, their flesh being very oily and indigestible. Many of the species exhibit great variation in colour.

KEY TO GENERA IN QUEENSLAND

A.   Some teeth granular or molar-like.   *Echidna*

AA. Teeth acute, not granular or molar-like.

    b. Form not greatly attenuated. Tail of moderate length.

      c. Dorsal and anal fin present, confluent with caudal and covered by thick skin. Colour uniform or varied.

        d. Body slender, its depth 36-51 times in the trunk. Colour uniform.   *Strophidon*

        dd. Body stouter, its depth less than 30 times in the trunk. Colour varied.   *Lycodontis*

      cc. Dorsal and anal fin reduced to rudiments close to and confluent with caudal. Colour uniform.   *Uropterygius*

    bb. Form greatly attenuated. Tail very long.   *Evenchelys*

Echidna

Teeth conical, granular or molar-like, changing with age in number, form, and arrangement, in one or more series in the jaws. Pectorals absent. Dorsal fin commencing on head. Gill-openings small, horizontal, in the middle of the height of the body.

The blunt teeth distinguish the members of this genus, which frequent the tropical seas. Two species are found in Queensland waters.

A. Roof of mouth posteriorly with a broad patch of irregularly placed rounded pebble-like teeth. Colour brown, with yellow rings. *polyzona*

AA. Roof of mouth with 2 large pebble-like teeth inside a semicircle of 10-12 similar but smaller ones. Colour yellowish or whitish, with star-like spots. *nebulosa*

96. CLOUDED REEF EEL *Echidna nebulosa* (Thunberg) [Plate 21]

Muraena nebulosa Ahl, De Muraena et Ophich., 1789, p. 5.
Muraena nebulosa Day, Fish. India, 1878-88, p. 673, pl. 172, fig. 2.

Head 3.5-4 or more in trunk; tail somewhat shorter than head and trunk; dorsal fin origin before gill-openings; vomerine teeth in 2 parallel series of varying size, mostly granular; 2 large granular mesial teeth inside a hemicircle of 10-12 similar but smaller ones. Colour yellowish or whitish, with a row of large black blotches, broken up into star-like spots.

A very pretty eel commonly seen among the corals on the Great Barrier Reef. Found in the waters of Queensland and New South Wales, also in the Indo-Australian region and Lord Howe Island. Grows to 30 inches.

OTHER SPECIES

Ringed Reef Eel, *E. polyzona*. Also found on the reefs and close inshore in North Queensland. A wide-ranging species found from the Red Sea to the Indo-Australian Archipelago and the Pacific Islands. Grows to 22 inches.

Lycodontis

Dorsal and anal fins present, well developed. Vent about midway. Sharp depressible canines in mid front of upper jaw. Posterior nostril before eye as a round or oval opening, sometimes with a rim but not tubular.

Pugnacious eels of tropical seas, inhabiting reefs, some attaining to a large size and considered dangerous. Species numerous, ten in Queensland. Identification is frequently difficult because of the great variation of colour pattern, but the following key will enable the Queensland species to be identified, and two of them will be described in greater detail.

A. Intermaxillary with 1-2 conical teeth, no larger than the outside row.

    b. Maxillary teeth in one series (2 in very young stage). *pictus*
    bb. Maxillary teeth in 2 series. *thyrsoideus*

AA. Intermaxillary with 1-4 depressible slender fangs.

    c. Gill-openings in a dark patch.   *flavomarginata*

    cc. Gill-openings not in a dark patch.

      d. Colour almost uniform green.   *prasinus*

      dd. Colour not uniform; patterned or spotted.

        e.1. Head, body, and fins covered with large rounded or polygonal spots, separated by narrow white lines.   *favagineus*

        e.2. Blackish, with wide network of white or yellow lines giving a mottled appearance, or reddish-brown with round or oval black spots.   *undulatus*

        e.3. Creamy-yellowish, overlaid with brown network; sides of head with brown spots.   *cribroris*

        e.4. A dark-brown streak behind corner of mouth, white spots on jaws; body brown, with incomplete wavy cross-bands.   *chilospilus*

        e.5. Brown or greenish-grey, with oval or round blackish spots, larger than the eye, on head, body, and dorsal.   *melanospilos*

        e.6. Brownish, with network of fine white or yellow lines; sometimes almost uniform dark brown.   *pseudothyrsoidea*

97. PAINTED REEF EEL *Lycodontis pictus* (Ahl)   [Plate 23]

Muraena picta Ahl, De Muraena et Ophich., 1759, p. 9 (*fide* Sherborn).
Gymnothorax pictus Bleeker, Atlas Ichth., 4, 1864, p. 87, pl. 172, fig. 3.

Speckled Reef Eel (Queensland).

Head and trunk somewhat longer than tail; maxillary teeth in one series (in young examples in 2 series) the anterior ones fixed and conical, not sharp; vomerine teeth in a single series in the young, becoming biserial in adults. Juveniles are yellow, with round blackish spots about the size of the eye and arranged in 3 longitudinal rows; adults are brownish-grey, covered with very small black spots; very variable in colour.

A common though very beautiful eel, frequently seen gliding between the coral growths on the Great Barrier Reef. Found in Queensland, Western Australia, and the Indo-Pacific. Grows to 4 feet.

98. TESSELLATED REEF EEL *Lycodontis favagineus* (Bloch and Schneider)
[Plate 23]

Gymnothorax favagineus Bloch and Schneider, Syst. Ichth., 1801, p. 525, pl. 105.
Muraena tessellata Day, Fish. India, 1878-88, p. 670, pl. 171, fig. 4.

Head about 3-4 times in trunk; tail somewhat longer or shorter than head and trunk; eye about 2-3 in snout; tube of anterior nostril much shorter than diameter of eye; maxillary teeth in a single row, but sometimes with a few canines on the inner side anteriorly; vomerine teeth in a single row, much shorter than the others. Colour blue-black, with white lines forming a tessellated pattern; juveniles have the white lines much wider, giving the effect of large black spots.

A very common eel on the entire coastline of Queensland. Found also in the South Seas, the Indo-Australian Archipelago, and other tropical seas. Grows to 4 feet.

Evenchelys

Form exceedingly elongate, the tail being twice as long as the body. Teeth conical, sharp. Cleft of mouth wide, extending far back behind eye, the eye being much nearer to end of snout than to gape of mouth. Pectorals absent. Dorsal and anal fins united with caudal and covered by thick skin. Gill-openings small oblique slits, margins prominent. One species.

99. LONG-TAILED EEL *Evenchelys macrurus* (Bleeker) [Plate 23]

Muraena macrurus Bleeker, Nat. Tijdschr. Ned. Ind., 7, 1854, p. 324.
Thyrsoidea macrurus Bleeker, Atlas Ichth., 4, 1864, p. 111, pl. 166, fig. 2.

Head and trunk 1.5-2 in tail; eye 2 in snout; gill-opening rather wider than eye. Colour uniform brownish-grey.

This species is probably the largest eel in the world. Certainly the specimen in the Queensland Museum is the largest on record; it is 12 feet 11 inches in total length and was caught in the Big Cod Hole, Maroochy River, South Queensland. Saville Kent[7] wrote of bêche-de-mer fishermen who told him of a ferocious eel said to reach 20 feet in length. Probably it was this species.

This large eel frequents shallow waters, entering and ascending rivers. It ranges through the Indo-Australian Archipelago and New Guinea to Formosa, India, and Natal.

Family **Myridae: Worm Eels**

Body elongate, worm-like, slightly compressed or short and much compressed. Origin of dorsal fin above or far behind gill-openings. Pectorals well developed or absent. Dorsal, caudal, and anal confluent. Vent in anterior half of length. Tongue not free. Nostrils on or very close to margin of upper lip, the anterior tubular, the posterior lobed.

---

[7] *The Great Barrier Reef*, p. 303.

Small worm-like eels of uniform coloration, found in most tropical seas, on coral reefs and sandy shores. One genus in Queensland.

Muraenichthys

Body long, cylindrical, worm-like. No scales. Lateral line present. Nostrils on margin of upper lip. Dorsal fin low or rudimentary, its origin far behind gill-openings, confluent with caudal and anal. Pectorals absent. Gill-openings very small. Two species in Queensland waters.

KEY TO SPECIES IN QUEENSLAND

A. Origin of dorsal fin well in advance of vertical of vent.   *godeffroyi*

AA. Origin of dorsal fin behind vertical of vent.   *iredalei*

100. IREDALE'S WORM EEL *Muraenichthys iredalei* Whitley   [Plate 23]

Muraenichthys iredalei Whitley, Rec. Austr. Mus., 16, 1927, p. 5, fig. 1.
Illustration by F. Olsen after Whitley.

Head 11.6 in the total length; tail longer than trunk; eye 2 in snout; head elongate, bag-like before gill-slits; cleft of mouth extending well behind eye; upper jaw longer than lower; a single row of backwardly curving teeth in each jaw and along narrow ridge of vomer; dorsal rudimentary, its origin behind vertical of vent and confluent with anal.

Colour brownish, darker along back, where there are innumerable blackish punctations; a fuscous area along each side of thorax; the viscera shows through just behind gill-slits; fins without pigment. (Whitley.)

Found on the North Queensland reefs, where it grows to about 6½ inches.

Family **Ophicthyidae: Snake Eels**

Body elongate, cylindrical, scaleless. Dorsal and anal fins not confluent, leaving tip of tail free; tail ends in a sharp point. These fins may be well developed, low, rudimentary, or absent. Caudal wanting. Pectorals present or absent. Vent far behind gill-openings, before or behind middle of length. Snout short or long, projecting beyond lower jaw, pointed. Cleft of mouth extending to below or behind eye.

The snake eels, whose elongate and worm-like bodies are mostly banded with snake-like markings, are denizens of shallow waters on the coral reefs, some species burrowing. Most of them are of moderate or small size, though some attain several feet in length.

Some peculiar habits of certain members of the family were noted by Deraniyagala,[8] who made his observations on the genus *Leiuranus*. He stated

[8] *Spolia Zeylanica*, 16, pt 1, 8th Sept. 1930, p. 107.

that the swimming female is gripped in the jaws of the male and is thus held for hours before the fertilization of the ova takes place. He also noted[9] that another species selects the urogenital passages of certain large fishes for shelter at certain periods of its existence.

Many species of snake eels are known from temperate and tropical seas. Seven genera are found in Queensland waters.

KEY TO GENERA IN QUEENSLAND

A.   Dorsal fin commencing before gill-openings.

        b. A conspicuous fringe of barbels on upper lip. Colour uniform.   *Cirrhimuraena*

        bb. No fringe of barbels on upper lip. Colour varied.

        c. Pectorals well developed. Head with small dark spots.   *Malvoliophis*

        cc. Pectorals rudimentary. No spots on head.   *Chlevastes*

AA. Dorsal fin (if present) commencing above or behind gill-openings.

        d. No teeth on vomer. Body banded.   *Leiuranus*

        dd. Teeth present on vomer. Body not or only half banded.

        e. Teeth on vomer granular or pebble-like. Colour uniform.   *Pisodonophis*

        ee. Teeth on vomer conical and acute or caniniform and in a single row. Colour uniform or varied.

        f. Snout produced, beak-like. Colour uniform.   *Ophisurus*

        ff. Snout not so produced, bluntly pointed. Nape with a broad black saddle-like patch.   *Ophichthus*

Of the above seven genera the first six are each represented in Queensland by a single species and the last by two species. A single genus and species has been dealt with here, the Half-banded Snake Eel.

Leiuranus

Head small, snout pointed, projecting beyond small mouth, the cleft of which extends back behind small eye. Tongue not free. Teeth pointed, of moderate size, none on vomer. Pectorals small. Dorsal and anal fins not confluent, the caudal wanting. One species, inhabiting the tropical parts of the Indo-Pacific region.

---

[9] *Ibid.*, pt 3, March 1932, p. 355.

101. HALF-BANDED SNAKE EEL *Leiuranus semicinctus* (Lay and Bennett)
[Plate 23]

Ophisurus semicinctus Lay and Bennett, Zool. Beechey's Voy. Fish., 1839, p. 66.
Leiuranus colubrinus (not of Boddaert) Bleeker, Atlas Ichth., 4, 1864, p. 42, pl. 163, fig. 1.

Head more than 6 times in trunk; head and trunk one-seventh longer than tail; eye 2 in snout; pectorals about equal to length of snout. Colour yellowish-brown, with 24 to 35 black saddle-like bands.

A handsome eel found on the coral reefs and near the shore. It is wide-ranging, being found in Queensland, the Indo-Pacific, China, and Japan. Grows to 20 inches.

Order SYNENTOGNATHI: LONG TOMS, GARFISHES, and FLYING-FISHES

In the members of this order the fins are without spines and the ventral fins are abdominal. The lateral line is situated low on the body, forming a raised ridge.

KEY TO SUB-ORDERS

A. Mouth large, jaws usually produced. Scales small.   SCOMBRESOCOIDEA

AA. Mouth small, only lower jaw produced. Scales large or moderate.   EXOCOETOIDEA

Sub-order SCOMBRESOCOIDEA

Family Belonidae: Long Toms or Needle-fishes

Body elongate, very slender, cylindrical or compressed, covered with small or very small cycloid scales. Lateral line very low, more or less elevated, sometimes forming a keel on caudal peduncle. Mouth very large, both jaws produced into a slender beak, the lower jaw the longer. Both jaws with bands of small teeth with a single series of wide-set distinct canines. Dorsal fin set far back, opposite anal, both fins rather long. No finlets. Pectoral fins moderate, inserted rather high. Caudal forked, emarginate, truncate or rounded.

Voracious carnivorous fishes inhabiting the coastal waters of all temperate and tropical seas, some species entering fresh water. They swim at or near the surface and feed upon small fishes. When startled they swim along the surface at great speed, often heaving their bodies into the air and riding the surface at great speed with their tails in the water. This curious habit has earned them the name of skipjacks among Queensland fishermen. Some of the larger species grow to a length of 6 feet and are dangerous to bathers. Most of them are good food-fishes but are rejected on account of their numerous bones. Three genera are found in Queensland waters.

A.   A bony keel beneath tip of lower jaw.   *Thalassosteus*

AA. No bony keel beneath tip of lower jaw.

    b. Body very little compressed, its height less than
      twice the breadth.   *Tylosurus*

    bb. Body strongly compressed, its height twice the
      breadth.   *Ablennes*

Thalassosteus

Agreeing with *Tylosurus* in general characters but differing in the presence
of a very peculiar bony keel on the lower side of the tip of the lower jaw. The
bones in this genus are all much more intensely green in life than in any others
of the Belonidae. The dorsal and anal are many-rayed, the anterior lobe of
each being high and falcate. A single species in Queensland.

102. KEEL-JAWED LONG TOM *Thalassosteus appendiculatus* (Klunzinger)
[Plate 24]

Belone appendiculatus Klunzinger, Zool. Bot. Ges. Wien, Verh., 21, 1871, p. 580.
Belone appendiculatus Günther, Mus. God. Journ., 8, pt 16, 1909, p. 351 (figure of head).

D. 26, hind rays somewhat elongated, last reaches caudal; A. 22-23; a large
compressed horny appendage below end of lower jaw; lower caudal lobe
longer than upper. Colour intense green above, silvery-white below, divided by
a broad silvery blue-green longitudinal band; vertical fins dusky, tinged bluish
with dark tips; caudal rusty-red with darker margins.

A rare species, its inclusion in Queensland fauna is based upon a single
example from Moreton Bay. It is also known from the Solomon Islands,
Hawaii, and the Red Sea. Readily recognized by the bony keel on the lower
jaw. Grows to about 40 inches.

Tylosurus

Form elongate, body cylindrical or compressed. Intermaxillaries and mandibles prolonged into a beak. No gill-rakers. Both jaws with a band of small
teeth and a series of well-developed canines. No teeth on vomer. Lateral line
sometimes forming an elevated keel on caudal peduncle.

Powerful surface-swimming fishes of most warm seas. Species numerous,
eight in Queensland waters.

A.   Caudal truncate or rounded; lateral line not forming a keel on caudal peduncle, or, if so, only rudimentary.

    b. A. 2/13-15. A black spot at base of caudal fin.   *strongylurus*

    bb. A. 2/17-23. No spot at base of caudal fin.

      c. A. 2/17-20.

        d. D. 2/14-16; A. 2/17-19; origin of dorsal fin opposite that of anal; body short and compressed; cheeks with wavy markings.   *kreffti*

        dd. D. 2/18; A. 19-22; origin of dorsal fin above 4th or 5th anal ray; body not so compressed, form more elongate.   *macleayanus*

      cc. A. 2/21-23; origin of dorsal above 7th divided anal ray. Pectorals with a black subterminal blotch.   *leiurus*

AA. Caudal forked, less so in the young.

    e. Lateral line forming a more or less elevated keel on caudal peduncle.

      f. D. 2/20-22; A. 2/18-20; P. 1/12-14; canines in upper jaw curved forwards.   *annulatus*

      ff. D. 2/23-24; A. 2/20-21; P. 1/11-12; canines in upper jaw vertical.   *melanotus*

      fff. D. 2/19; A. 2/22; P. 1/11. A dark blotch on caudal.   *terebra*

    ee. Lateral line not forming a keel on caudal peduncle.

      g. D. 2/19; A. 2/19; P. 1/13. A smoky blotch at upper part of inner pectoral axil.   *gavialoides*

103. BLACK-SPOT LONG TOM *Tylosurus strongylurus* (Van Hasselt)
[Colour-plate 5]

Belone strongylura Van Hasselt, Alg. Konst-en Letterbode, Deel 1, 1823, p. 130 (*fide* Weber and de Beaufort).
Illustration by G. Coates.

    D. 1/10-2/13; A. 2/13-15; L. 1. about 170; caudal truncate or rounded; lateral line not forming a keel on caudal peduncle; origin of dorsal fin above second divided ray of anal. Colour brownish or yellow-green above, sides silvery, white below; a silvery blue-bordered longitudinal band along posterior half of body; dorsal sometimes edged with orange; anal sometimes yellow; pectorals and ventrals clear; caudal yellowish or green, with median black blotch.

    A common species in the waters of Queensland, this also occurs in the Indo-Australian Archipelago and in the Philippines and India. Readily recognized by the black spot at the base of the tail. Grows to 18 inches.

104. STOUT LONG TOM *Tylosurus macleayanus* (Ogilby)   [Plate 24]

Belone macleayana Ogilby, Cat. Fish. N.S.Wales, 1886, p. 53.
Tylosurus macleayana Stead, Edib. Fish. N.S.Wales, 1908, p. 35, pl. 10.

D. 20; A. 19-22; C. 17; caudal acutely rounded or feebly emarginate; scales very small; origin of dorsal fin above fourth or fifth anal ray. Colour green above, silvery sides, white below; dorsal and caudal fins green, with dusky borders; outer half of pectorals black: ventrals yellowish.

This is the common Long Tom of Moreton Bay. Apparently it is not met with in the waters of northern Queensland. Found also on the coast of New South Wales. Grows to 4 feet.

OTHER SPECIES

Krefft's Long Tom, *T. kreffti*. A very common river species which swarms in the streams of North Queensland, especially far up in the fresh waters. Its range in Queensland extends southward as far as Maryborough. Also found in New Guinea. Grows to 26 inches and is known by its short, compressed, and deep body.

Tylosurus leiurus, *T. annulatus*, and *T. melanotus* inhabit northern waters. The small species known as *T. terebra* is from Michaelmas Cay, North Queensland, where the only known specimen was taken in 1926. *Tylosurus gavialoides*, known originally only from Western Australia, has now been recorded from North Queensland.

Ablennes

Body elongate, strongly compressed, the sides flattened. Jaws slender, the premaxillary elevated proximally. Base of mandible very deep. Anterior dorsal rays forming a lobe. No gill-rakers.

Fishes of moderate size inhabiting the warmer parts of the western Atlantic, Pacific, and Indian oceans. Three or four closely allied forms have been described, which, however, have been united into one species by some authors.

105. BARRED LONG TOM *Ablennes hians* (Cuvier and Valenciennes) [Plate 24]

Belone hians Cuvier and Valenciennes, Hist. Nat. Poiss., 1st ed., 18, 1846, p. 432; 2nd ed., p. 321.
Athlennes caeruleofasciatus Ogilby, Mem. Qld Mus., 5, 1916, p. 130, pl. 14.

D. 2/21-23; A. 2/23-25; P. 1/13; V. 1/5; body strongly compressed, height twice breadth of body. Colour: Back dark brownish, bluish or greenish, with bluish-green reflections; sides and below silvery and white; a narrow dark-green vertebral stripe from occiput to dorsal fin, below this a broad sea-green band extending to tail; 6 to 8 dark cross-bands on body, behind ventrals;

dorsal, ventrals and anal fins dark greenish-black, rusty-red on their anterior edges; caudal greenish-grey, dusky on extremities and with upper and lower edges rusty-red; inside of mouth scarlet.

A wide-ranging fish found in both the Pacific and Atlantic oceans. Apparently it is rare in Queensland. Grows to over 4 feet.

Sub-order EXOCOETOIDEA: HALF-BEAKS and FLYING-FISHES

In this sub-order there are only two families.

KEY TO FAMILIES

A. Lower jaw usually produced into a beak. Pectorals usually short (*Euleptorhamphus* excepted.) HEMIRAMPHIDAE

AA. Lower jaw not produced into a beak. Pectorals very long, used as an organ of flight. EXOCOETIDAE

Family **Hemiramphidae: Garfishes or Half-beaks**

These fishes are readily recognized by the prolongation of the lower jaw into a "beak" which is usually tipped with bright orange or scarlet. Though a few are pelagic in habit, most of the species live close inshore in shallow-water bays and in estuaries, some entering fresh water.

Garfishes are found in most warm seas and are herbivorous in habit, feeding upon minute scraps of vegetable matter, seaweeds, etc. Owing to their great habit of swimming at the surface in big shoals, numbers of them are captured by net fishermen. They frequently leap from the water or skip along its surface at a great pace, especially when surrounded by the nets.

Although small, they are relished as food-fishes, their flesh being firm, white, and well flavoured. Some of the species are viviparous, though most are oviparous. Five genera occur in Queensland waters.

KEY TO GENERA IN QUEENSLAND

A. Lower jaw produced into a beak, moderate or long.

   b. Pectoral fins short. Body moderately compressed.

    c. Caudal forked. No anal rays lengthened in males.

     d. Cutaneous flaps below and on each side of mandibles or beak greatly developed, the lateral ones broader than the beak itself. *Loligorhamphus*

     dd. Cutaneous flaps on beak not greatly developed. *Hemiramphus*

    cc. Caudal rounded or truncate. Some anal rays greatly lengthened and broadened in males. *Zenarchopterus*

   bb. Pectoral fins very long. Body slender and much compressed. Habit pelagic. *Euleptorhamphus*

AA. Lower jaw produced only into a very short beak. *Arrhamphus*

Loligorhamphus

Cutaneous folds below and on each side of mandibles greatly developed, the lateral ones broader than the beak itself. A genus with a single species, found in North Queensland.

106. SPATULA GARFISH *Loligorhamphus normani* Whitley   [Plate 24]

Loligorhamphus normani Whitley, Rec. Austr. Mus., 18, no. 3, 1931, p. 105, pl. 12, figs 2-3.

D. 14; A. 15; P. 12; V. 1/5; C. 14; L. 1. about 60; head from tip of upper jaw 4.1 in the length to hypural joint; entire head 2.2 in the total length; each lateral fold of skin on each side of beak broader than the beak itself. Colour in formalin brownish above, lighter below; beak and folds nearly all black; a blackish lateral stripe, probably silvery in life, extends from pectoral base to caudal base and is broadest between dorsal and anal fins. (After Whitley.)

Known only from the unique holotype, a specimen 127 mm. in standard length, or 205 mm. in total length, collected at Townsville, North Queensland, in 1924.

Hemiramphus

Form elongate, the body cylindrical or compressed. Mandibles produced into a long beak which bears teeth only on that part opposite the intermaxillaries. Beak bordered by a more or less conspicuous fold of skin on each edge and a third median one below, beginning on the chin. Teeth small, often tricuspid. Lateral line situated low on body. Scales moderate to large, somewhat deciduous.

Fishes of tropical and temperate seas, swimming in shoals, usually just offshore. Eight species occur in Queensland.

KEY TO SPECIES IN QUEENSLAND

A.   Triangular part of upper jaw longer than broad.   *georgii*

AA. Triangular part of upper jaw broader than long.

    b. Origin of ventrals nearer to axil of pectoral than to base of caudal.   *regularis*

    bb. Origin of ventrals midway between axil of pectoral and base of caudal.   *quoyi*

    bbb. Origin of ventrals nearer to base of caudal than to axil of pectoral.

      c. Origin of anal almost opposite that of dorsal.   *dussumieri*

      cc. Origin of anal about opposite fifth dorsal ray.

    d. Length of base of anal fin twice in that of dorsal.
       Body with black blotches.   *far*

    dd. Length of base of anal fin less than twice in that
        of dorsal. No black blotches on body or at most
        one only.

      e. Body strongly compressed, its breadth being
        one-half of its depth.   *marginatus*

      ee. Body not so compressed, its breadth being
        three-quarters of its depth.   *welsbyi*

AAA. Triangular part of upper jaw about equal in length
    and breadth.   *australis*

107. SHORT-NOSED GARFISH *Hemiramphus quoyi* Cuvier and Valenciennes
[Plate 24]

Hemiramphus quoyi Cuvier and Valenciennes, Hist. Nat. Poiss., 19, 1846, p. 35.
Illustration by G. Coates.

    Sea Garfish (Brisbane Fish Market).

    D. 16; A. 14-16; P. 12; origin of anal a little behind dorsal origin; ventrals inserted midway between preopercle ridge and caudal base or somewhat nearer the latter; body slightly compressed, its depth 9.3-13 in total length with caudal; entire head 3.2-3.8 in the length with caudal; lower jaw short, its length (beyond extremity of upper jaw) 7.3-11.4 in length with caudal.

    Colour yellowish-green, darker above, silvery on sides, with iridescent tints of bluish and pinkish posteriorly; white below; each scale on back with a golden-brown fleck, those in vicinity of dorsal being flecked with bright green; a silvery longitudinal band on side, bordered above by a bluish-black one, with which is a light-green one posteriorly; a row of bright light-blue spots beneath the scales on either side of base of anal fin; head dark greenish above; opercles and maxillary groove bright blue; fins hyaline; caudal and dorsal usually dusky tipped; beak orange-yellow. Young examples often have base of ventrals and pectorals blackish.

    A common fish along the whole coastline of Queensland, North Australia, and in New Guinea. It is frequently captured in the fishermen's nets along the ocean beaches and commands a ready sale in the markets. As a food-fish it is of first quality, having great breadth of body, which enables a good fillet to be cut. The species is recognized by the short beak. Grows to 14 inches.

108. BLACK-BARRED GARFISH *Hemiramphus far* (Forskål)

Esox far Forskål, Descr. Animal., 1775, p. 67.   [Colour-plate 6]
Illustration by G. Coates.

    Needle-fish, Candle-fish (South Africa).

    D. 12-14; A. 10-12; P. 11-13; entire head 2.3-2.4 in length without caudal; lower jaw (beyond extremity of upper) about 5 in length with caudal; origin of anal below about fifth dorsal ray; length of base of dorsal fin about twice that of anal; ventrals inserted about midway between base of caudal and tip of pectoral. Colour greenish-blue above, sides silvery, with 4 to 9 large black spots along sides; upper caudal lobe bright yellow, lower lobe vivid blue.

A most beautiful fish in life, this species is common on the Queensland coast, but is not so frequently met with in New South Wales waters. It ranges also through the waters of New Guinea and the Indo-Pacific region to the Indian Ocean, East Africa, and the Red Sea. A good food-fish. Grows to 20 inches.

109. FLAT-SIDED GARFISH *Hemiramphus welsbyi* Ogilby [Colour-plate 6]

Hemiramphus welsbyi Ogilby, Proc. Roy. Soc. Qld, 21, 1908, p. 91.
Illustration by G. Coates.

Three by Two Garfish (Brisbane Fish Market).

D. 13; A. 12-13; body robust, sides flattened; entire head $2\frac{2}{3}$ in length without caudal; lower jaw (beyond extremity of upper jaw) 5 in length without caudal; dorsal origin far in advance of that of anal, the length of its base being about $1\frac{3}{5}$ times that of the latter; ventrals inserted midway between root of caudal and middle third of pectoral.

Colour dark green above, silvery on sides, and pearly-white below; sides with a conspicuous silvery band, widest in the middle and tapering each extremity and bordered above by a blue-green band; fins dusky; caudal with upper lobe yellow, the lower bluish and both lobes edged blackish; a black spot is usually present on each side below dorsal fin.

This fine big garfish, which was first known from Moreton Bay, is now known all along the coast of Queensland and also in the Northern Territory and Torres Strait. It is well known as a food-fish in the Brisbane Fish Market, where it is sold as "Three by Two". It takes this name from its very flattened sides. Grows to 16 inches.

OTHER SPECIES

Long-jawed Garfish, *H. georgii*. A small species found in the waters of Queensland. Grows to 12 inches and is readily recognized by the triangular part of the upper jaw being longer than broad.

River Garfish, *H. regularis*. Known as the Needle Gar in Moreton Bay. Common in South Queensland, though not to the same extent as in New South Wales, where it is found in the coastal lakes, estuaries, and bays. It has a slender body and grows to only 14 inches.

Dussumier's Garfish, *H. dussumieri*. Frequents the waters of North Queensland and is wide-ranging outside Australia. Grows to only 12 inches.

Black-tipped Garfish, *H. marginatus*. A small and common gar from the waters of North Queensland, North Australia, New Guinea, and the Indo-Pacific region. Grows to 12 inches.

Sea Garfish, *H. australis*. A southern species which ranges round the southern coastline of Australia, entering Queensland waters only as a straggler. It is a lover of the outside waters and is common in New South Wales, where it enters the bays and estuaries during the early summer months for the purpose of spawning. Grows to 18 inches. A valuable food-fish in the southern States of Australia.

Zenarchopterus

The chief characteristic of this genus is the curious prolongation of some of the anal rays into a broad feather-like process in the males. Sometimes the dorsal fin in the males is also prolonged (see Plate 25). Two species in Queensland.

KEY TO SPECIES IN QUEENSLAND

A.   Base of anal fin 2-2.4 in that of dorsal; 6th and 7th anal ray in the male enormously enlarged, often reaching to end of caudal.   *dispar*

AA. Base of anal fin 2.5-3 in that of dorsal; sixth and seventh anal ray in the male enlarged, but not so much as to reach to base of caudal.   *buffonis*

110. SPOON-FIN GARFISH *Zenarchopterus dispar* (Cuvier and Valenciennes)
[Colour-plate 6; Plate 25]

Hemirhampus dispar Cuvier and Valenciennes, Hist. Nat. Poiss., 19, 1846, p. 58.
Colour illustration by G. Coates; monochrome by F. Olsen after Weber and de Beaufort.

D. 10-11; A. 11-12; compressed, the breadth of the body being somewhat more or less than 1.5 in the height; entire head 2.2-2.3 in the length with caudal; length of lower jaw (beyond extremity of upper jaw) 3.5-4 in the length with caudal; origin of anal about below third dorsal ray; base of anal 2-2.4 in that of dorsal; ventrals inserted about twice nearer to caudal than to corner of mouth. Colour olive-brown above, sides paler, whitish below, with a silver band with black line above it; fins dusky.

These little fishes, which are found in the sea as well as the creeks and rivers, more often seek the still waters of the mangrove creeks, where they float in small shoals at the surface. Readily recognized by the triangular part of the upper jaw being broader than long and the seventh anal ray (in the male) reaching almost to the end of the dorsal fin (see Plate 25). Grows to 6 inches. Ranges from Queensland through the East Indies.

102

OTHER SPECIES

Another East Indian species, *Z. buffonis*, also frequents North Queensland, being found both in the sea and in the estuaries. Grows to 11 inches.

Euleptorhamphus

Pelagic fishes related to the *Hemiramphus* but with the body much more slender and greatly compressed and with the pectoral fins very long as in the flying-fishes. Species few, inhabiting the Indo-Pacific region and the West Indies. One species in Queensland.

111. LONG-FINNED GARFISH *Euleptorhamphus longirostris* (Cuvier)
[Plate 25]

Hemirhamphus longirostris Cuvier, Règne Anim., 2nd ed., 2, 1829, p. 286.

Euleptorhamphus longirostris Jordan and Evermann, Bull. U.S. Fish. Comm., 23 (1903) 1905, pt 1, p. 128, fig. 43.

D. 22-25; A. 21-23; body greatly compressed; Pectorals very long, approaching those of the flying-fishes; lower jaw long, about 3-4 times in the total length.

Colour: "Pale bluish-silvery above; scales on back with darker edges; lower side and belly silvery; top of head dark bluish, side silvery; bill bluish-black; fins pale bluish, anal white; upper lobe of caudal with a diffuse curved black band parallel with the edge." (Jordan and Evermann.)

This interesting fish is seldom seen on account of its pelagic habits. Few specimens are met with. Only two specimens are known from Queensland so far. Both jumped aboard launches, one north of Gladstone and the other off Lady Elliott Island. The species grows to 18 inches. Its range is almost circumtropical.

Arrhamphus

Form elongate, somewhat compressed. Mandibles projecting beyond the upper jaw a short distance only, but not into a long beak as in the *Hemiramphus*.

Fishes of the Indo-Australian Archipelago and Australia, found both in the sea and in fresh water. Species few, one in Queensland.

112. SNUB-NOSED GARFISH *Arrhamphus sclerolepis* Günther
[Colour-plate 6]

Arrhamphus sclerolepis Günther, Cat. Fish. Brit. Mus., 6, 1866, p. 277.
Illustration by G. Coates.

Snubbie (South Queensland).

D. 13-15; A. 15-17; L. 1. 43-53; lower jaw short; body compressed, its height about $6\frac{1}{2}$-7 in the length to end of middle caudal rays; origin of dorsal and anal fins opposite, both fins with scaly bases. Colour sea-green above, with flushes of pink on body; 3 fine black lines dorsally from head to dorsal fin; fins almost hyaline, the dorsal, anal and caudal with minute black dots, giving the two former fins dusky edges anteriorly and the latter fin dusky on its edges, the whole fin black-tipped; tip of lower jaw pale orange; opercles opalescent; a patch of bright blue in region of maxilla and preorbital; a blue-black lateral stripe, beneath which is a broad silvery one, from pectoral base to caudal base; a faint black dot is usually present at hind edge of preopercle.

An Australian species found in Queensland, New South Wales, and northern Australia. Although found in the sea it is a lover of brackish and freshwater streams and is commonly seen far inland. A valuable food-fish, sold in the Brisbane Fish Market as "Snub-nose". Grows to 15 inches.

Family **Exocoetidae: Flying-Fishes**

Body oblong or elongate, more or less compressed, covered with cycloid scales of large or moderate size. Lateral line running low down along side of belly. Head with vertical sides, more or less scaly. Mouth moderate, terminal. Premaxillaries not protractile. Teeth small or minute, rarely tricuspid, in jaws and sometimes on palatines, by exception also on vomer, pterygoids, and tongue. Dorsal fin without spines, situated far back, above or behind origin of anal and more or less similar to it. Ventrals short, moderate, or long, of several soft rays. Pectorals inserted high, very long, forming an organ of flight. Caudal deeply forked, the lower lobe the longer.

In this group of fishes the pectoral fins are greatly enlarged and wing-like, enabling the fishes to undertake aerial excursions. They do not actually fly, as so many people suppose, but the fins are held rigid and act in the form of a parachute or glider. Speed is generated by the powerful tail whilst the fish is in the water, after which it launches itself into the air, usually turning into the wind.

In the "two-winged" types (*Exocoetus*) the fish launches itself straight from the water into the air, but in the "four-winged" types (*Cypselurus*) the fish, driven by the powerful tail, taxies along the surface of the water until the required speed is attained, when it hurls itself into the air at a speed which has been estimated at thirty-five miles per hour. They have been known to remain in the air for as long as half a minute.

Flying-fishes are usually met with at great distances from land in all tropical and subtropical seas, where they swim at the surface in shoals, and when disturbed rise from the sea like a swarm of grasshoppers in a field. Many of the flying-fishes are excellent food-fishes.

The three genera here dealt with are separated as in the key.

A. Pectorals short, reaching to middle of dorsal. Teeth on vomer and tongue. *Parexocoetus*

AA. Pectorals long, reaching to base of caudal, or nearly so. No teeth on vomer or tongue.

    b. Ventral fins much shorter than head, situated nearer to tip of snout than to base of caudal. *Exocoetus*

    bb. Ventral fins longer than head, situated nearer to caudal than to snout. *Cypselurus*

Parexocoetus

Body moderately elongate, compressed. Mandibles with a long triangular symphysial knob which projects beyond upper jaw. Teeth in jaws, on vomer, palatines, pterygoids, and tongue. Dorsal fin high. Anal as long as dorsal. Pectorals short or moderate, not reaching beyond middle of dorsal. Ventrals short, their origin about midway between point of snout and caudal base.

Fishes of the Indo-Pacific and Atlantic. One species in Queensland.

113. SHORT-FINNED FLYING-FISH *Parexocoetus brachypterus* (Richardson) [Plate 25]

Exocoetus brachypterus Richardson, Rept 15th Meet. Brit. Assn Adv. Sci., 1845, Cambridge, 1846 London, p. 265.
Parexocoetus mento Bleeker, Atlas Ichth., 6, 1866-72, p. 77, pl. 251, fig. 6.

D. 10-12; A. 10-12; L. 1. 38-40; compressed, the depth of the body about 4.5-5 in the length without caudal; head about 5 in the length with caudal; bony knob at front of lower jaw. Colour dark blue above, silvery below, a dark patch at base of dorsal; pectorals densely covered with small black spots, otherwise light blue-grey like the dorsal; caudal with the upper lobe light blue-grey, the lower lobe dark blue; ventrals and anal hyaline, blackish in the juveniles.

This fish, which is known by its short pectorals and black patch on the dorsal fin, is occasionally caught in northern Queensland waters. It ranges from the Indo-Australian region and China to Natal and the Red Sea. Grows to 8 inches.

Exocoetus

Body moderately elongate, compressed. Lower jaw but little projecting. Teeth very small. Palate and tongue toothless. Dorsal not elevated. Origin of dorsal fin about opposite to that of anal and about as long as that fin. Pectorals long, reaching to or almost to base of caudal. Ventrals short, inserted much nearer to snout-tip than to caudal base. Scales large. Lateral line low. Only one species, found in all warm seas.

114. COMMON FLYING-FISH *Exocoetus volitans* Linnaeus [Plate 25]

Exocoetus volitans Linnaeus, Syst. Nat., 10th ed., 1758, p. 316; 12th ed., 1766, p. 520.
Exocoetus evolans Day, Fish. India, 1878-88, p. 519, pl. 120, fig. 5.

D. 13-16; A. 12-14; L. 1. 40-43; height of body 6.5-7 in the length with caudal; head 5-5.3 in the length with caudal; pectoral reaching base of caudal or almost so. Colour bluish above, silvery on sides, whitish below; pectorals bluish-black or brownish, with a broad white posterior and with upper and lower borders white; other fins pale.

A widely distributed fish known by its long pectorals and short ventrals. In Australian waters it is known from Queensland, New South Wales, South Australia, and North Australia. Grows to 12 inches.

Cypselurus

Form elongate, more or less compressed. Snout blunt, jaws equal. Teeth small or very small, sometimes absent, none on vomer, pterygoids, and tongue. Dorsal fin not very high, its origin opposite to or far before that of anal and generally longer than last-named fin. Pectorals long, reaching to or not quite to caudal base. Ventrals well developed, often long, their origin much nearer to caudal base than to tip of snout. Scales large to moderate. Lateral line low.

Fishes of the Indo-Pacific and Atlantic oceans, two species being found in Queensland.

KEY TO SPECIES IN QUEENSLAND

A.   Origin of anal beneath that of dorsal. *oxycephalus*

AA. Origin of anal opposite middle of dorsal. *melanocercus*

115. FLYING-FISH *Cypselurus oxycephalus* (Bleeker) [Plate 25]

Exocoetus oxycephalus Bleeker, Nat. Tijdschr. Ned. Ind., 3, 1852, p. 771; and Atlas Ichth., 6, 1866-72, p. 75, pl. 248, fig. 1.

D. 10-12; A. 11; somewhat compressed; height of body 6-7 or more in the length with caudal; head 5-5.5 in the length with caudal; origin of dorsal opposite that of anal; pectorals reaching to end of dorsal or farther; ventrals reaching to middle of anal or beyond. Colour dark bluish above, silvery below; pectorals dusky, darkest at axil and in posterior half, thus forming a light transverse band; middle rays of ventrals and caudal fin dusky, other fins clear.

An Indo-Australian species which has been recorded from Torres Strait. As is the case of most species of flying-fishes, it is seldom met with owing to its pelagic habit. Grows to 9 inches.

OTHER SPECIES

Great Black-tailed Flying-fish, *C. melanocercus*. One of the largest of the flying-fishes, growing to at least 17½ inches. It is known only from Australian seas, where it has been captured off the coasts of Queensland and New South Wales. It is seldom that these fishes, other than the juveniles, are ever found in inside waters, but in October 1952 an adult of this species, measuring 15 inches in length and in good condition, jumped aboard a barge in the Brisbane River near the Grey Street bridge.

Order SOLENICHTHYES: FLUTE-MOUTHS, BELLOWS-FISHES, FIRE-FISHES and SEA-HORSES

The members of this order are distinguished chiefly by their elongated and tube-like mouths. The body in some species is encased in bony rings. There are five families in Queensland.

KEY TO FAMILIES REPRESENTED IN QUEENSLAND

A.   Jaws with minute teeth. Lateral line continuous. Form elongate.

    b. Body compressed, scaly. Soft dorsal fin preceded by isolated slender free spines.   AULOSTOMIDAE

    bb. Body depressed, without scales. No dorsal spines.   FISTULARIDAE

AA. Jaws toothless. No lateral line.

    c. Head and body with small rough scales.   MACRORAMPHOSIDAE

    cc. No scales, body more or less encased in dermal bony plates.

      d. Form knife-like. Two dorsal fins above ventrally deflected tail. Ventrals rudimentary.   CENTRISCIDAE

    dd. Form more elongate, angular or rounded. Bony plates forming rings round body. No ventrals.   SYNGNATHIDAE

Family Aulostomidae: Trumpet-fishes

Body compressed, elongate, covered with small ctenoid scales. Head long. Mouth small, at end of long tubiform and compressed snout. Lower jaw prominent, with a barbel at symphysis. Teeth minute, in bands on lower jaw and vomer. Spinous dorsal of 8 to 12 very slender free spines. Soft dorsal and anal rather long, similar, posterior, with 23 to 29 rays each, of which the four anterior ones are spine-like. Caudal small, rhombic, the middle rays longest. Ventrals abdominal, of 6 rays. Pectorals broad, rounded.

A small family of carnivorous fishes found in tropical and subtropical seas. They are mostly dwellers of shallow waters, swimming at or near the surface. One genus, *Aulostomus*, circumtropical.

116. SPINY-BACK TRUMPET-FISH *Aulostomus chinensis* (Linnaeus)
[Plate 26]

Fistularia chinensis Linnaeus, Syst. Nat., 12th ed., 1766, p. 515.
Aulostoma chinense Günther, Mus. God. Journ., 15, pt 7, 1881, p. 221, pl. 123, figs b-c.

Painted Flute-mouth (New South Wales).

D. 8-12 + 24-27; A. 4 + 22-26; P. 17; elongate, compressed; height 11-12.5 in the length without caudal; head about 3⅓ to 3⅔ with caudal, extremely compressed, especially the snout; scales small, ctenoid. Colour very variable, usually a uniform brown, with or without cross-bars or lines; some examples are yellow.

A widely distributed fish, though not commonly found on the Australian coast. Grows to 30 inches.

Family **Fistularidae: Flute-Mouths or Cornet-Fishes**

Body greatly elongate, much depressed, broader than deep. Skin totally naked, or covered with minute conical hooked spinelets which may disappear with age; there may also be a median longitudinal single row of narrow keeled scales on back and ventral surface. Head very long, the anterior bones of the skull much produced, forming a long tube, which terminates in the narrow mouth. Both jaws, and usually the vomer and palatines also, with minute teeth. No spinous dorsal. Soft dorsal short, posterior, somewhat elevated. Anal fin opposite and similar to soft dorsal. Caudal fin forked, the middle rays produced into a long filament. Pectoral small, with a broad base. Ventrals very small, wide apart, abdominal, far in advance of dorsal.

Fishes of the tropical seas, closely related to the preceding family and with similar habits. A single genus, *Fistularia*, with few species, one in Queensland.

117. FLUTE-MOUTH *Fistularia petimba* Lacépède   [Colour-plate 6]

Fistularia petimba Lacépède, Hist. Nat. Poiss., 5, 1803, p. 349.
Illustration by G. Coates.

Cornet-fish, Horsewhip-fish (China).

D. 14-17; A. 14-16; skin naked and smooth to touch; depth of body about 40 in the length (without caudal filament); head more or less than 2⅔ times in the length. Colour greenish-brown, whitish below, with two interrupted blue stripes running from nape to tail, above lateral line. Caudal with two median rays produced into a long filament. Some examples have the dorsal, anal, and caudal fins bright orange in colour.

When feeding upon a school of small fishes the Flute-mouths float straight and motionless, gradually drawing nearer as a stick would float with the tide. Suddenly, with a movement too quick for the eye to follow, they dart into a school and, seizing one, move back again by "going astern", repeating the "floating-stick" method until the school settles down again, when they repeat the attack.

This is a common and widely distributed fish, found in the estuaries and inshore waters from the east coast of Africa to the Indo-Pacific, Japan, and Australia; in Australia it frequents the waters of Queensland and New South Wales. It is also found in the Americas. Grows to at least 5 feet.

Family **Macroramphosidae: Bellows-fishes**

Form oblong or elevated, compressed. Head and body covered all over with small rough scales. Trunk also armoured with large bony plates, partly hidden by the scales, making it rigid and immovable. Head produced into a long tube which bears the short jaws at the end. No teeth. No lateral line. Spinous and soft dorsal continuous with or separated from each other, or connected by a series of short isolated spines. Soft dorsal and anal of moderate length. Ventrals small, abdominal, usually without a spine. Pectorals short. Caudal fin emarginate.

A small family of pelagic fishes found in both hemispheres. Their powers of swimming are feeble and the ocean currents aid their distribution. Species found on the coasts of Europe are known as snipe-fish or woodcock-fish on account of their attenuated snouts. One genus in Queensland.

Macroramphosus

Body compressed, oblong, back more or less straight. No lateral line, though lateral line canals present on head. Dorsal armour on each side of body, consisting of 2 series of bony plates, each series formed by 3 well-developed and a fourth much smaller plate. No patch of bristles on nape. First dorsal spine short. One species in Queensland.

118. LONG-SPINED BELLOWS-FISH *Macroramphosus elevatus* Waite
[Plate 26]

Macrorhamphosus scolopax var. *elevatus* Waite, Mem. Austr. Mus., 4, 1899, p. 59, pl. 7, fig. 1.

D. 4/11 to 5/12; A. 19; depth of body very variable, large examples being considerably deeper than small ones; length and position of second dorsal spine also variable, being longer than the head in some examples but little longer than the snout—or even shorter than it—in others. Colour orange-red.

A curious fish recorded from the deep water off the coast of South Queensland and found also in the waters of New South Wales, Tasmania, Victoria, and New Zealand. Grows to 8 inches.

Family **Centriscidae: Razor-fishes**

Small fishes living in the tropical inshore waters of the Indo-Pacific. Characterized by the transparent body encased immovably in a series of bony plates and with the head produced into a long tube with the mouth terminal, small, and toothless. The trunk ends posteriorly in a long strong spine, beneath which are situated the 2 dorsal fins. The spinous dorsal is close to the strong spine and the soft dorsal is directed downward. The ventral surface is extremely compressed, with a sharp knife-like edge.

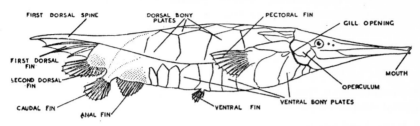

FIG. 7. External anatomy of a razor-fish, family Centriscidae.
AFTER MUNRO

These fishes swim in shoals in a vertical position, with the head down; some observers have stated that this position is a normal one for them; others state that the normal position is with the head upwards. Two genera, both represented in Queensland waters.

KEY TO GENERA

A. Dorsal spine with a movable spinous ray at its end. Interorbital space striated, convex, without a longitudinal groove. *Aeoliscus*

AA. Dorsal spine without a movable spinous ray at its end. Interorbital space convex or with a groove continued to crown of head, which is striated. *Centriscus*

Aeoliscus

Represented in Queensland by one species, *A. strigatus*, an Indo-Pacific fish recorded in Queensland from the far north at Torres Strait. Grows to 6 inches.

Centriscus

Represented in Queensland by two species, one of which will be described in detail here. The other can be identified from its description in the following key.

110

A. Interorbital space with a groove continued to crown of head; sutures of lateral plates serrated; postorbital part of head half or more than half distance of operculum from base of pectorals.   *scutatus*

AA. Interorbital space convex, without groove; sutures of lateral plates smooth; postorbital part of head thrice in distance of operculum from base of pectorals.   *cristatus*

119. RAZOR-FISH *Centriscus cristatus* (De Vis)   [Plate 26]

Amphisile cristata De Vis, Proc. Linn. Soc. N.S.Wales, 9, 1885, p. 872.
Centriscus cristatus McCulloch, Biol. Res. Endeavour, 3, pt 3, 1915, p. 105, pl. 36, fig. 1.

D. 3/12; A. 13-14; P. 12; V. 3; sutures of lateral plates smooth. Life colours silvery; a deep-red band from base of snout to eye, followed by a golden spot on temporal region; continuous with this is a red or orange band, which bisects the opercle, passes through base of pectoral, and extends along the side to root of terminal spine, the posterior portion being curved upward and sometimes supplemented by a short parallel superior band; abdominal ridge pale yellow, crossed by 8 to 10 oblique red bars directed downwards and backwards. (After Ogilby.)

A fairly common fish found only on the Queensland coast, and frequently found cast up on the beaches after heavy weather. It frequents the coral reefs where it may be seen swimming vertically in shoals. Numerous examples were trawled by the *Endeavour* at various points on the Queensland coast at depths of 5 to 16 fathoms. Grows to 12 inches.

OTHER SPECIES

Serrate Razor-fish, *C. scutatus* Linnaeus. A wide-ranging species found somewhat rarely in the waters of North Queensland. Grows to 6 inches.

Family **Syngnathidae: Pipe-fishes and Sea-horses**

Body slender, elongate, angular or laterally compressed or rounded, covered with bony plates arranged regularly in series, firmly connected, and forming a bony carapace. Head slender, the snout long, tube-like, bearing short toothless jaws at the end. Gill-opening reduced to a small aperture behind upper part of opercle. Tail long, prehensile or not. One dorsal fin, usually present (by exception absent), consisting of soft rays only, generally opposite the minute anal, which usually is present. Pectorals small or wanting. No ventrals. Caudal fin small, when absent the tail is more prehensile. Males with an egg-pouch, usually placed on underside of tail, sometimes on abdomen, commonly formed of folds of skin which meet on the median line. The eggs are received into the pouch and retained until some time after hatching, when the pouch opens and the young are released.

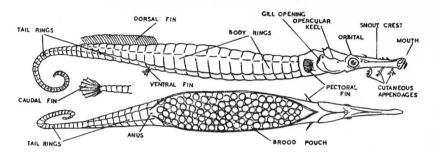

FIG. 8. Lateral view of a pipe-fish (top) showing external characters, and ventral view of male showing eggs implanted in the brood pouch.
AFTER MUNRO

Small fishes living in the coastal waters of tropical and temperate seas, some species entering fresh water. They swim mainly by undulating movements of the dorsal and pectoral fins or, in some species, with a snake-like motion. Those species having a prehensile tail anchor themselves to floating seaweeds, etc., maintaining an upright position and riding along like miniature horses. Sea-horses and pipe-fishes are poor swimmers and more or less drift with the currents.

Fourteen genera in Queensland waters.

KEY TO GENERA IN QUEENSLAND

Adapted from Weber and de Beaufort[10]

A. Caudal fin present.

  b. Dorsal keels of trunk and tail not continuous.

    c. Operculum with a complete, or basal incomplete, keel.

      d. Opercular keel rectilinear. Base of dorsal not elevated.

        e. Trunk-rings more numerous than tail-rings. Dorsal for its greater part inserted on trunk. Caudal longer than half length of head.   *Doryrhamphus*

        ee. Trunk-rings equal to or generally less numerous than tail-rings. Dorsal for its greatest part inserted on tail. Caudal equal to or shorter than postorbital part of head.

[10] *Fish. Indo-Austr. Archip.*, 4, 1922, p. 37.

f. Egg-pouch abdominal. .... *Microphis*

ff. Egg-pouch subcaudal.

g. Ventral keel of trunk and tail continuous. Median keel of trunk and median keel of tail discontinuous.

h. Upper profile of snout evenly continued in that of forehead. Orbits not prominent. .... *Syngnathus*

hh. Snout forming an angle with orbital part of head, which is prominent. .... *Corythoichthys*

gg. Ventral keel of trunk and tail discontinuous; median keel of trunk and ventral keel of tail continuous. Snout not forming an angle with orbital part of head. .... *Micrognathus*

dd. Opercular keel convex, bent upwards to gill-opening, with radial lines. Base of dorsal elevated.

i. Edges of shields spinous. Dorsal profile of snout and head spinous. Orbital part of head strongly prominent and sharply separated from snout. .... *Halicampus*

ii. All edges and ridges of head smooth. Orbits not prominent. .... *Yozia*

bb. Dorsal keels of trunk and tail continuous.

j. Egg-pouch abdominal. Operculum with a complete longitudinal keel. Vent behind middle of length. Trunk-rings less than 25. .... *Choeroichthys*

jj. Egg-pouch subcaudal. Operculum with or without a complete or incomplete longitudinal keel. Vent before middle of length. Trunk-rings about 30-50. .... *Ichthyocampus*

AA. Caudal fin absent, tail usually prehensile.

k. Body depressed or subcylindrical.

l. Snout very slender, more or less than twice as long as remaining part of head. Prenuchal and two nuchal shields present. Tail filiform but not prehensile. .... *Stigmatophora*

ll. Snout rather stout, nearly twice length of post-orbital part of head. No prenuchal shield. Tail prehensile. .... *Syngnathoides*

kk. Body compressed, not or scarcely dilated. Tail prehensile.

m. Base of dorsal not elevated. Dorsal situated on tail only. No cutaneous appendages. Operculum without keel, but with smooth or serrated radial ridges. .... *Runcinatus*

mm. Base of dorsal elevated. Dorsal situated on trunk and tail. Operculum with convex keel bent upwards to branchial opening.

n. Longitudinal axis of head and trunk nearly in same plane. Prenuchal shield without a coronet; numerous long cutaneous appendages. *Haliichthys*

nn. Longitudinal axis of head forming a right angle with axis of trunk. Prenuchal shield surmounted by a coronet; cutaneous appendages generally absent. *Hippocampus*

Doryrhamphus

Form short, stout. Edges of shields prominent, ending in a spine posteriorly, otherwise smooth. Dorsal keel on snout high and roughly serrated. Trunk-rings more numerous than tail-rings. Tail shorter than body. Pectoral, dorsal, anal, and caudal fins present. Dorsal keels of trunk and tail discontinuous. Dorsal fin for its greater part inserted on trunk. Brood-organ of male abdominal.

Pipe-fishes of the Indo-Pacific region. Several species, one in Queensland.

120. BLUE-STRIPED PIPE-FISH *Doryrhamphus melanopleura* (Bleeker)
[Plate 26]

Syngnathus melanopleura Bleeker, Nat. Tijdschr. Ned. Ind., 15, 1858, p. 464.
Doryrhamphus melanopleura Weber and de Beaufort, Fish. Indo-Austr. Archip., 4, 1922, p. 64, fig. 27.

D. 21-25; A. 4; P. 19-22; rings 16-18 + 13-15; snout stout, somewhat longer than postorbital part of head; tail much shorter than trunk; dorsal high, but less than depth of body; head $4\frac{1}{2}$-$5\frac{1}{2}$ times in the length. Colour greyish-brown; a dark band, narrow on snout and head, is continued as a broader band on sides of trunk and tail; posterior half of caudal blackish; in life bright orange-red, with ultramarine-blue longitudinal stripe from end of snout to caudal base; caudal bright blue, orange basally and with upper and lower edges white.

A handsome pipe-fish inhabiting northern Queensland coral reefs. Wide-ranging outside Australia. Grows to $2\frac{1}{2}$ inches.

Microphis

Snout larger than remaining part of head. Opercle with complete longitudinal keel and radiating ridges. Upper keels of trunk and tail discontinuous; lower keels discontinuous or continuous and median (lateral) keels of trunk and lower keels of tail continuous or not. Keels of shields or rings more or less serrated, usually ending in a free spine behind. Dorsal long, with over 30 rays, opposite vent, above at least 7 rings of largest part of tail. Caudal well developed, usually middle ray prolonged. Eggs small, numerous, on belly in glutinous skinny mass.

Fishes of fresh and brackish waters connected with tropical seas. One species in Queensland.

121. SHORT-TAILED PIPE-FISH *Microphis brachyurus* (Bleeker) [Plate 26]

Syngnathus brachyurus Bleeker, Verh. Bat. Gen., 25, 1853, pp. 11, 16.
Doryichthys bleekeri Day, Fish. India, 1878-88, p. 680, pl. 174, fig. 3.

D. 36-48; P. 18-23. Rings: trunk 19-22, tail 20-24. Much elongated. Shields transversely striated, their keels serrated and terminating in a spine in the young. Ventral keels of trunk and tail discontinuous. Median keel of trunk and ventral keel of tail continuous. Snout somewhat more than twice length of postorbital part of head; head $4\frac{1}{2}$ to 5 times in the length. Tail, without caudal, shorter than trunk. Colour dark olive-brown above, paler and profusely spotted with brown below; sides of snout with a series of 9 conspicuous black spots; caudal fin black.

This wide-ranging species has been recorded from Moreton Bay. Apparently rare in Queensland. Grows to 10 inches.

Syngnathus

Body long, very slender, hexagonal or tetragonal, not compressed, tapering into a long tetragonal tail. Head usually slender, tapering gently to a longer or shorter tube-like snout, with or without a median keel. Opercle with straight longitudinal keel, complete or restricted to basal part. Oblique lines radiate from keel or are wanting. Dorsal rays 21 to 45, fin inserted entirely on front tail-rings to ninth or also on 1 to 3 of last trunk-rings. Dorsal base not elevated. Anal, caudal, and pectoral present. Eggs isolated in cutaneous cells on ventral surface of front part of tail, entirely protected by cutaneous folds, which may contain more or less developed bony plates; the folds begin next to anus, reach far behind subdorsal rings of tail, and coalesce in median line, splitting lengthwise to release the young fishes.

122. BLACK-CHINNED PIPE-FISH *Syngnathus altirostris* Ogilby [Plate 26]

Syngnathus altirostris Ogilby, Rec. Austr. Mus., 1, no. 3, July 1890, p. 55.
Parasyngnathus altirostris Whitley, Austr. Zool., 10, pt 2, 30th April 1943, p. 177, fig 8.

D. 26-28; P. 14; rings 15-17 + 40-42; body deeper than broad; dorsal ridge of body ends below dorsal fin and median ridge ends a little before this, neither continuous with dorsal ridges of tail; a median ventral ridge present; eye small; snout longer than postorbital portion of head; dorsal fin situated on

7 anterior caudal rings, entirely behind level of vent, its base not elevated; brood-pouch subcaudal, from anal fin backwards over 16 rings as a very elongate slit with raised lips; tail very elongate.

Colour uniform brown, with a dark lateral stripe from tip of snout through eye to lower half of opercle where it is broken up into blotches; dorsal fin speckled with brown. (Ogilby.)

A pipe-fish from South Queensland and northern New South Wales, entering and living in fresh water. Grows to 6 inches.

Corythoichthys

Body short, somewhat stout. Plates rough, edges more or less prominent and smooth, slightly crenulated, in exception serrated. Operculum crossed by a complete longitudinal keel. Dorsal keel of tail and trunk discontinuous. Ventral keel of trunk and tail continuous. Median keel of trunk and dorsal keel of tail subcontinuous. Tail more or less twice as long as trunk.

Pipe-fishes of the shallow waters and coral reefs of the Indo-Pacific and South America. Two species occur in Queensland.

KEY TO SPECIES IN QUEENSLAND

A.   D. 25-32; rings 15-18 + 33-37; body with cross-bands.   *fasciatus*

AA. D. 29; rings 15 + 42; body without cross-bands.   *parviceps*

123. MESSMATE PIPE-FISH *Corythoichthys fasciatus* (Gray)   [Plate 27]

Syngnathus fasciatus Gray, Illust. Ind. Zool., 1, 1830-32, pl. 89, figs. 2, 2a (not of Risso, 1810).
Syngnathus haematopterus Günther, Fische der Sudsee, 1910, p. 431, pl. 167, fig. C.

D. 25-32; A. 3-4; rings 15-18 + 33-37; edges of shields on head, operculum, and body smooth, or those of body only slightly corrugated, even in the juveniles.

"Colour greyish, with numerous dark cross-bands composed of fine anastomosing longitudinal lines or there are dark blotches along the sides. Operculum with numerous darkish parallel longitudinal lines or it shows ventrally a dark longitudinal band. Throat between opercles with a black median streak or with a black marmoration and behind it two or three black cross-bars on the anterior 2 to 4 rings." (Weber and de Beaufort.)

This pipe-fish is said to live in the intestinal cavity of the bêche-de-mer. It ranges from Queensland through the Indo-Pacific to India and the Red Sea. Grows to 6½ inches.

OTHER SPECIES

Corythoichthys parviceps (Ramsay and Ogilby). A species originally described from the Clarence River, New South Wales, where several specimens, including the type, were collected. Rarely taken in Queensland waters. Recorded on a single example taken in Southport in October, 1916. Grows to 4½ inches.

Micrognathus

Body elongate, more or less stout, heptagonal anteriorly, tetragonal posteriorly. Rings smooth or only finely dentated or somewhat spinous posteriorly. Snout very short, more or less curved upward, about equal to postorbital part of head, rising more or less gently to orbits. Opercle keeled anteriorly. Tail equal to or somewhat more or less than twice length of trunk. Dorsal short, 17 to 23 rays, its base not elevated, situated on 1 or 2 of the last body-rings or none and on 3 to 5 tail-rings. Pectorals, anal, and caudal present. Eggs large, isolated in cutaneous cells on anterior 14 or 15 tail-rings.

Marine fishes of the Indo-Pacific region. One species in Queensland.

124. THORN-TAILED PIPE-FISH *Micrognathus brevirostris* (Rüppell) [Plate 27]

Syngnathus brevirostris Rüppell, Neue Wirbelth. Abyssin., Fische, 1840, p. 144.
Micrognathus brevirostris Herald, Fish. Marshall and Mariana Is., U.S. Nat. Mus. Bull. 202, Vol. 1, 1953, p. 260, fig. 39a.

D. 17-22; P. 9-14; rings 15-17 + 28-32; body somewhat compressed, its edges prominent; head 9 to 10 or more in the length; snout very short, slightly curved upward, equal to or shorter than postorbital part of head; tail more than 1.6 to about 2 in trunk.

Colour varying, usually dark brown with lighter cross-bars on back on each ring; females generally lighter. Operculum may have a brown ocellus with a pearl-coloured and a brown peripheral ring. (After Weber and de Beaufort.)

A small wide-ranging species recorded from Cape York Peninsula, North Queensland. Grows to 3 inches.

Halicampus

Form elongate, somewhat stout, trunk heptagonal. Tail tetragonal, about twice longer than trunk. All fins present. Opercle with a longitudinal convex keel, directed upwards and with numerous radiating lines. Occiput and neck elevated into a crest. Eyes prominent. Snout slender, more or less depressed, with rows of small spines and abruptly ascending to forehead. Edges of shields spinous, usually with cutaneous appendages. Dorsal situated above 4 or 5, its base elevated, its middle about above anus. Eggs numerous, isolated in cutaneous cells on tail and enclosed in a complete pouch which begins behind anus.

Species few, widely distributed, inhabiting the sea in rather deep inshore waters. One species in North Queensland.

125. GRAY'S PIPE-FISH *Halicampus grayi* Kaup [Plate 27]

Halicampus grayi Kaup, Arch. Naturges, 19, pt 1, 1853, p. 231.
Halicampus koilomatodon Weber and de Beaufort, Fish. Indo-Austr. Archip., 4, 1922, p. 103, fig. 43.

D. 19-22; P. 16-19; rings 17-18 + 33-36; head 8½-9 in the length, 3 times in trunk; tail about twice as long as trunk; snout about equal to postorbital part of head and provided with a series of spines; interorbital space concave and with a spiny median crest, and similar crests on occiput and neck. Colour brown, with whitish marblings; operculum with or without white stripes. (After Weber and de Beaufort.)

A rather distinctive wide-ranging little species which has been recorded from the waters of Torres Strait, North Queensland. Not commonly seen. Grows to 6 inches.

Yozia

Body slender, elongate. Trunk short, more or less swollen in middle of its length. Head not elevated, median keel present or absent, low, smooth, or with slight serrations, never spinous. Snout elongate. Front and orbits not prominent, cutaneous appendages sometimes present. Opercle with a keel, curving upwards toward gill-opening but distinct only at base or without a median keel but with radiating lines. Shields transversely striated. Dorsal and ventral keel of trunk and tail discontinuous; median keel of trunk and ventral keel of tail continuous. All fins present, dorsal about equal on trunk and tail, its base scarcely or only slightly elevated. Caudal small.

Pipe-fishes of the Indo-Pacific region. One species in Queensland.

126. BANDED PIPE-FISH *Yozia tigris* (Castelnau) [Plate 27]

Syngnathus tigris Castelnau, Proc. Linn. Soc. N.S.Wales, 3, pt 4, 1879, p. 397.
Syngnathus tigris McCulloch, Rec. West. Austr. Mus., 1, pt 2, 1912, p. 83, pl. 11, fig. 2.

D. 24-25; P. 15; C. 8; rings 17 + 36; head 3-3⅓ in trunk; head and trunk 1⅔ in tail; operculum with radiating lines, but without a median keel; dorsal fin opposite vent. Colour dark olive-green above, brownish on sides, white below; a few narrow stripes of reddish-brown on sides of head; body with 12 broad dark-reddish bands; a white half-oval spot on lower edge of each body scute.

A handsome pipe-fish recognized by its dark cross-bands. Found on the coasts of Queensland and New South Wales. Grows to 12 inches.

Choeroichthys

Small, short, arched dorsally and ventrally. Edges of shields finely serrated or granulated, those on head smooth. Tail-rings more numerous than body-rings. Snout rather short, slightly shorter or longer than postorbital part of head. Dorsal with 21 to 35 rays, situated above 5 to 9 rings, one or two of which belong to tail. Anal behind middle of length. Caudal small. Pectorals present. Eggs large, isolated in open cells in abdominal skin of male, laterally protected by ventrally diverging plates.

Widely distributed fishes, species few, two in Queensland.

KEY TO SPECIES IN QUEENSLAND

A. D. 21; P. 18; rings 18 + 20; 2 complete opercular keels each side. Colour brown; a row of reddish spots along upper sides anteriorly; light and dark pattern on snout; 3 pairs of light blotches across back.   *suillus*

AA. D. 20-24; P. 20-23; rings 14-15 + 18-19; opercle with a rough longitudinal keel above, with numerous diverging lines below; 2 series of black spots on each side of trunk.   *brachysoma*

127. PIG PIPE-FISH *Choeroichthys suillus* Whitley   [Plate 27]

Choeroichthys suillus Whitley, Rec. Austr. Mus., 22, no. 4, Aug. 1951, p. 393, fig. 2.

D. 21; A. 5; P. 18; C. 10; rings 18 + 20; subdorsal rings 5 + 1; brood-rings 14, thoracic; eyes and nostrils projecting; 2 complete opercular keels each side; no keels on shields between body or tail ridges; sculpture of shields striate, not reticulate; spines on rings not serrate.

Colour brown; light and dark pattern on snout, chin, and throat; dark-brown bar through eye; a row of reddish spots along upper sides anteriorly; 3 pairs of light blotches across back; brood-pouch with dark scalloping over light margin; anterior two-thirds of caudal fin dusky-brown, posterior third yellowish; other fins light yellowish. (After Whitley.)

A small pipe-fish found in North Queensland waters. Grows to about 2 inches.

OTHER SPECIES

Dotted Pipe-fish, *C. brachysoma*. Found in the waters of North Queensland and Torres Strait. Grows to 2½ inches.

Ichthyocampus

Body rather stout. Head short, with a shorter, sharp-ridged snout. Opercle round, swollen, higher than broad, smooth or shagreened, without keel or with a complete or basal keel with radiating lines. Tail almost as thick as body. All fins present. Caudal short. Eggs isolated in cutaneous cells on tail, completely enclosed in brood-pouch formed by lateral folds beginning at vent.

Marine shore-fishes of the Indo-Pacific, some living in deeper water or in brackish or fresh water. Two species are found in Queensland waters.

KEY TO SPECIES IN QUEENSLAND

A.   D. 25; rings 20 + 57.   *maculatus*

AA.   D. 17-20; rings 16-17 + 33-36.   *tryoni*

128. SPOTTED PIPE-FISH *Ichthyocampus maculatus* Alleyne and Macleay
[Plate 27]

Ichthyocampus maculatus Alleyne and Macleay, Proc. Linn. Soc. N.S.Wales, 1, pt 4, March 1877, p. 353, pl. 17, fig. 2.

D. 25; rings 20 + 57; form very elongate; body deeper than broad, the ridges well-defined; snout more than half length of head; operculum without a ridge; a prominence on occiput; tail twice as long as trunk; dorsal fin over 6 rings, three of which belong to body; caudal fin minute. Colour in preservative brownish, with a yellow spot on each body-ring below lateral line. (After Alleyne and Macleay.)

A little-known pipe-fish from the waters of Torres Strait. Grows to at least 11 inches.

OTHER SPECIES

Tryon's Pipe-fish, *I. tryoni*. Known only from Queensland waters. Grows to about 3 inches.

Stigmatophora

Body subcylindrical, scarcely broader than deep or strongly depressed and very broad. Lateral shields very oblique and produced into sharp edges, which form the median ridges of the trunk and border the flat abdominal surface; otherwise the edges are obsolete. Ridges of trunk continuous with those of tail. Pectoral fin developed, caudal absent, tail tapering to a very fine point. Dorsal fin very long, its middle above or somewhat before or behind anus. Anal small. Eggs large, isolated in cutaneous cells on lower surface of tail, in a completely closed brood-pouch.

Pipe-fishes of the waters of New Guinea, Australia (including Tasmania), and New Zealand. Two species in Queensland.

120

A.   Vent below or before middle of dorsal fin; D. 43-55.   *argus*

AA. Vent behind middle of dorsal fin; D. 35-43.   *nigra*

129. WIDE-BODIED PIPE-FISH *Stigmatophora nigra* Kaup   [Plate 28]

Stigmatophora nigra Kaup, Cat. Lophobr. Fish. Brit. Mus., 1856, p. 53.
Stigmatophora nigra McCulloch, Austr. Zool., 1, no. 1, June 1914, p. 29, figs 1-3.

D. 35-43; rings 16-18 + 58-72; head 2.3-2.8 in trunk; head and body 1.3-1.7 in tail, the latter longer in males than in females; dorsal fin placed on 11 or 12 body-rings and 6 to 8 tail-rings; vent well behind middle of its length.

Male: Body subcylindrical, scarcely broader than deep, with angular ridges but little elevated; pouch large, occupying 15 to 18 tail-rings. Colour pale green, closely speckled with minute black dots; a distinct patch of black dots on median line of each segment of abdomen; 2 longitudinal dark bars on lower surface of snout, extending backward to behind eye.

Female: Body strongly depressed, adults being twice as broad as deep. Upper surface pale green, speckled with minute black dots; outer edges of sides and abdomen deep pink, the latter crossed by pale-blue lines; breast with 1 to 2 broad dark cross-bars, which are represented on each abdominal segment by a black dot placed near the margin on either side; tip of snout white, chin pink; lower surface of snout with 2 dark longitudinal bars extending back behind eye.

A species from the southern portions of Australia, which has been recorded from South Queensland. Grows to about 4 inches.

OTHER SPECIES

Ocellated Pipe-fish, *S. argus*. Has not yet been recorded from Queensland, though recorded from the coasts of Australia (including Tasmania) and New Guinea. Grows to 8 inches.

Syngnathoides

Body elongate, depressed, tetragonal, with narrow dorsal surface. Lateral line running along margin of abdomen. Ventral surface much broadened and in the male covered by soft skin in which the eggs are embedded, uncovered by pouch-like folds. Tail shorter than body, without caudal fin, and prehensile. Shields smooth. Operculum without keel. A single species, inhabiting the Indo-Pacific.

130. HORNED PIPE-FISH *Syngnathoides biaculeatus* (Bloch) [Plate 28]

Syngnathus biaculeatus Bloch, Nat. ausl. Fische, 1, 1785, p. 10 (*fide* Sherborn).
Gastrotokeus biaculeatus Day, Fish. India, 1878, p. 681, pl. 174, fig. 5.

D. 37-50; P. 17-23; rings 15-17 + 40-54; subdorsal rings 1-2 + 8-10; superciliary margin terminating behind in a more or less distinct spine; skin often with numerous filaments on lower side of head, body, and tail; origin of dorsal nearly opposite to vent; females shorter than males. Colour pale green or brown, with or without dark-brown spots.

A poor swimmer, inhabiting shallow water and attaching itself to marine growths. Commonly seen. Said by Seale to be "used to a considerable extent in China as medicine". Ranges from the coasts of Queensland and New South Wales to North Australia and Western Australia, New Guinea, the Indo-Pacific, China, Japan, and the Red Sea. Grows to 10 inches.

Runcinatus

Body compressed, deeper than broad, nearly hexagonal. Tail prehensile. Shields hard, radially rugose or with radiating lines of well-developed spines and with a stronger one in the centre. Tail-rings with or without cutaneous excrescences on the inferior surface. Edges of rings rough or spiny. Dorsal ridges of trunk and tail continuous; the mediolateral ridges expand below the dorsal fin (at least in males) and terminate on sides of tail.

Pipe-fishes of the South Pacific; a single species known.

131. RED AND GOLD SEA-HORSE *Runcinatus dunckeri* (Whitley) [Plate 28]

Solegnathus dunckeri Whitley, Rec. Austr. Mus., 15, 1927, p. 294, pl. 24, fig. 1.

Colour: "Yellowish, darkest on the tail. A blackish band along the scutes forming the dorsal ridges, is continued on to the nape anteriorly, and becomes diffused below the last dorsal rays posteriorly. Lower surfaces of tail, behind brood-area, smoky brown. A faint brown stripe passes obliquely through the blue eye. Fins yellowish, an ill-defined smoky band along the lower part of the dorsal." (Whitley; colour from a spirit specimen.)

A large and very handsome fish found on the coasts of Queensland, New South Wales, and Lord Howe Island. Grows to 18 inches.

Haliichthys

Elongate, trunk as broad as deep, hexagonal or only slightly heptagonal, abdominal keel only feebly developed. Tail much longer than trunk, prehensile, the caudal wanting. Shields smooth, their edges with a prominent spine in the middle, except beneath end of tail. Long, more or less arborescent cutaneous appendages on spines on the edges of the trunk and the tail, also on the occiput and the orbits.

A genus with a single species, inhabiting North Australia, Western Australia, Torres Strait, and southern New Guinea.

132. SLENDER TANGLE-FISH *Haliichthys taeniophora* Gray [Plate 28]

Haliichthys taeniophorus Weber and de Beaufort, Fish. Indo-Austr. Archip., 4, 1922, p. 105, fig. 44.

D. 24-26; A. 4; P. 20-21; rings 19 + 44-45; subdorsal rings 3-4 + 2; body as broad as deep and as long as tail; head about 5 times in the length; vent below middle of dorsal fin. Colour brown, with irregular dark-brown bands across back; abdomen whitish; cutaneous appendages black.

A northern species found in North Queensland, Torres Strait, North Australia, Western Australia, and southern New Guinea. Grows to 12 inches.

Hippocampus

Body strongly compressed, more or less elevated, the belly gibbous, composed of 10 to 12 rings, tapering abruptly to a long quadrangular prehensile tail. Neck curved, head at about a right angle to axis of trunk. Occiput compressed and surmounted by a star-like coronet. Top and sides of head with spines. Bony shields of body-rings each with 6 spines or tubercles, those on tail with 4. Dorsal fin moderate, opposite vent, on elevated base on trunk and tail. Anal minute, usually present. Pectorals short and broad. Egg-pouch of male is a permanent sac at base of tail, ending near vent.

Species numerous in all warm seas, four in Queensland. They swim vertically in the water, head uppermost, by vibrating the dorsal fin. They are carried long distances by attaching their prehensile tails to seaweeds and other floating objects.

KEY TO SPECIES IN QUEENSLAND

A. Tubercles on keels developed into long slender spines; occipital keel behind coronet with 2 distinct spines; D. 17; P. 15; rings 11 + 34; snout equal to postorbital part of head. *spinosissimus*

AA. Tubercles on keels not developed into long spines; occipital keel behind coronet rough, but without distinct spines.

b. Coronet high, with 5-6 blunt tubercles; D. 16-17; P. 15-16; rings 11 + 32-36. *whitei*

bb. Coronet low.

c. D. 20-22; rings 11 + 36-41. *planifrons*

cc. D. 15-18; rings 11 + 33-37. *kuda*

133. COMMON SEA-HORSE *Hippocampus whitei* Bleeker [Plate 28]

Hippocampus whitei Bleeker, Verh. Kon. Akad. Wetensch. Amsterdam, 2, 1855, p. 17.
Hippocampus novaehollandiae Waite, Fish. Sth Austr., 1923, p. 85, plate unnumbered.

Colour very variable; usually brownish or olive-brownish, with snout, head, and body marbled and reticulated with brown; sometimes yellowish, with small red spots and the back streaked or marbled with brown.

A common species in the waters of South Queensland and New South Wales. Found also in South Australia. Grows to 6¼ inches.

134. LOW-CROWNED SEA-HORSE *Hippocampus planifrons* Peters [Plate 28]

Hippocampus planifrons Peters, Monatsb. Akad. Wiss. Berlin, 1876 (1877), p. 851.
Hippocampus planifrons Whitley, Proc. Roy. Zool. Soc. N.S.Wales, 1950-1 (1952), p. 29, fig. 2.

D. 20-22; trunk-rings 11; tail-rings 36-41; body slender; snout about twice in length of head, much longer than postorbital portion of head. Coronet low, preceded by short ridge, which terminates in a slightly hooked spine; its summit is surrounded by a star-like bunch of low, blunt tubercles.

Colour olive or orange-yellow, everywhere on head, body, and tail covered with irregular bright-orange spots, between which are numerous whitish dots; eye, pupil black, surrounded straw-yellow, with about 5 radiating black blotches; further radiating blotches continued outside orbit and on snout; a black stripe is usually present from throat to vent, along edge of body. Some examples exhibit dark-brownish closely set zebra-like stripes on head, body, and tail.

This common little species is known from the waters of north-western Australia and along the Queensland coast. It is commonly taken by the prawn-trawls in Moreton Bay, but otherwise is seldom seen. Grows to about 4 inches.

OTHER SPECIES

Spiny Sea-horse, *H. spinosissimus*. A small species from Torres Strait, readily recognized by its long spines. Grows to 3 inches.

H. kuda. A wide-ranging sea-horse which enters the waters of North Queensland. Reaches a length of 12 inches.

Order **ALLOTRIOGNATHI**

Sub-order TAENIOSOMI: OAR-FISHES and RIBBON-FISHES

The oar-fishes and ribbon-fishes are characterized by their greatly elongated and compressed ribbon-like bodies, which are extremely fragile and covered with shining silvery skin. A very long dorsal fin, usually pink or red in colour, extends from the head almost to the tail. The mouth is very protractile and its cleft vertical.

These curious fishes grow to a large size and no doubt have been the basis of many a sea-serpent story. They are found in arctic, temperate, and tropical seas, but are seldom seen alive, being mostly known from dead or dying ones found floating on the surface of the ocean or cast up on beaches after heavy storms.

Each of the two families is represented in Queensland by one species.

KEY TO FAMILIES

A. Depth of body 6-12 times in the length. Ventral fins normally present, consisting of several rays. Eye large. Teeth on both jaws and vomer. Upper profile of head convex.   TRACHIPTERIDAE

AA. Depth of body 12-30 times in the length. Ventral fins reduced to a single long filament-like ray which usually terminates in an expansion. Eye small. Teeth wanting. Upper profile of head markedly concave.   REGALECIDAE

Family Trachipteridae: Ribbon-fishes

The ribbon-fishes, sometimes called deal-fishes, are among the rarest of fishes, being mostly known from cast-up ones found on beaches. In Scandinavian countries the Deal-fish is known as the *Vaagmaer* or *Vogmar*, an Icelandic word meaning "maid of the bay". According to Norman, "The species from the Pacific coast of America is sometimes referred to as 'King of the Herrings'. Makah Indians west of the Straits of Fuca call it 'King of the Salmon' and they are reputed to have a saying that 'when the King is killed the salmon will cease to run'."[11]

Trachipterus

Lateral line with bony plates, each of which has a spine. Skin with scattered spines or tubercles.

135. SOUTHERN RIBBON-FISH *Trachipterus jacksonensis* (Ramsay) [Plate 29]

Regalaecus jacksonensis Ramsay, Proc. Linn. Soc. N.S.Wales, 5, pt 4, 20th May, 1881, p. 631, pl. 20.
Trachipterus jacksonensis Whitley, Rec. Austr. Mus., 15, 1927, p. 296, pl. 25, fig. 2.

Dorsal fin very long, at least 176 rays, preceded by 5-7 very short and fine rays; vent in middle of total length. Colour bright silvery with pink dorsal fin.

This species was first named from a specimen 4 feet 8 inches in length found at Manly, New South Wales, in 1881. Since then others have been reported,

---

[11] Norman and Fraser, *Giant Fishes, Whales and Dolphins*, 1937, p. 112.

including two from Queensland. In November 1921 J. O'May found one on the beach at Southport, South Queensland. It measured 6 feet 6 inches, and when brought to the Queensland Museum at night its silvery surface was glowing with luminescence. Another ribbon-fish was found at Coolangatta in October 1936 by J. E. Stewart and W. E. Bevan. Its length was 5 feet 9 inches.

The Southern Ribbon-fish is found in the waters of South Queensland, New South Wales, Tasmania, Victoria, and New Zealand.

Family **Regalecidae: Oar-fishes**

In the oar-fishes the ventral fins are reduced to a single ray which is long and filament-like and terminating in an expanded oar-like tip, and the dorsal fin in its anterior part usually forms a high lobe or crest more or less detached from the remainder. They grow to a great length, and specimens of more than 20 feet are known, weighing as much as 600 pounds. They are even rarer than the ribbon-fishes and are seldom seen alive. On the very few occasions when one has been seen, the observer has been impressed by its brilliant silvery body and scarlet mane and by its serpent-like movements.

The oar-fish is also known as the King of the Herrings. It was once believed that it accompanied the herring shoals and that to harm it would mean a poor harvest in herrings. The Japanese call it Dugunona-tatori, which means "Cock of the Palace Under the Sea". Norman[12] states: "The flesh is quite useless as food, and it is recorded that in Scandinavia even dogs refused to eat it, whether offered raw or cooked."

136. OAR-FISH *Regalecus pacificus* Haast [Plate 29]

Regalecus pacificus Haast, Trans. New Zeal. Inst., 10, May 1878, p. 246, pl. 7.
Regalecus banksi McCoy, Prodr. Zool. Vict., 2, dec. 15 1887, p. 169, pl. 145.

Colour: "Brilliant metallic-silvery, tinged with pale lavender-grey on back and anterior part of head; pectorals white; dorsal with bright red rays, the membranes rose-red, paler at base than at margin; about 19 vertical black streaks half an inch wide, of variable length, cross the anterior half of the body, and 5 or 6 longitudinal rows of longitudinally oval, blackish spots on posterior three-fifths; no spots near tail. Iris white. Inside of mouth black." (McCoy.)

Very few specimens of this rare fish have been found on the Australian coast. One was taken in the sea between the Tasmanian and Victorian coasts in May 1878. It measured 13 feet 7 inches and is the one from which the illustration was taken. McCoy states that "the silvering of the surface comes off at every touch, like the dust on a moth's wing".

---

[12] Norman and Fraser, *Giant Fishes, Whales and Dolphins*, 1937, p. 113.

Two specimens have been recorded from Queensland. One was picked up on the beach near the Tweed River (Queensland/New South Wales border) in January 1892. It measured 8 feet 9 inches.

On 15th August 1959 S. Clarke found one of these rare oar-fishes on the beach at Comboyuro, Moreton Island. It was lying at the water's edge and was still very much alive. Clarke stated that the fish was a blaze of purple and blue with the large spots or blotches very plain. When he picked the fish up, a large portion of the tail broke off, about 3 feet from the end. Total length of the fish was about 9 feet 10 inches. The specimen was brought to Brisbane in the hope that it could be preserved, but owing to its damaged state this was not possible.

Order **BERYCOMORPHI**

With this order we come to the great series of spiny-rayed fishes. About nine families constitute the order, five of which are found in Queensland seas. With the exception of the Holocentridae they are inhabitants of deep water and when caught are usually taken by dredge or trawl. They are a group of primitive fishes which were more abundant in Cretaceous and Eocene times than now, and represent the transition from the isospondylous or salmon and herring-like fishes to those of the mackerel and perch types.

KEY TO FAMILIES REPRESENTED IN QUEENSLAND

A. Caudal truncate or only slightly emarginate. No teeth
    on palate.   CAPROIDAE

AA. Caudal forked. Teeth on palate.

    b. Dorsal fin with 4-8 spines.

      c. Body encased in thick bony scutes.   MONOCENTRIDAE

      cc. Body scaled, not forming bony scutes.

        d. Ventrals with one spine and 7 rays. Anal with
          4 spines.   BERYCIDAE

        dd. Ventrals with one spine and 6 rays. Anal with
          2-3 spines.   TRACHICHTHYIDAE

    bb. Dorsal fin with 10-13 strong spines. Scales strongly
      ctenoid.   HOLOCENTRIDAE

Family **Caproidae**

Body deep, compressed, covered with small, ctenoid scales. Top of head bony. Mouth moderate or small, lower jaw projecting. Upper jaw very protractile. Bands of small teeth in jaws and sometimes on vomer. Dorsal fin with 7 to 9 spines. Anal with 2 to 3 spines. Ventrals with 1 spine and 5 rays, Caudal rounded.

Fishes inhabiting all tropical and subtropical seas, usually in deep water and obtainable only by dredging. A single genus and species in Queensland.

137. ROSEATE BOARFISH *Antigonia rubicunda* Ogilby [Plate 29]

Antigonia rubicunda Ogilby, New Fish. Qld Coast, 10th Dec. 1910, p. 103 (a suppressed publication).
Antigonia rubicunda McCulloch, Biol. Res. Endeavour, 3, pt 3, 1915, p. 113, pl. 18, fig. 2.

D. 9/28-29; A. 3/26-27; P. 1 + 12; V. 1/5; C. 12. Colour: "Rose-pink, with a darker band from the nape to the throat, curving forward through the eye, a second from the dorsal spines to the pectoral, and a third round the peduncle." (Ogilby.)

A rare fish known only from two examples trawled by the *Endeavour* in 70 fathoms off North Reef in the Capricorn Group. They measured 62 and 65 mm. respectively.

Family **Monocentridae: Knight-fishes**

Curious fishes in which the body is encased in a hard, bony "coat of mail". Two species are known, one of which is found only on the coasts of Australia, the other inhabiting parts of the Pacific, the East Indies, Japan, and South Africa. The Australian species is unique in that it possesses luminous organs on the lower lip.

138. KNIGHT-FISH *Cleidopus gloria-maris* De Vis [Plate 29]

Cleidopus gloria-maris De Vis, Proc. Linn. Soc. N.S.Wales, 7, pt 3, 1882, p. 368.
Cleidopus gloria-maris McCulloch, Rec. Austr. Mus., 13, no. 4, 1921, p. 124, pl. 23, fig. 1.

Port and Starboard Light Fish (New South Wales); Pine-cone Fish (South Africa).

D. 5-7/12; A. 11-12; Sc. 2/14-15/4-5. Colour: Scales of body canary-yellow, brighter anteriorly and with their margins broadly edged all round with black, forming a lattice pattern which is continued on to the head in markings similar to the scales; many of the scales on post-abdomen and caudal peduncle orange at their bases; lips, chin, and intermandibulary space jet-black; operculum golden, with a black oblique bar on lower limb; and elongate patch of bright scarlet on lower lip, bordered with a brilliant white line along upper edge; fins and tail clear rose-pink.

The bright scarlet patch with its brilliant white line, situated on the lower lips, is a luminescent organ. Live specimens placed in a tub of water have been observed to cast a gleam of light ahead from each mandibular organ, earning for the species the popular name of "Port and Starboard Light Fish".

This fish is occasionally found on the Queensland coast, more often among the debris on the beaches after storms. It is of sluggish habit, evidently depending on its luminous organs to lure its prey within reach. Since the prawn-trawlers began operating in the waters of South Queensland more specimens have come to light, and the species is not as uncommon as hitherto supposed.

Found on the coasts of South Queensland, New South Wales and Western Australia, also in South Africa. Grows to 9 inches.

Family **Berycidae: Nannygai**

Body oblong or ovate, compressed, covered with ctenoid or cycloid, foliate or granular scales. Cheeks and opercles scaly. Head with large muciferous cavities, covered by thick skin. Eye usually large or very large, lateral. Mouth wide, oblique. Premaxillaries protractile. Maxillary large, sometimes greatly dilated posteriorly, usually with supplemental bone. Teeth in villiform bands in jaws and usually on vomer and palatines. Canines present or absent. Dorsal fin continuous, with 2 to 8 weak spines. Anal with 2 to 4 spines. Ventral fins thoracic, mostly of 1 spine and 7 rays. Caudal usually forked.

139. NANNYGAI *Trachichthodes affinis* (Günther)   [Plate 29]

Beryx affinis Günther, Cat. Fish. Brit. Mus., 1, 1859, p. 13.
Hoplopteryx affinis Regan, Ann. Mag. Nat. Hist. (8), 7, 1911, p. 5, pl. 1.

Redfish (New South Wales); King Snapper (Western Australia).

D. 7/11-12; A. 4/12; L. 1. 42-44. Colour: Head and back bright red, with purplish and golden reflections, sides pale red, centres of scales darker, forming longitudinal bands; creamy-white below; dorsal, ventral, anal, and pectoral fins with rays red and membranes pink; caudal red, with a yellow band on posterior edge.

Very variable with age, the young being short in the body and round, and the depth only $2\frac{2}{3}$ in the total length, whilst large specimens are much more elongate with the depth $3\frac{1}{3}$.

A southern fish which occasionally enters Moreton Bay. Valued in the south as a food-fish. Nannygai was the name used by the aborigines round Sydney, but the same name as used at the Brisbane Fish Market refers to the Pearl Perch, *Glaucosoma scapulare*. Grows to 18 inches.

Family **Trachichthyidae: Roughies**

Body deep or elongate, compressed. Scales moderate or small, ctenoid or partly cycloid. Abdomen sometimes with a ridge or serrated scales. Head large. Mouth large, oblique. Jaws and palatines with bands of small teeth. Vomer with or without teeth. Eye large. Dorsal and anal spines few. Ventrals thoracic, with 1 spine and 6 rays. Caudal forked.

Members of this family are found in most seas, usually at considerable depths. Two genera are found in Queensland seas.

KEY TO GENERA IN QUEENSLAND

A.   Dorsal with 3 spines, anal with 2 spines. The fins covered
with asperities.   *Trachichthys*

AA. Dorsal with 4-7 spines, anal with 3 spines. The fins
not covered with asperities.   *Hoplostethus*

140. ROUGHY *Trachichthys australis* Shaw and Nodder   [Plate 30]

Trachichthys australis Shaw and Nodder, Nat. Miscell., 10, 1799, p. 378.
Trachichthys australis McCoy, Prodr. Zool. Vict., dec. 12, 1886, p. 57, pl. 114.

D. 3/12; A. 2/11; P. 13; L. 1. 65; L. tr. 24. Colour rich reddish-brown; a dark vertical band on opercle; all fins, with the exception of pectorals, with dark-brown areas as shown in the figure; a yellowish-white, almost colourless band at base of dorsal and anal fins.

This fish is another straggler into Moreton Bay from southern waters. It takes its name from its very rough skin. Inhabits rocky reefs. Grows to 6 inches.

141. SLENDER ROUGHY *Hoplostethus elongatus* (Günther)   [Plate 30]

Trachichthys elongatus Günther, Cat. Fish. Brit. Mus., 1, 1859, p. 10; and Challenger Rept Zool. 22, 1887, p. 22, pl. 5, fig. C.

D. 4/11; A. 3/9; V. 1/6; L. 1. 65. A black band along each side of caudal lobes and another in front of soft dorsal and anal fins.

A rare deep-water fish, its occurrence in Queensland waters based upon a single specimen trawled in Moreton Bay in 1889. Known also from New South Wales and New Zealand. Grows to 5 inches.

Family **Holocentridae: Soldier-fishes**

Brightly coloured fishes found living in shallow inshore waters of tropical seas. Most of the species are bright red in life, with silvery spots or bands along the rows of scales. They are extremely rough to the touch, and care must be used when handling them alive. The scales are large and strongly ctenoid with needle-like points. The head is armed with many spines and has a strongly serrated edge of parallel spines on the preopercle, and in one genus terminating in a long spine at its edge. Two genera are found in Queensland waters.

KEY TO GENERA IN QUEENSLAND

A.   Edge of preopercle armed with a long spine.   *Holocentrum*

AA. No spine at edge of preopercle.   *Myripristis*

Holocentrum

This genus is represented in the waters of Queensland by four species, two of which are exceedingly common on the Great Barrier Reef.

130

A. Four rows of scales between spinous dorsal and the lateral line; 43 scales on lateral line; Spinous dorsal vivid scarlet, other fins yellow. *spiniferum*

AA. Three rows of scales between spinous dorsal and lateral line.

    b. 46-47 scales on lateral line. Spinous dorsal dark maroon or blackish, crossed by a white line, continuous or discontinuous. *diadema*

    bb. 33-44 scales on lateral line.

    c. Nasal openings with spines. Spinous dorsal with spines pinkish-white and membrane scarlet-red and black. *cornutum*

    cc. Nasal openings without spines. Spinous dorsal with a broad black submarginal band. *rubrum*

142. SCARLET-FIN SOLDIER-FISH *Holocentrum spiniferum* (Forskål)
[Colour-plate 7]

Sciaena spinifera Forskål, Descr. Anim., 1775, p. 49.
Illustration by G. Coates.

D. 11/1/14; A. 4/9, or rarely 10; P. 1/14; V. 1/7; L. 1. 42-45; L. tr. 4/1/10. Colour: "Pinkish-red, lighter below; each scale with a silvery centre. A few violet dots along junctions of some lateral scale-rows. Cheek-scales with a bronze sheen. Pupil black, surrounded by a golden ring, rest of eye pinkish-brown. A gout of crimson on upper half of preoperculum, another in pectoral axil, and a third on the inner proximal half of the pectoral fin. Whole of the first dorsal vivid scarlet, other fins yellow." (Whitley.)

A wide-ranging species inhabiting the Great Barrier Reef, North Queensland. Grows to 15 inches.

143. CROWNED SOLDIER-FISH *Holocentrum diadema* (Lacépède)
[Colour-plate 7]

Holocentrus diadema Lacépède, Hist. Nat. Poiss., 5, 1903, pp. 372, 374 (*fide* Weber and de Beaufort).
Illustration by G. Coates.

D. 11-12/12-13; A. 4/8-9; V. 1/7; L. 1. 46-47; L. tr. 3/1/8. General colour tomato-red, with about 7 white longitudinal stripes; eye scarlet surrounding the black pupil and with white patches; a dark blotch through eye; spinous dorsal with spines reddish, passing into pinkish-white terminally, the membranes white anteriorly, very dark scarlet posteriorly; soft dorsal pale pink; pectorals hyaline-pink; ventrals hyaline-pink, the spine white, followed by scarlet on the first membrane; anal spines white, the first membrane blackish-scarlet, rest of rays red, membranes hyaline; caudal pink, with upper and lower edges scarlet; a large black spot as big as pupil of eye at caudal base and sometimes one on soft dorsal and anal.

Apparently a rare fish in Queensland waters, its occurrence being based upon two examples in the Queensland Museum labelled "Queensland Coast". Ranges from the Red Sea to the Indo-Pacific. Grows to 9 inches.

144. RED AND WHITE SOLDIER-FISH *Holocentrum cornutum* Bleeker
[Plate 30]

Holocentrum cornutum Bleeker, Nat. Tijdschr. Ned. Ind., 5, 1853, p. 240; and Atlas Ichth, 9, 1878, pl. 359, fig. 5.

D. 11-12/13-14; A. 4/9; L. 1. 35-36; L. tr. 3/1/7. Colour: Scarlet-red bands on a white background; spinous dorsal with spines pinkish-white and membrane scarlet-red and black; a black spot at base of caudal and sometimes one on soft dorsal and anal; pectorals and ventrals with pale-pink rays, the membrane hyaline; pupil of eye black, surrounded with scarlet and with white patches; a dark blotch through eye.

A strikingly handsome fish, common on the coral reefs of North Queensland. Also found in the Indo-Australian Archipelago and the Philippines. Grows to 6½ inches.

145. RED SOLDIER-FISH *Holocentrum rubrum* Bleeker   [Colour-plate 8]

Sciaena rubra Forskål, Descr. Anim., 1775, p. 48.
Illustration by G. Coates.

D. 11-12/12-14; A. 4/8-10; L. 1. 33-36; L. tr. 3/1/7. Colour red, each row of scales with a longitudinal silvery-white stripe; fins rosy; dorsal with a broad black submarginal band; membrane between second and third anal spine is black and also upper and lower margins of caudal.

This soldier-fish evidently lives in deeper water than the other species. George Coates of Townsville states: ". . . every one I have caught has come out of fairly deep water, fifteen fathoms and over. Rather fierce fighters when taking a bait. A wound caused by the spines has rather painful after-effects."

A wide-ranging species and the most common of the soldier-fishes in the Indo-Australian Archipelago. In Australia it is found on the coasts of Queensland, North Australia, and Western Australia. Grows to 11 inches.

Myripristis

There are two species of this genus in Queensland waters.

A. Eye twice the interorbital width or more; a patch of teeth
on the chin in addition to those on the lower jaw near the
symphysis. *australis*

AA. Eye less than twice interorbital width; no patches of
teeth on chin, only on lower jaw near symphysis. *murdjan*

146. BLUNT-NOSED SOLDIER-FISH *Myripristis australis* Castelnau
[Plate 30]

Myripristis australis Castelnau, Res. Fish. Austr. (Vict. Offic. Philad. Exhib.), 1875, p. 4.
Ostichthys australis Whitley, Austr. Zool., 9, pt 4, 1940, p. 417, fig. 28.

D. 11/1/14; A. 4/12; P. 1/14; V. 1/7; L. 1. 28; L. tr. $2\frac{1}{2}/1/5\frac{1}{2}$. Colour rose-
pink above, silvery-pink below, each scale edged with darker pink; head dark
rose-pink, lips and snout bright pink; pupil of eye black, with a large white
oblong sharp-edged blotch at its extreme posterior edge, the whole eye surrounded with scarlet; posterior edge of opercle on its upper half dark red,
almost blackish; spinous dorsal rose-pink, broadly margined with scarlet-red;
soft dorsal, pectorals, anal, and caudal rose-pink.

A common North Queensland species found among the coral reefs in both
deep and shallow water. Grows to $7\frac{1}{4}$ inches.

OTHER SPECIES

Blotch-eye, *M. murdjan*. A wide-ranging species found on the coral reefs
of North Queensland. Grows to 12 inches. In Hawaii it is a well-known food-
fish. Colour in life a clear red with a black bar on the edge of the opercle.
The fish takes its name from the black mark on the upper margin of the eye.

Order ZEOMORPHI

Family Zeidae: John Dories

Deep-bodied, compressed fishes, with long faces and large mouths and with
the upper jaw very protractile. The family is a small one, with species in both
the Atlantic and Pacific. Only one species has so far been found on the Queensland coast. The English name of John Dory is said to be a corruption of an
old Gascon name, Jan Doree, which meant Gilt Cock. In Germany the John
Dory is called Peter-fisch, as the spot on its side is said to represent the mark
of St Peter's thumb when he took the tribute money from its mouth.

147. JOHN DORY *Zeus faber* Linnaeus [Plate 31]

Zeus faber Linnaeus, Syst. Nat., 10th ed., 1758, p. 267.
Zeus faber Day, Fish. Gt Brit. and Irel., 1, 1880-4, p. 138, pl. 48.

D. 10/22-24; A. 4/21-22; V. 1/7; P. 14. Colour dull greenish or greenish-brown, paler on sides, silvery below; fins olive-green; a large blackish patch, bordered by a narrow silvery band, is situated on the side, below fifth and sixth dorsal spines.

Small specimens differ from larger ones in having much deeper bodies, marked with many wavy dark lines from snout to tail.

A rare fish in Queensland waters, where it very occasionally straggles into Moreton Bay from the south. In the southern States of Australia, where it is very common, the John Dory is highly esteemed as a food-fish, its capture usually being by means of the trawlers. Wide-ranging in all temperate seas. Grows to almost 24 inches. The John Dory of the Brisbane Fish Market is *Selenotoca multifasciatus aetatevarians*, the Southern Butter-fish.

Order **PERCOMORPHI**

The members of this large and important order, which contains about half of Australia's bony fishes and includes such diverse families as the mullets, mackerels, rock cods, and gobies, are characterized by having not more than one spine and six rays in the ventral fins. The order is subdivided into fifteen sub-orders, of which all but three are represented in Queensland.

Division **Perciformes**

Sub-order PERCOIDEA: PERCH-LIKE FISHES

The percoids are the predominant Australian food fishes, in contrast to the food-fishes of northern Europe and America where the staple food-fishes are the soft-rayed fishes of the orders Isospondyli, Anacanthini, and Heterosomata, which include the herrings, cods, and flounders respectively.

Family **Kuhliidae: Flag-tails**

Body oblong, strongly compressed. Scales large, ciliated. Mouth large, protractile. Maxillary exposed, without supplemental bone. Teeth in jaws in villiform bands, also on vomer and palatines. Tongue smooth. Preorbital and preopercle denticulate. Opercle with 2 spines. Spinous dorsal well developed, of 10 spines, connected at base with soft dorsal of 9 to 13 rays. Anal with 3 spines and 10 to 12 rays. Dorsal and anal fins fitting into a well-developed sheath. Pectorals obtusely pointed. Ventrals behind base of pectoral, with a strong spine. Caudal emarginate.

A small family of fishes with a single genus. Three species are found in Queensland waters. The spotted species live mainly in the estuaries and fresh-water streams, only occasionally being found in the sea.

Kuhlia

KEY TO SPECIES IN QUEENSLAND

A. 40-45 scales on lateral line; 16-19 gill-rakers on lower branch of first arch. Caudal fin with a single black blotch on each lobe; body with dark spots.   *rupestris*

AA. 46-56 scales on lateral line; 23-26 gill-rakers on lower branch of first arch.

    b. Caudal with 5 blackish bands, one median and a pair on each lobe, converging posteriorly; 53-56 scales on lateral line.   *taeniura*

    bb. Caudal with a blackish base and a broad black marginal band; 46-50 scales on lateral line.   *munda*

148. ROCK FLAG-TAIL *Kuhlia rupestris* (Lacépède)   [Colour-plate 8]

Centropomus rupestris Lacépède, Hist. Nat. Poiss., 4, 1802, pp. 252, 273.
Illustration by G. Coates.

Buffalo Bream (Townsville).

General colour bright silvery, darkest above, pure silver below; each scale strongly outlined in black, but the outline becoming grey below; head silver, with traces of pale olive-yellow sheen before eyes and on opercles and with numerous black spots on opercles; eye, pupil black, surrounded dark brown, with russet-brown ring outside; spinous dorsal pale hyaline olive-grey; soft dorsal blackish-grey, lighter terminally and light olive-greenish basally; pectoral hyaline with pale lemon-yellow tinge; ventrals white; anal with the rays whitish hyaline or pale yellowish, the membranes dusky; caudal blackish, pale yellowish terminally.

A handsome fish, mainly inhabiting the freshwater streams though occasionally found in the sea. Although found in South Queensland the species is much more common in the streams of the north. A good food-fish. Grows to 18 inches with a weight of $4\frac{1}{2}$ pounds. Wide-ranging.

OTHER SPECIES

Flag-tail, *K. taeniura*. Found on the coasts of Queensland and New South Wales, the young entering the tide-pools among the rocks. Grows to 9 inches. May be identified by the black bands on the tail. Outside Australia it is wide-ranging.

Clean Flag-tail, *K. munda*. Inhabits the waters of North Queensland, New Guinea, and the western Pacific. Grows to 11 inches.

Family **Apogonidae: Cardinal-fishes**

Fishes of the tropical seas, perch-like in form, small or of moderate size, with two distinct short dorsal fins. Many of them are bright red in colour, usually with dark stripes, bands, or spots. They inhabit coastal waters, usually in the vicinity of reefs, some being found in deep water. A few enter brackish water. Oral gestation occurs in several species, the impregnated ova being carried in the mouth and gullet until hatched (usually by the male).

This family is a large one, many genera and species being known. Six genera occur in Queensland waters.

KEY TO GENERA IN QUEENSLAND

A. Teeth on vomer, jaws, and palatines, minute or villiform, no true canines.

   b. Lateral line complete and continuous.

     c. No silvery tube-like prolongation on ventral surface of body. Body scales ctenoid.   *Apogon*

     cc. A silvery tube-like prolongation along each side of ventral surface of body extending to caudal peduncle.

       d. Scales ciliated or ctenoid.   *Siphamia*

       dd. Scales cycloid.   *Adenapogon*

   bb. Lateral line incomplete. Anal with 2 spines and 8 branched rays.

     e. A silvery subcutaneous tube on each side posteriorly.   *Fodifoa*

     ee. No silvery subcutaneous tube on sides.   *Foa*

AA. Jaws with minute or villiform teeth and with distinct canines.   *Cheilodipterus*

Apogon

Small fishes of tropical seas, frequenting the coral reefs in great numbers in both shallow and deep waters. Some of them are inhabitants of brackish and even fresh waters. Many of the species are brilliantly coloured. There are eighteen species and sub-species in Queensland and they can be identified by the descriptions in the following key. Three of the species will be described in detail.

KEY TO SPECIES AND SUB-SPECIES IN QUEENSLAND

Adapted from Weber and de Beaufort[13]

A.   Anal with not more than 8-10 soft rays.

    b. 7 dorsal spines (by exception A. *compressa*, which has usually 6).

      c. Free margin of preoperculum serrated.

       d. Caudal rounded.

        e. Reddish, with a series of small black spots along the lateral line.   *rüppelli*

        ee. Dark brown, with an oblique blackish bar below the eye and a blackish spot above the pectoral.   *atripes*

      dd. Caudal generally incised.

       f. Vertical part of preopercular ridge and orbital rim serrated.

        g. Height 2.9-3.3. A dark band from snout to caudal.   *frenatus*

        gg. Height 2.3-2.4. Seven to 8 dark bands from head to caudal; soft dorsal and anal with a dark ocellus.   *brevicaudatus*

       ff. Preopercular ridge smooth or at most with some spines at angle.

        h. Dorsal spines stronger, the third one generally much stronger than the others. Often dark longitudinal bands on the body.

         i. Maxillary reaching to below posterior half of eye. Dark longitudinal bands, often continued on caudal.

          j. Two bands on upper part of body only; orbital rim serrated.   *quadrifasciatus*

          jj. Bands also on lower part of body; orbital rim without serrations.

           k. Body usually with 3 distinct longitudinal bands; another may be present on back, and one along belly.

            l. The 3 principal bands extend onto the caudal fin, where the upper and the lower converge abruptly; no secondary band between the others.   *fasciatus novemfasciatus*

            ll. The bands not or scarcely extending beyond the caudal base.

---

[13] *Fish. Indo-Austr. Archip.*, 5, 1929, p. 278.

m. The 3 principal bands very broad, ending abruptly at the caudal base; no secondary intermediate bands. *fasciatus aroubiensis*

mm. Bands narrower, terminating less abruptly, a secondary band present or absent anteriorly.

n. A distinct secondary band anteriorly between median and dorso-lateral ones, which curves upwards and joins the latter. Some irregular spots at caudal base. *fasciatus compressa*

nn. Secondary band, if present, not joining the one above it. A dark spot usually present on caudal base. *fasciatus fasciatus*

ii. Maxillary reaching to below middle of eye. Bands, if present, seldom continued on caudal. *septemstriatus*

hh. Dorsal spines weaker, the third one not or only slightly stronger than the others. No dark longitudinal bands.

o. Height 2.4-2.8. Eye large, 2.1-2.5. A dark streak from eye to angle of preoperculum; a dark-brown band on upper part of caudal peduncle; sometimes transverse bands on body. *bandanensis*

oo. Height 2.1-2.3. Eye 2.7-3. A broad dark band encircling caudal peduncle. *aureus*

cc. Free margin of preoperculum smooth or with some serrations at angle only; caudal subtruncate or rounded; maxillary reaching behind middle of eye.

p. Third dorsal spine stronger and longer than the others. A blue-black ocellus on operculum. *auritus*

pp. Third dorsal spine not stronger than the others, equal to fourth and fifth. Upper part of first dorsal black; second dorsal with a marginal and a median black band, anal with a median black band. *ellioti*

bb. Six dorsal spines.

q. Preopercular ridge, preorbital and orbital rim serrated. More or less distinct dark transverse bands. *trimaculatus*

qq. Preopercular ridge and preorbital smooth.

138

r. Dorsal spines produced into filaments. Translucent olive or yellowish with dusky dots on head and foreparts of body; sometimes bronzy cross-streaks on head.   *hypselonotus*

rr. Dorsal spines not produced; nape concave. A large black spot on caudal base, also at bases of second dorsal and anal fins; a blackish spot may also be present on operculum.   *hyalosoma*

AA. Anal with 13-17 soft rays; 6 dorsal spines.   *lineolatus*

149. BLACK-FINNED CARDINAL-FISH *Apogon atripes* (Ogilby) [Colour-plate 9]

Amia nigripes Ogilby, Ann. Qld. Mus., no. 10, 1st Nov. 1911, p. 49 (preoccupied by *A. nigripes* Playfair).
Illustration by G. Coates.

D. 7/1/9; A. 2/8; P. 15. Colour dark brown, with a large round blackish spot between pectoral fin and lateral line; cheeks paler, with an oblique blackish bar from below middle of eye to angle of inner preopercular ridge; lower surface of head and throat pale yellow; dorsal, anal, and ventral fins black, the former broadly edged with yellow; caudal and pectorals uniform yellow. (After Ogilby.)

A Queensland species, mostly taken by the prawn-trawlers when capturing prawns in the otter-trawls along the coastline. Grows to 4 inches.

150. CARDINAL-FISH *Apogon fasciatus fasciatus* (Shaw)   [Colour-plate 9]

Mullus fasciatus Shaw, in White, Voy. N.S.Wales, 1790, p. 268.
Illustration by G. Coates.

D. 7/1/9; A. 2/8; L. 1. 25-27; L. tr. $1\frac{1}{2}/1/6\frac{1}{2}$-7. Colour olivaceous or pearly-grey, with three broad dark olive-green longitudinal stripes on the side, usually terminating in a dark spot on caudal base; another less distinct and narrower one along middle of back and base of dorsal; fins pinkish or brick-red; a dark band is usually present at base of soft dorsal and anal fins; caudal pinkish.

The Cardinal-fish swims in great numbers in the sheltered waters among the coral reefs. Great variation exists in both colour and form and there are many sub-species. It is very doubtful if they are anything but varieties of a common species. Grows to 5 inches. Wide-ranging.

151. BAR-CHEEKED CARDINAL-FISH *Apogon bandanensis* Bleeker
[Plate 31]

Apogon bandanensis Bleeker, Nat. Tijdschr. Ned. Ind., 6, 1854, p. 95; and Atlas Ichth., 8, 1876-7, pl. 345, fig. 2.

D. 7/1/9; A. 2/8; L. 1. 25-27; L. tr. 1½/1/6½. Colour: Back brown, sides and below paler, usually with brassy reflections; an obscure brown streak from below eye, down obliquely to angle of preopercle; a dusky brown saddle on upper surface of caudal peduncle; sides usually with traces of parallel and vertical obscure bars; spinous dorsal dusky, blackish anteriorly; soft dorsal greyish, dusky anteriorly; caudal greyish, margined darker above and below.

A very variable species, but readily recognized by the oblique streak below the eye. A common fish on the coral reefs of North Queensland. Wide-ranging. Grows to 4 inches.

Siphamia

A genus of small fishes in which a tube-like prolongation of the body cavity is contained at both sides along the lower part of the body and caudal peduncle to the base of the caudal fin.

Two species only are known, one from the island of Timor, the other from Queensland.

152. SIPHON-FISH *Siphamia cuneiceps* Whitley   [Plate 31]
Siphamia cuneiceps Whitley, Austr. Zool., 10, pt 1, Dec. 1941, p. 29, fig. 20.

D. 6/1/7-8; A. 2/8; P. 12; V. 1/5; C. 17. Colour in life brassy, everywhere covered with minute black dots; fins hyaline, except ventrals and anal, which have basal half blackish; eye with pupil brilliant metallic-blue, surrounded golden.

This curious little fish was first known from three examples which measured from 36 to 39 mm. in standard length or 1⅞ inches overall. They were taken by the M.V. *Warreen* of the Marine Biological Laboratory, C.S.I.R.O., Cronulla, New South Wales, and were secured in the Agassiz trawl when operating off Fraser Island, Queensland, in 15 fathoms on 14th September 1938. One example was a spawning female. Numerous other examples have now been taken by the otter-trawls operating in Moreton Bay, where the species appears to be fairly common. Grows to 2 inches.

Adenapogon

153. ROSE-BELLIED SIPHON-FISH *Adenapogon roseigaster*
(Ramsay and Ogilby)   [Plate 31]

Apogon roseigaster Ramsay and Ogilby, Proc. Linn. Soc. N.S.Wales (2), 1, 1886, p. 1101.
Adenapogon roseigaster McCulloch, Rec. Austr. Mus. 13, no. 4, April 1921, p. 133, pl. 21, fig. 2.

D. 6/1/10 (11); A. 2/9-10 (11); P. 12-14; V. 1/5; C. 17; L. 1. 26; L. tr. 1/1/5. Colour silvery white above, passing into pale rose-colour below, the tube-like prolongation on each side of the lower part of the body being the colour of quicksilver; head, with exception of opercles, with numerous minute dark olive-green dots, among which are several orange ones; scales of back and upper sides similarly dotted; fins hyaline pink; spinous dorsal with dense black dots forming a large dark spot or band medianally; soft dorsal and anal with a similar black band crossing their lower half; thick gland on each side of base of tongue silvery, black above.

A small fish commonly met with in the estuaries of the rivers and in the harbours along the coasts of South Queensland and New South Wales. The characteristic silvery peritoneal tubes are thought to be luminous organs.

In the Brisbane River the species is commonly taken at night in the trawl nets of the prawners. The eggs are carried in the mouth until hatched. Grows to 3 inches.

Cheilodipterus

Members of this genus are distinguished by the presence of distinct canines in the jaws, and the spinous dorsal fin has only six rather feeble spines. Two species occur in Queensland waters.

KEY TO SPECIES IN QUEENSLAND

A. Canine teeth weak; second dorsal and anal fin rounded.
Body with 5-6 longitudinal stripes, the first in the
median dorsal.   *quinquelineatus*

AA. Canine teeth strong; second dorsal and anal fin truncate
or slightly concave. Body with 8 longitudinal stripes, the
first in the median dorsal.   *macrodon*

154. FIVE-STRIPED PERCELLE *Cheilodipterus quinquelineatus*
Cuvier and Valenciennes   [Plate 32]

Cheilodipterus quinquelineatus Cuvier and Valenciennes, Hist. Nat. Poiss., 2, 1828, p. 167.
Paramia quinquelineatus Bleeker, Atlas Ichth., 7, 1873-6, p. 105, pl. 326, fig. 2.

D. 6/1/9; A. 2/8; P. 2/10; V. 1/5; L. 1. 25-27; L. tr. 2/1/6-7. Colour: Head and body pale iridescent pink, with 5 very dark horizontal stripes from head to tail; the centre one, which runs from snout through eye to tail, ends on caudal peduncle in a black spot a little smaller than pupil; this spot is surrounded by a lemon-yellow patch almost as wide as caudal peduncle; spinous dorsal with first two spines black, the membranes dusky; rest of spines light, membranes hyaline; ventrals dusky, the rays lightest; anal smoky, the membranes clear; caudal pink, the rays pencilled or ticked transversely with brownish, a dark-brown stripe along upper and lower edge.

A common fish among the coral reefs of North Queensland. Wide-ranging. Grows to 5 inches.

OTHER SPECIES

Big-toothed Percelle, *C. macrodon*. Another wide-ranging fish, common on the coral reefs of North Queensland. Grows to over 8 inches. Characterized by its strong canine teeth and the eight longitudinal stripes on the body.

Family **Plesiopidae: Long-fins**

Form oblong, compressed; body covered with ctenoid or ciliated scales. Large or moderate in size. Lateral line interrupted, mouth moderate, protractile, jaws equal. Maxillary with a supplemental bone. Jaws with villiform and slightly enlarged or canine teeth. Vomer and palatines with a few teeth or in villiform bands. Opercles entire. Dorsal fin single, the spinous portion as long as or much longer than soft portion. Anal with 3 spines. Base of dorsal and anal with or without scales. Pectorals short and rounded. Caudal rounded or pointed. Ventrals with 1 spine and 4 rays.

A small family of carnivorous fishes of small or moderate size, found in the littoral waters of the Indo-Pacific and Australian regions. They are somewhat similar to the Serranidae, but have only 2 to 4 rays in the ventral fin, the first being bifid, thickened, and elongate. Three genera are found in Queensland waters.

KEY TO GENERA IN QUEENSLAND

A. Two lateral lines, one close to dorsal base, the second along middle of sides to caudal base. Dorsal fin with 11-12 spines and 6-11 rays. Size moderate.

    b. Dorsal fin with 6-9 rays. Anal with 3 spines and 6-9 rays.   *Plesiops*

    bb. Dorsal fin with 9-11 rays. Anal with 3 spines and 10-11 rays.   *Paraplesiops*

AA. Three lateral lines, the third being above base of anal fin. Dorsal fin with about 18 spines and 6 rays. Anal with 10 spines and 5 rays. Size small.   *Belonepterygion*

Plesiops

KEY TO SPECIES IN QUEENSLAND

A. Dorsal fin with 12 spines. A black, blue-edged ocellus on opercle; head and body with blue spots.   *nigricans*

AA. Dorsal fin with 11 spines; no ocellus on opercle. Brownish with soft dorsal edged with red.   *melas*

155. BLUE-SPOTTED LONG-FIN *Plesiops nigricans* (Rüppell) [Plate 32]

Pharopteryx nigricans Rüppell, Atlas Fische. Roth. Meer., 1828, p. 15.
Plesiops corallicola Günther, Fische der Sudsee, 1, 1873-5, pp. 87, 88, pl. 58, fig. B.

D. 11/9; A. 3/7-9; scales 19 or 20 in upper section of lateral line plus 7 to 9 in lower section plus 3 more on caudal base; L. tr. 2-3/1/6. Colour blackish or very dark brown, each scale on body with a blue spot; several similar spots on shoulder and head; a large black, blue-edged ocellus on opercle (sometimes margined with red or orange); fins blackish, the spinous dorsal with a broad dull blue margin; soft dorsal, anal, and caudal with a blue or white marginal line; pectoral with its posterior margin red.

With regard to this fish and its habits in the New Hebrides, Herre notes:[14] ". . . at low tide they remain concealed under the boulders covering the beach and apparently are able to get along with an exceedingly limited supply of water, as long as they have wet sand in which to burrow." A wide-ranging fish recorded in Australia from South Queensland. Grows to 7 inches.

OTHER SPECIES

Crimson-tipped Long-fin, *P. melas.* A small fish 3 inches in length inhabiting the Indo-Australian region. It frequents the reefs of North Queensland.

Paraplesiops

156. BLUE-TIP LONG-FIN *Paraplesiops poweri* Ogilby [Plate 32]

Paraplesiops poweri Ogilby, Proc. Roy. Soc. Qld, 21, 1908, p. 17.
Paraplesiops jolliffei Ogilby, Mem. Qld Mus., 6, 1918, p. 49, pl. 17.

D. 12/10; A. 3/10-11; scales 28-30 in upper section of lateral line, plus 12 in lower section. Colour purplish-black or greenish-brown, with faint greyish transverse bands; a blue band from nostril to angle of preopercle; cheeks and opercles with a few blue spots; dorsal, caudal, anal, and ventral fins purple, edged with blue, the first two and the posterior rays of the third crossed by a network of greyish lines; pectorals greenish-yellow.

Although found on the Queensland coast as far north as Bowen, this fish appears to be more common in Moreton Bay. Grows to 8 inches.

Belonepterygion

Represented in Queensland by the Banded Long-fin, *B. fasciolatus* (Ogilby), a common little fish about 2 inches in length found under stones and in pools between tide-marks on the coral reefs of Queensland and at Lord Howe Island.

---

[14] Fish. Crane Pac. Exped., Field Mus. Nat. Hist., 21, 1936, p. 164.

Family **Priacanthidae: Bulls-eyes or Big-eyes**

Body oblong, somewhat elevated. Scales very small. Eyes large. Lower jaw prominent. Preopercle with flattened spine at angle. A single dorsal fin with 9 to 10 spines. Anal with 3 spines.

Fishes of moderate size, bright rosy-red in colour, with big eyes and short pectorals. They inhabit the tropical parts of the Indo-Pacific and Atlantic, usually in fairly deep water.

Two species belonging to the one genus, *Priacanthus*, are found in Queensland waters.

KEY TO SPECIES IN QUEENSLAND

A.   Dorsal with 10 spines and 12 rays; ventrals with distinct brown spots; caudal crescentic, the lobes produced with age.

tayenus

AA. Dorsal with 10 spines and 13 rays; ventrals without spots; caudal truncate, or only slightly emarginate.

macracanthus

157. RED BULLS-EYE *Priacanthus macracanthus* Cuvier and Valenciennes
[Colour-plate 10]

Priacanthus macracanthus Cuvier and Valenciennes, Hist. Nat. Poiss., 3, 1829, p. 108.
Illustration by G. Coates.

Bulls-eye Perch (Brisbane Fish Market).
D. 10/13-14; A. 3/13-15; L. 1. 85-96 + 12; L. tr. 12-14/1/40-42; lower gill-rakers 12. Colour red above, silvery on sides and below; vertical fins red or pink, with reddish to greyish spots on membranes; caudal dark-edged; pupil of eye black, surrounded scarlet; inside mouth orange-red.

An Indo-Australian species found along the coasts of Queensland and New South Wales. The young frequent the shallow bays and inlets of Moreton Bay in great numbers during the winter months. Common. Grows to 12 inches.

OTHER SPECIES

Spotted-finned Bulls-eye, *P. tayenus*. Found in the waters of North Queensland and the Indo-Australian region. Grows to 11 inches. Recognized by its brown-spotted ventral fins.

Family **Toxotidae: Archer-fishes**

Body oblong, compressed, back depressed. Scales moderate or small, ctenoid, extending on to head, soft dorsal, anal, and caudal fins. Head conical, pointed, flattened above and with a feeble occipital crest. Eyes moderate or large, in anterior half of head. Snout produced, lower jaw the longer. Mouth terminal,

144

oblique, protractile, gape wide. Maxillary slender throughout. Anterior margin of narrow preorbital serrated, as is also the lower border of preopercle. Villiform teeth in jaws, on vomer, palatines, and pterygoids. A single dorsal fin situated in posterior half of body and opposite the anal, with 4 to 5 (in one species 6) strong spines and 11 to 14 rays. Anal with 3 spines and 15 to 17 rays. Pectorals somewhat high, more or less acute, longer than ventrals, which are placed somewhat behind their base and have a strong spine and 5 rays and a large scaly axillary process. Caudal truncate or slightly emarginate.

Fishes of moderate size living in brackish waters of estuaries and in freshwater rivers of southern and south-eastern Asia from India and the Indo-Australian Archipelago northward to the Philippines, south to Australia, and east to the South Sea Islands.

A single genus, *Toxotes*, with few species, two in Queensland.

158. RIFLE-FISH or ARCHER-FISH *Toxotes chatareus*
(Hamilton Buchanan)   [Colour-plate 10]

Coius chatareus Hamilton Buchanan, Fish. Ganges, 1822, pp. 101, 370.
Illustration by G. Coates.

Spotted Bream (Normanton); Rifle-fish (North Queensland); Blowpipe-fish (Malaya).

D. 5/12-14; A. 3/17-18; L. 1. 33-34; L. tr. 4-5/11-13. Colour silvery, with flushes of golden; dorsal surface greenish-brown; 6 to 7 oblong or roundish blackish spots of unequal size between eye and end of dorsal fin, above lateral line; anterior and posterior angle of soft dorsal and outer half of anal blackish. The species is very variable in colour. In the young the blotches are larger and darker. The ventral fin is black and there is a black band along the base of the caudal.

This fish is a lover of brackish and fresh water, living in the mangrove-lined rivers and creeks and in the freshwater streams and billabongs, particularly where the trees and vegetation overhang the water. It delights in calm, still waters and there it congregates in small schools of a dozen or so, swimming just below the surface and immediately rising if a few grains of sand are thrown on the surface of the water. They readily take a bait, and at Townsville they are easily caught when the bait is a live cockroach.

This curious fish is remarkable for its habit of shooting down insects from overhanging foliage along the banks of streams by the aid of a jet of water. When the Rifle-fish has sighted an insect on a leaf or branch, it approaches

191

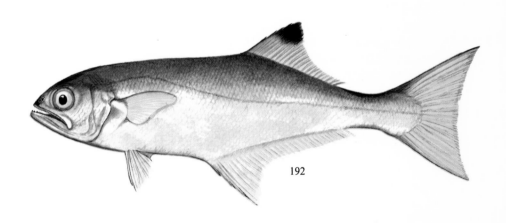

192

COLOUR-PLATE 17
191. Diamond-fish, *Monodactylus argenteus*, 5 in.
192. Steelback, *Leptobrama* mülleri, 11 in.

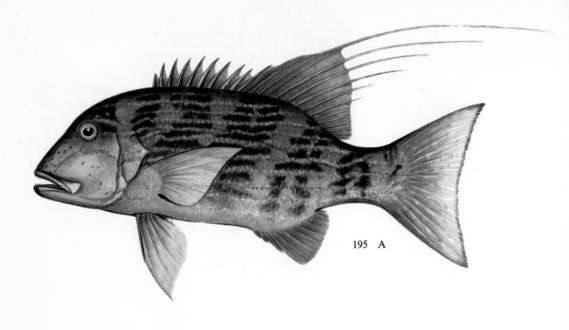

195 A

195 B

COLOUR-PLATE 18
195. Chinaman-fish, *Lutjanus nematophorus*. A, Juv., 12 in.;
B, adult, 27 in.

196

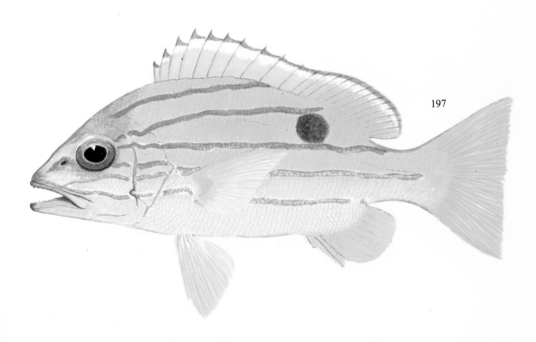

197

COLOUR-PLATE 19
196. Mangrove Jack, *Lutjanus argentimaculatus*, 14 in.
197. Blue-banded Sea Perch, *L. kasmira*, 11 in.

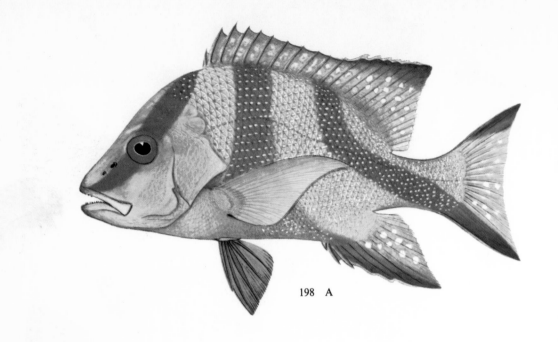

198 A

198 B

198. Red Emperor, *Lutjanus sebae*. A, Juv., 11 in.; B, adult,
36 in.

199

200 A

200 B

COLOUR-PLATE 21
199. Yellow-banded Hussar, *Lutjanus amabilis*, 12 inches.
200. Scarlet Sea Perch, *L. malabaricus*. A, Juv., 14 in.; B, Adult, 33 in.

201

202

COLOUR-PLATE 22
201. Black-spot Sea Perch, *L. fulviflamma*, 11 in.   202. Kelp Sea Perch, *L. coatesi*, 28 in.   203. Red-bellied Fusilier, *Caesio erythrogaster*, 10 in.

203

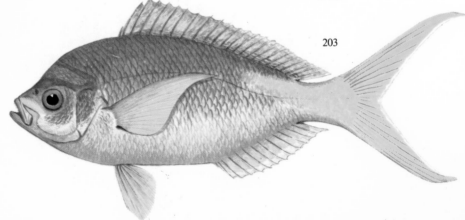

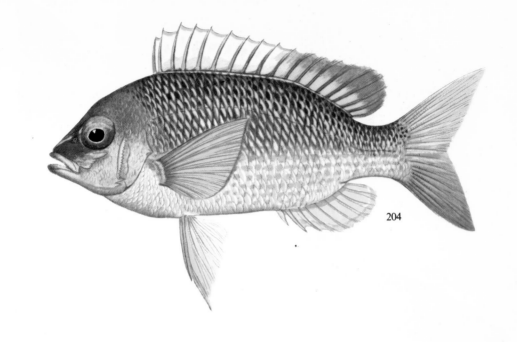

204

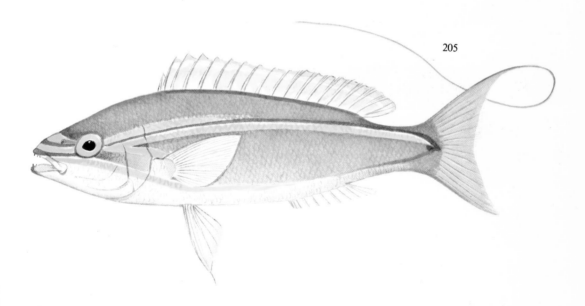

205

COLOUR-PLATE 23
204. Pearly Spine-cheek, *Scolopsis margaritifer*, 9 inches.
205. Blue-banded Whiptail, *Pentapodus setosus*, 11 in.

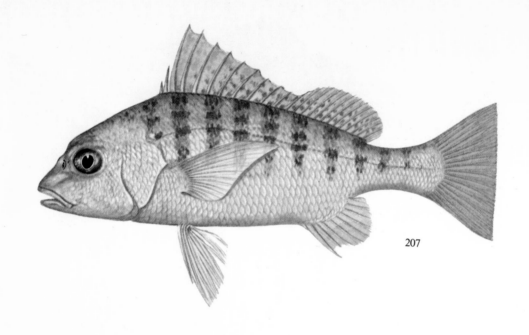

207

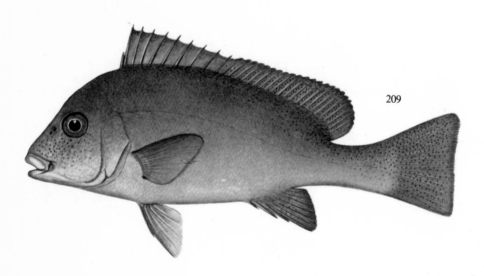

209

COLOUR-PLATE 24
207. Spotted Javelin-fish, *Pomadasys hasta*, 18 in.
209. Painted Sweet-lips, *Plectorhynchus pictus*, 12 in.

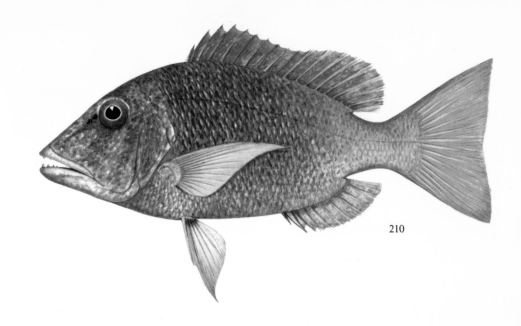

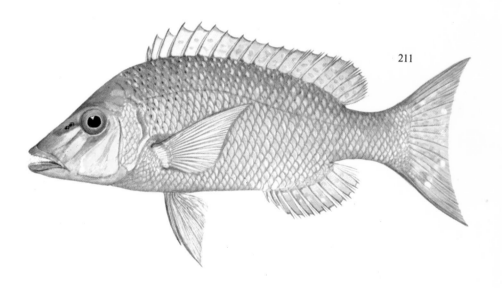

COLOUR-PLATE 25
210. Yellow-tailed Emperor, *Lethrinus mahsena*, 14 inches.
211. Spangled Emperor, *L. nebulosus*, 12 in.

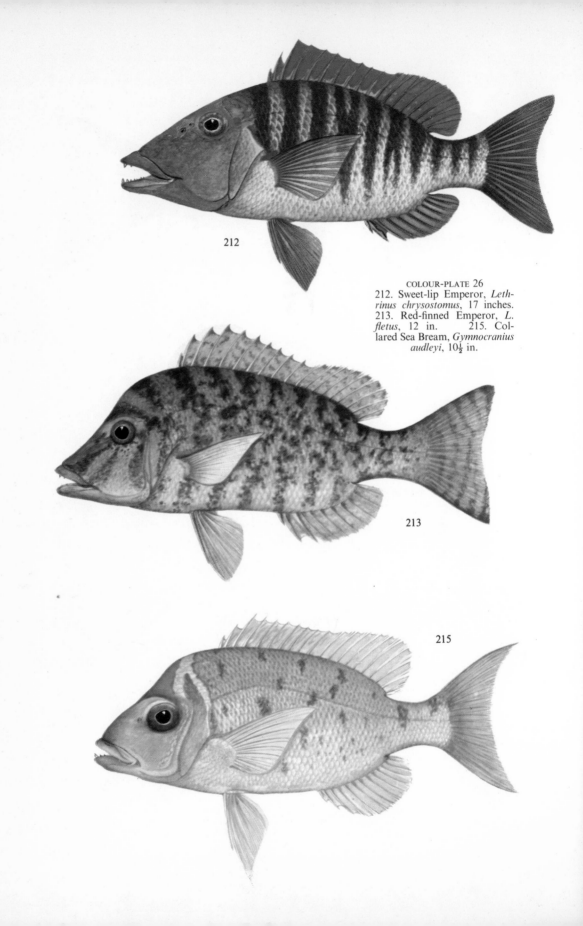

212

COLOUR-PLATE 26
212. Sweet-lip Emperor, *Lethrinus chrysostomus*, 17 inches.
213. Red-finned Emperor, *L. fletus*, 12 in.   215. Collared Sea Bream, *Gymnocranius audleyi*, $10\frac{1}{2}$ in.

213

215

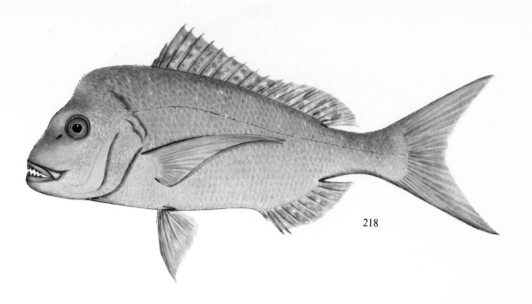

218

COLOUR-PLATE 27
218. Snapper, *Chrysophrys auratus*, 30 in. 219. Long-spined Snapper, *Argyrops spinifer*, 11 in.

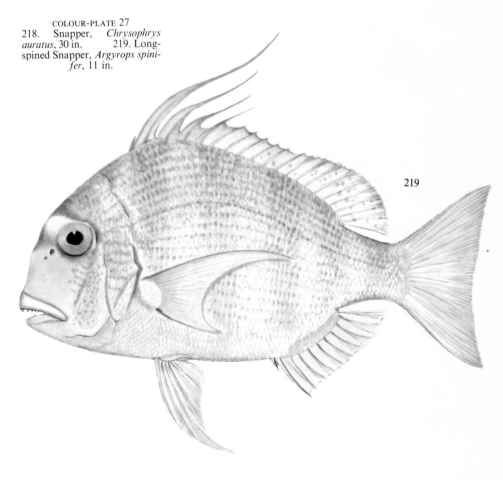

219

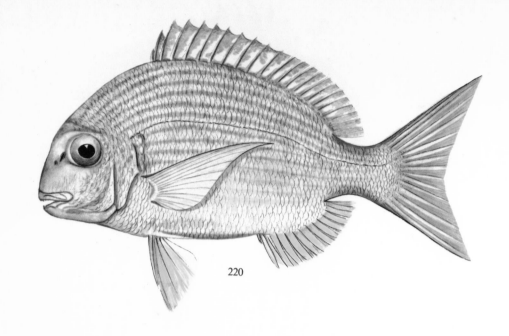

220

COLOUR-PLATE 28
220. Tarwhine, *Rhabdosargus sarba*, 12 in.   221. Yellow-fin or Common Bream, *Mylio australis*, $7\frac{1}{2}$ in.

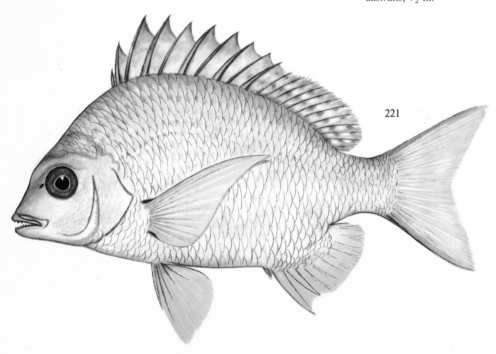

221

222

COLOUR-PLATE 29
222. Pikey Bream, *Mylio berda*,
14 in.   228. Bearded Jewfish, *Sciaena dussumieri*, 8 in.
232. Great Trevally, *Caranx
sexfasciatus*, 12 in.

228

232

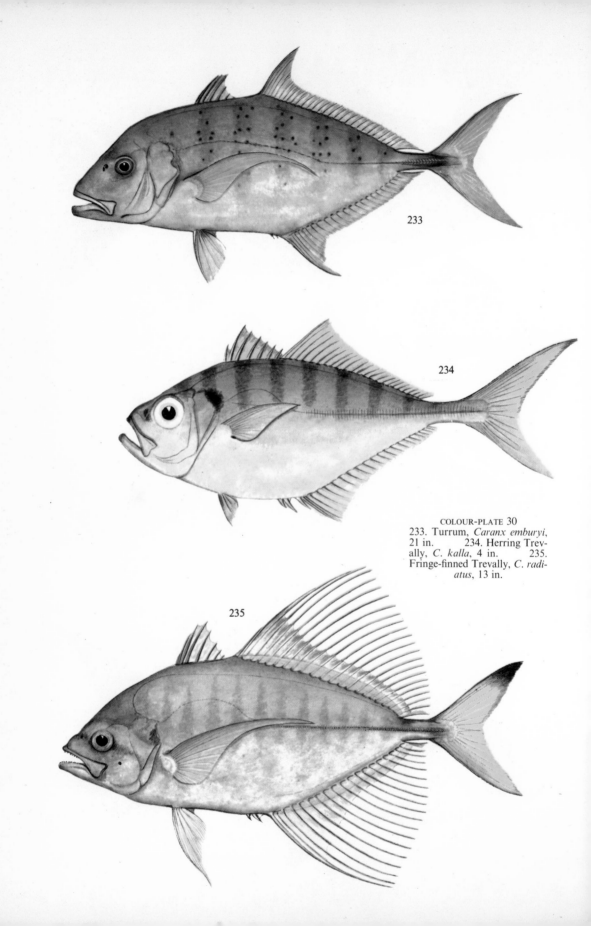

233

234

235

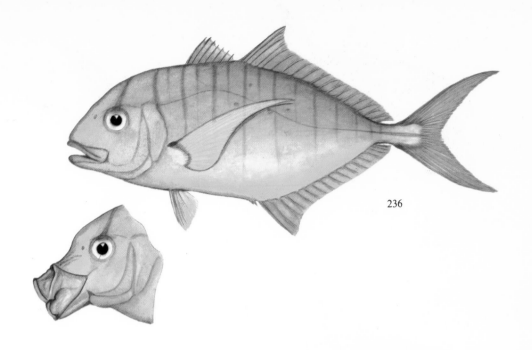

236

COLOUR-PLATE 31
236. Golden Trevally, *Caranx speciosus*, juv., 14 inches.
238a. Black Pomfret, *Parastromateus niger*, juv., 7 in.

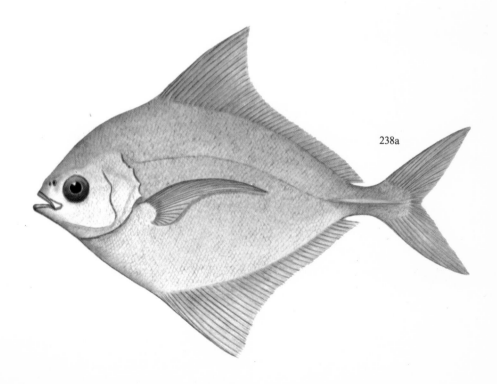

238a

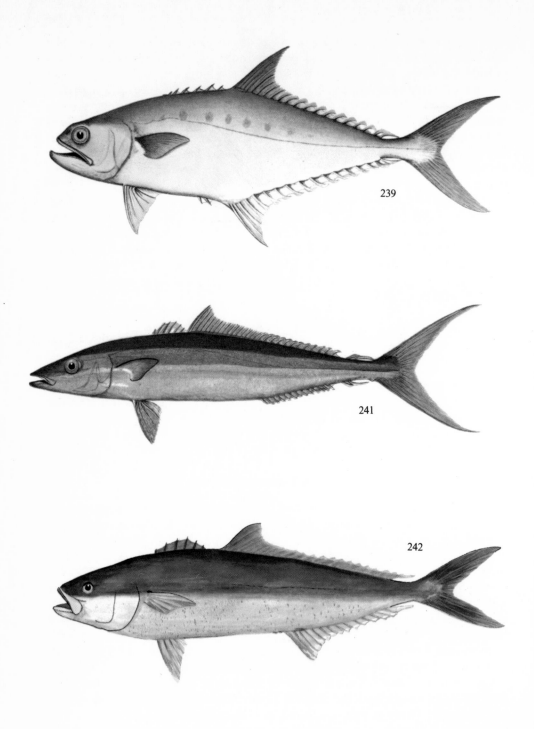

239

241

242

COLOUR-PLATE 32
239. Large-mouthed Leather-skin, *Chorinemus lysan*, 28 in.
241. Runner, *Elagatis bipinnulatus*, 23 in.   242. King
Amber-jack, *Seriola grandis*, 36 in.

with great stealth until within a striking distance of two or three feet. The fish then rises to the surface and projects only the tip of the closed mouth outside the water. When the mouth is closed a minute opening exists between the mandibulary symphysis and the upper jaw. Through this opening a few drops of water are propelled with force by the fish closing its gill-covers, compressing the opercular and branchiostegal apparatus and forcing up the floor of the mouth, the unsuspecting insect being knocked off the foliage and into the water. The distance the fish is able to shoot has been varied by many authors to as much as three feet and more, but my own observations suggest that a distance of two feet is probably a limit to accurate shooting.

The range of this species in Queensland is the northern portion of the State. On the east coast it ranges south to about Cardwell. On the west coast it is extremely common in the Gulf of Carpentaria, frequenting all rivers, creeks, and billabongs, often hundreds of miles inland in the fresh water. The species also occurs throughout the Indo-Australian Archipelago and New Guinea, and in India. It grows to almost 12 inches in length, and large ones have flesh of good edible quality.

OTHER SPECIES

Toxotes jaculator. A fish with only four dorsal spines. Ranges from the Andaman Islands and the East Indies to Queensland, where it is found in the northern parts only. Grows to 10½ inches.

Family **Centropomidae**

Body elongate or oblong, compressed, with elevated back and depressed or pointed head. Scales moderate to large, adherent or deciduous, cycloid or ctenoid. Lateral line continuous or by exception interrupted. Mouth moderate or large, horizontal or oblique, moderately protractile. Maxilla exposed, a supplemental bone present or absent. Preopercle with a single serrated border posteriorly or with two ridges, inferiorly serrated or spinous. Opercle with or without a spine. Teeth villiform, in bands in jaws and on vomer and palatines. Dorsal fins separated or united, subequal, the spinous portion with 7 to 9 strong spines, the soft portion with 1 spine and 9 to 15 rays. Anal short, with 3 spines and 6 to 17 rays. Ventrals thoracic, of 1 strong spine and 5 rays, with or without a scaly axillary process. Caudal rounded or forked.

Carnivorous fishes of small, medium, and large size inhabiting the fresh and brackish waters and the seas of North Australia, tropical Asia, Africa, and America. Three genera are found in Queensland waters.

F

A. Preoperculum with a single edge, serrated posteriorly. Ventrals with a scaly axillary process. Scales ctenoid. Caudal rounded.

    b. Maxillary reaching to below eye. Nostrils far distant. Inferior border of preoperculum entire. A patch of teeth on tongue.   *Psammoperca*

    bb. Maxillary reaching behind eye. Nostrils approximate. Inferior border of preoperculum spinous. No teeth on tongue or at most rudimentary.   *Lates*

AA. Preoperculum with a double ridge, the lower limb serrated. Ventrals without a scaly axillary process. Scales cycloid. Caudal forked.   *Ambassis*

Psammoperca

159. SAND BASS *Psammoperca waigiensis* (Cuvier and Valenciennes)
[Plate 32]

Labrax waigiensis Cuvier and Valenciennes, Hist. Nat. Poiss., 2, 1828, p. 83.
Illustration by G. Coates.

Glass-eyed Perch, Reef Barramundi, Sand Perch, Dwarf Palmer, Jewel-eye (North Queensland).

D. 7/1/12; A. 3/8-9; L. 1. 45-50; L. tr. $5\frac{1}{2}$-7/1/11-12. Colour uniform dull brown, the centres of scales a little darker; fins uniform brownish except pectorals and ventrals which are yellowish-white, the latter tinged greyish.

Another colour variety is light drab, darker on back, passing into dirty white, flecked with grey on belly, each scale clearly outlined in drab; 14 to 15 pale orange-cinnamon longitudinal lines on sides, strongest below lateral line; soft dorsal, anal, and caudal fuscous; spinous dorsal, pectorals, and ventrals hair-brown, darkest on edges; head darker than body, with lips pinkish-white.

A wide-ranging fish found on the coast of Queensland from north to south. George Coates, of Townsville, North Queensland, states that they are caught only on reefs and in rocky localities. A valuable food-fish in Borneo. Grows to 14 inches.

Lates

160. GIANT PERCH or PALMER *Lates calcarifer* (Bloch)   [Plate 32]

Holocentrus calcarifer Bloch, Nat. ausl. Fische, 4, 1790, p. 100.
Illustration by G. Coates.

Barramundi, Palmer (Mackay district); Nair-fish (Malabar); Cock-up (India).

D. 7-8/1/10-12; A. 3/7-9; L. 1. 52-61; L. tr. $5\frac{1}{2}$-7/1/10-14. Colour in adults greenish-grey above, silvery on sides, whitish below; head with tinges of purple;

spinous dorsal with membranes dark and spines silvery; pectorals and ventrals grey, other fins and caudal dark greenish-grey; eye brilliant pinkish-red.

Colour in young, olive-green, darkest along back, silvery below, each scale with an olive spot, forming longitudinal lines; a longitudinal wedge-shaped silver bar below eye, its narrowest end commencing above upper lip, below anterior nostril and passing backward below eye to pectoral base; fins pale olive-yellow; lateral line showing as a black-dotted line; eye like live coal.

When in the water and looked at from above the fish shows a whitish stripe on the dorsal surface from snout to first dorsal spine.

The Giant Perch inhabits the sea, tidal waters, and rivers of Queensland and North Australia. On the Queensland coast it is not found farther south than the Mary River. It is a valuable food-fish, its flesh being of excellent flavour. The name "Barramundi", by which it is generally though incorrectly known, belongs to *Scleropages leichardti*, a large-scaled freshwater fish found in the Dawson and all rivers to the north of that stream. The Queensland aborigines apparently used the name to designate any large-scaled river fish such as the Giant Perch, Barramundi, and the Queensland Lung-fish, *Epiceratodus forsteri*.

The Giant Perch grows to a length of almost 6 feet and a weight of 90 pounds and over. It ranges from the Persian Gulf to southern China, the Philippines, and North Australia.

From the point of view of edibility these fishes when taken in fresh water have not the flavour in their flesh that is to be found in those taken in salt water.

Ambassis: Perchlets

Small fishes of the Indo-Pacific regions living in the sea and round the river-mouths and also in fresh water, usually swimming in large shoals.

Their colours are generally brilliant silver or white. Although similar to the cardinal-fishes (Apogonidae) they are easily distinguished by their cycloid scales, continuous dorsals, though deeply notched between, the dorsal and anal fins with scaly basal sheaths, three anal spines, and by their silvery coloration. The freshwater species are popular aquarium pets, and their fondness for the larvae of the mosquito could be put to good account in the control of those pests. The marine species are a great nuisance to net fishermen on account of their spines fouling the nets and necessitating their removal by hand.

Most of the Queensland species are freshwater or estuarine forms and are not found on the reefs or coast. The three common saltwater species can be separated by means of the following key.

148

A.   Supraorbital with several (3-5) spines posteriorly.

    b. Tongue toothless; body slender, its depth 2.6 in the standard length; 9 dorsal and anal rays; total length not more than about 2½ inches.   *telkara*

    bb. Teeth on tongue; depth of body less than 2.5 in the standard length; 10-11 dorsal and anal rays; total length about 4½ inches.   *marianus*

AA. Supraorbital with one spine posteriorly.

    c. Tongue toothless; depth of body about 2 in the standard length (except in young); not more than 10 dorsal and anal rays; total length about 5 inches.   *macleayi*

161. YELLOW PERCHLET *Ambassis marianus* Günther   [Plate 33]

Ambassis marianus Günther, Voy. Challenger, Zool., 6, 1880, p. 32.
Priopis ramsayi McCulloch, Zool. Res. Endeavour, 1, 1911, p. 57, pl. 16, fig. 3.

D. 6-7/1/10-11; A. 3/10-11; L. l. 25-28; L. tr. 3/7. Colour whitish, the scales of the upper parts margined with olive-green dots; a thin dark line on median line of tail, and a silvery lateral band in specimens in spirits; upper portion of head, lips, and lower jaw densely spotted with olive-green: membrane between second and third dorsal spines blackish, and tips of soft dorsal and anal darker; caudal more or less spotted, its margin darker.

A marine and estuarine species which grows to about 4½ inches. It is found along the whole coastline of Queensland and also occurs in New South Wales.

OTHER SPECIES

Telkara Perchlet, *A. telkara*. A very common species in the waters of North Queensland. Grows to about 2½ inches.

Macleay's Perchlet, *A. macleayi*. Frequents the whole coastline of Queensland, where it is a common coastal and estuarine fish. Grows to 5 inches.

Family **Glaucosomidae**

Body robust to deeply ovate, compressed. Head large. Scales moderate or small, adherent, ctenoid, head well scaled almost everywhere. Lateral line nearly straight, extends to caudal. Mouth large, terminal, protractile, lower jaw prominent, cleft wide, oblique. Maxillary very broad, with narrow supplemental bone, scarcely slipping below preorbital. Teeth in narrow bands in jaws, some canine-like, also on vomer and usually on palatines and tongue. Preopercle with blunt teeth at angle or entire. Dorsal moderate or small, with 8 graduated spines and 12 to 14 soft rays, which are much higher than the spines and some anterior ones may be produced. Bases of dorsal and anal scaly. Anal with 3 short graduated spines and 12 soft rays, in form like soft dorsal. Caudal lunate, outer rays sometimes produced. Pectoral short, blunt. Ventrals a little smaller and inserted below pectorals.

A small family of large fishes found in the Pacific. They are represented in Australian waters by a single genus, *Glaucosoma*, containing two species, one of which, *G. scapulare*, is an important food-fish.

KEY TO SPECIES IN QUEENSLAND

A. Depth of body about 3 times in the total length; supra-clavicle developed into a prominent bony shield; eye 4 in the head.   *scapulare*

AA. Depth of body about 2.25 in the total length; no prominent bony shield; eye 2.3 in the head.   *magnificus*

162. PEARL PERCH *Glaucosoma scapulare* Macleay   [Plate 33]

Glaucosoma scapulare Macleay, Proc. Linn. Soc. N.S.Wales, 5, pt 3, Feb. 1881, p. 334.
Glaucosoma scapulare Marshall, Grant and Haysom, Know Your Fishes, 1959, p. 55.

Epaulette Fish, Nannygai (Queensland).
D. 8/11; A. 3/9; L. 1. 50; L. tr. 11/1/20. Colour silvery greenish-brown above, silvery below, with numerous small indistinct golden-brown spots; head light purplish-brown; supraclavicle deep iridescent blue-black; membranes of spinous dorsal and caudal pale fawn, the rays white; anal, ventrals, and pectorals hyaline; a small black axillary spot; irides silvery, clouded greyish.

One of the finest food-fishes in the Australian seas. Usually caught in the vicinity of sunken reefs and localities frequented by snapper. Found only in the waters of South Queensland and New South Wales. Grows to 24 inches.

The true Nannygai, *Trachichthodes affinis*, of New South Wales is quite distinct from this species.

Family **Serranidae: Sea Basses and Rock Cods**

The members of this large and varied family inhabit almost all tropical and temperate seas, frequenting rocky shores and reefs at moderate depths. A few species live in brackish or even fresh water. They are carnivorous fishes of small or large size, voracious feeders and of a vicious disposition, preying upon any living creatures they can overcome by strength or circumvent by cunning. To the family belong such well-known and large fishes as the Queensland Groper, *Epinephelus lanceolatus*; the Stone Bass or Wreck-fish of America, *Polyprion americanus*; and the Californian Jewfish, *Stereolepis gigas*—all fishes which attain to lengths of 7 feet and over, and weights of at least 800 pounds. The well-known Murray Cod, *Maccullochella macquariensis*, a large fish of the freshwater streams of the southern portions of the Australian continent, is also a member of this large and important family. Five sub-families are represented in Queensland waters.

The rock cods are commonly referred to by English-speaking peoples as groupers or gropers, a corruption of the name *garrupa*, which was applied by the Portuguese to a large species found on their coast. In Queensland and New South Wales the name is applied to the largest member of the family and also to an unrelated and quite distinct labroid of the genus *Achoerodus*.

Almost all the rock cods are excellent food-fishes and command a ready sale and good prices in the Queensland markets.

Sub-family DIPLOPRIONINAE

Body oblong-oval, very compressed, elevated anteriorly. Scales very small, ctenoid, adherent. Head large, mouth large, very oblique, protractile. Maxillary with a supplemental bone at posterior upper edge. Teeth in villiform bands on jaws, vomer, and palatines. No canines. Tongue toothless. Two dorsal fins, connected at the base, the first with 8 strong spines, the second with 14 to 15 rays. Anal with 2 spines and 12 to 13 rays.

This sub-family contains a single genus and species inhabiting the waters of the Indo-Australian Archipelago.

163. YELLOW EMPEROR *Diploprion bifasciatum* Cuvier and Valenciennes
[Colour-plate 11]

Diploprion bifasciatum Cuvier and Valenciennes, Hist. Nat. Poiss., 2, 1828, p. 137, pl. 21 (ex Kuhl and Van Hasselt, MS.).
Illustration by G. Coates.

D. 8/1/13; A. 2/12-13; L. 1. 110-115; L. tr. 17-18/1/43-46. Colour clear lemon-yellow, with 2 broad brownish or blackish cross-bands, the narrower anterior one commencing at the origin of the spinous dorsal and passing through the eye to end of upper jaw; the broader posterior band passes across the body from dorsal to anal.

A rare fish from India, China, Japan, and the East Indies which has been recorded from Queensland and the Northern Territory. Grows to 12 inches.

Sub-family EPINEPHELINAE

Body oblong or elongate, more or less compressed. Lateral line continuous. Scales small or minute, cycloid or ctenoid, adherent, often embedded in the skin. Head entirely scaled or only partly. Snout naked. Mouth large, protractile, and more or less oblique. Jaws subequal or the lower one the longer. Maxillary large, with well-developed supplemental bone, usually covered with small scales, exposed. Teeth in the jaws pluriseriate, the inner series enlarged, depressible. A few large canines usually present in front. Teeth on vomer and palatines. Tongue toothless. Nostrils subequal or the hind one the larger and slit-like. Preopercle serrate on its hind edge or entire, its lower limb with or without antrorse spines. Operculum with 1 to 3 strong spines. Dorsal fin with 6 to 12 spines and 11 to 21 rays. Anal with 3 spines and 8 to 12 rays. Caudal rounded, truncate or emarginate. Pectorals rounded.

Carnivorous fishes, many of large size, living in tropical and temperate seas, some species along the shore-line, others in the deeper offshore waters on shoals and coral reefs.

Determination of the species is in some cases extremely difficult to those who are not familiar with them in their native habitat, for they are subject to great variation in colour and also to considerable changes with growth. Six genera are found in Queensland waters.

KEY TO GENERA IN QUEENSLAND

Based on Weber and de Beaufort[15]

A. Canine teeth present.

    b. Palatines toothed.

        c. Lower border of preoperculum without antrorse or downward-directed spines. Head entirely scaly or nearly so. Anal and ventral spines strong.

        d. Dorsal spines 9; 13-14 rays.

           e. One or two curved canines on each side of mandible, besides those in front.   *Variola*

           ee. No curved canines on sides of mandibles.   *Cephalopholis*

        dd. Dorsal spines 11 (rarely 9 or 10); 14-18 rays.   *Epinephelus*

        cc. Lower border of preoperculum with strong antrorse spines. Head naked on front, snout and suborbital bones. Anal and ventral spines feeble and flexible.   *Plectropomus*

    bb. Palatines toothless. 11 dorsal spines; 14-15 rays. Lower border of preoperculum without antrorse spines. Head entirely scaly. Anal spines moderate.   *Anyperodon*

AA. No canine teeth. Palatines toothed. 10 dorsal spines; 10 rays. Lower border of preoperculum without antrorse spines, its angle with enlarged serrae. Anal spines moderate.   *Cromileptes*

---

[15] *Fish. Indo-Austr. Archip.*, 6, 1931, p. 11.

Variola

164. LUNAR-TAILED ROCK COD *Variola louti* (Forskål)

[Colour-plate 11]

Perca louti Forskål, Descr. Anim., 1775, p. 40.
Illustration by G. Coates.

D. 9/13-14; A. 3/8, 1; L. 1. 83-120; L. tr. 13-15/1/30-60. Colour: Head, body, and fins brownish-red, darkest on back and becoming rich reddish-orange below; scales with a dark-brownish centre; head, body, fins, and tail with prominent spots of crimson-lake, lilac, or purple, but mostly of the former colour; iris orange-red; posterior dorsal, ventral, and anal rays and a broad margin of each pectoral fin bright canary-yellow, as is also a crescentic area on the middle caudal rays.

A good game- and food-fish, frequently caught over the coral reefs of the Queensland coastline north of the Capricorns. Wide-ranging from the Red Sea to India and the Indo-Pacific. Grows to 30 inches.

Cephalopholis

Seven species of this genus are found in Queensland waters.

KEY TO SPECIES IN QUEENSLAND

A.   Anal with 8 soft rays.

     b. Brown, with or without darker vertical bands and bluish spots on head.   *pachycentron*

     bb. Red, dotted all over with blue spots.   *cyanostigma*

AA.   Anal with 9 soft rays.

     c. Caudal truncate. Colour blackish-brown with scarlet flush showing between scales.   *rogaa*

     cc. Caudal rounded.

      d. Dark saddle-like patches on back and tail.   *coatesi*

      dd. No dark saddle-like patches.

       e. Caudal with 2 oblique white bars, converging behind.   *urodelus*

       ee. No oblique bars on caudal.

        f. Red, with black-edged blue spots, much smaller than the interspaces, over head, body, and fins (except pectorals and ventrals).   *miniatus*

        ff. Red, with bluish mesh-work or closely set spots on head; those on body and fins larger than the interspaces.   *sonnerati*

165. BLUE-SPOTTED ROCK COD *Cephalopholis cyanostigma* (Cuvier and Valenciennes) [Colour-plate 12]

Serranus cyanostigma Cuvier and Valenciennes, Hist. Nat. Poiss., 2, 1828, p. 359.
Illustration by G. Coates.

D. 9/16; A. 3/8; L. 1. 85-97; L. tr. 21-23/1/25-31. Colour brownish-red, with about 6 indistinct mesh-like bands; head, body, fins, and tail with black-edged blue spots; dorsal, anal, and caudal dark brown edged with blue; the tips of spinous dorsal scarlet, also inside lips.

A small and pretty fish commonly found on the coral reefs of North Queensland, also in the Indo-Australian Archipelago. Grows to 14 inches.

166. FRECKLED ROCK COD *Cephalopholis coatesi* Whitley

[Colour-plate 12]

Cephalopholis coatesi Whitley, Mem. Qld Mus., 11, pt 2, 1937, p. 124, pl. 12.
Illustration by G. Coates.

D. 9/15; A. 3/9; L. 1. 85; L. tr. 10/1/40. Colour scarlet, with blue spots over head, body, dorsal, anal, and caudal fins; pectorals orange; 6 black saddle-like patches on dorsal surface, strongest posteriorly; ventrals and anal narrowly edged blue; eye with pupil black, surrounded by a narrow yellow ring.

A handsome species known only from the reefs of North Queensland. Grows to at least 30 inches and a weight of 15 pounds.

167. CORAL TROUT *Cephalopholis miniatus* (Forskål) [Colour-plate 12]

Perca miniata Forskål, Descr. Anim., 1775, p. 41.
Illustration by G. Coates.

Blue-spot Rock Cod, Garrupa (South Africa).
D. 9/15-16, 1; A. 3/9, 1; L. 1. 90-105; L. tr. 14-17/1/27-34. Colour scarlet above, orange-scarlet below; head, body, and fins (except pectorals) covered with small black-edged blue spots; dorsal and anal red, blackish posteriorly; caudal blackish or red, with blue spots; pectorals orange-yellow; soft dorsal, ventrals, anal, and caudal with dark-blue borders.

A very pretty fish, common on the reefs anywhere north of the Capricorns. Occurs also in the Indo-Pacific and across to India, Africa, and the Red Sea. Grows to 18 inches.

OTHER SPECIES

Spotted-faced Rock Cod, *C. pachycentron*. A small and common fish on the northern reefs of Queensland. Grows to only 8 inches.

Red-flushed Rock Cod, *C. rogaa*. A wide-ranging species which is also found, though somewhat rarely, in North Queensland. Grows to 22 inches.

154

Flag-tailed Rock Cod, *C. urodelus*. A small species, rare on the Queensland coast. Grows to only 10 inches. Recognized by the bars on its tail.

Tomato Rock Cod, *C. sonnerati*. A wide-ranging species taken on the northern reefs of Queensland. It reaches a length of at least 24 inches and like all the other members of the family is a good food-fish.

Epinephelus

This is the largest and most important genus of the sub-family Epinephelinae. The species, which are very numerous, are widely distributed and abound in all tropical seas. Most of them grow to a large size and all are valuable food-fishes. Fourteen species occur in Queensland waters.

KEY TO SPECIES IN QUEENSLAND

A. Caudal subtruncate, truncate or emarginate.

    b. Pale reddish-brown or greenish-brown, with large yellowish-green blotches over head, body, and fins.   *areolatus*

    bb. Lilac to purplish-blue, with or without numerous black dots; pectorals and sometimes other fins yellow.   *flavocaeruleus* var. *hoedtii*

AA. Caudal rounded.

    c. Pectorals longer than head without snout.   *megachir*

    cc. Pectorals shorter than head without snout.

    d. Last dorsal spine considerably shorter than the third.

    e. Brown, with distinct dark-brown spots over head, body, and fins.

    f. Head, body, and fins covered with large dark-brown spots, equal in size to pale interspaces.   *fario*

    ff. Black and brown spots of unequal size forming a mesh-work similar to *E. merra*.   *gilberti*

    fff. Brown, with darker brown spots, smaller and more numerous with age; dark blotches along dorsal base and caudal peduncle.   *corallicola*

    ee. Pale greenish or yellowish, with brown wavy markings or red or yellow spots, closely set to form wavy lines.

    g. Maxillary groove blackish; ventrals long, reaching anus. Pale green, with brown wavy markings enclosing green spots.   *summana*

    gg. No black in maxillary groove; ventrals short, not reaching anus. Creamy-brown or stone-grey with narrow golden stripes, oblique above, horizontal below lateral line.   *undulatostriatus* dd. Last dorsal spine not or but little shorter than third dorsal spine.

   h. Body usually with darker cross-bands or saddle-like blotches.

     i. Red; spinous dorsal with black spots terminally; dark ring round eye.   *fasciatus*

     ii. Olive-green, with scattered orange-red or brown spots; back with darker band-like blotches; with age uniform brown, spots indistinct.   *tauvina*

     iii. Young: Golden or olive-yellow, with 4 dark cross-bands. Adults: Uniform brown, fins yellowish.   *lanceolatus*

   hh. Body spotted; no cross-bands.

     j. Brownish or greenish, with numerous large hexagonal reddish-brown spots separated by honeycomb network of light lines.   *merra*

     jj. Purplish-brown, with more or less distinct whitish spots (large and few in young); maxillary groove black; body scales ctenoid.   *caeruleopunctatus*

     jjj. Light brown, with large irregular dark blotches and covered with small dark spots.   *fuscoguttatus*

168. YELLOW-SPOTTED ROCK COD *Epinephelus areolatus* (Forskål)
[Colour-plate 13]

Perca areolata Forskål, Descr. Anim., 1775, p. 42.
Illustration by G. Coates.

D. 11/15-17, 1 or 16; A. 3/8, 1; L. 1. 93-96 to caudal base and 12-15 more on latter; about 20 scales above lateral line. Colour reddish-brown or greenish-brown, with hexagonal spots or markings formed by bluish-white lines on head, body, and fins, the last-named having dark margins edged with white; sometimes the spots are bright golden-yellow.

A fairly common fish on the reefs of North Queensland. Grows to 16 inches.

169. MAORI ROCK COD *Epinephelus undulatostriatus* (Peters)   [Plate 33]

Serranus undulatostriatus Peters, Monatsb. Akad. Wiss. Berlin, 1866, p. 518.
Illustration by M. Hall.

Red-speckled Rock Cod (New South Wales); Maori (Moreton Bay).

D. 11/15; A. 3/7-8; L. 1. 96. Colour very light creamy-brown or stone-grey, with numerous narrow umber or golden-brown stripes, obliquely upwards above lateral line and more or less horizontal below; head profusely spotted with gold; fins tipped with gold and with numerous gold spots; pectorals yellow; dorsal, anal, and caudal edged bright yellow. In the young the colours are much deeper, the ground colour is lavender, and the stripes are fewer in number and wider, being rich rufous-brown, while the spots and stripes on the head are replaced by orange.

This species is only found on the reefs of South Queensland and New South Wales. It is one of the common rock cods on the snapper banks of Moreton Bay. Grows to 24 inches.

170. BLACK-TIPPED ROCK COD *Epinephelus fasciatus* (Forskål)
[Colour-plate 13]

Perca fasciata Forskål, Descr. Anim., 1775, p. 40.
Illustration by G. Coates.

Black-tipped Groper (Queensland); Rock Cod (South Africa).

D. 11/16, 1; A. 3/8, 1; scales about 80-98 on lateral line and about 9-12 above. Colour scarlet, with darker vertical bands; pectorals, ventrals, soft dorsal, and caudal scarlet, edged with orange-yellow; membrane between dorsal spines deep sepia in its upper part, rest of fin scarlet; a black circle round the eye and a black streak above the maxillary.

A very handsome and wide-ranging species, readily recognized by its distinct coloration. Very common. Grows to 15 inches.

171. ESTUARY ROCK COD *Epinephelus tauvina* (Forskål)
[Colour-plate 13]

Perca tauvina Forskål, Descr. Anim., 1775, p. 39.
Illustration by G. Coates.

Spotted River Cod, Estuary Cod (Brisbane); Groper, Cod, Greasy (Townsville); Brown-spotted Hind (New South Wales); Variegated Rock Cod, Garrupa, Rock Cod, Black Sea-bass (South Africa).

D. 11/15, 1, or 16; A. 3/8, 1; scales 84-108 in lateral line to caudal base and 11-15 on latter and about 15-19 above. Colour very variable; young usually dark olive-green, with rust-red spots and dark obscure band-like blotches on body; adults almost uniform dark brown, the spots indistinct.

One of the largest and most common species of rock cod in Queensland waters. Found on most reefs and in the mainland estuaries in brackish water. Grows to 7 feet and a weight of 500 pounds. Probably dangerous to man. Found also in the Indo-Australian Archipelago and the western Pacific.

172. GROPER *Epinephelus lanceolatus* (Bloch)   [Colour-plate 14]

Holocentrus lanceolatus Bloch, Nat. ausl. Fische, 4, 1790, p. 92.
Illustration by G. Coates.

Brindled Sea-bass (Natal); Garrupa (South Africa).

D. 11/14-15; A. 3/8, 1; scales 86-98 in lateral line to caudal base and 6-8 more on latter, and about 21-22 above. Colour: Young are a beautiful golden-yellow colour, with broad dark-brown or blackish cross-bands; adults are uniform brown or blackish, with fins and tail somewhat yellowish.

The largest fish in the Australian seas. It is a wide-ranging species and is known to attain a length of 10 feet, with a weight of some hundreds of pounds. The Groper is a dangerous fish and is feared by native divers far more than a shark. The pearling fleets of Torres Strait have at times mysteriously lost their divers when working over the reefs and it is held that their disappearance was due to gropers. These fish will follow a launch for hours, keeping in the stern-wash, and will take the baited hook on the trolling line.

Although found in the sea, gropers also love the mainland estuaries and several instances are known of their having been cut in halves by the propellers of steamers entering the rivers.

One large groper taken in Queensland was 7 feet 6 inches in length and weighed 606 pounds.

173. HONEYCOMB ROCK COD *Epinephelus merra* Bloch [Colour-plate 14]

Epinephelus merra Bloch, Nat. ausl. Fische, 7, 1793, p. 17, pl. 329.
Illustration by G. Coates.

Honeycomb Cod, Spotted Groper, Wire-netting Cod (Queensland); Matty McMahon (Gladstone).

D. 11-15/16, 1; A. 3/8, 1; L. 1. 92-102; L. tr. 10-17/1/27-35. Entire body covered with brown or purplish-brown spots, more or less hexagonal and separated by a network of pale yellowish or brownish lines. A very variable fish in both colour and pattern.

A common fish on the coral reefs of Queensland, where it is often found by turning over lumps of dead coral when the tide is out. Grows to 18 inches. Wide-ranging.

OTHER SPECIES

Purple Rock Cod, *E. flavocaeruleus* var. *hoedtii*. Apparently visits the shores of Queensland during the winter months only. Grows to 30 inches.

Long-finned Rock Cod, *E. megachir*. An Indo-Pacific species, apparently not common in Queensland. Grows to 14 inches.

Trout Rock Cod, *E. fario*. A wide-ranging fish found on the coral reefs of North Queensland. Grows to 18 inches.

Short-finned Rock Cod, *E. gilberti*. Found in Queensland, New South Wales, and the Northern Territory, also in the East Indies. Grows to 16 inches.

Coral Rock Cod, *E. corallicola*. Inhabits the reefs of North Queensland and the Indo-Pacific region. Grows to 18 inches.

Summana Rock Cod, *E. summana*. A small and very variable species, commonly found on North Queensland reefs and also in the East Indies. Grows to 13 inches.

158

Ocellated Rock Cod, *E. caeruleopunctatus*. A wide-ranging species not often met with on the Queensland coast. Grows to 22 inches.

Black Rock Cod, *E. fuscoguttatus*. A fairly common fish found along the whole coastline of Queensland, also in New South Wales and on Middleton Reef in the South Pacific. Grows to at least 36 inches.

Plectropomus

174. CORAL COD or LEOPARD-FISH *Plectropomus maculatus* (Bloch)
[Colour-plate 14]

Bodianus maculatus Bloch, Nat. ausl. Fische, 4, 1790, p. 48.
Illustration by G. Coates.

Coral Trout (Brisbane Fish Market and Townsville); Coral Cod, Leopard Cod (Townsville).

D. 7-8/11-12; A. 3/8; L. 1. 80-110; L. tr. 15-20/1/40-80. The colour of this fish varies considerably, being either salmon-pink, reddish, or light or dark brown, covered with numerous small round black-edged spots, or the spots may be less numerous and larger, some of them being elongate; one variety is mainly yellow, with very broad irregular bands, on the edge of which are the blue spots; other examples are almost black and with the blue spots almost absent.

The fish is very common over the coral reefs and will freely rise to the surface and take a bait trolled from a fast-moving launch. Grows to over 4 feet 2 inches in length and at least 50 pounds in weight. Wide-ranging.

Anyperodon

175. WHITE-LINED ROCK COD *Anyperodon leucogrammicus*
(Cuvier and Valenciennes)   [Colour-plate 15]

Serranus leucogrammicus Cuvier and Valenciennes, Hist. Nat. Poiss., 2, 1828, p. 347.
Illustration by G. Coates.

D. 11/14-15; A. 3/9, 1; L. 1. 75-85; L. tr. 12-15/1/55-65. Colour brownish or olive-greenish above, creamy-white below; 3 to 5 bluish or white longitudinal lines on body, three of which reach the caudal; body spotted all over with orange-rufous or reddish spots, more obscure above head and to a lesser degree on fins; all fins with the spines and rays greenish-brown, darker than the membranes which are hyaline; inner parts of mouth pinkish; with age the spots and lines become lost.

This fish is easily recognized by its pointed head and white longitudinal lines. It is a somwhat rare reef species, only occasionally taken in northern coastal waters. Grows to 20 inches. Wide-ranging.

Cromileptes

176. HUMP-BACKED ROCK COD *Cromileptes altivelis* (Cuvier and Valenciennes) [Colour-plate 15]

Serranus altivelis Cuvier and Valenciennes, Hist. Nat. Poiss., 2, 1828, p. 324.
Illustration by G. Coates.

Barramundi Cod (North Queensland).

D. 10/17, 1, or 18; A. 3/10, 1; L. 1. 74-100; L. tr. 21-24/1/34-37. Colour fawn, reddish-brown, or terra-cotta, covered all over with round blackish spots, largest on the back and in size smaller than the eye; larger and less numerous in the young.

A common fish found on northern reefs of Queensland and in the Indo-Pacific region. Only very occasionally taken in South Queensland. The name Barramundi Cod is bestowed because the head is somewhat similar in shape to that of the Giant Perch (erroneously called Barramundi). The Hump-backed Cod grows to 26 inches.

Sub-family CENTROGENYSINAE

Body oblong, compressed. Scales large, strongly ciliated. Head obtuse, convex, scaly. Mouth large, protractile. Maxillary exposed, with supplemental bone. Operculum with strong spine. Preoperculum denticulated, with 3 to 4 antrorse spines on lower limb. Minute teeth on jaws in villiform bands, on vomer in a ∧ shaped band and in a slender row on palatines; none on tongue. Spinous dorsal long, with 13 to 14 spines, soft portion with 9 to 11 rays, scaly at its base. Anal with 3 spines and 5 rays, also scaly at its base. Pectorals rounded, with 13 to 14 rays. Ventrals with a strong spine and situated behind pectoral base. Caudal slightly rounded.

A single genus consisting of one species inhabits the Indo-Australian Archipelago.

177. PRETTY-FINS *Centrogenys vaigiensis* (Quoy and Gaimard) [Plate 33]

Scorpaena vaigiensis Quoy and Gaimard, Voy. Uranie Physic., Zool., 1824, p. 324.
Myriodon waigiensis Bleeker, Atlas Ichth., Ned. Ind., 7, 1873-6, p. 68, pl. 297, fig. 1.

D. 13-14/9-10, 1 or 11, 1; A. 3/5-6; L. 1. 35-42; L. tr. 4-6/1/11-16. Colour light fawn over head and body, with large patches of darker brown and with varying spots of brown and grey; about 5 large blackish-brown spots, as big as the eye, along back adjacent to dorsal fin, the first at anterior spines, the last below middle of soft dorsal; eye, pupil black, surrounded with alternate brown and cream, like wheel-spokes; large brown spots on chin and opercles; spinous and soft dorsal creamy-fawn, with numerous spots of brown as large as the pupil, between which are much smaller spots and lines; pectorals banded alternately with pinkish-fawn and black, the colours much clearer on inside of fin; ventrals, anal, and caudal similar, though on the former more broken up with wavy lines between.

A small fish found along the coasts of Queensland, northern Australia, and New Guinea. It exhibits a striking resemblance to the scorpaenoid fishes. Grows to 6 inches.

Sub-family Hypoplectrodinae

Four genera of this sub-family are found in Queensland waters.

KEY TO GENERA IN QUEENSLAND

A. Lateral line ascending sharply and running high up along the back.

    b. 13 dorsal spines. Scales cycloid. Caudal rounded.   *Fraudella*
    bb. 11 dorsal spines. Scales ciliated. Caudal emarginate.   *Callanthias*

AA. Lateral line not running high up on back; evenly curved and continued along middle of side of caudal peduncle.

    c. Maxilla and mandible covered with rather large scales. Spinous and soft portions of dorsal fin nearly equal in height. Anal with 9-10 rays.   *Caesioperca*

    cc. Maxilla and mandible either naked or with imperfect scales. Spinous and soft portions of dorsal fin sub-equal in height. Anal with 7-8 rays.   *Ellerkeldia*

Fraudella

A genus of small fishes with a single species, and known only from the waters of Queensland. This species, the Golden Fraud, *F. carassiops* Whitley, is a reddish-orange-coloured little fish inhabiting the coral reefs of Queensland at various depths. It has been recorded only as far south as the Capricorns. It grows to 2¼ inches.

Callanthias

These fishes are found in South and south-eastern Australia, South Africa, the west coast of South America, and in the Mediterranean and neighbouring parts of the Atlantic. One species in Australia—namely, Allport's Perch, *C. allporti* Günther, a brilliantly coloured rosy-red or reddish-golden fish commonly taken in deep water in New South Wales by trawlers and found in South Queensland only as a straggler. Grows to 12 inches.

Caesioperca

This genus is represented in Queensland by the Bastard Long-fin, *C. lepidoptera*, (Bloch and Schneider), a red fish with a black spot on the body behind the tip of the pectoral fin. Grows to 12 inches. Common in New South Wales, but only occasionally straggles into South Queensland waters. Found also in South Australia.

Ellerkeldia

178. JAMESON'S ROCK COD *Ellerkeldia jamesoni* (Ogilby)   [Plate 33]

Hypoplectrodes jamesoni Ogilby, Proc. Roy. Soc. Qld, 21, 1908, p. 16.
Hypoplectrodes jamesoni McCulloch, Rec. Austr. Mus., 9, 1913, p. 359, pl. 13, fig. 1.

D. 10/20; A. 3/8; L. 1. 40; L. tr. 3/1/14. Colour dark olive-brown above, grey below; trunk and tail with about 9 narrow grey lines above lateral line, inconspicuous anteriorly; 7 to 8 irregular, transverse, slightly oblique reddish-brown bands below lateral line, becoming annular on tail; sides of head with 3 longitudinal series of brown spots; a black band behind chin and a pair of spots behind corners of mouth; outer half of soft dorsal and caudal pinkish-red; anal bright pinkish-red with 2 dark basal spots; pectorals strongly, ventrals faintly, tinged with red.

A small species from South Queensland and New South Wales. Grows to 4 inches.

Sub-family PSEUDOCHROMIDINAE

Body oblong, compressed, covered with ctenoid or ciliated medium-sized scales; those on head (including cheeks), may be cycloid or small, those on opercle large and irregular. Lateral line generally tubulate, interrupted. Mouth not or very little protractile, the cleft large, reaching beyond eye, or if less far, then very oblique. Teeth in jaws and on vomer and palatines, those in jaws minute or conical, pluriseriate, the anterior ones being caniniform. Preopercle entire or serrate, or with a flattened spine superiorly. Dorsal long, with 2 to 3 (by exception 7 or more) slender, weak or somewhat strong, pungent spines and numerous rays. Anal with 3 spines. Caudal rounded or obtuse.

Small marine fishes of the Indo-Pacific region, inhabiting coastal waters and coral reefs. They are related to the serranids but are readily distinguished by the reduced dorsal spines and the interrupted lateral line. Two genera are found in Queensland waters.

KEY TO GENERA IN QUEENSLAND

A. Dorsal fin with 2 slender and slightly pungent spines. Anal with 3 stronger spines. Both fins scaly at base. No palatine teeth.   *Dampieria*

AA. Dorsal fin with 3 spines, the first sometimes scarcely discernible. Base of dorsal and anal with a scaly sheath. Palatine teeth present.   *Pseudochromis*

Dampieria

Little-known small fishes found on the reefs of North Queensland and Western Australia. Two species have been recorded.

A. Dorsal rays 25, anal rays 14; anal fin originating below tenth dorsal ray. Each body-scale with a dark spot, forming longitudinal lines.   *lineata*

AA. Dorsal rays 35, anal rays 19; anal fin originating below the 17th dorsal ray. Colour uniform reddish-brown.   *longipinnis*

179. SHORT-FINNED CICHLOPS *Dampieria lineata* Castelnau   [Plate 34]

Dampieria lineata Castelnau, Res. Fish. Austr. (Vict. Offic. Rec. Philad. Exhib.), 1875, p. 30.
Cichlops lineatus Waite, Rec. Austr. Mus., 4, no. 5, 1902, p. 191, pl. 31.

D. 2/25; A. 3/14; L. 1. 60 + 21; L. tr. 4 + 17. Colour: "In spirits, the general hue is a rich brownish-yellow. A blue line encircles all but the anterior fourth of the eye, and 6 or more similar lines run obliquely forward and downward on the cheek; broken lines also exist on the opercle. Each scale of the body has a dark spot at the base with a blue centre; a series of lines, about 16 in number is thus formed, anteriorly they are very faint and thus appear to commence suddenly some distance behind the opercle; the scales of the lateral line are not spotted, it therefore seems more than usually distinct. The dorsal fin is ornamented with 8 to 9 wavy brown longitudinal lines equal in width to the interspaces; a black spot occurs between the second spine and first ray. The anal has lines similar to, but much fainter than those of the dorsal. On the caudal, lines pass obliquely from the upper and lower edges to the centre and if these edges were respectively joined to the dorsal and anal, the lines on these fins would be continuous with those of the caudal; the pectoral and ventral are without markings." (Waite.)

An uncommon fish from Western Australia and the reefs at Lady Musgrave Island, Bunker Group, Queensland. Grows to 10 inches.

OTHER SPECIES .

Long-finned Cichlops, *D. longipinnis*. A rare species, known only from the reefs off Bowen, North Queensland. Grows to 4 inches. In colour a uniform pale brown, the fins somewhat darker.

Pseudochromis

KEY TO SPECIES IN QUEENSLAND

Adapted from McCulloch[16]

A. Some anterior dorsal rays simple, the posterior branched.

Sub-genus *Pseudochromis*

    b. More than 30 dorsal rays; about 50 rows of scales between origin of lateral line and hypural joint; bases of dorsal and anal rays covered by scales. *P. (P.) novae-hollandiae*

    bb. Less than 30 dorsal rays; about 40 rows of scales between origin of lateral line and hypural joint; bases of posterior dorsal and anal rays covered with scales. *P. (P.) fuscus*

AA. All the dorsal and anal rays are branched. Sub-genus *Leptochromis*

    c. Less than 30 dorsal rays; bases of posterior dorsal and anal rays naked.

    d. Operculum armed with 4-5 flat spines on its posterior border; dorsal and anal spines pungent; 25-26 dorsal rays; about 40 rows of scales. *P. (L.) quinquedentatus*

    dd. Operculum unarmed.

    e. Dorsal and anal spines weak and flexible; 22 dorsal rays. *P. (L.) tapeinosoma*

180. NEW HOLLAND CICHLOPS *Pseudochromis (Pseudochromis) novae-hollandiae* Steindachner   [Plate 34]

Pseudochromis novae-hollandiae Steindachner, Sitzb. Akad. Wiss. Wien, 80, 1, 1879, p. 160.
Pseudochromis novae-hollandiae McCulloch, Mem. Qld Mus., 3, 1915, p. 48, pl. 16, fig. 1.

D. 3/37; A. 3/20; P. 18; L. 1. 42-43 + 12; L. tr. 20. A small species, variable in colour. Some may be dark brown, tinged with red, or head and foreparts of body deep pink, the rest sage-green. A dark-blue line extends round lower and hinder margins of eye, and two similar marks on cheeks. Dorsal green, margined with a yellow and blue line and a dark spot present between the spines, also longitudinal series of spots near base of fin. Anal similar. Caudal sage-green, with an oblique scarlet and blue marginal band on each lobe.

Known only from the reefs of North Queensland as far south as the Capricorns. Grows to $7\frac{1}{2}$ inches.

---

[16] *Biol. Res. Endeavour*, 5, pt 4, 1926, p. 186.

OTHER SPECIES

Brown Cichlops, *P. (P.) fuscus*. Grows to 4 inches and is found in Torres Strait and in the South Seas.

Five-spined Cichlops, *P. (L.) quinquedentatus*. A rare species known only from Bowen, North Queensland. Grows to 4 inches.

Banded Cichlops, *P. (L.) tapeinosoma*. Grows to 2 inches and is found on the reefs north of the Capricorns.

Family **Branchiostegidae**

Body elongate, head large. Scales small or moderate. Mouth large, with some strong canines and finer teeth in villiform bands. Palatines toothless. A single dorsal fin, the spines weak.

Fishes of moderate or large size found in temperate and tropical seas. They are closely related to the Serranidae, are carnivorous in habit, and with the exception of one or two species are found in shallow seas. The Tile-fish of North America belongs to this family, and was a well-known food-fish in the American markets until a vast destruction of them took place in 1882, when millions were found dead on the surface of the ocean over an area of some five to seven thousand square miles. The deaths were thought to be due to heavy gales and the displacement of much shore ice over the area, causing such a reduction of the water temperature as to kill off the fishes living in it, and causing the Tile-fish to become almost extinct. The destruction of this fish is one of the few cases known of the almost complete destruction of a species by natural causes.

A single species is known from Australian seas.

181. WARD'S HORSE-HEAD *Branchiostegus wardi* Whitley [Plate 34]

Branchiostegus wardi Whitley, Rec. Austr. Mus., 18, 1932, p. 335.
Illustration of an allied species, *B. ilocanus* Herre, Phil. Journ. Sci. 35, 1928, pl. 3.

D. 7/15 (16); A. 2/11 (12); P. 1/17; V. 1/5; L. 1. 76; L. tr. 8/1/23. General colour in formalin is light brownish above, shading to white below; crest of head, suprascapula, pectoral base, and axilla yellow; some faint orange or yellow blotches along lateral line; front of head faint lavender; pectorals light greyish, with a narrow black margin to the first two rays; dorsal greyish, with yellow along base and irregularly on membranes; a narrow, smoky, inframarginal stripe; anal and ventrals uniform smoky-grey; uppermost caudal rays grey, most of upper caudal lobe yellow, an oblique band of yellow across base of lower lobe and extends along parts of the rays, lowest part of caudal lobe dark greyish, with a whitish margin below. (After Whitley.)

A rare species from Port Stephens, New South Wales, trawled in 50 to 60 fathoms, and also taken off Noosa Heads, South Queensland. Grows to 17½ inches.

Family **Cepolidae: Band-fishes**

Carnivorous marine fishes of the temperate coastal waters of the Atlantic and Mediterranean Europe, and the tropical waters of India, China, Japan, the Indo-Australian Archipelago, Australia, and New Zealand. They are small fishes with attenuated and strongly compressed eel-like bodies, covered with minute scales and usually red or pinkish in colour. They are of little use as food, their flesh being dry and the bones stiff and numerous.

The family is a small one of only two genera, one of which, *Cepola*, is represented in Australia by one species.

182. BAND-FISH *Cepola australis* Ogilby   [Plate 34]

Cepola australis Ogilby, Proc. Linn. Soc. N.S.Wales, 24, 1899, pp. 184-5.
Cepola australis McCulloch, Biol. Res. Endeavour, 2, pt 3, 1914, p. 109, pl. 34, fig. 1.

D. 57-60; A. 48-55. Colour: Body and fins bright red or pink, passing into pale pink below; a row of orange-yellow spots along middle of sides from behind opercle almost to caudal base, those anteriorly being as large as pupil of eye but becoming progressively shorter toward tail; top of head brownish-pink, the cheek with a pink patch; eye, black pupil, surrounded scarlet; dorsal fin hyaline-pink, clear whitish basally; a dark intermaxillary spot usually present, much larger and more conspicuous in some examples than in others.

A southern species recorded from South Queensland with a specimen from Moreton Bay. Grows to 15 inches.

Family **Theraponidae: Grunters or Perch**

Body oblong or ovate, more or less compressed. Scales small or moderate, ciliated. Mouth terminal, protractile, the gape moderate or small, generally oblique. Teeth villiform in both jaws, the outer series enlarged or conical or flattened and in separate fixed rows or more or less trilobate and pluriseriate. Teeth on vomer and palatines are deciduous or wanting. Branchiostegals 6. Operculum with 2 spines. Preoperculum more or less strongly serrated. Dorsal fin more or less notched, with 12 or sometimes 13 spines (rarely 11 or 14). Anal with 3 spines and 7 to 12 rays. Caudal rounded, truncate or emarginate.

Fishes of small or moderate size which inhabit the waters of the Indian and Western Pacific oceans and the fresh waters of Australia and New Guinea. Some of them grow to a weight of 3 to 5 pounds and are valued as food-fishes, but the marine species, though edible, are little valued for food. Three genera constitute the family.

166

A. Teeth entire or simple.

   b. Teeth in villiform band in jaws, conic, undivided.   *Therapon*

   bb. Teeth flattened, 3 series in upper jaw, 2 more or
   less regular series below, brown-tipped.   *Pelates*

AA. Teeth flattened, tricuspid or trilobate.   *Helotes*

Therapon

There are five marine species of this genus in Queensland waters.

KEY TO SPECIES IN QUEENSLAND

A. Lower opercular spine greatly developed and produced
    beyond opercular lobe. A large dark blotch on spinous
    dorsal.

   b. Scales larger, 7½-8 supralateral scales.   *theraps*
   bb. Scales smaller, 13-15 supralateral scales.

      c. Preoperculum denticulated with strong and enlarged
         spines on the angle; 2-4 longitudinal straight bands.   *puta*

      cc. Preoperculum serrate, not or moderately enlarged
          on the angle; 3 dark curved longitudinal bands.   *jarbua*

AA. Lower opercular spine not greatly developed, not
    produced beyond opercular lobe. No large dark blotch
    on spinous dorsal.

   d. Suprascapular bone exposed, not hidden by scales;
      normally 12 dorsal spines. Silvery; young with
      stripes.   *argenteus*

   dd. Suprascapular bone not exposed, hidden by scales;
       normally 13 dorsal spines. Body spotted.   *caudavittatus*

183. CRESCENT PERCH *Therapon jarbua* (Forskål)   [Colour-plate 16]

Sciaena jarbua Forskål, Descr. Anim., 1775, p. 50.
Illustration by G. Coates.

Arrow Bass (Japan); Tiger (Natal).

D. 11/1/10; A. 3/8, 1; L. 1. 76-90; L. tr. 15-16/1/23-25. Colour brownish-
grey above, silvery below; 3 dark longitudinal downward-curved bands along
back and sides; spinous dorsal with a large black blotch; soft dorsal with 2
to 3 dusky spots on margin; caudal with an oblique blackish bar on each lobe
and the upper lobe tipped black.

This is readily distinguished from allied species by the curved bands. Wide-
ranging. Grows to 11 inches.

OTHER SPECIES

Grunter, *T. theraps*. A wide-ranging fish found in the sea, brackish waters, and rivers of North Queensland. Grows to 8 inches.

Three-lined Grunter, *T. puta*. Common on the northern coastline of Queensland in similar localities to the previous species. Grows to about 8 inches.

Silvery Grunter, *T. argenteus*. An Indo-Australian and South Seas species occasionally taken in North Queensland. It reaches a length of 12 inches.

Bar-tailed Grunter, *T. caudavittatus*. A handsome fish inhabiting the sea and rivers of North Queensland, North and West Australia, Torres Strait, and New Guinea. Grows to 8 inches.

Pelates

A genus with few species, inhabiting the coastal waters and rivers of the Indo-Australian Archipelago to China, Japan, and Australia. One species in Queensland.

184. TRUMPETER PERCH *Pelates quadrilineatus* (Bloch) [Colour-plate 16]

Holocentrus quadrilineatus Bloch, Nat. ausl. Fische, 4, 1790, p. 82 (*fide* Sherborn).
Illustration by G. Coates.

Croaker (South Africa).

D. 12/10, 1; A. 3/9-10, 1; L. 1. 70-73; L. tr. 12-14/1/23. Colour drab brown or dusky greenish above, whitish below, with a silvery hue; sides with deep-brown longitudinal bands; a large round dark mark above the shoulder and a large black blotch between the third and sixth or eighth dorsal spine is usually present; very young examples have 8 to 9 broad vertical blackish bands in addition to the usual horizontal ones.

A common fish on the coasts of Queensland, New South Wales, and the Northern Territory. Wide-ranging. Common on the sand-flats of Moreton Bay, South Queensland. Grows to 8 inches.

Helotes

This small genus, with few species, mainly Indo-Australian, is represented in Queensland by one species.

185. SIX-LINED PERCH *Helotes sexlineatus* (Quoy and Gaimard) [Plate 34]

Terapon sexlineatus Quoy and Gaimard, Voy. Uranie Physic., Zool., 1825, p. 340.
Helotes sexlineatus Bleeker, Atlas Ichth., 7, 1876, p. 118, pl. 342, fig. 5.

Trumpeter (South-west Australia).

D. 11-12/10, 1, or 11, 1; A. 3/10, 1, or 11, 1; L. 1. 90-98; L. tr. 17/1/19-20, Colour greyish or bluish above, silvery below; 4 to 6 (sometimes 8 to 9) dark longitudinal bands on back and sides, the first two on each side of back, run together on top of head and form a vermiculated pattern; upper half of spinous dorsal and front top of soft dorsal blackish; caudal with blackish border; in the young there are usually 3 dark blotches on the back, the largest on the shoulder.

A fairly common Indo-Australian fish found in North Queensland waters. Grows to 10½ inches.

Family **Sillaginidae: Whitings**

Body elongate, somewhat cylindrical, covered with rather small or moderate-sized ctenoid scales. Head conical, pointed, forehead flattened. Preoperculum slightly denticulate on upper limb. Operculum small, with a small spine. Mouth small, terminal, set low, lower jaw included, the cleft small. Broad villiform bands of teeth in jaws, and on vomer; none on palatines. Two dorsals, the first with 9 to 12 spines, the second approximate, long, with a weak spine and 16 to 26 divided rays. Anal with 2 weak spines and 15 to 27 divided rays. Caudal truncate or emarginate.

A small group of shore fishes of small or moderate size, inhabiting the Indo-Pacific regions from the east coast of Africa to China, Japan, and Australia. They are in no way related to the European whiting, a fish which is a member of the family Gadidae or true cod-fishes. From an edible viewpoint Australian whitings rank high, their flesh being white, of very good flavour and easily digested.

Of the few genera in the family, two are found in Australia. The genera *Sillaginodes* and *Sillago* inhabit the waters of the southern portion of Australia but only the latter genus extends its range into Queensland. Five species are found in Queensland waters.

KEY TO SPECIES IN QUEENSLAND

A.   A conspicuous blackish mark at base of pectoral fin.

    b. Body with dark blotches.   *maculata*

    bb. No dark blotches on body; colour uniform.   *ciliata*

AA. No blackish mark on base of pectoral fin, though a faint curved patch of fine blackish dots may be present.

    c. About 5-6 rows of scales between lateral line and anterior dorsal spines.

      d. Caudal truncate or slightly emarginate. Body uniform greenish-olive, with an indistinct silvery lateral stripe. No mark at pectoral base.   *sihama*

      dd. Caudal forked. Reddish brown above, white below, separated by a silvery lateral stripe against which

above is a reddish-brown one; a series of small
orange-red oblique stripes on back and upper
sides; a faint crescentic patch of blackish dots at
base of pectoral.   *bassensis*

  cc. Only 4 rows of scales between lateral line and
      anterior dorsal spines.

    e. Caudal emarginate. Uniform creamy-yellow above,
      lighter below; a silvery lateral stripe present; no
      spot at base of pectoral fin.   *robusta*

186. TRUMPETER WHITING *Sillago maculata* Quoy and Gaimard
[Plate 34]

Sillago maculata Quoy and Gaimard, Voy. Uranie Physic., Zool., 1824, p. 261, pl. 3, fig. 2.
Sillago maculata Bleeker, Atlas Ichth., 9, 1877, pl. 389, fig. 5.

Winter Whiting (Queensland); Diver Whiting (South Queensland); Trumpeter
Whiting (Western Australia); Smelt (South Africa).

D. 11-12/20-21; A. 21; L. 1. 70-74; L. tr. 5-7/10-12. Colour sandy-brown
above, sides silvery, white below; a median silvery band on sides; back and
sides with irregular dusky blotches, sometimes very indistinct; cheeks and
opercles golden-green; spinous dorsal mottled greenish, soft dorsal pale olive,
with rows of brownish-green spots; pectorals straw-yellow, with a blue-black
basal spot; ventrals orange-yellow; anal yellowish; caudal greyish green.

Though somewhat darker than *S. ciliata*, this species is more transparent-
looking when fresh. It frequents the inlets and salt-water lakes, and is seldom
found far off the coast. It is fond of somewhat muddy grounds, and moves
over the shallow flats in shoals, feeding on worms and crustaceans. When
encircled by the fishermen's nets both young and adult Trumpeter Whiting have
the habit of burying themselves in the sand. Ogilby noted:[17] ". . . the young
fish, measuring from one to two inches, may be found abundantly on shallow,
sheltered, sandy flats and lagunes—such as Manly Lagune, where great facilities
for their observation are available—during the early summer months; each
of these young fish is in possession of a hole in the sand, but whether self-
excavated, or having been deserted by, or taken from its rightful owner, we are
not in a position to state; at the mouth of the hole, which is only just large
enough to admit of the passage of its body, the little creature lies, and on the
approach of danger, or even the passage of a dark cloud over the sun, immediately disappears, the anterior half of the head, however, as quickly re-
appearing, thus showing that close beneath the surface a chamber must exist,
sufficiently large to permit of their turning round with ease."

A valuable food-fish. Not as frequently caught with hook and line as the
sand whiting, but mostly taken with the hauling net. Grows to 12 inches.
Ranges from the south-east coast of Australia to the Malay Archipelago.

---

[17] *Edib. Fish. Crust. N.S.Wales*, 1893, p. 101.

187. SAND WHITING *Sillago ciliata* Cuvier and Valenciennes [Plate 34]

Sillago ciliata Cuvier and Valenciennes, Hist. Nat. Poiss., 3, 1829, p. 415.
Sillago ciliata Marshall, Grant and Haysom, Know Your Fishes, 1959, p. 121.

Summer Whiting, Blue-nose Whiting, (Queensland); Sydney Whiting (New South Wales); Plain Whiting (Victoria); Silver Whiting (Western Australia).

D. 11/18; A. 17-18; L. 1. 63-65; L. tr. 6/10-11. Colour pale brown or olive-brown, lighter on sides, whitish below; cheeks and opercles with golden reflections; spinous dorsal yellowish-green with obscure brown spots; soft dorsal lighter, with rows of brown spots; ventrals and anal bright golden; pectorals with a dark blotch at base; caudal yellowish-green, tinged brownish.

One of the most important food-fishes in Queensland, great numbers being caught annually by line and net fishermen, especially during the summer months. These fishes move in shoals over the shallow bays and off the ocean beaches, where the very large ones are freely caught in calm weather. The average-sized fish is 10 to 12 inches, but they are known to grow to 18 inches and a weight of 2 pounds and over. The Sand Whiting is found along the coastline of eastern Australia, being much more commonly met with in South Queensland and New South Wales.

This species and *S. maculata* are the two most common Queensland species, being taken all the year round in commercial quantities.

OTHER SPECIES

Northern Whiting, *S. sihama*. Takes the place in North Queensland of southern Queensland's *S. ciliata*. Frequents the sea, estuaries, and brackish river waters, growing to a length of 12 inches. Wide-ranging outside Australia.

School Whiting, *S. bassensis*. A small but fine little food-fish, plentiful in the deeper waters of New South Wales and Tasmania. It grows to 10 inches and is recognized by its distinctive colour pattern and forked tail. In Queensland it is known only as a straggler taken in the prawn-trawls in outside waters off the South Queensland border.

Stout Whiting, *S. robusta*. Frequents the deeper offshore waters along the coastlines of South Queensland and New South Wales. Most specimens have been taken by trawlers using the otter-trawl. Grows to at least 9 inches.

Family **Coryphaenidae: "Dolphins"**

Body elongate, compressed, after the juvenile stage with a bony crest on frontal part of head, increasing in height with age. Scales small, cycloid. Mouth oblique, the cleft wide, chin slightly prominent. Opercles entire. Recurved teeth in bands on jaws, vomer, and palatines, those in the outer series on the jaws wide-set. Tongue with 2 patches of villiform teeth. A single long dorsal fin from nape almost to caudal base; anal similar but only about half as long.

No true spines. Pectorals falciform, their bases oblique. Ventrals long, slender, close together, and received into an abdominal groove below base of pectorals. Caudal deeply forked, the lobes very long.

Fast-swimming pelagic fishes found in all temperate and tropical seas. The use of the name Dolphin is unfortunate, for it rightly belongs to the marine mammals of the same name (family Delphinidae) Probably only a single genus and species, namely *Coryphaena hippurus*.

188. "DOLPHIN" *Coryphaena hippurus* Linnaeus   [Colour-plate 16]

Coryphaena hippurus Linnaeus, Syst. Nat., 10th ed., 1758, p. 261.
Illustration by G. Coates.

D. 55-67; A. 25-30. Colour brilliant blue or green above, shading into silvery-white or bright yellow with purple and golden reflections everywhere; head olive-green, chin and throat yellow; eye emerald-green, the pupil black; a series of bright-blue or greenish spots on head and back or lower sides of body; dorsal dark purplish-blue; caudal greenish-olive.

A brilliantly coloured fish whose colours fade rapidly after death. It lives in the open sea and is fast-swimming and predatory, pursuing and devouring the flying-fishes especially. With age it undergoes great changes in both colour and form, the elevation of the head and anterior part of the body becoming higher with increasing age.

Grows to at least 6 feet and a weight of 63 pounds. Wide-ranging.

Family **Rachycentridae**

Form elongate, subcylindrical. Head depressed, broad. Scales small. Lateral line wavy anteriorly. No caudal keel. Mouth terminal, almost horizontal, wide, the maxillary reaching front border of eye; intermaxillaries not protractile. Villiform teeth in jaws and on vomer, palatines, and tongue. Eyes small, encircled with narrow adipose eyelid. Preoperculum entire. Spinous dorsal fin with 7 to 9 (usually 8) short free spines, the soft dorsal with many rays and somewhat similar to anal. Ventrals inserted slightly in advance of base of pointed pectorals. Caudal with central rays prolonged in the juveniles, obtuse or slightly emarginate in half-grown examples, and lunate in the adults.

A single genus and species, pelagic in habit and found in the temperate and tropical seas of the Atlantic and Pacific oceans.

189. SERGEANT-FISH *Rachycentron canadus* (Linnaeus)   [Plate 35]

Gasterosteus canadus Linnaeus, Syst. Nat., 12th ed., 1766, p. 491.
Illustrations by G. Coates.

Black Kingfish, Crab-eater (Queensland and New South Wales); Bonito, Cobia (Americas).

D. 7-9 + 3-4/26-33; A. 2-3/22-28. Colour: In large adults the back and sides are deep brown, this colour being sharply defined by a narrow silvery band, the junction of the two forming a straight line from tip of lower jaw to middle of caudal peduncle; below the silver band is another brown band, which sharply defines an oblong patch of yellowish colour on the abdomen.

In the young examples there is a second light band, more dorsally, causing the dark band below it to form a median stripe; caudal dark brown with outer edges white.

In this fish the tail undergoes a great change with growth, the central rays being much prolonged in the juveniles, later becoming obtuse, then slightly emarginate, until its final lunate shape is reached.

A wide-ranging fish found in the warm waters of the Atlantic and Pacific oceans but not in the eastern Pacific. In Australia it occurs on the coasts of Queensland and New South Wales, the smaller ones being caught in the bays and estuaries whilst the larger ones are captured in outside waters by the big-game fishermen.

Grows to a weight of at least 150 pounds and a length of 6 feet or over. Its flesh is considered of good edible quality. A good sporting fish.

Family **Pomatomidae**

Body oblong, compressed, sturdy build, the head large and with a strong occipital ridge. Scales cycloid, of moderate size. Mouth wide, oblique, the intermaxillaries protractile. Lower jaw prominent. Maxillary with a large supplemental bone, exposed. Jaws with strong compressed teeth in a single series, unequal and widely set. An inner series of small depressible teeth in upper jaw. A triangular patch of villiform teeth on vomer and bands of similar teeth on palatines and tongue. Preoperculum finely serrated on its lower edge. Spinous dorsal with seven or eight weak connected spines, depressible into a groove. Second dorsal and anal of about equal length, long and densely scaled. No finlets. One or two small free spines before anal, sometimes hidden in the skin. Pectorals and ventrals short. Caudal forked.

A single genus and species, *Pomatomus saltatrix*, widely distributed in most tropical and subtropical seas.

190. TAILOR *Pomatomus saltatrix* (Linnaeus) [Plate 35]

Perca saltatrix Linnaeus, Syst. Nat., 10th ed., 1758, p. 293.
Illustration by M. Hall.

Pombah (Queensland aborigines); Skipjack (South Australia and the Americas); Elf, Elft, Shad (South Africa); Blue-fish, Snap Mackerel, Skipjack, Fat-back (Americas); Greenfish (North America).

D. 7-8 + 1/23-28; A. 2/23-27. Colour sea-green above, silvery on sides, white below; head darker green than body; spinous and soft dorsal and anal fins pale green, tinged yellowish; ventrals hyaline; caudal dull greenish with tinges of yellow; pectorals bluish at base, rest of fin hyaline; eye surrounded yellow.

A carnivorous and ferocious fish, powerful and fast-swimming. The young hunt their prey in shoals, the adults in small mobs, pursuing schools of mullet and other fishes as large as themselves, destroying great numbers far in excess of their needs and killing for the lust of destruction.

As a food-fish the Tailor is one of the most delicious of fishes. It must, however, be eaten when quite fresh, because the flesh deteriorates rapidly and becomes soft, making it difficult to market the fish in good condition. It is one of the best fishes when smoked, and treated in this manner commands a ready sale.

This fish is widely distributed over most tropical and subtropical seas. It grows to a length of 4 feet and a weight of 25 pounds, though such examples are rare, the average size being 18 inches. In North Queensland it is rarely met with, but in the south of the State huge quantities are caught by nets and hand-lines. It ranges also into the waters of New South Wales, Victoria, and South Australia. It is less commonly met with in Western Australia and Tasmania.

When these fishes are schooling at the surface great sport may be had, by trolling a line and spinner or feather lure behind a moving launch. The fish bite with great rapidity, and numbers can be caught in a short space of time.

Family **Monodactylidae**

Form deep and strongly compressed, silvery, with fine scales which extend over the fins also. Mouth small, teeth feeble. Fin-spines reduced. Ventrals rudimentary or reduced in size.

Marine fishes of the coastal waters of the Indo-Pacific, with one Atlantic representative and one Australian. They enter brackish waters and even ascend rivers beyond the tideway and into the fresh water.

191. DIAMOND-FISH *Monodactylus argenteus* (Linnaeus) [Colour-plate 17]

Chaetodon argenteus Linnaeus, Syst. Nat., 10th ed., 1758, p. 272; 12th ed., 1766, p. 461.
Illustration by G. Coates.

Butter Bream, Butter-fish (Brisbane); Silver Batfish (New South Wales); Leather-jacket (Lord Howe Island); Moony, Moon-fish, Kite-fish, Sea Kite (South Africa).

D. 7-8/28-30; A. 3/28-30. Colour silvery-green, with purplish reflections; back yellowish-green or brownish, changing to leaden colour at death; dorsal and anal lobes blackish; caudal yellow, with a narrow black edge; in the young there is a narrow brownish band crossing the eye, another from the nape through the base of the pectoral to the belly.

A very common species in both bay and river. They swim in small shoals and swarm round wharf-piles or vessels at anchor, and readily take a baited line, though they are difficult to hook, being adept at removing the bait. Although these fish are of small size, their flesh has a very good flavour.

In Australian waters the Diamond-fish ranges from northern Australia down the coast of Queensland to New South Wales. Grows to 9 inches.

Family **Pempheridae**

Form oblong-ovoid to elliptical, strongly compressed. Scales small or moderate, extending on head and usually on to vertical fins. Lateral line continued on to caudal fin. Head obtuse, snout short and blunt. Mouth oblique, slightly protractile. Small teeth in jaws, and present on vomer and palatines. Eye large, anterior, without eyelid or moderate with an adipose eyelid. Dorsal fin single, usually short; anal fin very long.

Marine fishes of small or moderate size living in coastal waters of tropical and temperate seas, usually in fairly deep water. The family is represented in Queensland by four genera, separated by the following key. One species, *Leptobrama mülleri*, will be described in detail.

KEY TO GENERA IN QUEENSLAND

Adapted from Fowler[18]

A. Eye large, without adipose eyelid. Maxillary greatly expanded behind. Dorsal fin pre-median.

　b. Body elongate or only slightly ovate. Teeth mostly uniserial in jaws. Preopercle entire. Anal naked. Fin-rays less than 30.　　　　　　　　　　　　　*Parapriacanthus*

　bb. Body ovate, deeper. Teeth in jaws pluriserial. Preopercle with 1-3 strong spines. Anal scaly. Soft rays over 30.

　　c. Scales of body cycloid.　　　　　　　　　　　　*Liopempheris*

　　cc. Scales of body ctenoid.　　　　　　　　　　　　*Pempheris*

AA. Eye small, with well-developed adipose lid. Maxillary spatulate, only slightly expanded behind. Dorsal fin post-median.　　　　　　　　　　　　　　　　　*Leptobrama*

192. STEELBACK *Leptobrama mülleri* Steindachner　　　[Colour-plate 17]

Leptobrama mülleri Steindachner, Sitzb. Akad. Wiss. Wien, 78, 1878, p. 388.
Illustration by G. Coates.

Flat Salmon (Mackay and Brisbane); Moreton Bay Tailor (Yeppoon); Silver Salmon (Mackay); Beach Salmon, Salmon Trout (Townsville).

D. 4/16-18; A. 3/26-30; L. l. 75-77; L. tr. 10-12/12-13. Colour silvery,

---

[18] U.S. Nat. Mus. Bull. 100, 11, 1931, p. 46.

with the back steel-blue, the line of demarcation well defined; fins dusky; tip of dorsal lobe usually with a black blotch; caudal green; pectorals and lobe of anal tinged yellow.

A very common fish in Queensland waters, particularly in the northern parts. It is known also from Western Australia and New Guinea. It grows to a length of 17 inches and a weight of at least 2 pounds and is a good food-fish.

Family **Kyphosidae: Blackfishes and Drummers**

The members of this family are thickly built and heavy-looking fishes, found frequenting coral reefs and rocky shores in most tropical and subtropical seas. The species are chiefly herbivorous, feeding upon algae and other marine growths. They have no molars, the front of the jaws having incisors which are often serrated, loosely attached and fixed or movable. Some species are valued as food-fishes whilst others are tough and tasteless.

The two Australian genera, usually placed in two families by most authors, are sufficiently related to be included in one family.

KEY TO AUSTRALIAN GENERA

A.   Soft part of dorsal and anal naked; dorsal base partly covered with scales. Teeth all movable, incisors tricuspid or truncate.   *Girella*

AA.   Soft part of dorsal and anal closely scaled. Teeth not freely movable; fine teeth on vomer, palatines, and tongue.   *Kyphosus*

Girella

Herbivorous fishes found only in the Pacific Ocean. Four species in Australia, one of which is found in Queensland.

193. BLACKFISH *Girella tricuspidata* (Quoy and Gaimard)   [Plate 35]

Boops tricuspidata Quoy and Gaimard, Voy. Uranie Physic., Zool., 1824, p. 296.
Girella tricuspidata McCulloch, Rec. Austr. Mus., 13, 1920, p. 60, pl. 14, fig. 1.

Nigger (South Queensland and New South Wales); Black Bream, Blackfish (Queensland and New South Wales); Darkie (New South Wales); Cocky Salmon (Tasmania); Luderick (New South Wales and Victoria); Black Perch (Victoria).

D. 15/12; A. 3/12; P. 17; V. 1/5; C. 17; L. l. 46. Colour grey or brownish-grey above, lighter below, passing into white below; five to eight dark transverse narrow bands on back and sides in life, which fade out and become lost after death; fins dusky; a pale canary-yellow tinge on cheeks, lips, and throat.

Blackfish are lovers of rocky headlands and weed-covered reefs, congregating in shoals in such places. They readily take a bait of green weed and are caught in great numbers by rod fishermen. A favourite bait is an ascidian known as cunjevoi, which is found on the submerged rocks.

The flesh of the Blackfish is of fair edible quality but like that of all weed-eating fishes it must be gutted soon after capture because it deteriorates rapidly. The fish is commonly sold in the Brisbane Market under the name of Black Bream. It is an important food-fish in New South Wales and is commonly seen at markets in that State at all seasons of the year.

Blackfish are found in the rivers, estuaries, and outside coastal waters of Queensland, New South Wales, South Australia, and Western Australia, also in Tasmania and New Zealand. In Queensland they are mainly confined to the more southern waters as far north as Maryborough, though stragglers have been taken north of that port. The species grows to 28 inches, but the average length is about 13 inches.

In the males the teeth of the outer series in both jaws are distinctly trilobate, whereas in the females these teeth are almost all truncate. In South Queensland these fish are most plentiful during the months of June, July, and August, when they frequent the rivers and estuaries.

Kyphosus: Drummers

Body elongate, ovate, moderately compressed. Head short, snout blunt, mouth small. Teeth obtusely lanceolate, in a single row in each jaw, not freely movable. Fine teeth on vomer, palatines, and tongue. Scales small, ctenoid, entirely covering vertical fins and extending up on paired fins. Dorsal fin low, continuous, depressible into groove of scales.

Marine fishes of median size, mainly herbivorous in diet, feeding upon algae or sometimes molluscs and crustaceans, and frequenting rocky situations in tropical and subtropical seas. Some of the species are valued as food-fishes, whilst others are rejected as tough and tasteless. In other parts of the world these fishes are called rudder-fishes from their habit of following ships. Four species are found in Queensland waters.

KEY TO SPECIES IN QUEENSLAND

A. Base of soft dorsal much shorter than that of spinous dorsal.

    b. Anterior dorsal rays much longer than longest dorsal spine; scales L. 1. 52.   *cinerascens*

    bb. Anterior dorsal rays much shorter than longest dorsal spine; scales L. 1. about 55.   *sydneyanus*

AA. Base of soft dorsal nearly equal to or longer than that of spinous dorsal.

    c. Dorsal rays 14-15; scales L. 1. 65-70.   *vaigiensis*

    cc. Dorsal rays 13; scales L. 1. 59.   *gibsoni*

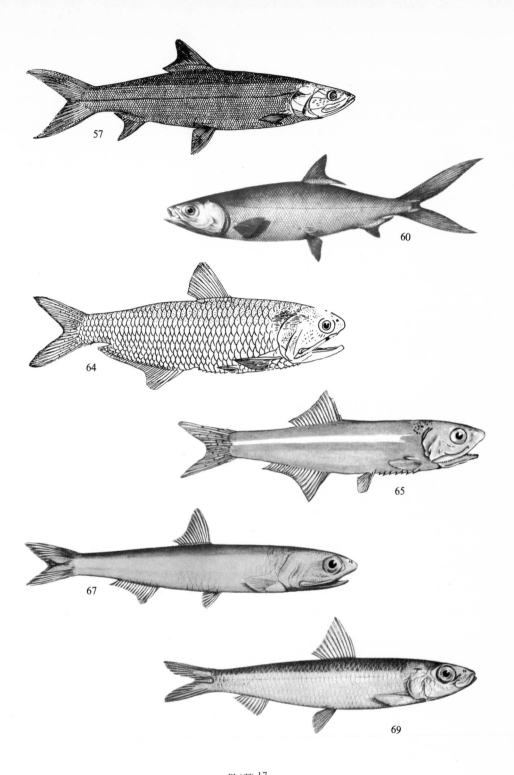

PLATE 17
57. Giant Herring, *Elops saurus*, 13 in.   60. Salmon Herring, *Chanos chanos*, 10 in.   64. Estuary Anchovy, *Thrissina aestuaria*, 5 in.   65. Gulf Anchovy, *Amentum carpentariae*, 2 in.   67. Australian Anchovy, *Engraulis australis*, $4\frac{1}{4}$ in.   69. Blue Sprat, *Stolephorus delicatulus*, $2\frac{1}{2}$ in.

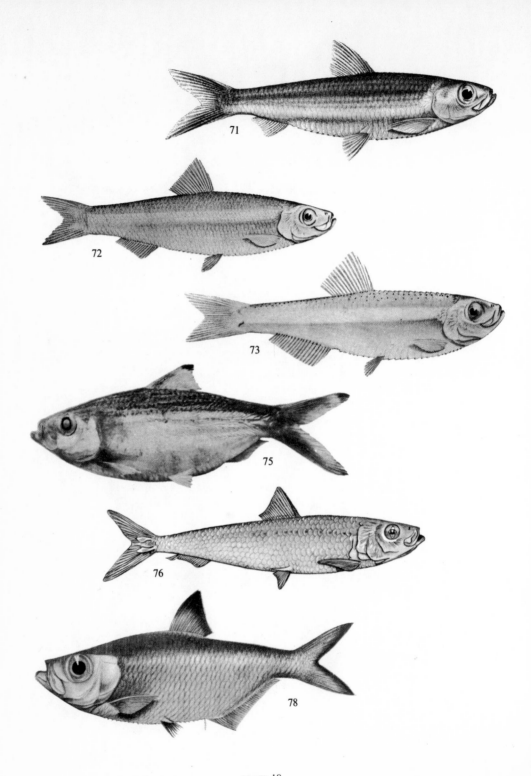

PLATE 18

71. Freshwater Herring, *Potamalosa richmondia*, 7½ in.   72. Sandy Sprat,
Hyperlophus vittatus, 81 mm.   73. Glassy Sprat, *H. translucidus*, 58 mm.
75. Southern Herring, *Harengula castelnaui*.   76. Dakin's Pilchard, *Arengus
dakini*, 7¼ in.   78. Ditchelee Herring, *Pellona ditchela*, 6¾ in.

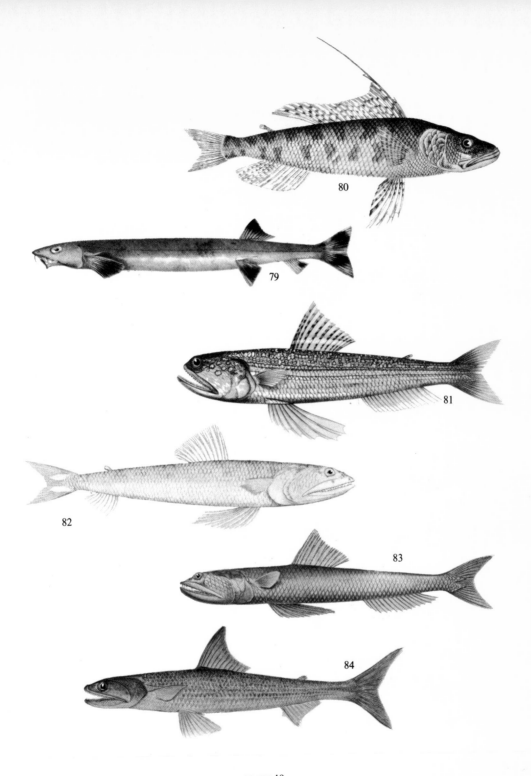

PLATE 19

79. Rat-fish, *Gonorhynchus gonorhynchus*. 80. Sergeant Baker, *Aulopus purpurissatus*, male, 21 in. 81. Painted Grinner, *Trachinocephalus myops*, 12 in. 82. Hoult's Grinner, *Synodus houlti*, 8 in. 83. Spear-toothed Grinner, *Xystodus sageneus*, 10½ in. 84. Yellow-banded Grinner, *Saurida tumbil*, about 12 in.

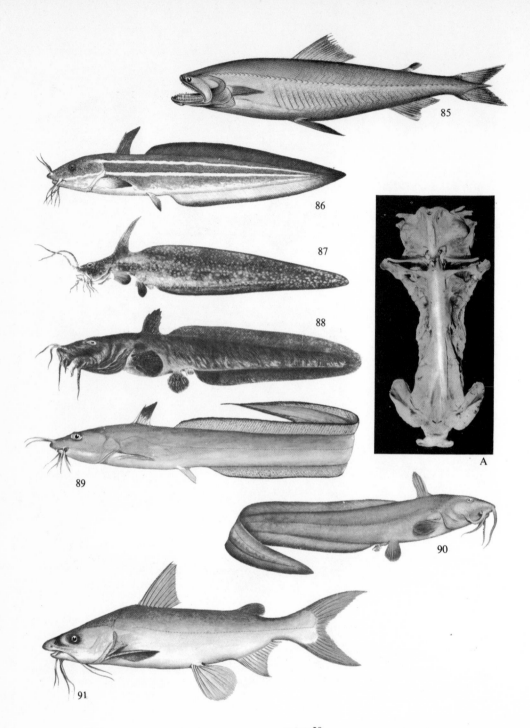

PLATE 20

85. Glassy Bombay Duck, *Harpadon translucens*, 15½ in.   86. Striped Catfish, *Plotosus anguillaris*, 7 in.   87. White-lipped Eel Catfish, *Paraplotosus albilabris*, 9 in.   88. Estuary Catfish, *Cnidoglanis macrocephalus*, 20 in. 89. Nettle-fish, *Exilichthys nudiceps*, 10½ in.   90. Long-tailed Catfish, *Euristhmus lepturus*, 14½ in. A, Skull of a catfish (not same species) showing "crucifix" on undersurface (photo from Brisbane *Telegraph*).   91. Giant Salmon Catfish, *Tachysurus thalassinus*, 15 in.

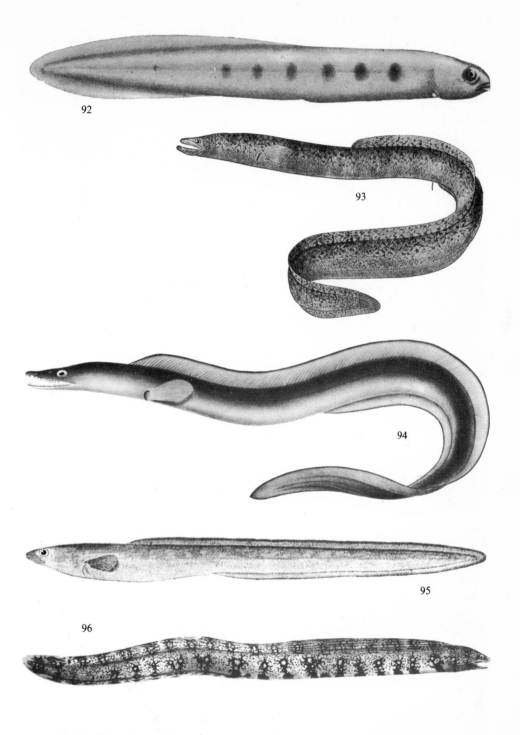

92. Red-banded Pygmy Eel or Shore Eel, *Alabes rufus*. 93. Long-finned
Freshwater Eel, *Anguilla reinhardtii*. 94. Pike Eel, *Muraenesox arabicus*,
21 in. 95. Australian Conger Eel, *Conger labiatus*. 96. Clouded Reef
Eel, *Echidna nebulosa*.

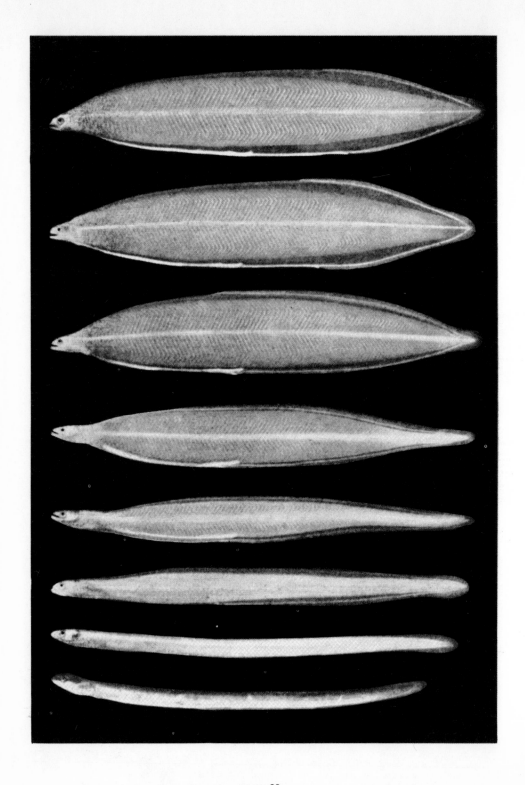

PLATE 22
Development of a young freshwater eel from the flat and transparent glass-eel
stage to the cylindrical elver or young eel. After Schmidt.

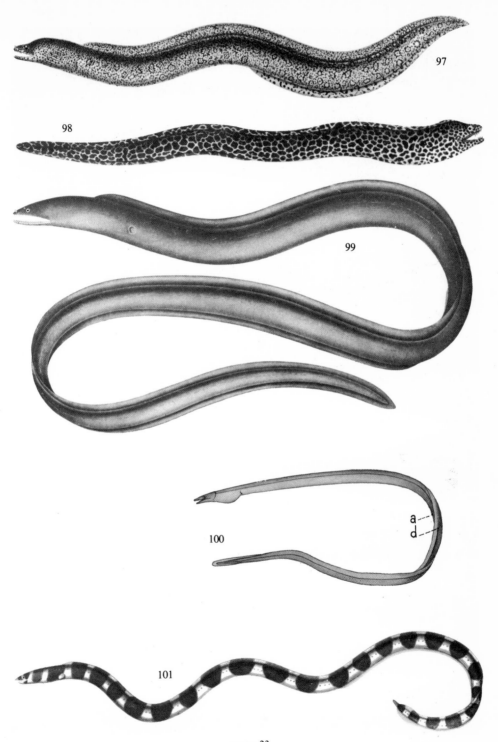

97. Painted Reef Eel, *Lycodontis pictus*, 14 in.   98. Tessellated Reef Eel,
L. favagineus, 28 in.   99. Long-tailed Eel, *Evenchelys macrurus*, 46 in.
100. Iredale's Worm Eel, *Muraenichthys iredalei*, $6\frac{1}{2}$ in. Position of anal fin is
indicated at *a*, and of dorsal fin at *d*.   101. Half-banded Snake Eel, *Leiuranus
semicinctus*, 19 in.

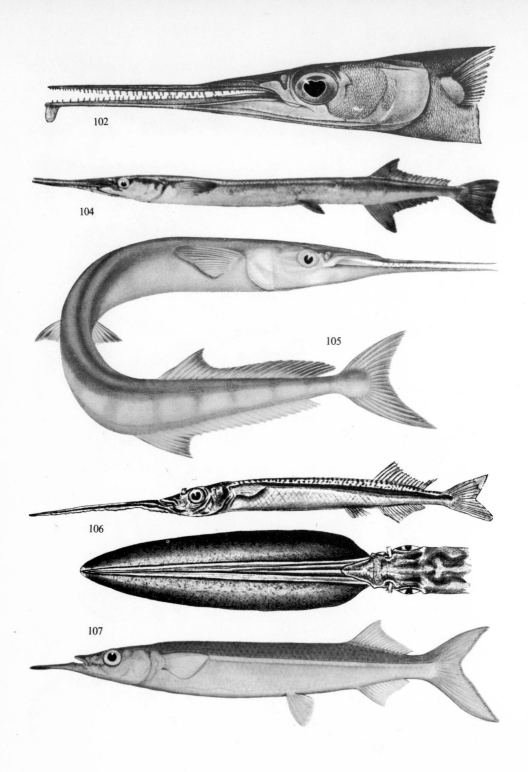

102. Keel-jawed Long Tom, *Thalassosteus appendiculatus*.   104. Stout Long
Tom, *Tylosurus macleayanus*.   105. Barred Long Tom, *Ablennes hians*, 24 in.
106. Spatula Garfish, *Loligorhamphus normani*, $8\frac{1}{2}$ in., with detail of upper surface
of head.   107. Short-nosed Garfish, *Hemiramphus quoyi*, 12 in.

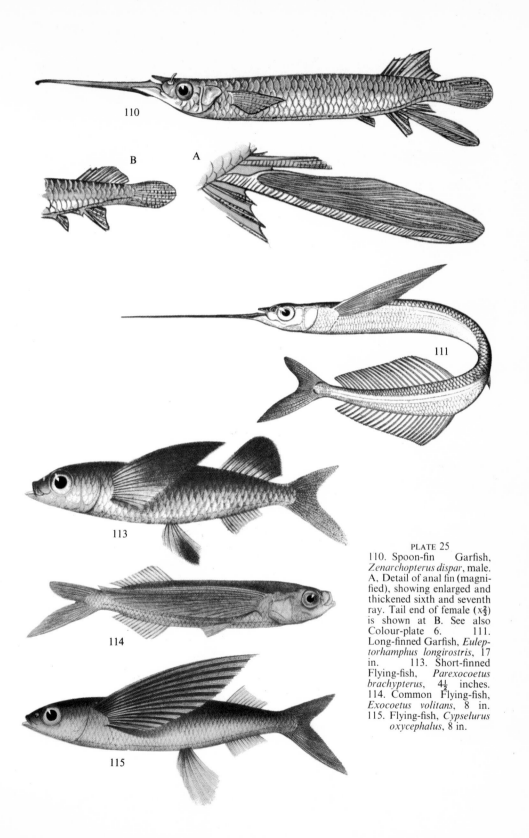

PLATE 25

110. Spoon-fin Garfish, *Zenarchopterus dispar*, male. A, Detail of anal fin (magnified), showing enlarged and thickened sixth and seventh ray. Tail end of female (x⅔) is shown at B. See also Colour-plate 6.   111. Long-finned Garfish, *Euleptorhamphus longirostris*, 17 in.   113. Short-finned Flying-fish, *Parexocoetus brachypterus*, 4½ inches. 114. Common Flying-fish, *Exocoetus volitans*, 8 in. 115. Flying-fish, *Cypselurus oxycephalus*, 8 in.

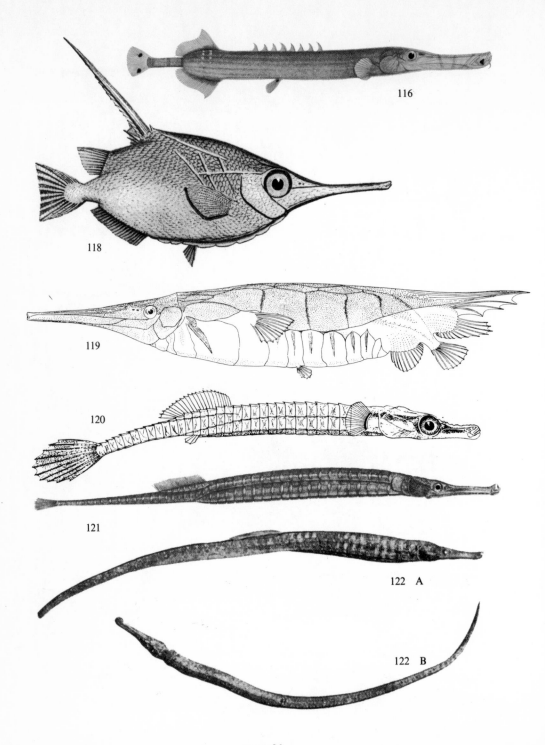

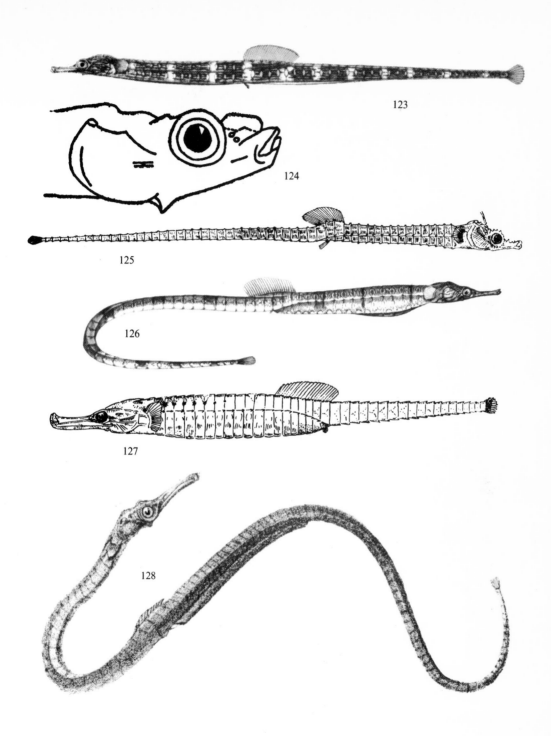

123. Messmate Pipe-fish, *Corythoichthys fasciatus*. 124. Head of Thorn-tailed Pipe-fish, *Micrognathus brevirostris*. 125. Gray's Pipe-fish, *Halicampus grayi*, $3\frac{1}{2}$ in. 126. Banded Pipe-fish, *Yozia tigris*, 11 in. 127. Pig Pipe-fish, *Choeroichthys suillus*, 2 in. 128. Spotted Pipe-fish, *Ichthyocampus maculatus*, 11 in.

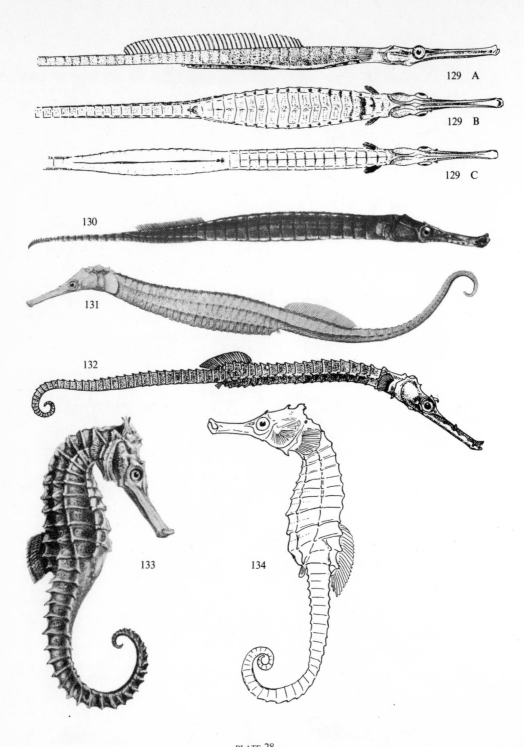

129 A

129 B

129 C

130

131

132

133

134

129. Wide-bodied Pipe-fish, *Stigmatophora nigra*. A, Lateral view of female; B, ventral surface of female; C, ventral surface of male.   130. Horned Pipe-fish, *Syngnathoides biaculeatus*.   131. Red and Gold Sea-horse, *Runcinatus dunckeri*, 18½ in.   132. Slender Tangle-fish, *Haliichthys taeniophora*.   133. Common Sea-horse, *Hippocampus whitei*.   134. Low-crowned Sea-horse, *H. planifrons*, 4 in.

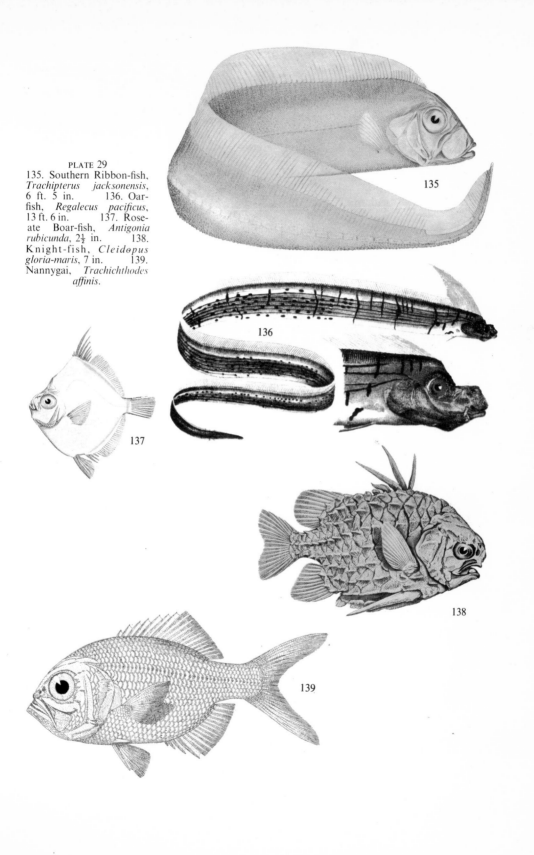

PLATE 29
135. Southern Ribbon-fish, *Trachipterus jacksonensis*, 6 ft. 5 in. 136. Oar-fish, *Regalecus pacificus*, 13 ft. 6 in. 137. Rose-ate Boar-fish, *Antigonia rubicunda*, 2½ in. 138. Knight-fish, *Cleidopus gloria-maris*, 7 in. 139. Nannygai, *Trachichthodes affinis*.

135

136

137

138

139

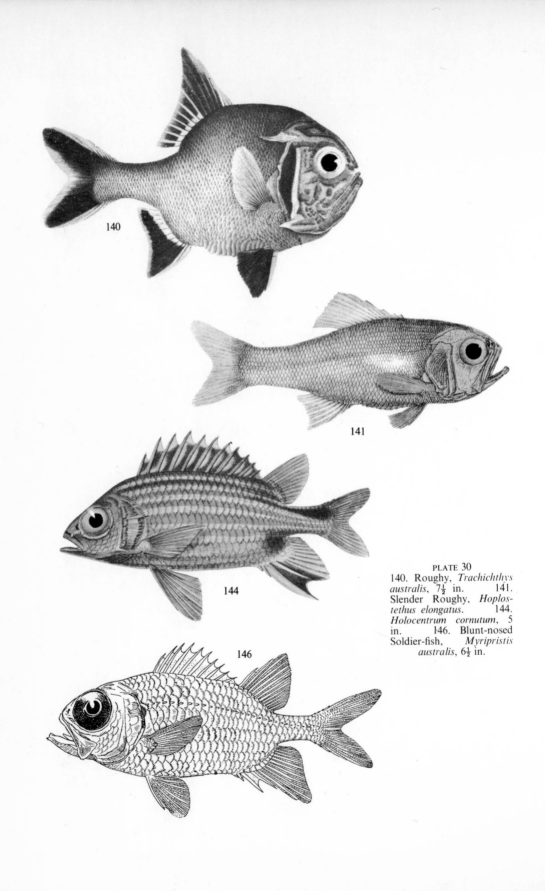

PLATE 30

140. Roughy, *Trachichthys australis*, 7½ in.   141. Slender Roughy, *Hoplostethus elongatus*.   144. *Holocentrum cornutum*, 5 in.   146. Blunt-nosed Soldier-fish, *Myripristis australis*, 6½ in.

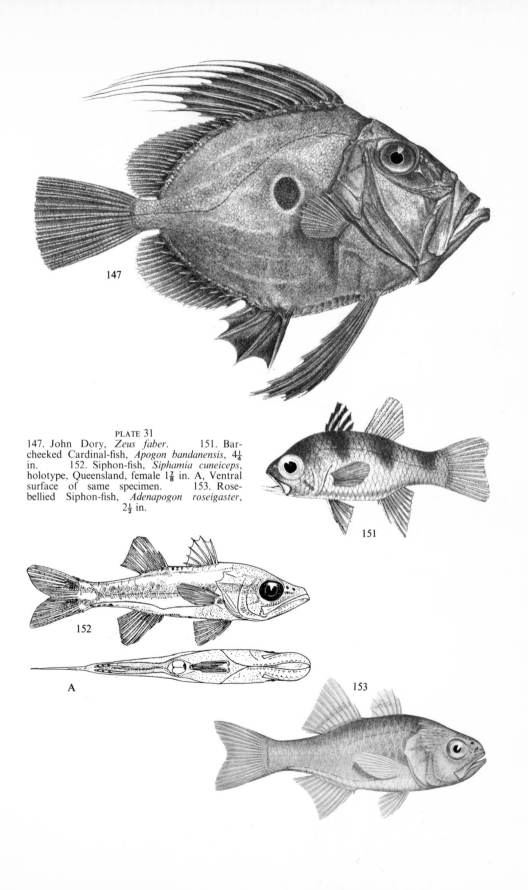

147. John Dory, *Zeus faber*.   151. Bar-cheeked Cardinal-fish, *Apogon bandanensis*, $4\frac{1}{4}$ in.   152. Siphon-fish, *Siphamia cuneiceps*, holotype, Queensland, female $1\frac{7}{8}$ in. A, Ventral surface of same specimen.   153. Rose-bellied Siphon-fish, *Adenapogon roseigaster*, $2\frac{1}{2}$ in.

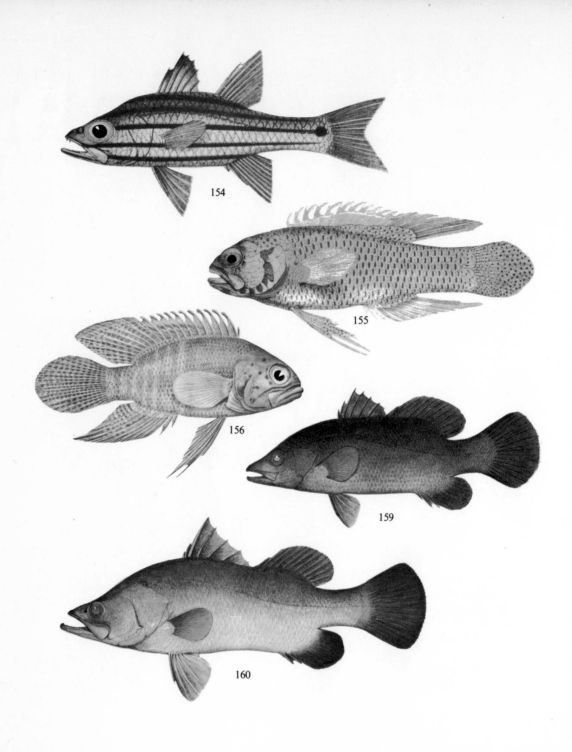

PLATE 32
154. Five-striped Percelle, *Cheilodipterus quinquelineatus*, 3¾ in.   155. Blue-
spotted Long-fin, *Plesiops nigricans*.   156. Blue-tip Long-fin, *Paraplesiops
poweri*, 6½ in.   159. Sand Bass, *Psammoperca waigiensis*, 12 in.   160.
Giant Perch or Palmer, *Lates calcarifer*, about 15 in.

194. TOPSAIL DRUMMER *Kyphosus cinerascens* (Forskål) [Plate 35]

Sciaena cinerascens Forskål, Descr. Anim., 1775, p. 53.
Pimelepterus cinerascens Bleeker, Atlas Ichth., 9, 1876, p. 15, pl. 364, fig. 4.

Blue-fish, Rudder-fish, Chub (South Africa).

D. 11/12, 1; A. 3/11, 1; scales 61-64 along above lateral line to caudal base; 48-56 in lateral line to caudal base, 7-10 more on latter; 11 scales above and 18 below. Colour silvery-grey, with golden longitudinal bands on sides; fins dusky.

A wide-ranging fish found on the Queensland coast from north to south. Its flesh is of good edible quality. The species is readily recognized by its high soft dorsal fin. Grows to 18 inches.

OTHER SPECIES

Silver Drummer, *K. sydneyanus*. A southern species only very occasionally recorded from South Queensland. Grows to 30 inches but a poor food-fish.

Low-finned Drummer, *K. vaigiensis*. A wide-ranging fish which inhabits North Queensland waters, where it grows to 16 inches.

Gibson's Drummer, *K. gibsoni*. A South Queensland fish with similar habits to other members of the family. It reaches a length of 17 inches but has flesh of poor quality.

Family **Lutjanidae**

Four sub-families are represented in the waters of Queensland.

KEY TO SUB-FAMILIES REPRESENTED IN QUEENSLAND
From Weber and de Beaufort[19]

A.   Preoperculum with three or more transverse rows of scales. Palate toothed or edentulous.

    b. Vomer and palatines often with teeth. If palate toothless either the dorsal is deeply notched, appearing as two separate fins, or A. III. 11-14, or the lower jaw has a symphysial knob and D. IX. 9-10, or the teeth in jaws are minute or deciduous. D. IX-XIII. 9-17. Subocular shelf strong. Outer face of palatines without distinct ridge. LUTJANINAE

    bb. Palate always toothless. Dorsal and anal spines rather weak. Preorbital naked. D.X. 9-16. A. III. 7-11. Subocular shelf present, sometimes small. Outer face of palatines with a strong ridge from the base of the maxillary process to the pterygoid. NEMIPTERINAE

---

[19] *Fish. Indo-Austr. Archip.*, 7, 1936, p. 233.

G

bbb. Palate always toothless. Dorsal and anal spines robust. Preorbital scaly. D. IX-XV. 12-20. A. III. 7 (8). No subocular shelf. Outer face of palatines with a ridge along their posterior edge.   POMADASINAE

AA. Preoperculum without scales. Palate always toothless. Often molar teeth in sides of jaws.   LETHRININAE

Sub-family LUTJANINAE

Form oblong, more or less compressed. Scales ctenoid, moderate or small. Head more or less covered with scales; vertical fins with scales or scaleless. Preorbital generally naked, preopercle always scaly. Mouth large or small, terminal, more or less protractile. Teeth in several rows in jaws, often with an outer row of enlarged ones, with or without canines. Sometimes teeth in upper jaw are minute and deciduous or wanting. Vomer and palatine teeth present or absent. Preopercle denticulate or entire. A single dorsal fin, continuous or deeply notched, with 9 to 13 spines and 9 to 17 soft rays. Anal with 3 spines and 7 to 14 soft rays. Pectorals long and pointed. Ventrals with a spine and 5 branched rays. Caudal truncate or more or less deeply forked. Five genera in Queensland waters.

KEY TO GENERA IN QUEENSLAND

A.   Dorsal and anal fins usually more or less scaly.

     b. Mouth large, protractile. Teeth on vomer and palatines well developed. Preoperculum with a more or less distinct notch, to fit a knob of the interoperculum. Dorsal with 10-12 spines. Caudal truncate or somewhat emarginate.   *Lutjanus*

     bb. Mouth moderate or small, somewhat protractile. Teeth on vomer and palatines present or absent. Preoperculum entire, without serrations. Caudal deeply forked.

       c. Dorsal rays 14-15. Anal rays 11-12. Spinous dorsal not elevated into a lobe.   *Caesio*

AA. Dorsal and anal fins scaleless. Preoperculum entire or feebly serrate.

     d. Spinous dorsal elevated into a lobe.

     e. Dorsal rays 10. Anal rays 8.   *Paracaesio*

     dd. Spinous dorsal not elevated into a lobe.

     f. Mouth rather small. Villiform teeth on vomer, palatines, and jaws; outer series on jaws somewhat enlarged and canine-like. No teeth on tongue.   *Aprion*

     ff. Mouth large. No teeth on vomer, palatines, or tongue; teeth in each jaw in a narrow villiform band or deciduous. No enlarged canine-like teeth.   *Aphareus*

Lutjanus: Sea Perch or "Snappers"

A very large genus with many species, inhabiting most temperate and tropical seas. Many of them grow to a large size and almost all are valuable food-fishes. Some species, however, are said to be poisonous when eaten, causing the disease known as ciguatera, the symptoms of which are violent sickness followed by paralysis, and even death. The poison appears to be seasonal, for at times no ill-effects have been noted from eating a species previously known to have been poisonous. The large Red Mumea, *L. bohar*, is regarded as always poisonous in Samoa, and according to David Starr Jordan is the most dangerous fish in the islands. Two Queensland species, the Chinaman-fish, *L. nematophorus*, and Coates Sea Perch, *L. coatesi*, are also known to have flesh which is poisonous at certain times.

The species of *Lutjanus* living close inshore are usually greenish in colour and banded, spotted, and streaked, whilst those from the deeper outside waters are red. Most of the species are lovers of the reefs off the coast, but some enter the rivers and estuaries of the mainland and at times are found far up mangrove creeks.

In America these fishes are known as Snappers, a name which must not be confused with that of the Australian Snapper, *Chrysophrys auratus*, which is a member of the family Sparidae.

The genus *Lutjanus* shows much variation in form, dentition, and scaling, and the species are somewhat difficult to determine. The following key to the eighteen species occurring in Queensland has been adapted from Weber and de Beaufort's splendid key.[20]

KEY TO SPECIES IN QUEENSLAND

A. Longitudinal rows of scales above lateral line parallel to it or ascending somewhat below posterior part of soft dorsal only.

    b. Fourth to seventh dorsal rays prolonged into long filaments; a deep and conspicuous fossa before the eye. Body with blue longitudinal bands in the young; adult pink, with network of yellow lines on head.   *nematophorus*

    bb. Dorsal rays without filaments.

     c. Scales on head beginning behind eye; temporal region naked.   *longmani*

     cc. Scales on head beginning above middle of eye; temporal region scaly; 7 transverse rows of scales on preoperculum.   *johni*

---

[20] *Fish. Indo-Austr. Archip.*, 7, 1936, p. 236.

AA. Longitudinal rows of scales above lateral line parallel to it in their anterior part only, ascending to dorsal profile below posterior part of spinous dorsal; scales on head beginning behind eye. Anterior part of soft anal and the ventrals dark. *argentimaculatus*

AAA. Longitudinal rows of scales above lateral line obliquely ascending to dorsal profile, those in front of and below anterior part of spinous dorsal sometimes parallel to lateral line.

d. Scales on head beginning above middle of eye or nearly so. Temporal region scaly.

e. Vomerine teeth in a $\triangle$ or a $\triangle$; preopercular notch slightly developed.

f. 10 dorsal spines, exceptionally 9 or 11.

g. 6-7 scales between lateral line and median dorsal spines. A dark band from hind border of eye to caudal. *vitta*

gg. 9½-11 scales between lateral line and median dorsal spines. Axil of pectoral black.

h. Pinkish-brown, with darker brown and faint yellow longitudinal bands on sides. *carponotatus*

hh. Bluish-grey, with bright golden-yellow longitudinal bands on sides. *chrysotaenia*

ee. Vomerine teeth in a $\wedge$; preopercular notch deep. Often a dark blotch below origin of soft dorsal, for the greater part above lateral line. 10-11 dorsal spines. Longitudinal light-blue bands, bordered above and below by dark lines. *kasmira*

dd. Scales on head beginning behind eye; temporal region naked or nearly so.

i. Longitudinal rows of scales below lateral line ascending, those on lower part of sides sometimes parallel to axis of body.

j. Anal with 3 spines and 10-11 rays; dorsal with 11 spines and 15-16 rays. Young pinkish-white with 3 broad red bands (arrow-like); adult salmon-pink, yellow wavy marks on head. *sebae*

jj. Anal with 3 spines and 8 rays. No dark transverse bands, or a band on head only.

k. Dorsal with 10 spines and 13-15 rays; soft dorsal rounded; preopercular notch very deep and narrow. Posterior part of caudal peduncle and base of caudal dark brown in young. *gibbus* kk. Dorsal with 11 spines and 14 rays; soft dorsal rounded; preopercular notch deep. Pinkish-red, with a vivid yellow longitudinal band from head to caudal base. *amabilis*

kkk. Dorsal with 11 spines and 15 rays; soft dorsal rounded; preopercular notch almost absent. A black saddle, bordered by margaritaceous, especially anteriorly, on caudal peduncle. 9-10 scales between lateral line and median dorsal spines. *sanguineus*

kkkk. Dorsal with 11 spines and 14-15 rays (12/13-14); soft dorsal pointed; preopercular notch shallow. A margaritaceous saddle-like patch on caudal peduncle usually present. 7-8 scales between lateral line and median dorsal spines. Dorsal and caudal with a narrow dark marginal border. *malabaricus*

ii. All the longitudinal rows of scales below lateral line parallel to axis of the body.

l. A large black blotch in lateral line below last spines and anterior rays of dorsal.

m. 13 dorsal rays. A dark blotch largely below the lateral line. *fulviflamma*

mm. 14-15 dorsal rays. A dark blotch largely above the lateral line. *russelli*

ll. No black blotch in lateral line.

n. Caudal more or less totally dark.

o. 6½-7 scales between lateral line and median dorsal spines; preopercular notch well developed, at least in adults; 6 transverse rows of scales on preoperculum. *vaigiensis*

oo. 7-7½ scales between lateral line and median dorsal spines; preopercular notch indistinct; 7-8 rows of scales on preoperculum. *janthinuropterus*

nn. Caudal not totally dark, at most with a dark border.

p. 10 scales between lateral line and median dorsal spines; a conspicuous fossa before eye. Colour dark red. *coatesi*

pp. 7-7½ scales between lateral line and median dorsal spines; no fossa before eye.

lll. A chalk-white blotch in lateral line, above anterior part of soft dorsal, preceded by a dark-brown blotch. Blue spots on scales, forming lines; head with blue lines. Dorsal spines 10, rays 15. *rivulatus*

195. CHINAMAN-FISH *Lutjanus nematophorus* (Bleeker) [Colour-plate 18]

Mesoprion nematophorus Bleeker, Act. Soc. Sci. Indo-Neerl., 8, 1860, p. 56.
Illustrations by G. Coates.

Chinaman-fish (North Queensland), Thread-finned Sea Perch (Queensland).

D. 10/15-17; A. 3/9; L. 1. 55-56; L. tr. 7-9/1/21-22. Young: Roseate, lighter below, with yellowish tinge; body with about 10 to 12 more or less wavy, longitudinal blue bands which extend on to head; a narrow blue cross-bar between eyes; fins pale pink, with the exception of pectorals, which are yellowish; a few blue spots on soft dorsal; caudal pale pink, edged blackish; eye, pupil blackish, surrounded scarlet.

Adults: Crimson-pink, with dusky, somewhat obscure transverse bands on body and some violet spots; head with a network of fine yellow lines; eye scarlet, with an orange-yellow ring round the black pupil.

The Chinaman-fish is an Indo-Australian species found along the entire coastline of Queensland, though very rarely met with in the southern half of the State. It is fairly plentiful over the coral reefs in water varying in depth from about 8 to 25 fathoms. Average fish weigh about 10 pounds, but the species grows to 36 inches in length and 34 pounds in weight.

Chinaman-fish are avoided as food-fishes on account of the ill-effects caused from eating them. Dr W. E. J. Paradice, who studied the fish in the far north, stated: "In most cases it can be eaten with impunity, but in certain cases (not depending on the time of the year) the fish is very poisonous. The symptoms are, pains in the joints and abdomen, with diarrhoea and perhaps vomiting. There is usually a rise in temperature and the patient is very weak for some days after." Dr P. S. Clarke, of Cairns, said: "Fish caught during June, July, and August appear to be more poisonous than those caught during the other months. Natives of Murray Island attribute the poisonous qualities to some noxious variety of seaweed eaten by the fish."

The deep fossa before the eyes and the prolonged dorsal rays, often lost in the adult, distinguish this fish from all other species.

196. MANGROVE JACK *Lutjanus argentimaculatus* (Forskål)
[Colour-plate 19]

Sciaena argentimaculata Forskål, Descr. Anim., 1775, p. 47.
Illustration by G. Coates.

Mangrove Jack, Creek Red Bream, Dog Bream (Townsville); Rock Barramundi (Gladstone); Rock Salmon, Red Snapper, Red Salmon (South Africa); Red Bream (Brisbane Fish Market); Red Bass, Purple Sea Perch (Moreton Bay).

D. 10/14; A. 3/8; L. 1. 45-48; L. tr. 6-6$\frac{1}{2}$/1/17-19. Colour reddish-brown, cherry-red, or pinkish-red above, lighter below; sometimes the scales on the sides with a silvery or pearly centre or with a dark basal spot and the horizontal rows of scales below lateral line with a pale brassy or yellowish spot forming lines; spinous dorsal and distal part of soft dorsal reddish-brown. Sometimes one or two horizontal blue lines on the cheeks may be present in the young, though absent in the adult. Young fish up to 6 inches in length, with 8 to 11 transverse silvery bands on body, disappearing with age.

A widely distributed fish, found in the rivers and mangrove creeks of Queensland and the Northern Territory, often travelling long distances from the ocean. In the East Indies it is said to penetrate into fresh water and remain there until sexually mature, when it returns to the sea to spawn. Grows to 36 inches in length and at least 25 pounds in weight and is a good sporting fish as well as an excellent food-fish.

197. BLUE-BANDED SEA PERCH *Lutjanus kasmira* (Forskål)
[Colour-plate 19]

Sciaena kasmira Forskål, Descr. Anim., 1775, p. 46.
Illustration by G. Coates.

Moon-lighter (Cairns); Blue-banded Hussar (Queensland and New South Wales); Blue-banded Snapper, Snapper (South Africa); Tanda Tanda (East Indies).

D. 10-11/13-16; A. 3/8 (9); L. 1. 53-78; L. tr. 6-9/1/21-24. Colour: Head reddish-brown above and on snout, passing into canary-yellow on cheeks and opercles; body golden-yellow or lemon-yellow, with 4 to 5 longitudinal blue stripes from head to tail, each margined narrowly above and below with deep violet; fins and tail yellowish; sometimes a more or less distinct black blotch is present between lateral line and anterior dorsal rays. All the colours are very brilliant.

This handsome and wide-ranging fish frequents the waters of Queensland and New South Wales. It apparently does not exceed a length of 15 inches and is not a common species in Queensland.

198. RED EMPEROR *Lutjanus sebae* (Cuvier and Valenciennes)
[Colour-plate 20]

Diacope sebae Cuvier and Valenciennes, Hist. Nat. Poiss., 2, 1828, p. 411.
Illustrations by G. Coates (juv.) and T. C. Marshall (adult).

King Snapper (Moreton Bay); Government Bream, Queenfish (North Queensland); Seba's Snapper, Red Snapper (South Africa).

D. 11/15-16; A. 3/10-11; L. 1. 48-57; L. tr. 7½/1/22-26. Young (up to about 12 inches): Very pale pink or almost white, with 3 vivid red transverse bands forming a broad arrow, the posterior one curving downwards and backwards to end of lower caudal lobe; soft dorsal, ventrals, and anal broadly edged black, caudal lobes also black-tipped.

In an example of about 5 or 6 pounds, the colour is bright red or pinkish-red, each scale with a white spot. The broad arrow is much darker red or blackish, distinct or almost wanting; head salmon-pink with a vermiculated pattern of yellow; eye surrounded scarlet; the black on edges of soft dorsal and anal and the caudal tips not so pronounced.

Adult: Salmon-pink, with a white spot on each scale; no traces of the broad arrow or of the black tips of the fins; the dorsal is white-edged and there are a few white spots on the spinous dorsal; anterior edges of pectorals, ventrals, anal, and caudal white; the yellow vermiculations are present on the head; eye surrounded scarlet, pupil black; lips and throat greyish.

In the young the soft dorsal is pointed, but it becomes rounded in the adult.

A wide-ranging and valuable food-fish found in the waters of Queensland, New South Wales, and the Northern Territory. Somewhat rare in the southern portions of Queensland, but commonly met with on the reefs off Gladstone and northwards, where many thousands of pounds are taken for the markets. It is a great sporting fish, fighting with fury when hooked. A peculiar feature is that the flesh of the adult or of the old fish is just as tender to eat as that of the very young fish. This fish grows to a length of at least 40 inches and a weight of 48 pounds.

199. YELLOW-BANDED HUSSAR *Lutjanus amabilis* (De Vis)

[Colour-plate 21]

Genyoroge amabilis De Vis, Proc. Roy. Soc. Qld, 1, 1884 (1885), p. 145.
Illustration by G. Coates.

Hussar (Queensland).

D. 11/14; A. 3/8; L. 1. 52; L. tr. 7/1/21. Colour rose-doree, caudal darker, each scale picked out darker; head, between eyes, begonia-red; spinous dorsal rose-doree, becoming darker towards and including soft dorsal, the rays and spines a little lighter than the membranes; pectorals geranium-pink, with a brilliant lemon-yellow spot at their upper bases; ventrals white; anal with first two spines and outer edge of fin white, rest rose-doree, with lighter rays; eye, large pupil black, surrounded with lemon-yellow and pale scarlet; a brilliant lemon-yellow band runs from opercle to caudal base and there are pale lemon-yellow bands running obliquely back from preopercle to base of caudal; tail pink, edged with yellow.

This handsome fish apparently has a very restricted range. It is very common in South Queensland to as far north as the Capricorns, north of which it becomes rare, and at Townsville it is seldom met with. It is an excellent food-fish and grows to about 18 inches.

200. SCARLET SEA PERCH *Lutjanus malabaricus* (Bloch and Schneider)
[Colour-plate 21]

Sparus malabaricus Bloch and Schneider, Syst. Ichth., 1801, p. 278.
Illustration by G. Coates.

Red Jew, Red Bream, Nannygai (North Queensland); Scarlet Emperor, Red Snapper (Thursday Island).

D. 11/14-15; A. 3/8-9; L. 1. 57-62; L. tr. 7-8/1/18-22. Colour deep red, with narrow oblique yellow lines above lateral line, and longitudinal ones below it; head with a dark scarlet broad band from snout, through eye, to dorsal origin; sometimes a violet-purple longitudinal band from behind eye along base of dorsal fin, at the end of which it is interrupted by a faint light band or saddle over base of caudal; fins red or pink, the dorsal and caudal with a fine black edge.

A wide-ranging species found on the reefs of North Queensland. According to G. Coates it grows to a weight of 30 pounds.

201. BLACK-SPOT SEA PERCH *Lutjanus fulviflamma* (Forskål)
[Colour-plate 22]

Sciaena fulviflamma Forskål, Descr. Anim., 1775, p. 45.
Illustration by G. Coates.

Finger-mark Bream, Red Bream (North Queensland); Black-spotted Sea Perch (Queensland); Moses Perch (Queensland and New South Wales); Johnny, Spot Snapper (South Africa).

D. 10/13-14; A. 3/8-9; L. 1. 46-50; L. tr. 7-8/14-15; preopercle feebly notched. A fish which is most variable in colour. One variety is olive-green, belly silvery, with 8 yellow-orange horizontal bands on the side; edges of soft dorsal, anal, and caudal orange; a black spot on lateral line below origin of soft dorsal and a dark pectoral axil spot. Another variety is purplish-red or pink above, silvery-white below, with oblique yellow lines above lateral line, following the rows of scales, and horizontal ones below; fins and tail yellow, the usual black patch or "finger-mark" on lateral line below soft dorsal origin. Sometimes the yellow stripes are wanting altogether, the fish being reddish, pink, or greenish, but the black blotch is always present.

A wide-ranging species commonly found on the coasts of Queensland and the Northern Territory. It is also found in the northern portions of New South Wales. The young are common in the mangrove creeks of North Queensland. A good food-fish. Grows to 17 inches.

202. KELP SEA PERCH *Lutjanus coatesi* Whitley [Colour-plate 22]

Lutjanus coatesi Whitley, Mem. Qld Mus., 10, pt 4, 1934, p. 176.
Illustration by G. Coates.

Red Bass, Kelp Bream (Townsville).

D. 10/14 (15); A. 3/9; L. 1. 50; L. tr. 10/1/19 to 5/1/7 on caudal peduncle. Colour victoria-lake along back and top of head to tip of snout, merged laterally into rose-doree and passing into eosine-pink on belly; very faint narrow lines of darker pink run longitudinally through centre of scales below lateral line; opercles, cheeks, and throat creamy-yellow; head with several small wavy lines and blotches of dark lavender, thickest in preorbital areas; eye, pupil black, with a narrow border of cadmium-orange, the orbit peach-red; spinous dorsal dark scarlet medially, its spines, base, and terminally almost black; soft dorsal, ventrals, anal, and caudal maroon or rose-doree, passing into black on their edges; pectoral pale rose-doree, its anterior half dusky-black.[21]

A large and handsome fish first known from specimens caught off Townsville by G. Coates, but since found to occur at Elizabeth Reef, about a hundred miles north of Lord Howe Island, South Pacific, also north-west Australia and Papua.

Apparently it has the same poisonous properties when eaten as the Chinaman-fish, *L. nematophorus*. G. Coates, writing of the fish, states that it has the reputation of producing a form of muscular paralysis of a rather severe nature, and that others of the same kind, together with Chinaman-fish, have at various times been displayed in the local fish-shops. He went on: "These fish are fairly common on the reefs outside Townsville. A few months back I came into contact with a case of fish-poisoning and a 'Red Bass' was the cause. A whole family was affected and had a bad time, one adult being sick for several weeks. As these fish are brought in and eaten nearly every week, it is evident that only certain fish have the poisonous effect. They are mostly caught on the outside reefs and grow to at least 20 pounds." In length the Kelp Sea Perch grows to 31 inches.

OTHER SPECIES

Longman's Sea Perch, *L. longmani*. Common in the Whitsunday Passage. Colour uniform rosy-pink. Grows to 12 inches.

Spotted-scale Sea Perch, *L. johni*. An olive-green or dull salmon-coloured fish, each scale with a darker spot forming rows along the body. It is wide-ranging and is not commonly met with in South Queensland. Grows to 36 inches.

Striped Sea Perch, *L. vitta*. A rose-pink, reddish, or golden-yellowish fish with a reddish, brown, or blackish lateral band from snout to caudal base.

---

[21] Colours from *Ridgway's Colour Standard*, 1912.

It is an Indo-Australian fish, common on the reefs of Queensland and the Northern Territory, where it grows to 14 inches.

Stripey Sea Perch. *L. carponotatus*. Colour reddish with three or four dark-brown longitudinal stripes above, passing into yellow ones below. It is a some-what rare fish found on the reefs of northern Australia. Grows to 14 inches.

Gold-banded Sea Perch, *L. chrysotaenia*. This Indo-Australian species is apparently not common on the Queensland coast. Grows to 14 inches.

Paddle-tail, *L. gibbus*. A reddish or scarlet-coloured fish which frequents the waters of Torres Strait. Wide-ranging outside Australia. Grows to 24 inches.

Saddle-tailed Sea Perch, *L. sanguineus*. A wide-ranging fish which in colour is a bright rose-pink with a zone of deep scarlet between the eyes. Found on the coast of Queensland and North Australia. Grows to 36 inches. A good food-fish.

Moses Perch, *L. russelli*. Very similar in colour to the Black-spot Sea Perch, *L. fulviflamma*, but differing as shown in the key. In Australia it is found in Queensland, New South Wales, and the Northern Territory. Grows to 17 inches. A good food-fish.

Yellow-margined Sea Perch, *L. vaigiensis*. A species which is most variable in colour but mostly with a dark-coloured tail. A wide-ranging fish, common in the South Seas and the Northern Territory, but not commonly met with in Queensland. Grows to 24 inches.

Dark-tailed Sea Perch, *L. janthinuropterus*. An orange-red fish with each scale outlined yellow. The tail is very dark red, sometimes almost black. An Indo-Australian and South Pacific species found also on the coast of North Queensland. Grows to 24 inches.

Maori Sea Perch, *L. rivulatus*. A wide-ranging fish occasionally taken in North Queensland waters. Colour olivaceous or reddish above, silvery below, with a slaty-blue spot on each scale, forming lines. Grows to 25 inches.

Caesio

Body elongate. Scales moderate or small. Mouth small. A single dorsal fin with fin-spines slender.

Fishes mainly of the Indo-Pacific region. They are denizens of the coral reefs, some species swarming among the corals. Valued as food. Four species are found in Queensland waters.

KEY TO SPECIES IN QUEENSLAND

A. Teeth in jaws in several rows, the outer ones enlarged; teeth on vomer and palatines; height 2.3-3.2. Belly rosy, caudal uniform yellow.   *erythrogaster*

AA. Teeth in jaws in a single row or nearly so; generally no teeth on palate; height 3.4-4.1.

  b. 60-65 scales in lateral line. Blue, with yellow lateral band.

    c. Yellow lateral band above lateral line; caudal lobes with blackish, median longitudinal band on each.   *caerulaureus*

    cc. Yellow lateral band below lateral line on body and above it on caudal base; tips of caudal lobes blackish.   *chrysozona*

  bb. Scales very small, 70-80 in lateral line. Purplish or blue, with 2 narrow brown or greyish-white longitudinal bands; caudal with dusky tips.   *digramma*

203. RED-BELLIED FUSILIER *Caesio erythrogaster* Cuvier & Valenciennes
[Colour-plate 22]

Caesio erythrogaster Cuvier and Valenciennes, Hist. Nat. Poiss., 6, 1830, p. 442.
Illustration by G. Coates.

Yellow-tail (Thursday Island).

D. 10/14-15; A. 3/11; L. 1. 50-58; L. tr. 6-7/1/15-16. Colour dark blue above, lighter on sides, passing gradually into rosy-red below; caudal bright yellow, the three colours blending into each other below soft dorsal; head very dark blue above, cheeks pale pink with a few yellow scales; 2 violet bands across snout; eye, pupil black, surrounded scarlet; spinous dorsal blackish, merging into yellow soft dorsal and with a red spot between each spine terminally; pectorals and ventrals pink; anal hyaline.

A common and beautiful fish found among the coral reefs of North Queensland and the Northern Territory and also in the Indo-Pacific region. A good food-fish. Grows to at least 14 inches.

OTHER SPECIES

Blue and Gold Fusilier, *C. caerulaureus*. A common fish on the snapper banks off Moreton Bay, also found in the Indo-Pacific. Grows to 12 inches.

Black-tipped Fusilier, *C. chrysozona*; Dark-banded Fusilier, *C. digramma*. Two wide-ranging species which frequent the reefs along the Queensland coast. They grow to 10½ and 9 inches respectively.

Paracaesio

This genus is represented in Queensland by Pedley's Fusilier, *Paracaesio pedleyi* McCulloch and Waite, a handsome fish, blue and yellow in colour, found on the coasts of South Queensland and New South Wales and also at Lord Howe Island, South Pacific. Grows to 15 inches.

Aprion

This genus of few species is represented in Queensland by two species—the Job-fish, *Aprion (Aprion) virescens* (Cuvier and Valenciennes), and the Roseate Job-fish, *A. (Pristipomoides) microlepis* (Bleeker). Both are excellent food-fishes. The Job-fish reaches a length of 40 inches with a weight of 26 pounds. The Roseate Job-fish grows to 24 inches. Both are wide-ranging outside Australia.

Aphareus

A genus of two closely related species living in the warmer waters of the Indo-Pacific. The Small-toothed Job-fish, *A. rutilans* Cuvier and Valenciennes, is occasionally taken in North Queensland waters where it grows to at least 32 inches and a weight of 20 pounds. Although soft, the flesh is of good flavour.

Sub-family NEMIPTERINAE

Form oblong or elongate, more or less compressed. Scales moderate or small, ctenoid, not usually present on snout, jaws, preorbital, suborbital, or on vertical fins. Opercles scaled. Mouth moderate or small, terminal, more or less protractile. Preopercle denticulate or entire. Jaws with or without canines, posterior teeth sometimes molar-like. Palate toothless. One dorsal fin of 10 spines and 9 to 10 (by exception 16) soft rays. Anal with 3 spines and 7 to 11 rays. Pectoral long, pointed. Ventrals with a spine and 5 branched rays. Caudal emarginate or forked. Four genera are found in Queensland waters.

KEY TO GENERA IN QUEENSLAND

Adapted from Weber and de Beaufort[22]

A. Suborbital with a distinct spine below eye, directed backwards, generally with a few small points below it. No canines.   *Scolopsis*

AA. Suborbital without distinct spines. Canines at least in upper jaw.

    b. Sides of jaws with round, flat molar teeth.   *Monotaxis*

    bb. No molar teeth.

        c. 5-7 transverse rows of scales on preoperculum.   *Pentapodus*

        cc. Only 3 rows of scales on preoperculum.   *Nemipterus*

Scolopsis

Fishes of wide distribution characterized by the presence of a sharp spine immediately under the eye on the suborbital generally followed by some shorter ones below. Six species occur in Queensland waters.

---

[22] *Fish. Indo-Austr. Archip.*, 7, 1936, p. 325.

190

A. Scales on lateral line 36-40.

    b. Scales on head beginning before front border of eye; no bands. Scales with pearly or yellow spots.   *margaritifer*

    bb. Scales on head beginning between eyes. Two dark longitudinal bands on body, with white or yellow band between.   *longulus*

AA. Scales on lateral line more than 40.

    c. 3½ scales between lateral and median dorsal spines.

      d. Scales on head beginning between anterior part of eyes, at some distance behind nostrils.

        e. 49-50 scales on lateral line. A white longitudinal band from eye to caudal, pale-blue band across interorbital.   *personatus*

        ee. 44-46 scales on lateral line. One to 3 white or yellowish parallel bands, connected behind by short pale bars.   *cancellatus*

      dd. Scales on head beginning before eye, reaching on snout to a line connecting anterior nostrils.

        f. A broad white curved band, bordered above and below by a narrow dark-red line from eye to dorsal; longitudinal bands in the young.   *bilineatus*

    cc. 4½ scales or five between lateral line and median dorsal spines.

      g. 3 light bands across snout; a dark ring usually present on temporal region.   *temporalis*

204. PEARLY SPINE-CHEEK *Scolopsis margaritifer*
(Cuvier and Valenciennes)   [Colour-plate 23]

Scolopsides margaritifer Cuvier and Valenciennes, Hist. Nat. Poiss., 5, 1830, p. 337.
Illustration by G. Coates.

D. 10/9; A. 3/7; L. 1. 36-40; L. tr. 4-5/1/10-14. Living colours: General colour above dark olive-brown, the centre of each scale being a very light pearly-green or pearly-bluish, forming a checkered pattern, which on the pearly-white belly is as a series of yellow spots, which become gradually smaller and disappear on the belly; head with flushes of pinkish on cheeks; lips salmon-pink; eye, pupil black, surrounded dark brown; dorsal hyaline-white, the spines and membranes brownish-red which, on the last eight or nine rays and membranes forms a large patch on the outer half and leaves a whitish patch basally—there is a very narrow yellow edge to the whole fin; pectoral pale canary-yellow; ventrals hyaline, except the membrane between the first two rays, which is bright yellow; anal pale yellow, the edge broadly bordered bluish-white; caudal with upper lobe pale yellow, the lower one maroon-red.

An Indo-Australian and South Seas fish found on the reefs of North Queensland and North Australia. Common. Grows to 10 inches.

OTHER SPECIES

Yellow-banded Spine-cheek, *S. longulus*. An Indo-Australian and South Seas species that frequents the reefs of North Queensland and the Northern Territory. Grows to $5\frac{1}{2}$ inches.

Masked Spine-cheek, *S. personatus*. Another wide-ranging fish occasionally found in the far northern waters of Queensland, where it grows to 10 inches.

Green-lined Spine-cheek, *S. cancellatus*. An Indo-Pacific and South Pacific fish which is also found on the reefs of North Queensland. It reaches a length of only 8 inches.

Yellow-finned Spine-cheek, *S. bilineatus*. An Indo-Australian fish commonly found on the reefs of North Queensland. Grows to only 8 inches. Readily recognized by the curved pearly-white band (bordered above and below by a dark-red line) curving from the mouth to the soft dorsal fin.

Barred-face Spine-cheek, *S. temporalis*. A large species that reaches 17 inches in length. Fairly common on the Great Barrier Reef. It ranges throughout the Indo-Pacific region.

Monotaxis

A small genus of only two species, one ranging from the Pacific through the Indo-Malay Archipelago to India and the Red Sea, the other, *M. affinis* Whitley, known only from the unique holotype, a specimen $14\frac{1}{2}$ inches in length was captured at North Gardiner Bank, off Fraser Island, South Queensland, in September, 1938.

Pentapodus

Body oblong, somewhat compressed, covered with ctenoid scales of moderate size. Maxillary scaleless, its end fitting into the naked or scaly preorbital which is scalloped to receive it. Lower canines, when present, flaring outwards. Sometimes one or both lobes of the forked caudal produced into a filament.

Small fishes of the Indo-Pacific. Species few, one in Queensland.

205. BLUE-BANDED WHIPTAIL *Pentapodus setosus*
(Cuvier and Valenciennes) [Colour-plate 23]

Pentapus setosus Cuvier and Valenciennes, Hist. Nat. Poiss., 6, 1830, p. 270.
Illustration by G. Coates.

Long-tailed Perch (North Queensland); Paradise-fish, China-fish (Queensland).

D. 10/9/1; A. 3/7/1; L. 1. 46; L. tr. $2\frac{1}{2}/1/13$-16. Colour olivaceous above, whitish or yellowish below; snout bluish-silvery, with two yellow cross-bands; a pearly-blue or silvery longitudinal band, slightly curved from middle of eye to caudal base, where it meets a similar band and ends in a dark spot; a pearly-blue coloured band along the back at base of dorsal; fins yellowish. The young have a broad dark band from the snout through the eye in a straight line to caudal base and a narrow indistinct one on either side, separated by a yellowish stripe. The dark bands are wanting in large specimens.

The presence of the caudal filament and the colours distinguish this common fish, which ranges from Western Australia round the northern parts of Australia and along the Queensland coast to New South Wales. Grows to 10 inches.

Nemipterus

Form somewhat elongate. Scales moderate, easily shed. Opercles with large cycloid scales, leaving a broad or narrow flange naked. Mouth moderate, with rows of conical teeth and a few small canines in front. Spinous and soft dorsal continuous, not notched. Caudal forked, in some species the upper lobe produced into a filament.

Somewhat small, brightly coloured fishes of the Indo-Pacific. Species numerous, five in Queensland. They are food-fishes of excellent flavour and are usually found offshore and over sandy bottoms in great numbers.

KEY TO SPECIES IN QUEENSLAND

A. Both jaws with distinct canines.

    b. Spinous dorsal lower than soft dorsal.   *hexodon*

    bb. Spinous dorsal higher than soft dorsal.   *peronii*

AA. Lower jaw without distinct canines.

    c. Median dorsal spines longest. Ventrals reaching not quite to or but little beyond vent.

        d. Upper caudal ray produced. Body with yellow bands.   *aurifilum*

        dd. Upper caudal ray not produced. Colour uniform.   *upeneoides*

    cc. Posterior dorsal spine longest. Ventrals reaching to second anal spine.   *theodorei*

206. THEODORE'S BUTTERFLY BREAM *Nemipterus theodorei* Ogilby
[Plate 35]

Nemipterus theodorei Ogilby, Proc. Roy. Soc. Qld, 28, 1st Dec., 1916, p. 113; and Mem. Qld Mus., 6, 1918, p. 55, pl. 19.

D. 10/8/1; A. 3/7; L. 1. 48; L. tr. 3/1/9. General colour lilac-pink above, passing into mauve on sides and pearly-pink iridescence below; about 7 pale greenish-yellow longitudinal stripes on body from shoulders to caudal base;

head deeper lilac-pink above, the cheeks and opercles shot with iridescent pinks and blues; a deep curved stripe of pale magenta commences below eye forward to beneath nostrils, then down snout to lip; upper lip clear canary-yellow; eye-pupil black, surrounded pale scarlet, tinged green above; dorsals hyaline canary-yellow, hyaline-blue basally, 2 hyaline-blue longitudinal stripes (upper one wider than lower) extend the full length of the fins on their outer half; edge of fin narrowly hyaline-yellow; pectorals hyaline; ventrals hyaline, except for first spine and ray, which is deep mauve; anal hyaline with alternate bright-blue and canary-yellow longitudinal wavy lines on basal two-thirds; caudal pale rose-pink, the upper lobe dusky-tipped.

A beautiful fish known from a few specimens caught off Caloundra (South Queensland) and in New South Wales. No doubt this species and the others of this genus will prove to be quite common along the Queensland coast when trawling is engaged in on a large scale. Grows to 10 inches.

OTHER SPECIES

Yellow-banded Butterfly Bream, *N. hexodon*. Trawled in North Queensland waters in depths of 12 to 33 fathoms. Grows to 16 inches and is known in the north as Rainbow Perch and Gold Perch.

Peron's Butterfly Bream, *N. peronii*. An Indo-Australian fish which grows to 11 inches. Found in North and north-eastern Australia.

Yellow-lip Butterfly Bream, *N. aurifilum*. Common at depths ranging from 13 to 70 fathoms along the Queensland coast. Grows to 12 inches.

Red Butterfly Bream, *N. upeneoides*. An East Indian species, once recorded from the coast of South Queensland. Grows to $6\frac{1}{2}$ inches.

Sub-family POMADASINAE

Form oblong, compressed. Scales small or moderate in size, ctenoid, adherent. Head scaled, with the exception of snout anteriorly, lips and chin. Mouth small or moderate, more or less oblique, terminal, somewhat protractile. Lips thick or swollen. Maxillary slipping under the high preorbital. A median groove sometimes present on chin and often a row of pores. Teeth in several rows in jaws, at least anteriorly, an outer row of enlarged ones usually present. Palate toothless. Outer face of palatines with a ridge on posterior edge. Opercle with a weak spine, preopercle serrate. Preorbital not serrated. Suprascapular generally exposed. Dorsal fin single, more or less deeply emarginate and with a basal sheath, the spinous portion of 9 to 15 spines, the soft of 12 to 20 rays. Anal short, of 3 spines, the first very small, and 7 to 8 rays. A basal sheath more or less developed. Pectorals long and pointed. Caudal rounded, truncate or emarginate.

Shore-fishes of all tropical and subtropical seas. Two genera comprise this sub-family.

A.   A median pit or groove behind chin. Generally 2 pores
     present on chin.   *Pomadasys*

AA. No median pit or groove behind chin. Chin with a
     row of 6 pores immediately behind lower lip.   *Plectorhynchus*

Pomadasys: Javelin-fishes

Body oblong, compressed. Scales moderate, ctenoid on body. Mouth small
or moderate. Jaws subequal, upper little protractile. Teeth in jaws in bands,
villiform, pointed. No canines, no teeth on palate. Lower jaw with median
longitudinal groove below chin and usually with 2 pores on the chin anteriorly.
Preopercle serrated. No opercular spine. Dorsals notched, consisting of 11
to 15 spines and 12 to 18 rays. Anal with 3 spines and 7 to 13 rays. Bases of
both fins scaly.

A small genus containing only a few species, some entering rivers into
fresh water. They emit a grunting noise when caught, such habit having earned
them the name of "Grunts" or "Grunters" in other parts of the world. The
name of Javelin-fish refers to the very large anal spine in some species. Four
species on the shores of Queensland.

A.   Body and dorsal fins with blotches or spots.

   b. Body with dark cross-bars or series of large dark
     blotches.

     c. Back with 4-5 large blackish blotches; a large
       dark blotch on the spinous dorsal.   *maculatus*

     cc. Body and dorsal fins with somewhat indistinct
       blackish spots usually in series to form transverse
       bands on body.   *hasta*

   bb. Body and dorsal fins with many distinct small
     blackish spots; no transverse bars.   *opercularis*

AA. Body and dorsal fin uniform silvery, without spots or
     blotches; a large blue-black blotch usually present on
     the opercle.   *argyreus*

207. SPOTTED JAVELIN-FISH *Pomadasys hasta* (Bloch)   [Colour-plate 24]

Lutjanus hasta Bloch, Nat. ausl. Fische, 4, 1790, p. 109.
Illustration by G. Coates.

Grunter Bream, Trumpeter, Queensland Trumpeter (Queensland); Grunter
(Townsville); Spear-spined Grunter, Banded Grunter, Silver Grunter (South
Africa).

D. 13/14, 1; A. 3/7, 1; L. 1. 45-54; L. tr. 7-8/1/11-12. Colour olivaceous above, silvery on sides, whitish below, each scale on back and sides with a dark olive-brown spot, forming more or less irregular longitudinal rows; spinous dorsal olive-grey, sides of the spines burnished silver; both spinous and soft dorsal with about 3 rows of deep blackish-brown spots placed longitudinally; upper dorsal edge greyish-black; anal and caudal olive-grey; ventrals greenish-yellow. Sometimes the spots of the body are indistinct and are replaced by transverse rows of larger spots, which may be formed into cloudy transverse bands on the back and upper sides.

A large and valuable food-fish commonly found on the Queensland coast, especially in the north. Grows to 24 inches. Wide-ranging.

OTHER SPECIES

Blotched Javelin-fish, *P. maculatus*. A wide-ranging species found in North Queensland waters. Grows to 18 inches. Readily recognized by the large blackish blotches across its back.

Small-spotted Javelin-fish, *P. opercularis*. Another wide-ranging species, a valued food-fish in northern Queensland waters. In South Africa it is said to reach a weight of 25 pounds, though such a size is never seen in Queensland. Like the other members of the genus it is an excellent food-fish.

Silver Javelin-fish, *P. argyreus*. Wide-ranging outside Australia. Known from the waters of North Queensland, where it attains 16 inches but is apparently rare.

Plectorhynchus: Sweet-lips

Form oblong, compressed. body and head covered with small or moderate scales, usually ctenoid. Dorsal fin with spinous portion of 9 to 14 spines, sometimes very strong, and 15 to 26 rays. Anal short. Chin with a row of pores. Mouth small, lips usually thick. Conical pointed teeth in jaws in several rows anteriorly, the outer ones enlarged, one row posteriorly. No canines. No palatines. Preopercle margin serrate.

A large genus of Indo-Pacific fishes of striking colours, usually horizontally banded in yellow and black. They vary considerably in colour within each species, undergoing great changes with age. They may be strongly banded when young and only spotted in the adults, the number of body-bands and ornamentation of the fins varying with age. The shape of the caudal alters with age, being rounded in the young, truncate or emarginate in the adult. All are good food-fishes. Seven species occur in Queensland seas.

KEY TO SPECIES IN QUEENSLAND

A. Dorsal with 14 spines and 15-16 rays; height 1.9-2.2 in the length. Colour uniform.   *nigrus*

AA. Dorsal with 12-13 spines and 18-22 rays; height 2.5-3 in the length. Usually striped or spotted in part or whole.

b. Dorsal with 12-13 spines and 18-19 rays; 75-90 scales in a longitudinal row. Colour usually uniform grey; young olive, with blue lines on snout and cheeks. *schotaf*

c. Dorsal with 12 spines and 19 rays; 90-95 scales in a longitudinal row. Colour greyish, with black spots. *punctatissimus*

d. Dorsal with 13 spines and 19 rays; 75 scales in a longitudinal row. Colour blue, with longitudinal yellow bands. *chrysotaenia*

e. Dorsal with 13 spines and 21 rays; 55 scales in a longitudinal row. Colour brownish or greenish, with darker reticulating pattern on upper part of body. *reticulatus*

f. Dorsal with 12-13 spines and 19-20 rays; 77-93 scales in a longitudinal row. Colour brownish, with longitudinal bands on body, continued on head, where the superior ones are bent downwards; 9 bands in young, 18 in adult; caudal spotted. *goldmanni*

AAA. Dorsal with 9-10 spines and 23-26 rays; 88-100 scales in a longitudinal row; height 2.5-2.7 in the length. Striped in young, spotted or uniform in old examples. *pictus*

208. BROWN SWEET-LIPS *Plectorhynchus nigrus* (Cuvier and Valenciennes)
[Plate 36]

Pristopoma nigrum Cuvier and Valenciennes, Hist. Nat. Poiss., 5, 1830, p. 258.
Pristopoma crassispina Bleeker, Atlas Ichth., 8, 1876-7, p. 15, pl. 342, fig. 4.

D. 13-14/16, 1, to 18, 1; A. 3/7, 1; L. 1. 53-64; L. tr. 10-11/1/16-21. Colour usually dark brown, blackish or greyish, but little paler on the sides; fins blackish. In young examples the distal part of caudal, soft dorsal, and anal white. Another variety is whitish-grey, with a broad black saddle on the back above the pectoral fin and extending over the anterior half of the spinous dorsal, the rest of the fin being white; soft dorsal mostly black; caudal black; other fins same as body; eye with pupil black, surrounded red and set in a broad black oblique band; opercle narrowly edged with scarlet.

A wide-ranging and common fish which grows to about 24 inches. Commonly met with on the Queensland coast but becoming rarer in New South Wales waters.

209. PAINTED SWEET-LIPS *Plectorhynchus pictus* (Thunberg)

[Colour-plate 24]

Perca picta Thunberg, Kon. Vet. Akad. Nya Handl. 13, 1792, p. 141 (*fide* Weber and de Beaufort).
Illustration by G. Coates.

Morwong (Brisbane Fish Market); Blackall (Queensland); Bluey, Morwong, Slate Bream (North Queensland); Thick-lip Bream (Townsville).

D. 9-10/23, 1, to 25, 1; A. 3/7, 1; L. 1. 82-134; L. tr. 17-19/20-22. Young whitish or yellowish, with chestnut-brown or blackish longitudinal bands from head to tail, the median one running to end of tail and terminating in a wedge-shaped band and with a cross-band over its upper and lower angles; dorsal with a narrow black margin and a broad dark band from upper two-thirds of second spine backwards and downwards to basal half of fin; this band is sometimes interrupted, causing a black spot to exist between third and fourth spines. In half-grown examples the bands begin to break up into rows of oval or roundish spots and the adults become silver-greyish with more or less distinct spots over body and fins, or, in some examples, on fins only, the body being washed with iridescent pink. Others may be drab-grey, with numerous yellow or olive-yellow spots. The banded young are quite unlike the spotted adult, but the long second dorsal spine and the small scales are characteristic.

A common species on the coast of Queensland from north to south and occurring rarely in the northern portions of New South Wales. Wide-ranging. Grows to at least 26 inches.

OTHER SPECIES

Sombre Sweet-lips, *P. schotaf*. A wide-ranging fish recorded in Australian waters only from Torres Strait. Grows to 20 inches.

Multi-spotted Sweet-lips, *P. punctatissimus*. In Australian waters this fish has been recorded only from North Queensland, where so far it has been rarely met with. Grows to 22 inches. Wide-ranging.

Golden-lined Sweet-lips, *P. chrysotaenia*. A handsome species from the Indo-Australian region and South Seas, occasionally found on the coast of Queensland. Grows to 20 inches.

Netted Sweet-lips, *P. reticulatus*. A somewhat rare fish known from the waters of Queensland, New South Wales, Western Australia, and China. Grows to 15 inches.

Many-lined Sweet-lips, *P. goldmanni*. An Indo-Australian species found in the northern parts of Australia. Grows to 24 inches.

Sub-family LETHRININAE: EMPERORS

Form oblong, somewhat compressed. Scales of moderate size. Head naked, with the exception of opercles and nape. No scales on preopercles. Mouth terminal, little protractile. Teeth in jaws cardiform anteriorly, with canines.

Lateral teeth in a single row, conical or molar-like. Palate toothless. Single dorsal fin, of 10 spines and 8 to 9 branched rays. Anal with 3 spines and 5 branched rays. Pectoral long and pointed. Caudal emarginate.

This family consists of a single genus, *Lethrinus*, with many species widely distributed, twelve of which occur in Queensland.

Although closely resembling the Sea Perch, *Lutjanus*, the members of this genus are readily recognized by their naked cheeks, only the opercles being scaled. The teeth are cardiform in front, with a few large canines, the lateral teeth in a single series, conical and pointed in the young, and in some species remaining so throughout life, in others becoming rounded, flat, and molar-like posteriorly. Some of the species grow to a large size and most of them are valued as food. The emperors feed upon other fishes, molluscs, crustaceans, and coral growths. They are great sporting fishes, biting voraciously and putting up a good fight when hooked. They swarm on the coral reefs, where great numbers are caught by line fishermen.

The emperors inhabit the waters from the east coast of Africa to Japan and the Indo-Pacific, with one species on the west coast of Africa.

Whilst the members of the genus are easily recognized, the species are difficult to determine, for the colour, shape of the head, and general form vary greatly with age. A good character in distinguishing the species is the number of scales between the middle of the spinous dorsal and the lateral line.

KEY TO SPECIES IN QUEENSLAND

Adapted from Weber and de Beaufort[23]

A. Maxillary reaching to below anterior border of eye; base of soft anal less than longest soft anal rays; $4\frac{1}{2}$ scales between lateral line and median dorsal spines. Soft dorsal with dark marmorations.   *kallopterus*

AA. Maxillary reaching to below nostrils; base of soft anal longer than longest anal rays.

   b. 4-$4\frac{1}{2}$ scales between lateral line and median dorsal spines.

     c. Lateral teeth in jaws conical, in young and adults.

      d. Second dorsal spine produced.   *nematacanthus*

      dd. Second dorsal spine not produced, shorter than third one.

       e. Height 3.3-3.5; eye 3-3.8.   *variegatus*

       ee. Height 2.8-3.1; eye 3.4-4.5.   *reticulatus*

     cc. Lateral teeth in jaws molar-like, at least posterior ones in adults. Greenish, each scale edged brown; caudal yellow.   *mahsena*

---

[23] *Fish. Indo-Austr. Archip.*, 7, 1936, p. 43.

bb. 5-5½ scales between lateral line and median dorsal
spines.

  f. Lateral teeth in jaws conical, pointed, even in
large specimens; snout long and pointed.   *miniatus*

  ff. Posterior teeth in jaws molar-like, at least in adults.

    g. A black blotch above origin of anal, near lateral
line.   *rhodopterus*

    gg. No black blotch above origin of anal.

      h. Third anal spine as long as eye. Olive-green, each
scale with a pearly-blue spot; a vermilion spot at
edge of operculum.   *nebulosus*

      hh. Third anal spine more than eye.

        i. Greenish-brown, with reddish longitudinal bands.   *ornatus*

        ii. Olive-green, with darker oblique transverse
bands; forehead, dorsal and pectoral axil scarlet.   *chrysostomus*

        iii. Olive-green, each scale with a pearly-blue
central spot and usually a much smaller basal
spot.   *glyphodon*

  fff. Lateral teeth in jaws molar-like.

    j. Olive-fawn, with pink horizontal lines following
scale rows; 3-4 blue lines and some spots radiating
from eye.   *fletus*

210. YELLOW-TAILED EMPEROR *Lethrinus mahsena* (Forskål)
[Colour-plate 25]

Sciaena mahsena Forskål, Descr. Anim., 1775, p. 52.
Illustration by G. Coates.

Yellow Morwong (Gladstone); Tricky Snapper (Cairns).

D. 10/9, 1; A. 3/8, 1; L. 1. 47-48; L. tr. 4½-6/1/14-16. Colour veronese-green,
becoming white below, every scale outlined with fawn-brown and blackish
marbling at base; belly tinged pink anteriorly; head brownish-grey between
eyes, green and bronze reflections on sides of face, cheeks grey; upper lip
salmon, scarlet at gape; lower lip white, tinged fawn; inside lips scarlet;
throat white; eye, pupil black, with a narrow gold line and surrounded
gold and yellow; dorsal spines brown, the membranes reddish-brown, becoming
pale grenadine-red on soft dorsal; extreme edge of both fins grenadine-red;
pectoral rays orange-rufous, the membranes hyaline, first ray blue; anal spines
and rays greenish-brown, the membranes orange-rufous, merging into
grenadine-red terminally and with the same colour splashed at base of fin;
caudal yellow, edged red.

Although varying greatly in colour this species is readily recognized by
its yellow caudal fin, which colour sometimes extends well across the body
to a line between soft dorsal and anal.

Said to be rarely met with in the Indo-Australian Archipelago, but very common on the coral reefs of North Queensland. Grows to 17 inches. Wide-ranging.

211. SPANGLED EMPEROR *Lethrinus nebulosus* (Forskål) [Colour-plate 25]

Sciaena nebulosa Forskål, Descr. Anim., 1775, p. 52.
Illustration by G. Coates.

Morwong (Queensland); Sand Snapper, Green Snapper, Sand Bream, Yellow Sweet-lip (North Queensland); Scavenger, Parrot-fish (South Africa).

D. 10/9, 1; A. 3/8, 1; L. 1. 48; L. tr. 5-7/1/14-16. Colour: Upper surface of body pale olive-green or fawnish, shading into silvery-grey or whitish below; each scale with a pearly-blue central spot and usually a much smaller basal spot, the upper and lower edges narrowly edged dull gold, forming more or less parallel rows; head dull violet or purplish above, sometimes with a broad, lighter cross-band between the eyes; cheeks violet-grey, with numerous small blue spots, usually not apparent until after death; 3 light-blue bands radiating from eye; blue spots on opercles and a brilliant red spot at their edges; inside mouth vermilion; dorsal spines olive, the membranes with traces of pink, becoming rose-pink in the soft dorsal, both fins with hazy wavy lines; similar wavy lines in caudal, which is purplish-pink; pectorals yellow, with a basal vermilion spot; ventrals pale yellow; anal tinged with vermilion.

A handsome and valuable food-fish found on the coral reefs of North Queensland and on the east coast of that State as far south as Moreton Bay. In the latter locality they are caught by means of meshing nets over the coral. Grows to at least 30 inches. Wide-ranging outside Australia.

212. SWEET-LIP EMPEROR *Lethrinus chrysostomus* Richardson
[Colour-plate 26]

Lethrinus chrysostomus Richardson, Ichth., Voy. Erebus and Terror, 1848, p. 118, pl. 60, figs 6-7.
Illustration by G. Coates.

Sweet-lip (Queensland); Sweet-lip, Nannygai, Lipper, Tricky Snapper (Townsville); Yellow-mouthed Perch, Island Snapper, Yellow-mouthed Snapper (New South Wales).

D. 10/8; A. 3/8; L. 1. 51; L. tr. 5/1/17. Colour: Body olive-greenish, lighter below, with darker oblique transverse bands which fade rapidly after death; head blood-red above to between and below eyes and on to snout; cheeks pinkish; gape of mouth with gout of crimson and short one posterior to it; spinous dorsal with brownish or bluish spines and scarlet membranes; soft dorsal with purplish-black rays and scarlet membranes; pectoral rays bluish, darkest at their base, the membranes pale pink; a scarlet-red patch in the axil; ventrals dusky-red, the rays pinkish and with a scarlet blotch basally; anal with spines and rays bluish, the membranes black at the bases and pinkish-red terminally; caudal red, the rays bluish.

This is the commonest *Lethrinus* on the Queensland coast, especially on the reefs. It is a splendid food-fish and grows to a length of 36 inches and a weight of 20 pounds. Like many other reef-fish it is caught from drifting boats over the patches between coral reefs.

213. RED-FINNED EMPEROR *Lethrinus fletus* Whitley   [Colour-plate 26]

Lethrinus fletus Whitley, Proc. Linn. Soc. N.S.Wales, 68, pts 3-4, 1943, p. 138.
Illustration by G. Coates.

Morwong, Sw Breameeps, C,et-lioral, Squir Piggy (Townsville).

D. 10/9; A. 3/8; L. 1. 47; L. tr. 6/1/17. Colour fawnish-olive above, lighter below, with pale-pink horizontal lines following scale rows; blue lines radiating from eye and breaking into spots of blue on snout and cheeks; 3 to 4 blue lines from eye to eye; inside mouth scarlet; dorsal, anal, and caudal pale olive-pink, with oblique pink wavy bands; anterior edge of pectorals, ventrals, and edge of anal blue; eye, pupil black, surrounded with rich brown and gold. Some examples have the body blotched with small dusky greyish-brown blotches.

A very common fish on the Queensland coast, its favourite haunts when young being the mangrove creeks along the coastline. Grows to at least 18 inches, but the average size caught is about 13 inches.

Coral Bream, Sweet-lips (Queensland); Grey Sweet-lip (Brisbane Fish Market); Grass Sweet-lip (Moreton Bay); Brown Kelp-fish (Mooloolaba); Red-throat (Gladstone); Snapper Bream (Whitsunday Passage); Brown

OTHER SPECIES

Yellow-spotted Emperor, *L. kallopterus*. A large emperor which ranges through the waters of North Queensland and New Guinea, Samoa, the East Indies, and the Philippines. Grows to at least 24 inches.

Lancer, *L. nematacanthus*. Wide-ranging and common, being found on the coasts of Queensland and New South Wales. Grows to only 9 inches.

Variegated Emperor, *L. variegatus*. Another wide-ranging emperor which is occasionally caught in North Queensland. Grows to 15 inches.

Reticulated Emperor, *L. reticulatus*. An Indo-Australian species, common in North Queensland and North Australia. Grows to 16 inches.

Long-nosed Emperor, *L. miniatus*. A species which ranges from the Red Sea to the South Pacific. Common on northern coral reefs of Queensland. Grows to a length of 36 inches and a weight of at least 10 pounds.

Black-bloch Emperor, *L. rhodopterus*. An Indo-Australian and South Pacific species found in the northern waters of Queensland. Grows to 16 inches.

Ornate Emperor, *L. ornatus*. Another Indo-Australian and South Seas species found in North Queensland. Grows to 18 inches.

Blue-spotted Emperor, *L. glyphodon*. A handsome and little-known fish from the Louisiade Archipelago, now known on the coast of North Queensland, where an example 10 inches in total length was taken at Townsville by G. Coates.

Family **Lobotidae**

Form oblong, compressed, scales of moderate or large size, weakly ctenoid, those on the head and bases of median fins smaller, forming a shallow sheath for the spinous dorsal. Jaws about equal or the lower more prominent, Jaws with narrow bands of villiform teeth and an outer series of somewhat enlarged conical ones. Vomer, palatines, and tongue toothless. Preoperculum serrated, operculum with 1 to 2 flat spines. Dorsal continuous, the spinous portion much longer than soft, with 12 strong spines and 13 to 17 rays. Anal with 3 spines, the soft portion opposite that of the dorsal, both fins rounded. Pectorals rounded. Ventrals with a spine and 5 rays and with a scaly axillary process. Caudal rounded.

A small family of two genera, related to the Serranidae but differing in the toothless palate and shortened forepart of the head. One genus, *Lobotes*, with its single species is found in the seas of Queensland.

214. TRIPLE-TAIL *Lobotes surinamensis* (Bloch) [Plate 36]

Holocentrus surinamensis Bloch, Nat. ausl. Fische, 4, 1790, p. 98.
Lobotes surinamensis Bleeker, Atlas Ichth., 8, 1876, p. 12, pl. 311, fig. 4.

Queensland Dusky Perch, Jumping Cod (North Queensland); Black Perch (Brisbane Fish Market); Flasher, Dormeur (America).

D. 11/15, 1; A. 3/11, 1; L. 1. 42-50; L. tr. 9-10/16-19. Colour umber or blackish, especially darker on the head, silvery-grey below, mottled paler and darker, or sometimes with yellowish tinge; pectorals and margin of caudal pale yellowish, rest of caudal and other fins usually darker than the body.

This species, which attains a length of 40 inches and a weight of 30 pounds, inhabits the coastal waters of Queensland and New South Wales. Though not occurring very plentifully in these States it is elsewhere a common and widely ranging species and is found in the West Indies and on the east coast of America (as far north as Cape Cod), in the Mediterranean, India, China, and the Malay Archipelago. It is a fish of sluggish habits, frequenting the coastal waters and entering the muddy creeks. G. Coates states: "When trapped or caught in a net it exhibits great jumping ability. This no doubt accounts for the local name of Jumping Cod." Its flesh is considered of good edible quality.

Family **Sparidae: Snapper and Sea Bream**

Body oblong, more or less compressed. Scales cycloid or minutely ctenoid, not extending on to snout, preorbital or suborbital. Mouth moderately protractile. Teeth in the jaws conical, incisors or molar-like. Canines present or absent. Palate toothless. A single dorsal fin formed by a spinous and soft portion, their bases of nearly equal extent. Anal with 3 spines. Pectorals long, pointed. Ventrals with a spine and 5 branched rays.

Large or moderate-sized fishes found in all temperate and tropical seas. Most of them are valued food-fishes, the family including such well-known species as the snapper, *Chrysophrys auratus*, and the breams, *Mylio*.

The members are best characterized by their dentition, which in some species takes the form of incisor or cutting teeth in the front of the jaws or molar-like crushing teeth posteriorly. The palate is edentulous. Six Australian genera.

KEY TO GENERA IN QUEENSLAND

A. Lateral teeth of jaws in a single series, conical or peg-like.

    b. Dorsal fin with 10 spines and 9-11 rays. Anal with 3 spines and 10-11 rays. Head scaly between eyes.   *Gymnocranius*

    bb. Dorsal fin with 12 spines and 10 rays. Anal with 3 spines and 8 rays. Head naked between eyes.   *Allotaius*

AA. Lateral teeth of jaws in several rows, conical or rounded, becoming larger and molar-like posteriorly.

    c. Molars in 2 series.   *Chrysophrys*

    cc. Molars in 3 or more series.

      d. Dorsal spines flexible and flattened, the second to fifth, produced into long filaments. Dorsal profile of head steep. Colour pinkish.   *Argyrops*

      dd. Dorsal spines rigid, none of them produced. Colours mainly silvery or blackish.

        e. One enlarged molar posteriorly in each jaw. Not less than 13 dorsal and anal rays. Body with longitudinal golden stripes.   *Rhabdosargus*

        ee. No single greatly enlarged molar posteriorly. Not more than 12 dorsal and 9 anal rays.   *Mylio*

Gymnocranius

Body deep, compressed, covered with large ctenoid scales. Head naked, except the opercles, subopercle, parietal region, and the posterior portions of the cheeks. Lateral line continuous, extending on to base of caudal. Dorsal 10/9-11, anal 3/10-11, both fins without scaly sheaths.

204

Marine shore fishes of moderate size, valued as food, having flesh of excellent flavour. They frequent the shore-line of the western Pacific; one species from the Red Sea. Of the few species, two occur in Queensland.

KEY TO SPECIES IN QUEENSLAND

A. Eye 3.3 in head. A broad milk-white nuchal collar, ending on each side in a semi-triangular mark behind the eye. *audleyi*

AA. Eye 4.3 in head. No nuchal collar; cheeks with a series of wavy blue bands. *marshalli*

215. COLLARED SEA BREAM *Gymnocranius audleyi* Ogilby
[Colour-plate 26]

Gymnocranius audleyi Ogilby, Mem. Qld Mus., 5, 1916, p. 170, pl. 22.
Illustration by G. Coates.

Bastard Bream (Gladstone); Sand Snapper (Townsville); Coral Bream (Brisbane Fish Market).

D. 10/10, 1; A. 3/10, 1; L. 1. 48; L. tr. 6/1/15-16. Colour silvery, head with fawn-brown tinge and bluish reflections; eye, pupil black, surrounded with silver above and gold below; spinous and soft dorsal fawn colour, the edge tinged narrowly with red; pectorals pale citron-yellow; ventrals whitish; anal pale citron-green, narrowly edged with pale red; caudal rays whitish, the membranes green, the whole fin narrowly edged all round with red.

A common fish on the Queensland coast from the Capricorns northwards. Found as far south as Moreton Bay, though never in any great numbers. A good food-fish, comparing favourably with other sea breams. Grows to 14 inches.

An aberrant specimen, thought to be this species, is in the collection of the Queensland Museum. It is 23½ inches in length and weighs 9½ pounds.

216. MAORI SEA BREAM *Gymnocranius marshalli* (Whitley)

Paradentex marshalli Whitley, Mem. Qld Mus., 11, pt 1, 1936, p. 27.

D. 10/10 (11); A. 3/11; L. 1. 50; L. tr. 7/1/17. Colours taken several hours after death were: General colour silvery, with purplish reflections; numerous wavy blue lines before and below eyes; all fins hyaline, with traces of pale green, edges of dorsal, caudal, and anal orange; inside of mouth pale orange.

Known only from a single specimen in the collection of the Queensland Museum, caught on Rib Reef, near Townsville by G. Coates. Its length is 24 inches.

Allotaius

Form of body deep. More than 45 scales in lateral line. Body scales fairly uniform in size. Cheek scales in 5 rows. Eye large. Posterior nostril slit-like. Preopercular flange scaly. Preorbital shallow, not crenulated. Dorsal spines 12. No fin spines or rays produced.

A single species, known only from South Queensland.

217. CAPE MORETON SEA BREAM *Allotaius spariformis* (Ogilby)

[Plate 36]

Dentex spariformis Ogilby, New Fish. Qld Coast, 20th Dec. 1910, p. 91 (a suppressed publication).
Dentex spariformis Ogilby, Mem. Qld Mus., 5, 1916, p. 169, pl. 21.

D. 12/10; A. 3/8; L. 1. 49-51; L. tr. 5/1/15-16. Colour: Upper surface of body pink, washed with gold, lower surface and sides silvery; head dull red above, shading imperceptibly into the paler body-colour; dorsal and caudal fins saffron-yellow, the base and lateral borders of the latter pink; anal and ventral fins colourless; pectoral with upper half yellow, the lower hyaline. (After Ogilby.)

A species evidently inhabiting fairly deep water. It was first taken by the last haul of the *Endeavour* in 1910, when 141 examples were trawled in 73 fathoms on a bottom of fine sand and mud at a distance of 36.5 miles S. 12° W. from Cape Moreton, Southern Queensland. It has since been taken several times in New South Wales. Grows to 10 inches.

Chrysophrys

Form oblong, ovate, somewhat deep, compressed. Head large, deep. Mouth terminal, small, low. Anterior teeth in jaws cardiform, outer series usually little enlarged, canine-like, not compressed. Teeth behind canines slender, acute. Two or three rows of rounded molars, sometimes mixed with slender teeth. Preopercle entire. Opercle unarmed. Twelve dorsal spines.

Carnivorous fishes found in the waters of Asia, Australia, and New Zealand, the young close inshore, the adults in deeper outside waters. Two species are listed by some authors—*C. major* and *C. auratus*. According to Fowler[24] they are indistinguishable structurally. He states: "I am therefore obliged to leave the species simply as provisional geographic expressions, *C. major* Indo-Chinese-Japanese and *C. auratus* Australian."

---

[24] U.S. Nat. Mus. Bull. 100 .12 .1933, p. 139.

218. SNAPPER *Chrysophrys auratus* (Bloch and Schneider) [Colour-plate 27; Plate 36]

Labrus auratus Bloch and Schneider, Syst. Ichth., 1801, p. 266.
Illustration by G. Coates; photograph (cast of head) from *Courier-Mail*, Brisbane.

Cockney, Red Bream, Squire, Schnapper (Australia).

D. 12/10; A. 3/8; L. 1. 54-55; L. tr. 9-10/16-17. Colour delicate pink above, passing into silvery-white below, with numerous irregular bright-blue spots which fade out and become lost in very old examples; upper parts of head darker pink or dark reddish-brown in old fish; cheeks flushed with purplish or sometimes yellowish-gold; dorsal fin pink, with or without blue spots; pectorals pink; caudal pinkish, the colour deeper on the upper lobe; ventrals and anal pale pink or white.

Very young fish up to about 4 inches have dark transverse bands on the body, which become lost after the first year. It is at this age that they are known as cockneys. From one to two years and a weight of one pound is the red bream stage, and from two to three years and a weight of 3 pounds they are called squire. From this stage onward they are Snapper.

The Snapper up to the squire stage of its life is to be found in the sheltered bays and inlets along the coast, the adults preferring the deeper outside waters, usually in the vicinity of reefs where they move in schools.

As the age of the fish increases, the hump on the head develops to a remarkable degree, whilst the mouth becomes more fleshy and the snout more pronounced, the head resembling the face of an old man. It is this likeness which has earned them the name of Old Man Snapper. These old fish cease to school and lead a solitary existence. They grow to a large size, and examples up to 4 feet 3 inches and weighing 43 pounds are known. The Snapper is a valuable food-fish and always commands a good price in the markets. Its range is along the eastern and southern coastline of Australia. In Queensland the most northerly point at which it is caught in any numbers is off Mackay. North of this locality it is scarce, and at Bowen and Townsville it is almost unknown.

Argyrops

Distinguished from *Rhabdosargus* and *Mylio* chiefly by the anterior dorsal spines (usually third to fifth or sixth) being greatly lengthened and filamentous. A single wide-ranging species.

219. LONG-SPINED SNAPPER *Argyrops spinifer* (Forskål) [Colour-plate 27]

Sparus spinifer Forskål, Descr. Anim., 1775, p. 32.
Illustration by G. Coates.

Bowen Snapper, Steamboat Bream (North Queensland); Redfin (South Africa).

D. 11-12/10, 1, or 11; A. 3/8, 1; L. 1. 49-53; L. tr. 7-8/1/16-18. Colour reddish or rose-pink above, darkest on snout and nape, paler or silvery below; faint longitudinal pink lines along each row of scales and with 4 to 5 deeper broad transverse bands across body; anal and ventrals whitish, other fins pale pink or hyaline; pupil of eye black, surrounded red. The vertical bands are much plainer in the young, becoming lost with age.

A handsome and uncommon fish which frequents sunken shoals and reefs. It ranges from Africa to the Indo-Australian region and Australia and is found on the Queensland coast from north to south. Grows to 24 inches. A good food-fish.

Rhabdosargus

Differing from *Mylio* in having the dorsal and anal spines slender to moderate. The second anal spine is slender and not greatly larger than the third. Soft dorsal and anal fins without scaly basal sheaths.

Fishes of the waters of Africa, the Indo-Australian Archipelago, and Japan. Three species, one in Australia.

220. TARWHINE *Rhabdosargus sarba* (Forskål)   [Colour-plate 28]

Sparus sarba Forskål, Descr. Anim., 1775, p. 31.
Illustration by G. Coates.

Silver Bream, River Stump-nose (South Africa); Yellowfin Bream, Silver Bream (Natal).

D. 11/13-15; A. 3/11-12 (10); L. 1. 55-70; L. tr. 7/12-16. Colour silvery-greyish, each scale with a golden centre, forming longitudinal lines on body; head golden-brown above, cheeks silvery, with blue tinges; a bright longi-tudinal band above base of ventrals; dorsal fin hyaline at its base, rest of fin dusky; anal with basal half hyaline, the terminal half yellow; caudal olive-yellow, edged black; pectorals and ventrals yellow; eye brown.

In Australian waters this wide-ranging fish is found in Queensland, New South Wales, and Western Australia. It is, however, most common in South Queensland and the northern parts of New South Wales. Rarely seen in North Queensland. A good food-fish with habits similar to the bream. Grows to a length of 16 inches and a weight of at least 4 pounds. Said to reach a weight of 25 pounds in South Africa.

Mylio: Bream

Dorsal fin-spines strong. Second anal fin-spine very stout and greatly enlarged. Soft dorsal and anal fins densely scaled at their bases. Four to six incisiform teeth anteriorly in each jaw.

The genus *Mylio*, restricted to Africa, Indo-Australia, and Japan, whilst not containing many species nevertheless includes several fishes which are of economic importance in many parts of the world, especially in Australia. There are two species in Queensland.

These splendid food-fishes, known as bream in our seas, are to be seen in Australian markets in large quantities at all times of the year, the busy months in the Brisbane Fish Market being from May to August.

Bream frequent the inshore waters and ocean beaches as well as the rivers and estuaries, travelling far up the streams in dry weather when the salinity of the water is high, but they return down the rivers when the "freshes" occur. The usual method of capture for the market is by means of hauling nets, though great numbers are also taken by hook and line. They are popular game-fishes with amateur anglers on account of the good fight they put up when hooked.

Bream are carnivorous in habit, feeding chiefly upon molluscs, crustaceans, and small fishes. The molluscs are crushed with the aid of the powerful molars. On the oyster banks the Yellowfin Bream is a pest on account of the great damage it does to the immature oysters.

KEY TO SPECIES IN QUEENSLAND

A. Second anal spine not or scarcely enlarged. Body colour silvery or golden-olive with streaks lengthwise along scale-rows; ventral and anal fins yellow or brownish.   *australis*

AA. Second anal spine enlarged. Body colour dusky-grey or black, without longitudinal streaks; ventral and anal fins dusky.   *berda*

221. YELLOWFIN or COMMON BREAM *Mylio australis* (Günther)
[Colour-plate 28]

Chrysophrys australis Günther, Cat. Fish. Brit. Mus., 1, 1849, p. 494.
Illustration by G. Coates.

Bream, Sea Bream, Surf Bream (Queensland); Black Bream, Silver Bream (New South Wales).

D. 10-12/10-13; A. 3/8-10; L. 1. 47-58; L. tr. 4-6/11-15. Colour silvery olive-green, the edges of the scales white; silvery-white below; head olive-green above, cheeks blue with golden reflections, chin whitish; dorsal spines silvery, the membranes pearly, edged dusky; rays hyaline; pectorals yellow, a black axillary spot at the base; ventrals yellow on the rays, the membranes hyaline; caudal brownish-yellow with a darker broad margin.

One of the best known food-fishes in Queensland. It occurs on the coast as far north as Townsville but is more plentifully met with in the southern waters of the State where it occurs in great numbers. It is also found in the waters of New South Wales and Victoria. Caught by both net and hand-line.

According to Roughley[25] the largest example of this species, of which there

---

[25] *Fish and Fisheries oj Australia*, 1951.

is an authentic record, is one landed by an angler named Negus in the Georges River, New South Wales, in April 1916. It weighed 7 pounds 6 ounces.

Writing about the spawning and early life-history of bream, S. R. Munro, a biologist who has made an extensive study in Australia of this fish, states:[26] "Bream on the Australian east coast spawn once a year, but in any particular locality this is spread over a period of several months. The peak is usually during mid-winter. Large bream appear to enter river mouths from the sea during the spawning seasons, but there is no defined seasonal coastal migration that can be correlated directly with the spawning behaviour, as is the case with mullet. Large bream often carry as many as from $2\frac{1}{2}$ to 3 million eggs, but there is evidence that all of these are not spawned. It is unlikely that many of the resulting fry reach maturity.

"The eggs are very small and spherical, and when shed into the sea float near the surface. They appear to be spawned and fertilised at night on a flooding tide when the moon is full. These eggs are shed at the mouths of rivers just inside the turbulent zone where the surf breaks on the sand bars which characterise the mouths of most eastern rivers. Hatching occurs about $2\frac{1}{2}$ to 3 days after fertilisation. When the tiny larvae have grown in length to about half an inch, they cease to be planktonic, and move to the food and shelter afforded by the grassy flats and brackish creeks situated within a mile or so of the river mouth and the sea.

"Most of the first year of life is spent in the weed shallows of the lower reaches of the rivers in which they were spawned. The coloration and shape of the adult fish are rapidly acquired, and as growth continues the Bream assemble in small schools of a dozen or more, and move further afield and into deeper water in search of food. Little is definitely known about the movements of more mature fish, but a tagging programme is being undertaken by the C.S.I.R. to throw some light upon that question."

222. PIKEY BREAM *Mylio berda* (Forskål) [Colour-plate 29]

Sparus berda Forskål, Descr. Anim., 1775, p. 32.
Illustration by G. Coates.

Black Bream (Townsville); Black Bream, River Perch, River or Mud Bream, Sly Bream, Picnic Bream (South Africa).

D. 11-12/10-13; A. 3/8-9; L. 1. 46-54; L. tr. 4-5/9-13. Colour grey to dark silvery-grey or dull olive-brown, darkest at bases of scales above, lower surface of head and body white, everywhere with silvery and brassy reflections; dorsal and anal with dark edges, the spines of the dorsal silvery; caudal darker terminally; pectorals straw-yellow; anal and ventrals blackish.

A wide-ranging species found in the northern waters of Australia from Darwin in the Northern Territory to the North Queensland coast about as

---

[26] *Fisheries Newsletter*, 4, no. 5, Sept. 1945, p. 2.

H

far south as Mackay. It is a very common species and can usually be captured around wharf piles. Known by the long and very stout second anal spine and by its dark coloration. Grows to 15 inches. A good food-fish. In India it is said to reach a length of 30 inches.

Family **Sciaenidae**

Form oblong to more or less elongate, somewhat compressed; scales somewhat thin, adherent, ciliated or cycloid, extending more or less on to median fins. Lateral line complete, often continued on to caudal. Head scaled. Muciferous pores usually present on chin and often on snout. Sometimes a barbel or barbels under symphysis of mandible. Eyes lateral, anterior. Mouth more or less protractile, in front of or below the snout, oblique to horizontal. Jaws equal, subequal, or the lower prominent. Muciferous pores on head well developed. Teeth in jaws in a villiform band or a narrow band with an outer and inner row of conical distant or close-set, often enlarged teeth which become true canines in some genera in a restricted number. Vomer, palatines, and tongue toothless. Cheeks unarmed. Opercles sometimes with weak spines. Dorsal fin more or less deeply notched or incised (by exception *Pama*), the spinous portion sometimes depressible into a scaly groove, shorter than soft dorsal. Anal usually much shorter than soft dorsal and with 1 or 2 spines. Ventrals thoracic, with 1 spine and 5 rays. Caudal rounded.

This large family of coastal fishes, important from an economic point of view, inhabits the sandy shores of all warm seas, except those of the Pacific Islands, from which they are unaccountably absent. Most of them grow to a large size, and species such as the European Maigre, *Johnius hololepidotus*, and the Jewfish, *J. antarctica*, a closely related species, attain a length of over 6 feet and exceed a weight of 100 pounds.

Most of the species freely enter the estuaries, making their way upstream far beyond tidal influence, pursuing and feeding upon the shoals of small mullet, garfishes, herrings, and other small fishes. Some species are wholly confined to fresh water.

Jewfish are good sporting fishes, biting greedily and putting up a good fight when hooked. All are good food-fishes, but the larger species, when over 2 feet in length, are coarse and tasteless. The air-bladders or "sounds" of these fishes are very large and are used in the manufacture of an inferior brand of isinglass, and on the coast of India they are extensively collected and exported.

Otoliths or ear-bones, found in the skulls of many fishes, are especially large in the Sciaenidae. The ear-bones of the European Maigre were well known to the ancients, who called them "colic-stones". Some of the species have the power of producing loud sounds which can be heard plainly by occupants in a boat when the fish is some distance below the surface. The production of this noise, which has been called "drumming" and which has caused the names of drums, croakers, and grunters to be bestowed on them, is considered to be due to muscular action on the air-bladder. The name of jewfish is apparently a corruption of "dewfish"—which was given on account of their beautiful silvery-grey colour. The Salmon Bass or Kabeljaauw of South Africa belongs to this family. Four genera occur in Queensland waters.

KEY TO GENERA IN QUEENSLAND

A. No barbel on chin.

b. No pores on chin.

c. Strong, curved, conspicuous canines anteriorly in
both jaws. Caudal rounded or cuneate.   *Otolithes*

cc. Bands of villiform teeth in jaws, with enlarged
series in both, though no canines. Caudal lunate.   *Atractoscion*

bb. Pores present on chin.   *Johnius*

AA. Single barbel on chin, with a wide pore at its base.   *Sciaena*

Otolithes

Fishes of the Indo-Pacific region, some growing to a large size and living both in the sea and in brackish waters, even penetrating far up into fresh water. One species in Queensland.

223. SILVER TERAGLIN *Otolithes argenteus* (Cuvier and Valenciennes)
[Plate 36]

Otolithus argenteus Cuvier and Valenciennes, Hist. Nat. Poiss., 5, 1830, p. 62.
Otolithus argenteus Ogilby, Mem. Qld Mus., 6, 1918, p. 63, pl. 20.

Yankee Whiting (Townsville); Wire-tooth (Rockhampton district).

D. 10-11/1/29; A. 2/7; L. 1. 72-75; L. tr. 8/1/19. Colour: Silvery, darker along the back and washed with blue and pink iridescence above the lateral line; a dark blotch on the opercle; paired fins yellowish; dorsal bordered dusky; caudal yellowish.

A wide-ranging fish found in the northern waters of the east coast of Queensland. A good food-fish. Grows to 32 inches.

Atractoscion

Shore-fishes of large size from the coasts of south-eastern Australia and South Africa, inhabiting the more open waters of the bays and beaches. Valuable food-fishes. One species.

224. TERAGLIN *Atractoscion aequidens* (Cuvier and Valenciennes) [Plate 36]

Otolithus aequidens Cuvier and Valenciennes, Hist. Nat. Poiss., 5, p. 66.
Cynoscion atelodus Roughley, Fish. Austr., 1916, p. 115, pl. 36.

Teraglin-jew (Brisbane Fish Market); Geelbek, Cape Salmon (South Africa). D. 10, 1/29-31; A. 2/9; L. l. 74-77; L. tr. 16/1/33. Colour bluish above, silvery on sides and white below; cheeks washed with gold; inside of mouth, lips and edges and inside opercles bright yellow; irides golden; dorsals yellowish-grey, with darker spots at base; caudal greenish-yellow, with outer edges and tips darker; anal silvery-white, the anterior rays clouded; pectorals grey, with a black axillary spot; ventrals pinkish-white.

This fine food-fish is captured fairly commonly in the waters of South Queensland, mainly during the winter months, when it wanders into these waters as far north as Mooloolaba. It is more frequently met with in New South Wales, where at times great shoals are seen off the coastline.

Unlike the Jewfish it seldom ventures close inshore, being more a lover of the outside waters and deep bays. On account of these habits it is only occasionally caught in the fishermen's nets. It is, however, frequently taken by hook and line, and always commands a ready sale in the fish markets. As a food-fish it ranks high, its flesh being considered greatly superior to its congener, the Jewfish. Found also in South Africa. Grows to 4 feet 2 inches in length and 20 pounds in weight.

Johnius

Snout obtusely rounded, sometimes overhanging lower jaw, frequently with conspicuous slits and pores. Chin with pores, rarely with rudimentary barbel.

A genus of many species of sciaenids inhabiting the waters of all warm seas. Seven species occur in Queensland waters.

KEY TO SPECIES IN QUEENSLAND

A. Second anal spine short and weak.

    b. A pale band containing the lateral line in its entire course.   *carutta*

    bb. No pale band along lateral line.

      c. Preorbital and interorbital region narrow, the former about 2.5 in the eye-diameter, the latter about 5.25 in the head; scales above lateral line in 85-96 series; size large.   *antarctica*

      cc. Preorbital and interorbital region wider, the former 1.5 in the eye-diameter, the latter about 3.75 in the head; scales above lateral line in 54-56 series; size small.   *australis*

AA. Second anal spine long and strong.

    d. Second anal spine stout, about half the length of the head, or almost so.

      e. Body sub-ovate, its depth more than one-third of its length; second anal spine very strong, almost half as long as the head; size large.   *soldado*

      ee. Body elliptical, its depth less than one-third of its length; second anal spine half as long as head; size small.   *mulleri*

    dd. Second anal spine rather short, about one-third of the length of the head.

      f. Body, dorsal and caudal fins with many black spots; young banded and spotted; snout not swollen.   *diacanthus*

      ff. Body and fins not spotted; snout swollen   *novae-hollandiae*

225. JEWFISH or MULLOWAY *Johnius antarctica* (Castlenau)   [Plate 37]

Sciaena antarctica Castlenau, Proc. Zool. Acclim. Soc. Vic., 1, 1872, p. 100.
Sciaena hololepidota antarctica Ogilby, Mem. Qld Mus., 6, 1918, p. 70, pl. 21.

Silver Jew (New South Wales); Butter-fish, Mulloway (South Australia); Kingfish (Victoria and south-west Australia); River Kingfish (Western Australia).

D. 10, 1/27-28; A. 2/7; L. 1. 85-90; L. tr. 11-12/1/19-21. Colour: The young are steel-blue above, becoming dark grey-blue or brownish-green in adults, shading through the silvery-grey of the sides to pure white on throat and abdomen; dorsal and caudal brownish; ventrals and anal white; pectorals greenish, with a black axillary spot; sides of head gold; inside of mouth and inner border of opercles orange. The young usually have narrow oblique bars running upwards and backwards following the rows of scales above the lateral line.

A common fish in South Queensland waters, being found in the sea, bays, and rivers at all times of the year, but especially plentiful during the winter months. Rarely met with north of the Burnett River, but extremely plentiful from Moreton Bay down along the south-eastern to the southern seaboard of Australia and across to the west.

Jewfishes are cunning, powerful, and voracious fishes, capable of great speed, and are relentless killers. They cause great havoc with the shoals of spawning mullet as these fishes enter the estuaries, rounding them up and making fierce onslaughts, killing and maiming far in excess of what they can consume.

Examples to a length of 24 inches are called Silver Jew, and to this stage are of good edible quality, but older ones are coarse and tasteless. They grow to at least 6 feet in length and at least 134 pounds in weight.

226. LITTLE JEWFISH *Johnius australis* (Günther) [Plate 37]

Corvina australis Günther, Rept Voy. Challenger, Zool., 1, 6, 1880, p. 33.
Sciaena australis Ogilby, Mem. Qld Mus., 6, 1918, p. 75, pl. 22.

Perch (Moreton Bay district); Little Jew-perch, River Perch (South Queensland).

D. 10, 1/29-31; A. 2/7; L. 1. 54-56; L. tr. 9/1/16-18. Colours when received fresh, silvery-grey above, pure silver on sides, passing into whitish below, over which is a tinge of ochre-yellow over chest, belly, and underparts of caudal peduncle; upper and lateral scales densely powdered with dusky dots to form 4 broad, sometimes indistinct, bands of dark greyish; scales of breast and belly with margins of copper-coloured dots; head dark brownish above, nape purplish; inside mouth golden; dorsal (spinous) closely dotted, blackish on outer third; soft dorsal densely dotted blackish, the centre longitudinally much less so, thus forming a greyish band in the central third of the fin; pectorals, ventrals, and anal yellowish, the former less so, all with a few blackish dots; caudal yellowish, densely covered with dusky dots, edged terminally with blackish.

These fish enter the rivers of South Queensland during the early winter months (usually about the month of March) in great numbers, evidently for the purpose of feeding only, retiring again to the deeper waters of the bays in the spring to spawn. When travelling in the rivers they bite freely, and dozens may be caught in a few hours, the usual bait being prawns.

The species has a very limited range, being known only from Queensland. It is seldom seen in the northern parts of the State. Although small it is an excellent eating fish. Grows to only 12 inches.

227. SILVER JEWFISH *Johnius soldado* (Lacépède) [Plate 37]

Holocentrus soldado Lacépède, Hist. Nat. Poiss., 4, 1802, pp. 344, 389.
Sciaena soldado Ogilby, Mem. Qld Mus., 6, 1918, p. 81, pl. 24.

Silver Perch, Grassy Jew, Banana Jew (North Queensland).

D. 10, 1/28-32; A. 2/7; L. 1. 62-65; L. tr. 8/1/16. Colour greyish or silvery, darkened with greenish or pinkish above, becoming white on sides and below; dorsals dusky, the spines and rays darker and sometimes with a small brown spot in front of each ray; outer edges of fins dark in some examples, except the ventrals which are white; rest of fins yellow.

A wide-ranging jewfish commonly found in North Queensland waters. It is extremely common in the Gulf of Carpentaria, where it penetrates the rivers far up into the fresh water. As a food-fish it is said to have flesh of fair edible quality. Grows to at least 30 inches.

OTHER SPECIES

Banded Jewfish, *J. carutta*. A small species from the Indo-Australian Archipelago which has been recorded in Australian waters from the Gulf of Carpentaria, where it is extremely common. Grows to only about 12 inches.

Sharp-nosed Jewfish, *J. mulleri*. Frequents the waters of the Northern Territory and North Queensland. A small fish, growing to only about 12 inches.

Spotted Jewfish, *J. diacanthus*. An Indo-Australian fish which frequents the waters of North Queensland. It is said to reach a length of 5 feet. G. Coates of Townsville states: "I have caught them up to 50 pounds and have seen one nearly 100 pounds." Known by its spotted pattern.

Bottle-nose Jewfish, *J. novae-hollandiae*. Another small species found on the coasts of Queensland and New South Wales. Grows to 11 inches. Recognized by its bottle nose.

Sciaena

Body ovate, oblong. Snout prominent, conspicuous pores present; similar pores on chin, on which is also situated a somewhat short, thick barbel.

Fishes of most warm seas, some entering rivers. Species few, one in Queensland.

228. BEARDED JEWFISH *Sciaena dussumieri* (Cuvier and Valenciennes) [Colour-plate 29]

Umbrina dussumieri Cuvier and Valenciennes, Hist. Nat. Poiss., 9, 1833, p. 481.
Illustration by G. Coates.

D. 11/23, 1, or 24; A. 2/7, 1; L. 1. 52-57; L. tr. 8/10-12. Colour dark brown or greyish above, sometimes nearly black and often with a coppery tinge and shot with golden reflections; silvery below, tinged yellow; fins reddish-brown, first dorsal stained with black, other fins powdered brown, with grey edges; ventrals yellow.

A wide-ranging fish, rare on the coast of Queensland where it has been recorded off Townsville and Yeppoon. Grows to 10 inches.

Family **Carangidae**

A large and varied family of pelagic or coastal fishes, found in all tropical and temperate seas, a few species ascending rivers and entering fresh water. They are powerful, active, and fast-swimming fishes of moderate or large size, many having the habit of moving through the water with the dorsal fin above the surface. Most of the species are widely distributed, and almost all are valued food-fishes. Four sub-families are represented in Australian waters.

A. Lateral line armed with a series of enlarged bony scutes, at least posteriorly. Pectorals long, falcate. Anal base about as long as that of the soft dorsal.   CARANGINAE

AA. No enlarged body scutes on the lateral line.

    b. Bases of dorsal and anal fins of equal length, both much longer than abdomen. Pectorals short, not falcate.

        c. Dorsal and anal fins with several more or less detached finlets.   CHORINEMINAE

        cc. Dorsal and anal fins without finlets.   TRACHINOTINAE

    bb. Base of anal fin much shorter than that of soft dorsal, its base not longer than the abdomen. Pectorals short, not falcate.   SERIOLINAE

Sub-family CARANGINAE

Form oblong, ovate or rhombic, usually strongly compressed; scales small, cycloid (minute and embedded in the skin in one genus) on cheeks, top of head, and opercles, sometimes wanting to a greater or lesser degree on breast. Lateral line more or less curved anteriorly followed by a straight part with usually keeled scutes, larger than the other scales. Teeth in villiform bands in jaws and on vomer, palatines, and tongue. Jaws sometimes with an outer row of enlarged conical teeth or only a single series, or the dentition may be variously incomplete. Spinous dorsal fin with 7 to 8 weak connected spines, preceded by a procumbent spine, more or less hidden in the skin. In some genera one or more of the posterior rays of the dorsal and anal fins are detached finlets. Pectorals long, falcate. Caudal deeply forked.

A. One or more finlets behind soft dorsal and anal fins.

    b. Several finlets behind soft dorsal and anal fins.   *Megalaspis*
    bb. One finlet behind soft dorsal and anal fins.   *Decapterus*

AA. No true finlets behind soft dorsal and anal fins.

    c. Lateral line armed along its entire length.   *Trachurus*
    cc. Lateral line armed on part of its length only.

[27] *Fish. Indo-Austr. Archip.*, 6, 1931, p. 192.

    d. Dorsal spines 7-8, connected by membrane; none of the anterior dorsal and anal rays equal the length of the body.

        e. Gill-rakers of moderate length and shape.   *Caranx*

      ee. Gill-rakers extremely long, feather-like in shape and reaching into the mouth.   *Ulua*

  dd. Dorsal spines less than 7, rudimentary, not connected by membrane; anterior dorsal and anal rays at least equalling the length of the body.   *Alectis*

 ddd. Dorsal spines rudimentary, hidden (except the last one), about 4 in number. Anterior dorsal and anal rays short, not equalling length of body.   *Parastromateus*

Megalaspis

This genus includes only one species, the Finletted Mackerel Scad, *M. cordyla* (Linnaeus), a wide-ranging fish rarely seen in Australian waters. Known by the presence of several finlets behind the dorsal and anal fins. Grows to 24 inches.

Decapterus

Body elongate, subfusiform. Scales small, cycloid. Lateral line feebly curved, with enlarged scales throughout its length, those on straight portion spinigerous. Dentition weak, teeth in jaws minute, mostly in a single series. Similar teeth on vomer and palatines, and usually on tongue. Eyes large, with well-developed adipose lid. Spinous dorsal well developed, with 7 to 9 flexible spines. Soft dorsal and anal lobes low, each followed by a single finlet, the former with 27 to 36, the latter with 23 to 30 soft rays. Free anal spines strong. Caudal small, narrowly forked. Pectoral falcate, 21 to 23 rays. Ventrals moderate, below pectoral base.

    Small scombriform trevallies found in most temperate and tropical seas. Species numerous, one in Queensland.

229. NORTHERN MACKEREL SCAD *Decapterus russellii* (Rüppell)
[Plate 37]

Caranx russellii Rüppell, Atlas Fische Roth. Meer., 1828, p. 99.
Decapterus russellii Ogilby, Mem. Qld Mus., 3, 1915, p. 59, pl. 19.

    Lajang (East Indies).
    D. 8, 1/31, 1; A. 2, 1/25-27; L. 1. scutes 32-33. Colour dark blue or greenish-blue above, silvery below, with a diffused yellow longitudinal lateral band; snout, interorbital region, and upper head blackish; a narrow black spot on opercle; hinder base of pectoral blackish, axillary spot absent or small; fins hyaline or yellowish, tinged with red; caudal narrowly edged with yellow.
    Another wide-ranging species, only occasionally found on the coast of Queensland. Grows to 18 inches.

Trachurus: Horse Mackerels

Form long, slender, somewhat compressed. Scales small. Eye large, with broad adipose lids. Mouth moderate, snout rather conic. Lateral line armed throughout its whole length with large bony scutes. Two dorsal fins, the first preceded by a procumbent spine. Anal preceded by 2 spines. No finlets.

Species few, found in all warm seas, two in Queensland.

KEY TO SPECIES IN QUEENSLAND

A. Depth of body 4-4.4 in the total length; less than 73 scutes on the lateral line. *declivis*

AA. Depth of body 4.7-5.2 in the total length; more than 73 scutes on the lateral line. *novae-zelandiae*

230. SCAD *Trachurus declivis* (Jenyns) [Plate 37]

Caranx declivis Jenyns, Voy. Beagle, Zool., 3, Fish., 1841, p. 68.
Trachurus declivis McCulloch, Biol. Res. Endeavour, 3, pt 3, 1915, p. 125, pl. 34, fig. 2.

Bung (Queensland); Horse Mackerel (New South Wales and Victoria); Yellow-tail (New South Wales).

D. 8, 1/30-34; A. 2, 1/26-31; L. 1. 26-28 + 7-9 + 35-38. Colour yellowish-green above, darkest on head; sides golden, silvery below, with reflections of bluish or pinkish iridescence; dorsal, anal, and pectoral fins greenish-yellow; ventrals hyaline; caudal greenish-yellow, the lobes yellow.

Old adults of this species have the last rays of the dorsal and anal fins much enlarged and forming semi-detached finlets which approach somewhat to *Decapterus*. A common fish in the inlets and bays of the coasts of South Queensland and the southern half of Australia. Grows to 13 inches.

OTHER SPECIES

Jack Mackerel or "Cowanyoung", *T. novae-zelandiae*. An oceanic species found in large shoals in the open seas of southern Australia and Tasmania, the young sometimes entering the inlets. It also occurs in New Zealand. Grows to 18 inches and is a food-fish of fair quality.

Caranx: Trevallies

Body ovate to oblong-ovate, compressed. Scales very small. Breast scaly or naked. Hind part or straight section of lateral line armed with strong bony scutes, largest on caudal peduncle and each scute with a spine. Dorsal spines rather low, connected by membrane, both fins depressible into groove. Second dorsal long, front portion usually elevated into a lobe. Anal similar, preceded by 2 spines. Caudal strongly forked.

Fishes occurring in all warm seas. Many species of the true trevallies, all of which are valuable food-fishes, are found in the seas of Queensland. The young are netted in numbers in the sandy bays along the coastline or inside the estuaries, whilst the adults are lovers of the outer waters and open ocean. The adults congregate in great schools on the foreshore banks during the breeding season to shed their spawn. Many of the species grow to a large size, and all are good game-fishes, putting up a stubborn fight when hooked.

The species are somewhat difficult to determine, and the following key, which has been adapted from McCulloch's splendid key to the family, is preceded by a note of caution. McCulloch states: "Care is necessary in using this key, as the principal characters, the dentition and the squamation of the breast are evidently somewhat variable with growth. Further, their gradation from one type to another is so complete in the numerous species that some forms are intermediate between two sections, and can be placed almost equally well in either of two divisions."

KEY TO SPECIES

Adapted from McCulloch[28]

A. Teeth present on jaws and usually on vomer and palatines also.

    b. A row of larger teeth along front and sides of each jaw, which are exterior to and markedly different from the smaller depressible inner teeth, when these are present.

    c. Breast wholly or partially naked.

     d. Breast entirely naked before a line between pectorals and ventrals.

      e. Straight portion of the lateral line much longer than the very short curved portion and armed with strong scutes. *bucculentus*

     dd. Breast partially naked ventrally.

      f. A patch of scales before the ventral fins surrounded by a naked area; body deeper. *ignobilis*

      ff. Breast wholly naked on the ventral surface; general form more slender. *papuensis*

    cc. Breast entirely scaly.

     g. Straight portion of lateral line much shorter than curved portion; a single row of teeth in each jaw; maxillary not reaching the anterior margin of eye. *georgianus*

---

[28] *Mem. Qld Mus.*, 8 pt 1, 30th Jan. 1924, p. 67.

gg. Straight portion of lateral line longer than curved portion; upper jaw with an inner band of villiform teeth; maxillary reaching backward beyond the vertical of the anterior margin of the eye. — *sexfasciatus*

bb. No outer row of larger teeth in jaws, though some fixed conical teeth may be present exterior to the smaller inner depressible ones, if those are present.

h. Breast wholly or partially naked.

i. A band of teeth in each jaw; microscopic teeth on vomer and palatines.

j. Straight portion of lateral line shorter than curved part.

k. Depth between origin of first dorsal and ventrals greater than length of soft dorsal.

l. Anterior dorsal and anal rays longer than bases of those fins.

m. Dorsal with 22-24 rays; anterior anal ray reaching beyond base of posterior ray. — *altissimus*

mm. Dorsal with 20-21 rays; anterior anal ray not reaching base of posterior ray. — *armatus*

ll. Anterior dorsal and anal rays shorter than bases of those fins.

n. Eye shorter than postorbital portion of head. — *chrysophrys*

nn. Eye nearly as long as postorbital portion of head. — *malabaricus*

kk. Depth between origin of first dorsal and ventrals distinctly less than length of second dorsal.

o. Eye small, nearly 3 in snout; scutes on lateral line 40 or more. — *emburyi*

oo. Eye larger, equal to snout; scutes on lateral line 27-31. Body with 5 very broad dark bands in the young; a large dark blotch above shoulder. — *humerosus*

jj. Straight portion of lateral line slightly longer than curved portion. — *oblongus*

jjj. Straight portion of lateral line equal to curved portion. — *gymnostethoides*

ii. Teeth in single rows on sides of jaws, in 2 rows anteriorly; straight portion of lateral line longer than curved portion. — *aurochs*

hh. Breast entirely or almost entirely scaly.

p. Abdominal profile markedly more deeply convex than the dorsal; eye longer than snout.

q. Body greatly compressed; lateral line armed with broad scutes; premaxillary teeth in 2 series, the outer tubercular, stout, and in a single row, the inner villiform and in a narrow band; mandibular teeth in a single row, except anteriorly. *kalla*

pp. Abdominal profile equally or less convex than the dorsal.

r. Eye longer than snout. *parasitus*

rr. Eye shorter than snout.

s. Body stout, its depth subequal to length of head; teeth minute, curved, not juxtaposed. *mate*

ss. Body compressed, its depth greater than length of head.

t. Many dorsal and anal rays usually more or less produced into long filaments. *radiatus*

tt. None of the dorsal and anal rays produced.

u. Teeth in a single row, cardiform and juxtaposed (palate toothless?); eye about equal to snout; scutes on straight portion of lateral line 48-56. *malam*

uu. Teeth in upper jaw in a villiform band with an outer row of enlarged, conical ones; a single series of teeth in lower jaw; eye much shorter than snout; scutes on straight portion of lateral line 36-38. *melampygus*

AA. Teeth in the jaws either lacking or infinitesimal.

v. 19-21 dorsal rays; 16-17 anal rays; palate toothless. Body with transverse bands in the young. *speciosus*

vv. 26-27 dorsal rays; 23 anal rays; palate with microscopic teeth. A dark blotch on shoulder. *leptolepis*

231. WHITE TREVALLY *Caranx georgianus* (Cuvier and Valenciennes)
[Plate 38]

Caranx georgianus Cuvier and Valenciennes, Hist. Nat. Poiss., 9, 1833, p. 85.
Caranx georgianus McCulloch, Biol. Res. Endeavour, 3, pt 3, 1915, p. 126, pl. 20

Skipjack (south-western Australia).

D. 8, 1/27; A. 2, 1/22; L. 1. scutes 18-22. Colour silvery yellow, with a bluish tint on back; operculum with a well-defined round black spot; fins yellow, excepting the caudal which is blackish towards tips of lobes.

A widely distributed species found in the coastal and outside waters of the southern portions of the continent from Moreton Bay, South Queensland, to Western Australia and also in the South Pacific. The young enter the inlets and are frequently caught in the fishermen's nets. Grows to at least 44 inches. A good food-fish.

232. GREAT TREVALLY *Caranx sexfasciatus* Quoy and Gaimard
[Colour-plate 29]

Caranx sexfasciatus Quoy and Gaimard, Voy. de l'Uranie, 1824, p. 358.
Illustration by G. Coates.

Turrum (North Queensland); Kingfish (Natal).

D. (1 procumbent) 7-8, 1/19-22; A. 2, 1/15-17; L. 1. scutes 30-33. Colour silvery, darker above; dorsal, anal, and caudal dusky; pectoral bright yellow; no dark opercular spot or a very small one; young usually with broad dark vertical cross-bars. Sometimes the dorsals and ventrals have the anterior rays yellow, the anal and caudal saffron-yellow, and a tinge of yellow on upper half of body and head. The young are golden, with four or five broad vertical bands on the body.

A fine large trevally commonly found along the entire coastline of Queensland and in the waters of the Northern Territory, New Guinea, and in the western Pacific. The young move in shoals over the shallow sandy bays. Grows to a length of at least 4 feet and a weight of 80 pounds.

233. TURRUM *Caranx emburyi* (Whitley) [Colour-plate 30]

Turrum emburyi Whitley, Rec. Austr. Mus., 18, no. 6, 1932, p. 337.
Illustration by G. Coates.

Albacore (Whitsunday Passage).

D. 8, 1/29; A. 2, 1/24; L. 1. scutes 40 or more. "General colour opalescent bluish above, with a few yellow spots on upper parts of sides, and light silvery below. Fins smoky olive. A small black opercular blotch and a broken line of dark brown marks along anal base. Pectoral axil black." (Whitley.)

A fine game-fish that is usually caught on trolling lines from a moving launch, though fishermen sometimes hook it when they are fishing on the bottom, and it puts up a terrific fight for freedom. Known only on the Queensland coast from the north southwards to the Capricorns. Average weight about 20 to 30 pounds, but it reaches 71 pounds.

234. HERRING TREVALLY *Caranx kalla* (Cuvier and Valenciennes)
[Colour-plate 30]

Caranx kalla Cuvier and Valenciennes, Hist. Nat. Poiss., 9, 1833, p. 49.
Illustration by G. Coates.

D. 8, 1/25-26; A. 2, 1/21-22; L. 1. scutes 41-45. Colour: "Blue above, shading into bronze on the upper side, the lower side and breast silvery. Upper surface of head, snout, and tip of mandible bronze; a large blackish shoulder-spot, encroaching well on the upper edge of the opercle; sides and lower surface of head, a blotch on the throat, and the bases of the pectoral, ventral, and anal fins washed with dull gold. Fins hyaline, except the anterior dorsal spines and the outer ray and tip of the upper caudal lobe, which are blackish." (Ogilby.)

A wide-ranging species found in the waters of North Queensland—most examples have been trawled at depths ranging from 14 to 25 fathoms. Apparently does not grow longer than about 12 inches.

235. FRINGE-FINNED TREVALLY *Caranx radiatus* (Macleay)
[Colour-plate 30]

Caranx radiatus Macleay, Proc. Linn. Soc. N.S.Wales, 5, 1881, p. 537.
Illustration by G. Coates.

Reef Herring (Mackay district).

D. 7, 1/22; A. 2, 1/19-20; L. 1. scutes 38-45. Colour pale greenish-blue above and on sides, silvery-white below, with or without 6 or more dark vertical bands extending from back to middle of sides; a large black opercular blotch present; dorsal rays almost hyaline at their bases, passing gradually into blackish-brown towards the outer two-thirds, the membranes bluish-hyaline on the anterior half and orange-yellow posteriorly; anal with the rays white, anterior half of membranes hyaline, posterior half pale orange-yellow; caudal yellowish, edged posteriorly dusky and with end of upper lobe black; pectorals and ventrals whitish.

This trevally is readily recognized by the prolonged dorsal and anal rays which in some examples are only very slightly prolonged whilst in others they are of great length. The species is known only from the waters of North Queensland, the Northern Territory, and Western Australia. Grows to 13 inches.

236. GOLDEN TREVALLY *Caranx speciosus* (Forskål)   [Colour-plate 31]

Scomber speciosus Forskål, Descr. Anim., 1775, p. 54.
Illustration by G. Coates.

Banded Trevally (Queensland); Kingfish (South Africa).

D. 8-5, 1/19-21; A. 2, 1/16-17; L. 1. with 10-18 feeble scutes, increasing in size and strength with age. Young: Clear canary-yellow on head, sides, and below, suffused with purple and blue above; head with a greenish tinge above and on snout; 10 to 12 alternately wide and narrow black cross-bands which reach a little over half-way down the sides or even the full depth of body; fins yellow, the dorsal and caudal narrowly edged black, the anal edged white; pectoral with a small black axillary spot which is mostly concealed.

Adults: "Silvery, washed above with plumbeous-blue and without any trace of bands or spots, only the yellowish tinge of the fins and the dusky tips of the spinous dorsal and caudal persisting." (Ogilby.)

A large and handsome trevally commonly found in the northern waters of the continent, from Western Australia to Queensland, where it is found as far south as Moreton Bay. Grows to 40 inches. Wide-ranging.

OTHER SPECIES

Blue-spotted Trevally, *C. bucculentus*. A little-known fish found in the Gulf of Carpentaria and along the coast of Queensland as far south as Bustard Heads. Grows to 26 inches.

Lowly Trevally, *C. ignobilis*. A wide-ranging fish occasionally taken in the Northern Territory and North Queensland. Grows to 35 inches.

Papuan Trevally, *C. papuensis*. This Papuan species frequents the coast of North Queensland. Grows to at least 14 inches.

Trevally, *C. altissimus*. An uncommon trevally which has been recorded from North and South Queensland and also from China and the Philippines. Grows to 11 inches.

Long-finned Trevally, *C. armatus*. A wide-ranging fish which frequents the waters of North Queensland, also of North Australia and Western Australia, New Guinea, the East Indies, etc. Grows to 24 inches.

Long-nosed Trevally, *C. chrysophrys*. A small trevally of the northern waters of Queensland. Grows to 14 inches. Wide-ranging.

Hunch-back Trevally, *C. malabaricus*. Another small and wide-ranging species occasionally found on the coast of North Queensland. Grows to about 15 inches.

Dusky-shouldered Trevally, *C. humerosus*. A small trevally known only from the Queensland coast north of Gladstone. Grows to 10 inches.

Coach-whip Trevally, *C. oblongus*. Although recorded from as far south as Caloundra this species is more frequently met with in the far north of Queensland. Grows to about 15 inches.

Bludger, *C. gymnostethoides*. A large trevally commonly taken in the northern waters of Queensland. Grows to 30 inches.

Black-crested Trevally, *C. aurochs*. Known only from the Queensland coast, where it is apparently widely distributed though not common. It has been trawled at depths of 15 to 26 fathoms. Grows to 7 inches.

Round-finned Trevally, *C. parasitus*. A small trevally usually found sheltering beneath the tentacles of a jelly-fish, *Crambessa mosaica*. It is known only from the waters of North Queensland and the Gulf of Carpentaria. Grows to about 2 inches.

Deep Trevally, *C. mate*. A wide-ranging species recorded from Australian waters in North Queensland and north-west Australia. Grows to 12 inches.

Malam Trevally, *C. malam*. Found throughout the Indo-Pacific region. Frequents the Queensland coast from north to south. Grows to 10 inches.

Blue-finned Trevally, *C. melampygus*. A small Indo-Pacific species found on the Queensland coast from north to south. Grows to 13 inches.

Thin-scaled Trevally, *C. leptolepis*. An Indo-Pacific fish found along the whole Queensland coastline. Grows to 13 inches.

Ulua

Gill-rakers numerous, exceedingly long, feather-like, projecting far into the mouth on each side of the tongue. Lips sharp-edged. Distribution that of the single species known.

237. CALE-CALE TREVALLY *Ulua mandibularis* (Macleay) [Plate 38]

Caranx mandibularis Macleay, Proc. Linn. Soc. N.S.Wales, 7, 1883, p. 356.
Ulua mandibularis McCulloch, Mem. Qld Mus., 8, pt 1, 1924, p. 75, pl. 14.

Cale-Cale (New Guinea natives).

D. 7, 1/20; A. 2, 1/17; about 20 scutes on lateral line. Colour: "Olive-green above, silver below; the junction of the two colours sharply defined above the middle line of the body. The edges of the caudal and anal blackish, the inner axil of the pectoral black." (McCulloch.)

An interesting species distinguished from all other Carangidae by the presence of long feather-like gill-rakers which extend into the mouth on each side of the tongue. It is known only from North Australia, North Queensland, and New Guinea. Grows to 12½ inches. Apparently not common.

Alectis: Thread-fishes

Carangoid fishes with strongly compressed bodies, deeply rhombic in form, with 5 to 6 rudimentary dorsal spines, not connected by membrane and with the anterior rays of soft dorsal and anal fins greatly produced into long filaments in the young but becoming shorter with age (Plate 38). Three or four species are known, two being found in Queensland waters.

KEY TO SPECIES IN QUEENSLAND

A. Snout long and pointed; eye small; maxillary not nearly extending to the vertical from the eye; gill-rakers short and stout; vent much nearer ventrals than anal.   *indica*

AA. Snout short and rounded; eye large; maxillary extending to below eye; gill-rakers long and slender; vent about midway between ventrals and anal.   *ciliaris*

238. DIAMOND TREVALLY *Alectis indica* (Rüppell) [Plate 38]

Scyris indicus Rüppell, Atlas zu Rüppell, Reise (Senck. Nat. Ges.) Fische, 1830-1, p. 128.
Alectis indica Ogilby, Mem. Qld Mus., 3, 1915, p. 83, pl. 26.

Old Maid, Mirror-fish (Townsville); Diamond-fish (North Queensland); Plumed Trevally (Queensland); Silvery Moon-fish (New South Wales); Straight-nosed Thread-fish (South Africa).

D. 6, 1/19; A. 2, 1/16 (spines disappearing with age); 8-12 weak scutes on caudal peduncle. Colour: Upper surface golden-bronze, shading imperceptibly into the iridescent silvery of lower sides and breast; young lighter in colour than adult, with five or six broad dull-blue bands extending from the back to below middle of sides; nuchal ridge blackish; upper surface of head, snout, and jaws light brownish-yellow, the cheeks and opercles silvery; opercular spot small and inconspicuous or absent; first dorsal ray, tips of produced rays, and a narrow bar along base of each interradial membrane black; caudal washed with gold; anal and pectorals colourless; ventrals colourless, the elongate rays blackish in the young.

A wide-ranging species found on the coast of Queensland from north to south, in the northern waters of New South Wales, and also in the Northern Territory. It is common in the far north of Queensland. Said to reach a length of 5 feet, though such a size is uncommon.

OTHER SPECIES

Pennant Trevally, *A. ciliaris*. More commonly found in the southern waters of Queensland and also in New South Wales. Like *A. indica* it is very wide-ranging and is found in the warmer parts of the Indian, Pacific, and west Atlantic oceans. Apparently grows to only 15 inches.

Parastromateus

Body strongly compressed, elevated. Scales small, covering vertical fins. Lateral line gently curved, straight on caudal peduncle, keeled and armed with scutes posteriorly. Mouth moderate. Small teeth in a single row, disappearing with age; none on palate. A single long dorsal and anal fin with rudimentary spines anteriorly. No finlets. Ventral fins absent with age. Caudal forked. A single species. Wide-ranging.

238a. BLACK POMFRET *Parastromateus niger* (Bloch) [Colour-plate 31]

Stromateus niger Bloch, Nat. ausl. Fische, 9, 1795, p. 93.
Illustration by G. Coates.

Turbot, Halibut (Townsville); Blue Skate (Cairns); Black Batfish (North Queensland); Butter-fish (Thursday Island); Slade (Rockhampton); Sweep (Brisbane Fish Market).

D. 4 + 1/41-46; A. 2/35-40; P. 23-24; L. 1. about 100. Colour of body, fins, and tail greyish, greyish-brown, or brownish, tinged bluish; fins and tail sometimes edged with black.

A fish commonly taken in the fish-traps of North Queensland but very occasionally caught in South Queensland. It frequents the anchored lightships in northern waters around which it is captured. Found also in the East Indies and is wide-ranging elsewhere. Grows to 24 inches and is an excellent food-fish.

Sub-family CHORINEMINAE: LEATHER-SKINS

Fishes of small or large size, found along the shores of both tropical and subtropical seas, the young ascending the estuaries and tidal rivers. Their elongate compressed bodies are brilliant silvery and usually with a row of dusky spots on the sides of the adults, but often missing in the young. In these fishes the scales are rudimentary and are embedded in the skin, being needle-like, broadly lanceolate or rhombic in form.

This sub-family contains an Atlantic genus, *Oligoplites*, and an Indo-Pacific genus, *Chorinemus*. The species are few.

Chorinemus

Body elongate-oblong, compressed, with small elongate scales more or less embedded in the skin. Teeth feeble or needle-like. Spinous dorsal of 6 to 7 spines connected by membrane in the young, but nearly free in the adult. Soft dorsal and anal equal in length, the anterior rays elevated, the posterior rays detached or semi-detached. Anal spines strong.

Species few, inhabiting the coastal waters of tropical and subtropical regions of the Indo-Pacific, three in Queensland. As food-fishes their flesh is somewhat poor in quality.

KEY TO SPECIES IN QUEENSLAND

A. Snout pointed, equal to eye or somewhat longer in the adult; maxillary reaching centre or hind border of eye. Soft dorsal with a black blotch anteriorly.

  b. Body higher than length of head; scales rhombic. A row of indistinct dark blotches above lateral line usually present. *tolooparah*

  bb. Height of body and length of head almost equal; scales lanceolate, pointed in their exposed part and giving the skin a crinkled appearance. A bluish band from occiput to pectoral; a series of distinct spots on lateral line and a second indistinct series below. *sancti-petri*

AA. Snout blunt, shorter than, in adult nearly equal to, eye; maxillary surpassing hind border of eye. No black blotch on soft dorsal. *lysan*

239. LARGE-MOUTHED LEATHER-SKIN *Chorinemus lysan* (Forskål)
[Colour-plate 32]

Scomber lysan Forskål, Descr. Anim., 1775, p. 54.
Illustration by G. Coates.

Tailor or Taylor (North Queensland); Queenfish (North Queensland and South Africa); Talang (East Indies).

D. (1 procumbent) 6, 1/19-20; A. 2, 1/18. Colour: Head above and back golden-greenish-olive, rest of head and body golden-citrine or sulphur-yellow; second dorsal, anal, pectoral, and caudal like the body; margin of caudal posteriorly, blackish; anterior dorsal, ventral, and post-anal spines white; 6 to 8 greyish indistinct large round spots along sides above lateral line.

A large, wide-ranging fish commonly found in the waters of North Queensland, southwards to about Gladstone. It grows to at least 4 feet with a weight of 20 pounds. Numbers are netted by the natives of Palm Island, North Queensland. As food-fishes they are not held in high esteem, their flesh being dry and tasteless. This also applies to the other members of the genus.

OTHER SPECIES

Five-barred Leather-skin, *C. tolooparah*. A small and very common species on the Queensland coast. Wide-ranging. Grows to only 12 inches.

Slender Leather-skin, *C. sancti-petri*. Though common in the waters of the Northern Territory, this species is not frequently met with on the Queensland coast. Grows to 36 inches. Wide-ranging outside Australian waters. Its flesh is of fair edible quality.

Sub-family TRACHINOTINAE: SWALLOW-TAILS

Body strongly compressed, oblong or elevated, breast and belly rounded, nape more or less trenchant. Scales cycloid, adherent, almost wanting on head. Lateral line without scutes. No keel on caudal peduncle. Head small, opercles entire (preoperculum with spines in the young). Mouth small, with obtuse snout. Intermaxillaries protractile. Small teeth in jaws and on vomer and palatines, generally becoming lost with age. Spinous dorsal with an anterior procumbent spine and 5 to 6 erect spines, well developed in the young and connected by membrane, which disappears with age, the spines becoming rudimentary. Soft dorsal and anal fins of equal length and similar form, highly falcate anteriorly. Pectorals and ventrals short. Caudal deeply forked, the lobes long and pointed.

Large, deep-bodied, carangoid fishes inhabiting tropical and temperate seas. They are pelagic and partially migratory in habit, visiting the shores of Queensland in large schools during the winter months, usually with the schools of sea-mullet. Swallow-tails swim high in the water and are often to be seen travelling along in the breakers, which habit has earned for them the name of

Surf Trevally. Their food consists of crabs, squid, and molluscs. They take a hook readily, and a very good bait is the shellfish known as Eugarie, *Donax deltoides*. Four species belonging to the one genus, *Trachinotus*, are found in Queensland seas.

KEY TO SPECIES IN QUEENSLAND

Based on Ogilby[29]

A. Body elevated, its depth half or more than half its length; snout high, anteriorly vertical; upper jaw the longer; gill-rakers short and stout.   *blochii*

AA. Body ovate, its depth less than half its length; snout low, anteriorly rounded; gill-rakers longer and more slender. Sides with row of dark spots.

    b. Dorsal with 23 or more, anal with 21 or more soft rays. Sides usually with a row of dark spots.

      c. Snout slightly gibbous anteriorly; caudal fin longer; ventrals shorter. Dark spots on sides small, situated on lateral line.   *bailloni*

      cc. Snout pointed anteriorly; caudal fin shorter; ventrals longer. Dark spots on sides large, situated above lateral line.   *botla*

    bb. Dorsal with 20 or less, anal with 17 or less soft rays; snout gibbous. Sides uniform, without spots.   *anak*

240. SWALLOW-TAIL or DART *Trachinotus botla* (Shaw)   [Plate 38]

Scomber botla Shaw, Gen. Zool. Pisc., 4 (2), 1803, p. 591 (after Russell).
Trachinotus botla Ogilby, Mem. Qld Mus., 3, 1915, p. 93, pl. 28.

Surf Trevally (South Queensland); Surf Bream, Dart (New South Wales).

D. (1 procumbent) 6, 1/23-26; A. 2, 1/21-25. Colour: Upper surfaces dark blue-grey, shading to silvery below lateral line, the breast and abdomen milk-white; a series of 6 to 7 vertically oval dark spots on each side; these are mostly above the lateral line, only the anterior two, or rarely three, crossing it; these spots are sometimes obscure or, though rarely, absent in the young; dorsal, caudal, and anal lobes indigo-blue.

This fast-swimming fish, a lover of the surf and breakers, is caught in numbers during the winter months by rod fishermen. Average-sized fish caught are 12 inches, but specimens of 24 inches are known. Common on the coasts of northern New South Wales and South Queensland, becoming rarer northwards. A splendid food-fish. Wide-ranging outside Australia.

---

[29] *Mem. Qld Mus.*, 5, 1916, p. 149.

OTHER SPECIES

Snub-nosed Dart, *T. blochii*. A wide-ranging fish found in the waters of the Northern Territory and Queensland. A good food-fish, growing to at least 34 inches in length and 16 pounds in weight.

Black-spotted Dart, *T. bailloni*. Another wide-ranging fish which visits the coast of North Queensland where it is quite common. Grows to 24 inches.

Oyster-eater, *T. anak*. Frequents the waters of South Queensland (Moreton and Wide bays). It is probably the largest of all the carangoid fishes, attaining a length of 6 feet. It is said to be very destructive on the oyster-banks, which according to J. D. Ogilby are visited by the fish in the months of October to January.

Sub-family SERIOLINAE

Form attenuated or oblong, slightly compressed, belly rounded, head without occipital ridge. Scales small, cycloid. Lateral line slightly curved anteriorly, without scutes, but with a more or less distinct keel on caudal peduncle. Mouth terminal, the cleft small or wide. Intermaxillaries protractile. Opercle and preopercle entire in adults. Teeth in villiform bands in jaws, on vomer, palatines, and usually on tongue. Spinous dorsal with 6 to 7 spines, connected by membrane in the young, with age becoming free, weak, and obsolete. Soft dorsal with anterior rays somewhat elevated. Anal similar but much shorter and in the young preceded by 2 weak spines which become obsolete with growth. Dorsal and anal with or without finlets. Caudal deeply forked. Pectorals short. Ventrals longer than pectorals and with their origin behind the base of those fins.

Coastal or pelagic fishes of tropical and temperate seas, some attaining to a large size and valued as food and sporting fishes. Three genera occur in Queensland waters.

KEY TO GENERA IN QUEENSLAND

A. A 2-rayed finlet behind the dorsal and anal fins.   *Elagatis*

AA. No finlets behind dorsal and anal fins.

    b. Dorsal spines in adult 5-7, and connected by membrane.   *Seriola*

    bb. Dorsal spines in adult totally free and reduced to 4-5.   *Naucrates*

Elagatis: Runners

Form long, slender, somewhat compressed, belly rounded. Head long, pointed. A 2-rayed finlet behind the long soft dorsal and anal fins. No keel on caudal peduncle. A single species known.

241. RUNNER *Elagatis bipinnulatus* (Quoy and Gaimard) [Colour-plate 32]

Seriola bipinnulata Quoy and Gaimard, Voy. Uranie Physic., Zool., 1, 1824, p. 363, pl. 61, fig. 3.
Illustration by G. Coates.

Yellow-tail (North America); Rainbow Runner, Prodigal Son (South Africa).

D. 6, 1/24-27 + 2; A. 2, 1/15-17 + 2; L. 1. 100. Colour very dark blue or greenish above, lighter on sides, whitish below; 3 pale-yellow longitudinal bands from head to tail, between which are 2 blue ones; dorsal and anal fins dark greenish; pectorals and ventrals pale yellowish, the latter with dusky greenish streaks; caudal dark greenish or sometimes yellowish.

A widely distributed pelagic fish found in all tropical and temperate seas. Grows to at least 4 feet. A good food-fish, with flesh of excellent flavour.

Seriola: Amber-jacks or Yellow-tails

Form oblong to elongate, moderately compressed, the belly usually rounded. Scales small. Snout blunt, gape of mouth wide. Caudal peduncle without scutes but with a keel. First dorsal preceded by a procumbent spine, more or less obsolete. No finlets. Caudal deeply forked.

Robust fishes of moderate or large size inhabiting the coastal and offshore waters of all tropical and subtropical seas. Species few, four in Queensland. Some grow to a length of 5 to 7 feet and a weight of 100 pounds and are valued food-fishes, especially when canned. The colours vary in the different species, but the caudal is nearly always yellow. Young examples often have dark transverse bands which become lost with age. Yellow-tails swim in large schools and feed upon other fishes, crustaceans, etc. They are game when hooked and are much sought after by anglers. Four species are found in Queensland.

KEY TO SPECIES IN AUSTRALIA

A. Body slender, its depth equal to or somewhat less than length of head. A longitudinal yellow stripe usually present from head to caudal base.

    b. Maxillary extending to below anterior third of eye; eye smaller, 6-6.7 times in head. Colour dark purplish-blue, the lateral stripe bright yellow; silvery below.   *grandis*

    bb. Maxillary extending to below middle of eye; eye larger, 5.5 times in head. Colour purplish-brown, lateral stripe dull dirty-yellowish; creamy-white below.   *simplex*

AA. Body deeper, its depth much greater than length of head; profile of head strongly convex. Body with darker cross-bars in the young.

232

c. Maxillary greatly dilated posteriorly, its width almost equal to eye; scales minute, not visible to the eye. *hippos*

cc. Maxillary not greatly dilated posteriorly, its width about half that of eye diameter; scales small, but visible to the eye. *nigrofasciata*

242. KING AMBER-JACK *Seriola grandis* Castelnau [Colour-plate 32]

Seriola grandis Castelnau, Proc. Zool. Acclim. Soc. Vict., 1, 1872, p. 115.
Illustration by T. C. Marshall.

Albacore, Silver Kingfish (Gladstone); Yellow-tail (Victoria and South Australia).

D. (1 procumbent, usually obsolete) 6-7, 1/31-34; A. 2, 1/20-22. Colour brilliant purplish-blue above, the head with a greenish tinge; lower half silvery, the two colours sharply defined and separated by a greenish-yellow longitudinal stripe from eye to tail base; dorsal pale greenish, edged with yellow; anal whitish, edged with yellow; pectorals greenish; ventrals with rays yellow, the membranes white; caudal olive-green, the lobes yellowish-green. Sometimes the yellow lateral band is wanting.

A large and powerful fish found in South Queensland and New South Wales, Victoria, South Australia, Tasmania, and Lord Howe Island. It swims in schools, and numbers are caught by fishermen when they are trolling for mackerel. As food-fish the young are of fair edible quality, but the adults are coarse, tough, and tasteless; others at certain periods of the year have flesh which when boiled or steamed disintegrates into a watery and tasteless mass. Grows to a length of 6 feet and a weight of 150 pounds. On the Queensland coast the species does not appear to occur north of the Capricorns. Considered by some authorities to be the same species as the American Amber-jack, *S. lalandi*.

OTHER SPECIES

Yellow-banded Amber-jack, *S. simplex*. A common fish on the Queensland coast, where it is taken by line over the many reefs by the mackerel fishermen, particularly during the colder months. Grows to 5 feet with a weight of 80 pounds.

Samson-fish, *S. hippos*. A powerful and very active fish in the waters of southern Queensland and New South Wales, and also in Western Australia. It is a lover of the open seas but is also found close inshore. Its flesh is of fair edible quality in the young but inclined to toughness in the adults, which reach a length of at least 30 inches.

Black-banded Amber-jack, *S. nigrofasciata*. A wide-ranging species found along the whole Queensland coastline. It does not appear to be commonly met with in Queensland. Grows to 28 inches.

Naucrates

Body oblong, moderately compressed. Scales minute. Dorsal spines low, weak, connected by membrane only in the young. Caudal peduncle with fleshy keel. Caudal strongly forked, less so in young. A single pelagic species found in all warm seas.

243. PILOT-FISH *Naucrates ductor* (Linnaeus)   [Plate 38]

Gasterosteus ductor Linnaeus, Syst. Nat., 10th ed., 1758, p. 295.
Naucrates ductor McCulloch, Rec. Austr. Mus., 15, no. 1, 1926, p. 34, pl. 1.

D. 3-6/27-30; A. O-2/16-18. Colour bluish or blackish above, silvery on sides, lighter below, with 5 to 7 vertical dark cross-bands, less conspicuous with age, the posterior ones intruding on to dorsal and anal fins; tip of pectorals dark; caudal blackish with white tips to the lobes.

The young of the Pilot-fish take shelter and swim about beneath the jellyfishes, the Portuguese man-o'-war (*Physalia*), floating wreckage, or seaweeds. The adults swim in the company of sharks or even ships, following them for long periods. They are said to associate with the sharks in order to obtain the scraps of food overlooked by their hosts and to which they had piloted them.

A pelagic fish of wide distribution and found in all warm seas. Grows to 24 inches.

Family **Menidae**

Body very strongly compressed, nearly triangular, the dorsal profile being slightly rounded, nearly horizontal. The ventral profile with prominent trenchant abdomen. Scales minute. Mouth small, almost vertical. Teeth in villiform bands in jaws, none on palate. A single long dorsal fin with 9 spines in the young but without spines in the adult, the anterior undivided rays somewhat elevated. Anal with 2 spines and normal rays in the young but without spines in the adult and with the numerous rays enveloped in the skin with their widest free edges broad and flat. Ventrals with a short spine and 5 rays, filiform in the young and the first compressed and very long in the adult. Caudal deeply forked.

A family with a single genus and species, with affinities to the trevallies (Carangidae). Wide-ranging.

244. MOON-FISH *Mene maculata* (Bloch and Schneider) [Colour-plate 33]

Zeus maculatus Bloch and Schneider, Syst. Ichth., 1801, p. 95.
Illustration by G. Coates.

D. 3-4/40-42; A. 30-32. Colour deep blue along back; sides and belly silvery; 2 to 4 irregular rows of large slaty-blue oval spots on upper part of body, above level of pectoral fin; fins pale; dorsal grey, front lobes dusky; caudal and long ventrals dusky; anal and pectorals white.

This distinctively shaped fish is occasionally found in North Queensland waters. It lives mainly in the deeper coastal waters but has also been caught in the fish-traps on the coast. Grows to 8 inches. Wide-ranging.

Family **Mullidae: Surmullets or Goat-fishes**

Carnivorous fishes of small or moderate size, inhabiting the shore waters of tropical seas. Some species range into temperate waters and are known at times to enter estuaries. Most of the species are noted for their brilliant colours, reds and yellows being predominant. They are characterized by having 2 long, unbranched barbels attached behind the symphysis of the lower jaw, a feature which has earned then the name of Goat-fishes. They are bottom-dwellers, swimming about with the highly sensitive barbels constantly in motion, by means of which they are able to feel all objects in their search for food. They feed mainly upon marine worms, crustaceans, etc.

The species are numerous and almost all are valued food-fishes, their flesh being white, tender, and of excellent flavour. Wherever the species are found they are usually numerous in numbers.

The goat-fishes were the favourites on the tables of the old Roman epicures, and fabulous prices are said to have been paid for them in ancient times. These fishes rarely take a bait, so that they are seldom seen in the Queensland markets. In the Philippines they are caught by means of traps or bobos, or in trammel- or gill-nets.

Four genera are found in Queensland waters.

KEY TO GENERA IN QUEENSLAND

A. Dentition complete, teeth in both jaws and on vomer and palatines. *Upeneus*

AA. Dentition incomplete; no teeth on palate.

b. Teeth in both jaws in several rows of narrow villiform bands. *Mulloidichthys*

bb. Teeth in both jaws short, conic, in 2 rows anteriorly, one row laterally. Teeth on vomer, none on palatines. *Upeneichthys*

bbb. Teeth in both jaws in a single series; rather strong, acute. No teeth on vomer or palatines. *Pseudupeneus*

Upeneus

Body somewhat compressed. Mouth low, rather small. Minute teeth in bands in each jaw and on vomer and palatines.

A genus of Indo-Pacific fishes of about eighteen species, four of which occur in Queensland.

A.   Second dorsal spine greatly produced, extending beyond base of soft dorsal.   *filifer*

AA. Second dorsal spine not produced.

    b. Head and body with blackish spots; first dorsal with upper half black, sprinkled with yellow spots; caudal lobes with oblique dark bars.   *tragula*

    bb. Head and body without dark spots.

      c. A bright-yellow stripe from eye to caudal and another from pectoral axil to caudal; caudal uniform.   *sulphureus*

      cc. 4-5 longitudinal stripes of yellow, orange, or reddish colour on each side; caudal yellow, with oblique black bars on both lobes.   *vittatus*

245. MOTTLED GOAT-FISH *Upeneus tragula* (Richardson)   [Plate 39]

Upeneus tragula Richardson, Ichth. China Japan, 1846, p. 220.
Upeneus tragula Bleeker, Atlas Ichth., 9, 1877, pl. 392, fig. 2.

D. 8 + 1/8; A. 1/6-7; L. 1. 33-38; L. tr. 2-3/6-7. Colour dark umber-brown or greyish-yellow, with head and body more or less mottled or speckled with black or brownish spots; a dark lateral stripe from snout through eye to caudal base; upper half of spinous dorsal black, sprinkled with yellow spots, basal half with 2 faint dusky bands; soft dorsal with 2 to 3 faint dusky bands; caudal with broad oblique dusky bars on both lobes; other fins with obscure dusky bands, frequently broken as spots. The colour is variable but the dark lateral stripe is always present.

A wide-ranging species common on the coast of Queensland and entering New South Wales. Grows to about 14 inches.

OTHER SPECIES

Thread-fin Goat-fish, *U. filifer*. A rare species known only from Cape Gloucester, North Queensland, where twelve examples were trawled. Grows to almost 7 inches.

Sunrise Goat-fish, *U. sulphureus*. Does not exceed 8 inches in length. Found from the Red Sea to the Indo-Australian Archipelago and the South Seas. Very common in North Queensland.

Bar-tailed Goat-fish, *U. vittatus*. Another wide-ranging fish, common in the Indo-Australian Archipelago and the South Seas, where it is a valued food-fish, growing to 12 inches.

Mulloidichthys

Form elongate, rather slender. Maxillary short, not reaching eye in adult. Small teeth in jaws in narrow villiform bands; no teeth on vomer and palatines. Dorsal and anal fins without scales. Lateral line complete. No carinate ventral scales.

Species few, living in all tropical seas, mostly in the Indo-Pacific. Valued as food. One species in Queensland.

246. GOLD-STRIPED GOAT-FISH *Mulloidichthys auriflamma* (Forskål)
[Plate 39]

Mullus auriflamma Forskål, Descr. Anim., 1775, p. 30.
Mulloides flavolineatus Bleeker, Atlas Ichth., 9, 1877, pl. 394, fig. 3.

D. 7, 1/8; A. 1-2/6; L. l. 35-38; L. tr. 2/7. Colour scarlet, rose-pink, orange, yellow, or olive above, lighter below, and darkest on head; a bright lemon-yellow or orange-yellow stripe from snout to caudal base; reddish or yellow spots may be present on cheeks; dorsals and caudal lemon-yellow, orange, or red; other fins pinkish, yellowish, or colourless.

A very variable species but readily recognized by the yellow lateral stripe. Ogilby notes that in a few cases the yellow lateral stripe is replaced by one of bright red. It is a rare species in Australia, recorded only from the Queensland coast. Wide-ranging. Grows to 16 inches.

Upeneichthys

This small genus is represented in Queensland by the Blue-spotted Goat-fish, *U. lineatus* (Schneider), a very handsome fish with each scale having a blue central spot. It is found in the waters of the southern half of Australia from Western Australia to Moreton Bay in South Queensland, and also in Tasmania and New Zealand. Grows to 10 inches.

Pseudupeneus

Head moderate to large. Eye large, smaller with age. Mouth low, almost horizontal. Both jaws with rather strong teeth, unequal, in a single or double series. Palate toothless. Barbels shorter than head.

Many species, widely distributed in all tropical seas, four in Queensland.

KEY TO SPECIES IN QUEENSLAND

A. Black longitudinal band from snout through eye to below middle or last dorsal rays; a black spot at caudal base. *barberinus*

AA. No distinct black band from snout to below dorsal, though an obscure band may be present from opercle to below dorsal.

b. A black saddle-like spot on upper half of caudal peduncle.

c. Red, with 3 curved olive-yellow stripes from snout to below dorsal; the black caudal spot preceded by a yellow blotch. — *spilurus*

cc. Red, clouded with olive-brown; an obscure dusky stripe from opercle to below soft dorsal; the black caudal spot frequently preceded by a pinkish blotch. — *signatus*

bb. A large round black spot in lateral line on posterior half of caudal peduncle.

d. A large elongate yellow spot on lateral line, below posterior part of spinous dorsal and anterior dorsal rays; colour violet, yellowish, olive-green, or pinkish, each scale with a yellow edge, those posteriorly with violet or blue spots; 3 to 4 violet or blue lines on head. — *indicus*

247. BLACK-SPOT GOAT-FISH *Pseudupeneus signatus* (Günther) [Plate 39]

Upeneus signatus Günther, Ann. Mag. Nat. Hist. (3), 20, 1867, p. 59.
Upeneus signatus Tosh. Rept Marine Dept. Qld, 1902-3 (1903), pl. 3, fig. 2.

Spotted Goat-fish, Spotted Red Mullet (New South Wales).

D. 8, 1/8, 1; A. 1/6, 1; L. l. 26-28 + 3-4; L. tr. 2-3/6-7. Colour: "Red, the upper surface clouded with olive-brown; a broad, rather obscure, dusky band from the opercles to beneath the rayed dorsal; caudal peduncle with a large black spot extending over its upper surface, and frequently preceded by a pinkish blotch." (Ogilby.)

The common Goat-fish of South Queensland (Moreton Bay) and New South Wales. Found also at Lord Howe Island. Grows to 18 inches in length and 3 pounds in weight but those usually met with are about 7 inches long.

OTHER SPECIES

Dot and Dash Goat-fish, *P. barberinus*. A very wide-ranging fish which, in Australian waters, has only rarely been recorded from Queensland. Grows to 20 inches. A valued food-fish in the Philippines.

Japanese Goat-fish, *P. spilurus*. Has been recorded from North Queensland and is also found in New Guinea, the Andamans, the Philippines, and Japan. Grows to 13 inches.

Indian Goat-fish, *P. indicus*. Commonly captured in North Queensland. A wide-ranging fish which grows to 16 inches.

DIVISION *Cirrhitiformes*

Carnivorous percoid fishes inhabiting the tropical coastal waters and southern temperate parts of the Pacific. The species of the families closely resemble the smaller Serranidae, but the lower rays of the pectoral fins are enlarged and undivided.

Of the five families represented in the waters of southern Australia three are to be found in Queensland and then only as stragglers.

KEY TO FAMILIES REPRESENTED IN QUEENSLAND

A. 10 dorsal spines.   CIRRHITIDAE

AA. 14-22 dorsal spines.

  b. Vomer toothless.   CHEILODACTYLIDAE

  bb. Vomer with teeth.   CHIRONEMIDAE

Family **Cirrhitidae: Hand-fishes**

A single genus and species represents this small family in Queensland. It is the Many-rayed Hand-fish, *Cirrhitichthys polyactis* Bleeker, a species which is also known in the East Indies. A single example only has been taken in Queensland waters; it was caught near the Capricorns and in length was 4 inches.

Family **Cheilodactylidae: Morwongs**

Two genera of this family are found in Queensland waters.

KEY TO GENERA IN QUEENSLAND

A. Anal fin almost oblong, with 12 or more rays. *Nemadactylus*

AA. Anal fin with less than 12 rays, the anterior much
  higher than the posterior.   *Cheilodactylus*

Nemadactylus

Fishes of the cooler waters of the southern portion of the continent of Australia and the waters of New Zealand. Species few, one in Queensland.

248. MORWONG *Nemadactylus morwong* (Ramsay and Ogilby) [Plate 39]

Chilodactylus morwong Ramsay and Ogilby, Proc. Linn. Soc. N.S.Wales (2), 1, 1886, p. 879.
Cheilodactylus carponemus Ogilby, Edib. Fish Crust. N.S.Wales, 1893, p. 55, pl. 18 (not *C. carponemus* Cuvier and Valenciennes).

D. 19-18/27-29; A. 3/16-17; L. l. 55 on body, 6 on tail; L. tr. 7/18-19. Colour purplish-grey, darkest on head; each of the scales with a greenish-golden dark-edged spot, forming inconspicuous bands; sides and below silvery; a golden band, margined above and below with iridescent purple, extends from below middle of eye along snout; area before pectoral axil yellow, dotted with black; dorsal purplish-grey, the membranes of spinous portion canary-yellow; similar colour in the form of spots on membranes of soft dorsal and anal; other fins uniform purplish-grey.

A southern species which occasionally visits Moreton Bay. It is found in the waters of New South Wales, Victoria, and Tasmania, but does not appear to be anywhere common. It is evidently not a shore-frequenting fish, for those captured in Moreton Bay have always been taken in the deeper outside waters. A good food-fish which grows to 24 inches.

The vernacular name Morwong is used in the Brisbane Fish Market for several species of Emperors (*Lethrinus*).

Cheilodactylus

Fishes of the southern waters of Australia, from Queensland to Western Australia. Species few, two in Queensland.

KEY TO SPECIES IN QUEENSLAND

A. Margin of spinous dorsal evenly convex. Body nearly uniform. — *fuscus*

AA. Spinous dorsal elevated in front. Body white, with oblique blackish bands. — *gibbosus*

249. MAGPIE MORWONG *Cheilodactylus gibbosus* Richardson [Plate 39]

Cheilodactylus gibbosus Richardson, Trans. Zool. Soc. Lond., 1841, pp. 21, 102 (ex *Chaetodon gibbosus* Banks).
Goniistius gibbosus Stead, Edib. Fish N.S.Wales, 1908, p. 72, pl. 41.

D. 17/33-35; A. 3/8; L. l. 63. Colour silvery-white, with oblique brownish or blackish bands; the longest one begins on posterior half of spinous dorsal and runs along back and caudal peduncle and covers lower lobe of caudal fin; another runs from before anterior dorsal spine to belly; a narrower one in front of this, down and along edge of opercle where it is almost joined to another which runs down across cheek from eye; 3 short bars on face, two between eyes and one below on snout; mouth encircled by a dark brownish ring; soft dorsal, pectorals, and anal yellowish, the latter with a dusky tip; pectoral with a blackish bar on base; upper lobe of caudal dusky yellow; ventrals black; edge of opercle scarlet.

A handsome fish which is occasionally caught by line fishermen in Moreton Bay, where it wanders from New South Wales. It has also been recorded from Western Australia. Grows to 12 inches.

240

OTHER SPECIES

Red Morwong, *C. fuscus*. A fine food-fish which inhabits the rocky reefs
and shoals off the coasts of New South Wales and Moreton Bay in South
Queensland. It is more common in New South Wales where the young are
found in the rocky inlets. Grows to 18 inches.

Family **Chironemidae: Kelp-fishes**

Dorsal with 15 spines. Lower 6 to 7 pectoral rays simple. Villiform teeth in
both jaws; no canines; teeth on vomer, none on palatines.

Fishes of the Australian seas, principally in the southern portion. Species
few, one in Queensland.

The Kelp-fish, *Chironemus marmoratus* is the only representative of the
family in Queensland. In colour it is reddish-brown, yellowish-brown, or
olive-green, blotched and marbled darker and densely covered with small
spots, yellow in the adults and red in the young. In Queensland it is taken
only in Moreton Bay on weed- and rock-strewn grounds. It is a good food-fish
and grows to 16 inches.

Family **Leiognathidae: Pony-fishes or Pouters**

Small or moderately sized fishes living in shoals in coastal waters of all tropical
seas. They are mostly silvery in colour, with or without dusky or black markings,
the body compressed, generally elevated, and covered with small cycloid scales
which are wanting on the head. The eyes are large, the mouth remarkably
protractile, and the lower edge of the preoperculum is generally serrated. The
dorsal is continuous, with 8 spines and 15 to 17 rays, the anal with 3 spines
and 13 to 14 rays.

Some species enter the estuaries and also fresh water. They take the name
"pony-fishes" from their extremely protractile mouths, which give them quite
a horse-like appearance.

About three genera, which include a couple of dozen species, are found in
Australian waters.

KEY TO GENERA IN AUSTRALIA

A. Teeth weak, small, uniserial in the jaws.

    b. Mouth very small, oblique, when fully protracted
      directed upward, when closed mandible ascending
      vertically.   *Secutor*

    bb. Mouth small, protractile horizontal or directed
      downward when fully protracted, when closed
      mandible ascending obliquely.   *Leiognathus*

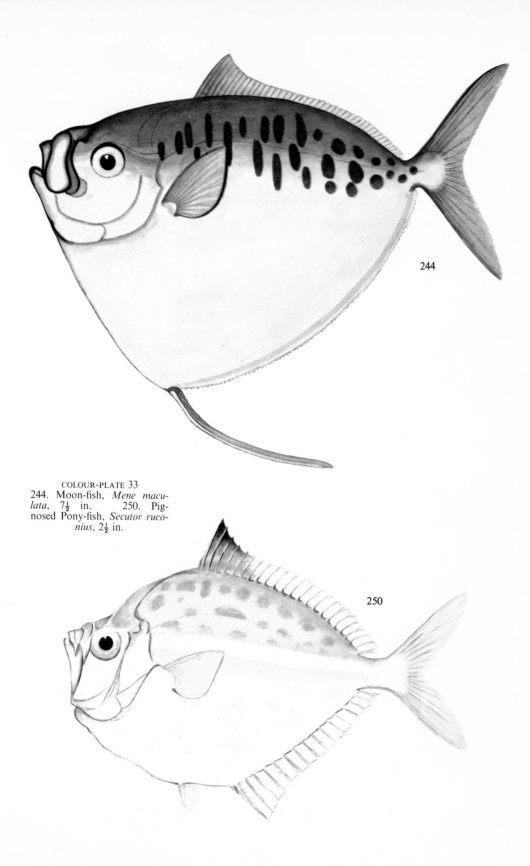

244

250

COLOUR-PLATE 33
244. Moon-fish, *Mene maculata*, 7½ in.   250. Pig-
nosed Pony-fish, *Secutor ruconius*, 2½ in.

254

256

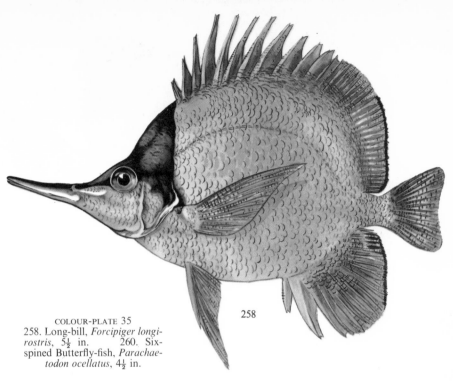

258

COLOUR-PLATE 35
258. Long-bill, *Forcipiger longi-rostris*, 5½ in. 260. Six-spined Butterfly-fish, *Parachae-todon ocellatus*, 4½ in.

260

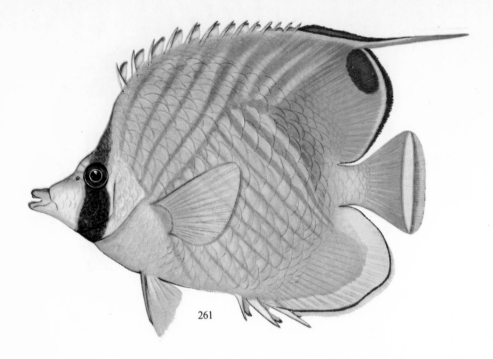

261

COLOUR-PLATE 36
261. Threadfin Butterfly-fish, *Chaetodon auriga*, 9 inches.
262. Criss-cross Butterfly-fish, *C. vagabundus*, 4½ in.

262

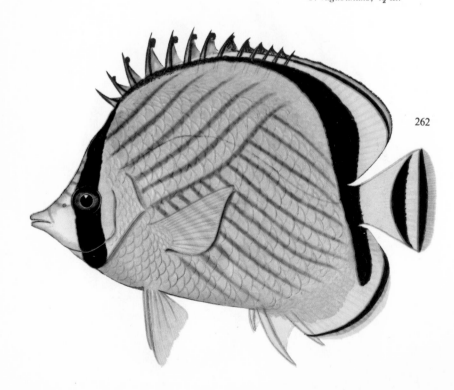

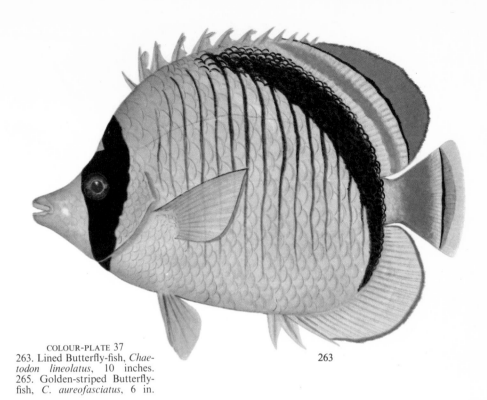

263. Lined Butterfly-fish, *Chaetodon lineolatus*, 10 inches.
265. Golden-striped Butterfly-fish, *C. aureofasciatus*, 6 in.

263

265

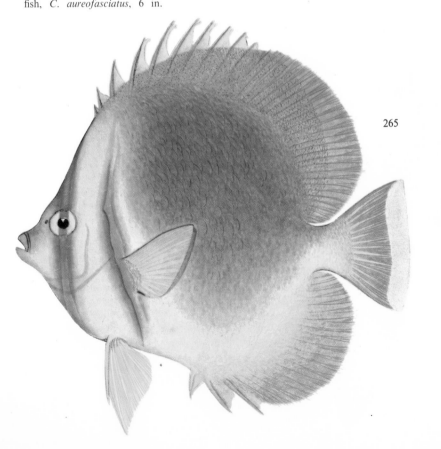

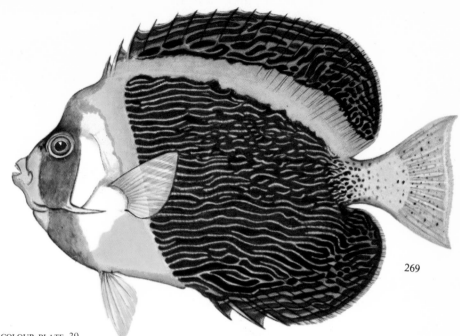

269

COLOUR-PLATE 39
269. Scribbled Angel-fish,
Chaetodontoplus duboulayi 8 in.
274. Sickle-fish, *Drepane punctata*, 8 in.

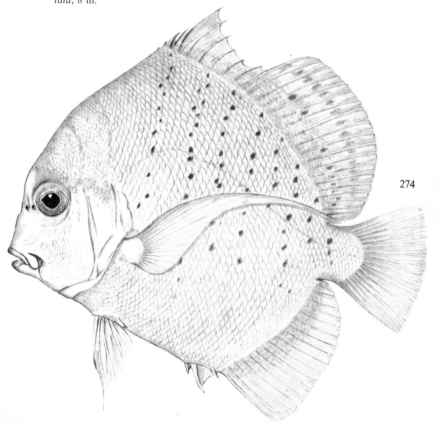

274

275   A

COLOUR-PLATE 40
275. Batfish, *Platax pinnatus*, juv., 4 in.

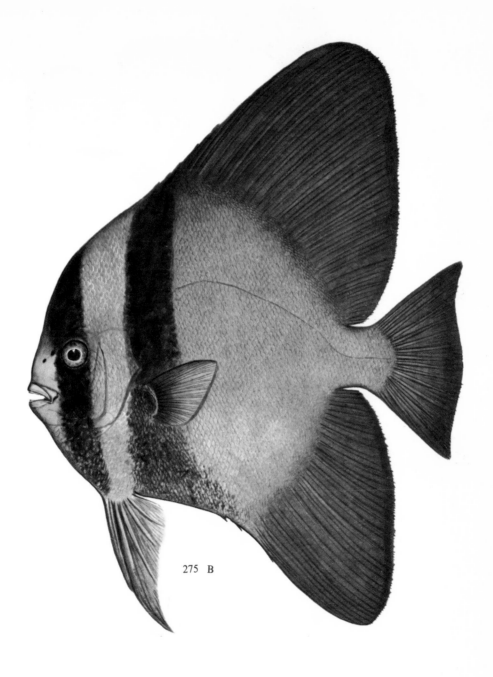

275 B

275. Batfish, *Platax pinnatus*, adult, 12 in.

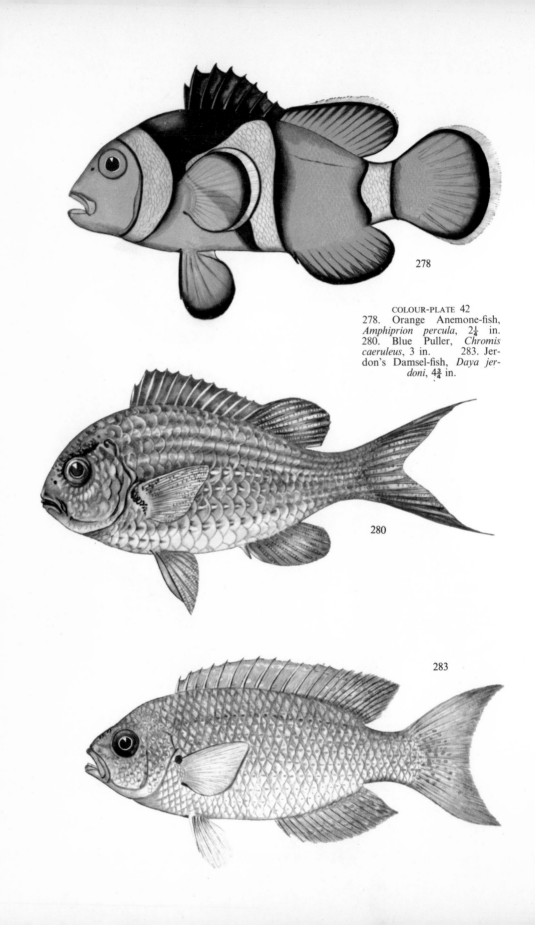

278

COLOUR-PLATE 42
278. Orange Anemone-fish, *Amphiprion percula*, 2¼ in. 280. Blue Puller, *Chromis caeruleus*, 3 in. 283. Jerdon's Damsel-fish, *Daya jerdoni*, 4¾ in.

280

283

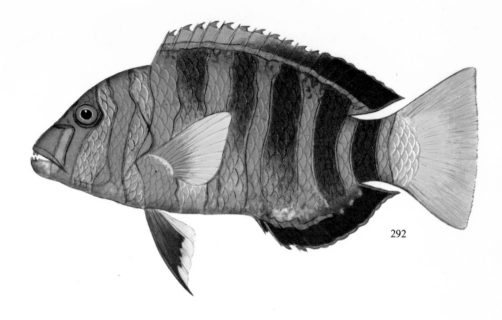

292

293

COLOUR-PLATE 43
292. Harlequin Tusk-fish, *Lienardella fasciatus*, 9 in.
293. Purple Tusk-fish, *Choerodon cephalotes*, 15 in.

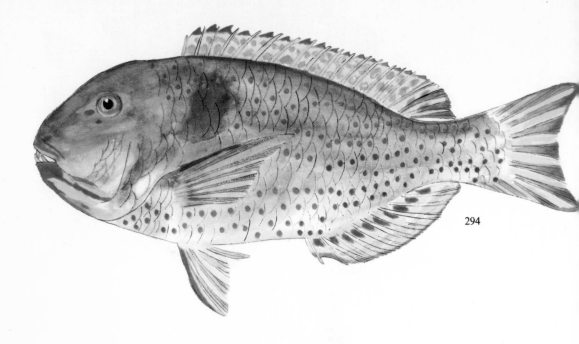

294

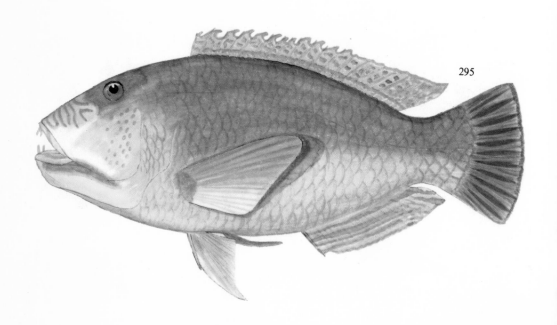

295

COLOUR-PLATE 44
294. Venus Tusk-fish, *Choerodon venustus*, 20 in.
295. Blue Tusk-fish, *C. albigena*, 12 in.

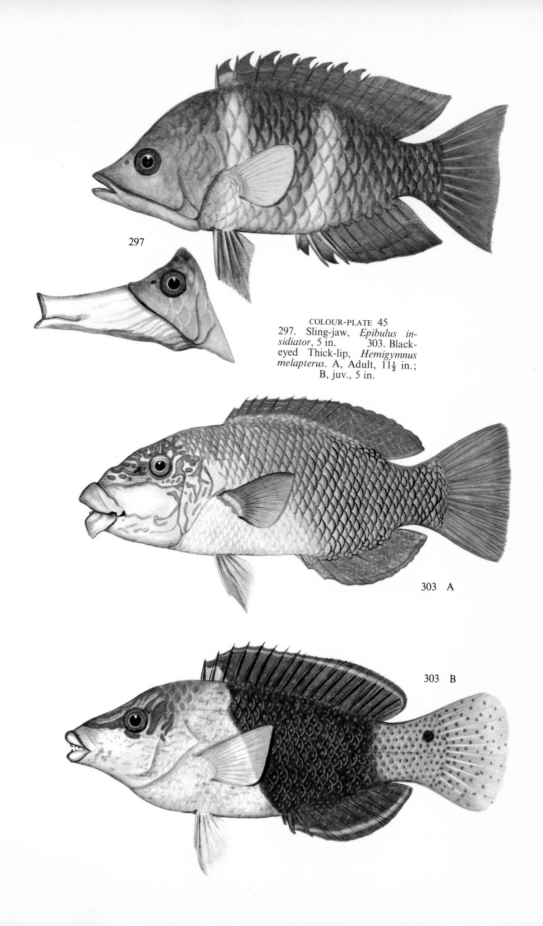

297

COLOUR-PLATE 45
297. Sling-jaw, *Epibulus insidiator*, 5 in. 303. Black-eyed Thick-lip, *Hemigymnus melapterus*. A, Adult, 11½ in.; B, juv., 5 in.

303 A

303 B

304

305

304. Clouded Rainbow-fish, *Halichoeres nebulosus*, 3¼ in.
305. Saddled Rainbow-fish, *H. margaritaceus*, 4 in.

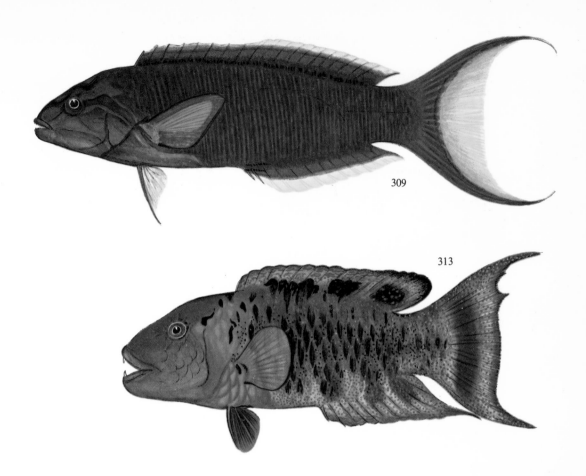

309

313

COLOUR-PLATE 47
309. Moon Wrasse, *Thalassoma lunare*, 8 in.   313.
Scarlet-breasted Maori Wrasse, *Cheilinus fasciatus*, 12 in.
314. Hump-headed Maori Wrasse, *C. undulatus*, 4 ft. 8 in.

314

319   A

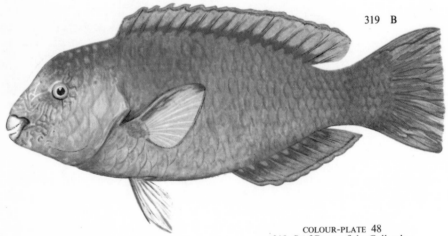

319   B

323

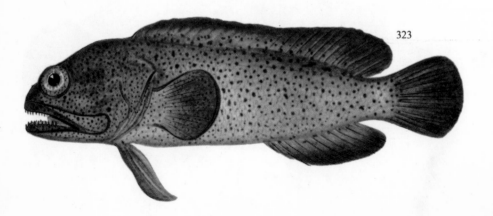

AA. Teeth strong, hooked, with curved canine each side of symphysis; lower teeth curved, pointed, with a pair of symphysial canines, with notch between to receive upper one.   *Gazza*

Secutor

Easily distinguished from the other genera of Leiognathidae by having the mouth practically vertical and protractile horizontally. Species few, one in Queensland.

250. PIG-NOSED PONY-FISH *Secutor ruconius* (Hamilton Buchanan)
[Colour-plate 33]

Chanda ruconius Hamilton Buchanan, Fish. Ganges, 1822, pp. 106, 371.
Illustration by G. Coates.

Slimy, Soapy (South Africa); Chakkara-mullan (India).
D. 8/16; A. 3/14-15. Colour bluish-silvery or brownish above, silvery on sides and below; a series of dark vertical lines or spots along side of back; a blackish streak from lower front edge of eye to throat; a blackish line along base of dorsal; a dark spot on upper part of opercle; pectoral axil black; fins pale, the spinous dorsal tipped with black.
Although not met with by casual observers this wide-ranging species is apparently common in North Queensland waters, for trawling has yielded numerous examples. Grows to 5 inches.

Leiognathus

Top of head with bony ridges and a nuchal spine. Mouth horizontal, more or less directed downwards, closed mandible oblique. Lower preopercle edge serrate.
Small silvery fishes living in shoals in the waters of the Indo-Pacific, some entering fresh water. Species numerous, at least twelve in Queensland.

251. BLACK-BANDED PONY-FISH *Leiognathus moretoniensis* Ogilby
[Plate 39]

Leiognathus moretoniensis Ogilby, Mem. Qld Mus., 1, 1912, p. 59.
Equulites moretoniensis Whitley, Mem. Qld Mus., 10, pt 2, 1932, p. 108, pl. 14, fig. 2.

D. 8/16 (last divided); A. 3/14; P. 17; L. l. less than 40, becoming obsolete below last dorsal ray. Colour in life iridescent pink above, silvery-white below, with oblique wavy light-blue bars and spots above the lateral line (greyish or dark after death) and vertical blue bars and round spots between it and the median line of the sides; below this is a wider blackish band, rarely absent, having a downward curve anteriorly free from pectorals to caudal peduncle;

I

sides of snout with black dots crowded together, also sparsely scattered over cheeks and opercles; spinous dorsal, anal and lower lobe of caudal canary-yellow; a narrow blackish stripe along dorsal base.

A common Moreton Bay species. In 1910 the *Endeavour* trawled 149 examples at a depth of 9 fathoms on a muddy bottom in Moreton Bay. The species has also been recorded from the Gulf of Carpentaria but so far has not been taken between these localities. Grows to $3\frac{1}{4}$ inches.

OTHER SPECIES

Some of the other more comon species of *Leiognathus* are the Orange-tipped Pony-fish, *L. virgatus*, found in the waters of North Queensland and recognized by the orange-tipped dorsal fin; the Black-tipped Pony-fish, *L. splendens*, which bears a large black blotch marginally on the spinous dorsal fin and frequents the waters of the northern part of the State; and the Hump-nosed Pony-fish, *L. decora*, also found in the northern waters. None of these grows to a greater length than approximately $5\frac{1}{2}$ inches.

Family **Gerridae: Silver-bellies**

Small or moderate-sized fishes inhabiting tropical and temperate seas, some entering fresh water. They somewhat resemble the pony-fishes, Leiognathidae, in which family they are included by some authors. In *Gerres*, which is the only genus of the family in Queensland waters, the top of the head is smooth, without a nuchal spine. The scales are large and more or less deciduous and are present on the head. There are 9 to 10 dorsal spines and 10 to 11 rays, the anal having 3 spines and 7 to 8 rays. A noticeable feature is the very protractile jaws which are somewhat similar to those in the pony-fishes.

The species do not display bright colours, all being more or less brilliant silvery-white, some having slightly darker longitudinal or transverse lines, bands, or blotches.

Silver-bellies abound in great numbers in shallow bays and estuaries and are often to be seen among the catches of bream and mullet in the fishermen's nets. The species are numerous and most are valued as food-fishes in other parts of the world. The genera are few, one (*Gerres*) being well represented in Queensland by five species.

KEY TO SPECIES IN QUEENSLAND

A. Second dorsal spine greatly elongated; usually greater than depth of body.   *punctatus*

AA. Second dorsal spine not greatly elongated, usually much less than depth of body.

b. Pectoral short, about equal to length of head.   *splendens*
bb. Pectoral long, more than length of head.

c. Pectoral reaching to or beyond origin of anal.

    d. Scales larger, 32-36 in lateral line to caudal base. Dorsal profile elevated anteriorly; depth of body 2-2.2 in the length.   *abbreviatus*

    dd. Scales smaller, 40-45 in lateral line to caudal base. Dorsal profile not so elevated; depth of body 2.4-2.65 in the length.   *argyreus*

cc. Pectoral not reaching to origin of anal.   *ovatus*

252. THREAD-FIN SILVER-BELLY *Gerres punctatus* (Cuvier and Valenciennes)   [Plate 40]

Gerres punctatus Cuvier and Valenciennes, Hist. Nat. Poiss., 6, 1830, p. 480.
Diapterus filamentosus Bleeker, Atlas Ichth., 8, 1876-7, p. 124, pl. 362, fig. 3.

Kapas-kapas (East Indies).

D. 9/10-11; A. 3/7-8; L. l. 45; L. tr. 5-6/1/12-13. Colour bluish-grey above, silvery on sides and below; rows of short, oblong, horizontal bluish spots on upper half of body, forming, when the scales are rubbed off, continuous lines; young with 10 to 12 pale dusky vertical lines, often broken as a series of dark blotches; snout black; spinous dorsal blackish terminally and a row of blackish spots on each membrane below the middle and just below each spine and ray, above the scaly sheath; spinous dorsal dark-edged; other fins yellowish with numerous fine dots on the membranes. The young have vertical bands.

Another common Indo-Australian and Pacific species commonly found in North Queensland and in the Northern Territory. Occasionally stragglers have been captured as far south as Moreton Bay. Grows to 10 inches.

253. SILVER-BELLY *Gerres ovatus* (Günther)   [Plate 40]

Gerres ovatus Günther, Cat. Fish. Brit. Mus., 1, 1859, p. 343.
Xystaema ovatum Waite, Mem. Austr. Mus., 4, 1899, p. 83, pl. 13.

Pilchard (Moreton Bay).

D. 9/10, 1; A. 3/7, 1; L. l. 36-40; L. tr. 5/9-10. Colour brilliant silvery, the back bright greenish or brownish, fading into silvery sides; fins opaline, the posterior third of the ventrals golden; spinous dorsal dusky, the dorsals black-edged.

A very common fish which inhabits the shallow sandy flats and bays in shoals. Great numbers are netted by the fishermen when they are capturing mullet, bream, etc. Silver-bellies are not known to take a bait. Their flesh is sweet, but on account of their small size they are of no importance as food-fish. They are found in Queensland, New South Wales, the Northern Territory and Western Australia and grow to 10 inches.

OTHER SPECIES

Shining Silver-belly, *G. splendens*. A northern species found only in the waters of North Queensland. Grows to 7½ inches.

Short Silver-belly, *G. abbreviatus*. An Indo-Australian species commonly found in the waters of North Australia. Grows to 9 inches.

Darnley Island Silver-belly, *G. argyreus*. A wide-ranging fish which enters Australian waters commonly in Queensland, and occasionally strays into New South Wales. Grows to 9 inches.

Family **Chaetodontidae**

This big family, also called Squamipinnes (scaly-finned fishes), is represented in all tropical seas, a few species being found in subtropical waters. They are marine, littoral fishes of small or median size, the majority of the species living among coral reefs. The family is represented by five sub-families in Australian seas. Although the majority of the species are of little value as food-fishes, some attain a large size and are excellent to eat.

KEY TO AUSTRALIAN SUB-FAMILIES

Based on Weber and de Beaufort[30]

A. Anal with 4 spines. Spinous dorsal differentiated from soft dorsal, the first spine procumbent, Mouth small, transverse, not protractile. .... SCATOPHAGINAE

AA. Anal with 3-4, rarely 5, spines. Spinous dorsal without procumbent spine, sometimes differentiated from, usually totally confluent with, soft dorsal. Mouth protractile. Scales moderate or small.

    b. Preoperculum serrate or not, but in adult without a strong spine. Anal with 3-4 (5) spines. Ventrals with an axillary scale. .... CHAETODONTINAE

    bb. Preoperculum strongly armed, including a long spine at the angle. Anal with 3 spines. Ventrals without an axillary scale. .... POMACANTHINAE

AAA. Anal with 3 spines.

    c. Spinous dorsal differentiated from soft dorsal; first spine procumbent. Mouth protractile. Maxilla distally exposed. Pectorals falcate, elongate. .... DREPANINAE

    cc. Spinous dorsal confluent with soft dorsal; no procumbent spine. Mouth not protractile, maxilla not exposed. .... PLATACINAE

---

[30] *Fish. Indo-Austr. Archip.*, 7, 1936, p. 2.

Sub-family SCATOPHAGINAE: BUTTER-FISHES

Form much compressed, elevated, covered with minute adherent ctenoid scales which extend over the head and on soft dorsal and anal fins. Head small, with an occipital crest abruptly ascending. Mouth small, square, terminal, not protractile, the maxilla hidden. Teeth in jaws setiform, tricuspidate, movable; none on vomer and palatines. Opercles entire. Two dorsal fins, united at base, spinous portion long, preceded by a procumbent spine and with 11 to 12 strong spines; soft portion of 16 to 18 rays. Anal with 4 strong spines and 14 to 15 rays. Pectorals small, rounded. Ventrals with a spine and 5 branched rays; a small scaly axillary process present. Caudal truncate.

A small sub-family of fishes consisting of two genera and but two or three valid species. They are found from the east coast of Africa across the Indian Ocean to the Indo-Australian Archipelago, living in the sea, in brackish estuaries, and in freshwater streams. In Australia and other countries they are valued as food, though some peoples reject them on account of their foul habit of feeding upon excrement and other obnoxious substances. The flesh is very soft but of good flavour. It must, however, be eaten fresh, because it deteriorates rapidly. The common name is bestowed on account of the flesh being "as soft as butter".

In their young stages butter-fishes feed upon algal growths, conferva, etc., and when small make admirable aquarium pets, living well in fresh water. They should be handled with care, for they are capable of inflicting painful wounds with their many spines. Their scales are ctenoid and very small, with a sand-paper-like feeling to the touch. There are two genera, both represented in Australian waters.

KEY TO GENERA

A. Gill-membranes forming a distinct, deep, free fold across the isthmus. Posterior margins of the soft dorsal and anal fins sloping backwards from the last ray. *Scatophagus*

AA. Gill-membranes not forming a fold across the isthmus, though sometimes grooved across it. Posterior margins of soft dorsal and anal sloping forward from last ray. *Selenotoca*

Scatophagus

For characters of the genus see those given under the sub-family heading and in the above key. One species in Queensland.

246

254. SPOTTED BUTTER-FISH *Scatophagus argus* (Linnaeus)

[Colour-plate 34]

Chaetodon argus Linnaeus, Syst. Nat., 12th ed., 1766, p. 464.
Illustration by G. Coates.

Mia-Mia (Townsville).

D. 11/16-18; A. 4/14-15. Colour bluish-grey, greenish, olive or blackish above passing into silvery below or even sometimes yellowish, with smaller or larger, more or less numerous, round or oval brownish spots, sometimes in the form of dots or blotches over body, in some examples extending on to fins and tail.

Young fish about one inch in length are olive-brown, with about 5 black transverse bands which disappear with growth; above the head and along the back, between the black bands, is bright orange-red.

A common fish on the coasts of Queensland, New South Wales, and the Northern Territory. Found also in the western Pacific and the Indo-Australian Archipelago. In India, where it is esteemed, its flesh is said to resemble trout, though many reject it on account of its disgusting habits. Grows to 12½ inches. Stings from the spines of this species are said to be much worse than from allied species.

Selenotoca

For characters of the genus see those given under the sub-family heading and in the preceding key.

KEY TO SPECIES IN QUEENSLAND

A.   About 12-18 narrow black vertical bands on upper sides
of body, some surpassing the lateral line; spotted below.   *multifasciata*

AA. About six wide black vertical bands on sides, extending
to ventral surface, broken into a dotted line in young
examples. Adults have the irregular abdominal spots
arranged in 2-3 longitudinal stripes.   *multifasciata* sub-sp. *aetatevarians*

255. SOUTHERN BUTTER-FISH *Selenotoca multifasciata* var. *aetatevarians* (De Vis)

[Plate 40]

Scatophagus aetatevarians De Vis, Proc. Linn. Soc. N.S.Wales, 9, 1884, p. 456.
Illustration after Marshall, Grant and Haysom.

Johnny Dory (Queensland and New South Wales).

D. 12/16; A. 4/15. Colour: Back and upper sides greenish, sides and below silvery; 5 to 6 broad vertical dark-green bands composed of elongate spots; 2 to 3 horizontal stripes on belly, usually more faint than the vertical bands, are usually present in adult specimens; spinous dorsal dusky; dorsal and anal rays white, the membranes greenish; ventrals and pectorals pale yellowish-green; caudal brownish basally, the posterior half greenish.

A common fish in South Queensland and New South Wales. Great numbers are captured by net fishermen, usually when netting in the estuaries and bays which have dirty sandy or somewhat muddy banks. Grows to 16 inches. A good food-fish, though the flesh is rather soft.

OTHER SPECIES

Northern Butter-fish, *S. multifasciata*. Ranges across the northern waters of the continent from Western Australia to North Queensland. Grows to 10½ inches. Common. Also found in New Guinea and New Caledonia.

Sub-family CHAETODONTINAE: BUTTERFLY-FISHES

Brilliantly coloured fishes of exquisite beauty and design living among the coral reefs of the Indo-Pacific and especially plentiful on the Great Barrier Reef of Queensland. Their predominant combination of colours is yellow and black. Many of the species have a black vertical band passing down through the eye, and an eye-like spot at the root of the tail or on the fins. They are carnivorous, and feed upon small invertebrates, crabs, and other crustaceans. The mouth is small and in some species is set at the end of an extremely long snout, which enables the fish to feed among the coral branches. The teeth are close-set, minute, and slender, a feature signified by the name of the family, which means "bristle-toothed". Their bodies are compressed laterally and covered with small scales which extend on to the dorsal and anal fins. Eight genera occur in Australian seas.

KEY TO GENERA IN QUEENSLAND
Based on Fowler and Bean[31]

A. Snout tubiform, elongated, produced.

b. Dorsal spines 9-11.
c. Dorsal spines 9.   *Chelmon*
cc. Dorsal spines 11.   *Chelmonops*
bb. Dorsal spines 12-13.   *Forcipiger*

AA. Snout conic, moderate or short, not especially produced.

d. Dorsal spines not greatly elongated or prolonged in flexible filaments.
e. Teeth rudimentary or absent. Dorsal spines 8-10. *Coradion*
ee. Teeth well developed.

---

[31] U.S. Nat. Mus., Bull. 100, 8, 1929, p. 41.

f. Dorsal spines 6-7. Front dorsal and anal rays
prolonged.   *Parachaetodon*

ff. Dorsal spines 10-16.

  g. Scales large, 30-50 from operculum to caudal
base. Lateral line terminating before or near
end of dorsal.   *Chaetodon*

  gg. Scales small, 55 or more from operculum to
caudal base. Lateral line terminating on caudal.   *Microcanthus*

dd. Dorsal spines elongated and at least one prolonged
into a filament. Front of head with bony protuberance. Scales moderate.   *Heniochus*

Chelmon

The two Australian forms of this genus are separated as shown in the following
key. Further study of numerous specimens from various localities will probably
prove them to be varieties of but a single species which ranges from the east
coast of Africa to China and the Indo-Australian region.

KEY TO AUSTRALIAN SPECIES

A.   Snout short, 2.3 in the head; upper profile more or less
gibbous on occiput. Ventrals black; dorsal and anal
fins with light margins.   *rostratus mulleri*

AA. Snout longer, nearly twice in head; upper profile concave from snout to neck. Ventrals light coloured, with
median longitudinal dusky area; dorsal and anal fins
with dark margins.   *rostratus marginalis*

256. BEAKED CORAL-FISH *Chelmon rostratus marginalis* (Richardson)
[Colour-plate 34]

Chelmon marginalis Richardson, Ann. Mag. Nat. Hist., 10, 1842, p. 28.
Illustration by G. Coates.

D. 9/30; A. 3/21; L. l. 50; L. tr. 9-10/21-24. Colour pearly-white, becoming
somewhat yellowish posteriorly; very pale, faint mauve longitudinal lines
follow the scale rows; 4 vertical orange-yellow bands, the first three with dark-
brown margins, the last bordered with pale blue; the first band from nape
through eye to throat; second band from origin of spinous dorsal to ventrals,
widest before pectoral origin; third from posterior spinous dorsal to first
anal spine; fourth band from soft dorsal to anal, fading at each end into the
yellow of those fins; a blackish band across caudal peduncle, bordered on either
side by pale blue; dorsal spines orange, the membranes pale blue, continued on
to soft dorsal as a submarginal band, beneath which the soft dorsal is canary-
yellow, with a large black ocellus, edged with pale blue; margin of fin orange-

brown; anal with submarginal pale-blue band, edged terminally orange, which colour is continued across caudal peduncle to edge of dorsal; caudal and pectoral hyaline, the latter with a pale-orange stripe across its base; ventrals yellow basally, the outer half orange, separated by a wide blue band.

A common fish on the coast of Queensland from Moreton Bay to Torres Strait and across North Australia to Western Australia. Grows to 8 inches.

OTHER SUB-SPECIES

Black-fin Coral-fish, *C. rostratus mulleri*. A handsome fish which frequents the waters of the Northern Territory and North Queensland. Grows to 5½ inches.

Chelmonops

In this genus the snout is produced but is shorter than in *Chelmon*, and the dorsal fin has 11 spines. Two species, found only in Australia, one in Queensland.

257. TRUNCATE CORAL-FISH *Chelmonops truncatus* (Kner) [Plate 40]

Chaetodon truncatus Kner, Sitzb. Akad. Wiss. Wien, 34, 1859, p. 442, pl. 2.

D. 11/26-27; A. 3/18-21; L. l. 43-55. General colour white, all the spines yellow, with 6 dark-brown or black vertical bands, the first from upper lip upwards between nostrils to a point above eyes, the last on caudal peduncle. Dorsal and anal fins coloured similar to the body markings; pectorals colourless, the ventrals black.

In small examples there is a large and distinct ocellus on the anterior dorsal rays and included in the fourth body-band which becomes lost with age.

A well-known and fairly common fish in New South Wales. It is rare in Queensland waters and has not been recorded farther north than Double Island Point, where four examples were trawled at 29 to 30 fathoms. It has also been recorded from Western Australia and Lord Howe Island. Grows to 8 inches.

Forcipiger

A genus containing a single species, closely related to *Chelmon* and *Chelmonops* but differing in the long snout, long pectorals, high spinous dorsal, and distinctive coloration.

258. LONG-BILL *Forcipiger longirostris* (Broussonet) [Colour-plate 35]

Chaetodon longirostris Broussonet, Ichth., 1782, p. 23.
Illustration by G. Coates.

D. 11-12/22, 1, to 24, 1; A. 3/17, 1, or 18, 1; L. l. 63-75; L. tr. 12-13/29-31. Colour brilliant yellow, deeper and shaded with orange posteriorly; a large black triangular patch covers the nape, upper surface of head, and side down to level of lower edge of eye from tip of snout to opercular region; lower parts of head and breast livid white; caudal fin greyish, other fins yellow; anal fin with a large black circular spot at its posterior angle; soft dorsal and anal with a narrow black margin. (After Herre and Montalban.)

A wide-ranging species found from the east coast of Africa to China and through the Indo-Pacific. It is everywhere rare and is not known from many intermediate localities. In Australian waters it is known only from Queensland, where it has been recorded from each end of the State, but is unknown between Cape York and Moreton Bay. It is apparently confined to coral reefs and rocky coasts of a similar nature. Grows to 9 inches. The species varies greatly in the length of the rostrum.

Coradion

A small genus of fishes allied to *Chaetodon* but differing in the more angular form, the base of most of the soft dorsal and anal being nearly vertical, in the very small teeth, and the small number of dorsal spines. One species in Queensland.

259. HIGH-FIN CORAL-FISH *Coradion altivelis* McCulloch [Plate 40]

Coradion altivelis McCulloch, Biol. Res. Endeavour, 4, pt 4, 1916, p. 191, pl. 56, fig. 1.

D. 8/33-34; A. 3/22-23; P. 17; V. 1/5; C. 17; L. l. 47. Colour yellowish; a broad ocular band from nape through eye to throat; a second band below anterior dorsal spines crosses end of operculum and base of pectoral fin, to the ventrals; it is joined below with another band extending from bases of posterior spines to belly; a less definite and broader grey band crosses the body between middle of soft dorsal and anal, extending on to bases of those fins; a broad blackish band encircles base of tail and has its posterior margin angular with the apex directed backwards, membrane between second and third dorsal spines black; soft dorsal and anal fins with 2 intramarginal narrow dark lines, separated by a white interspace, and with broad lighter borders. (After McCulloch.) Young examples have a large ocellus on the soft dorsal.

This little-known species inhabits the Wide Bay district, South Queensland. Nothing is known concerning its habits. The largest of the two known specimens measures 135 mm.

Parachaetodon

Small dorsal spines graduated to the last, which is the longest. Soft dorsal higher than spinous dorsal and the anterior rays elevated, the fin graduated low posteriorly. Species few, one in Queensland.

260. SIX-SPINED BUTTERFLY-FISH *Parachaetodon ocellatus* (Cuvier and Valenciennes) [Colour-plate 35]

Platax ocellatus Cuvier and Valenciennes, Hist. Nat. Poiss., 7, 1831, p. 229.
Illustration by G. Coates.

D. 6/28, 1, or 29, 1; A. 3/19, 1, or 20, 1; L. l. 39-42; L. tr. 14-15/27-28. Colour silvery, with 5 cross-bars, the first yellow, black-edged, and forked on the occiput, whence it sends back a spur along median ridge of nape; it curves downward through eye, across cheek and interopercle, and backward to meet its fellow or be lost on side of throat. The second is olive-brown, mesially golden, and black-edged; it extends from first dorsal spine over and behind opercular edge through base of pectoral, and bends strongly backward to behind ventral. The third and fourth are olive-brown, with a slightly backward obliquity; the third is between last three dorsal and two anterior anal spines, and the fourth between sixth and fourteenth dorsal and sixth and ninth anal rays. The fifth is between median dorsal and anal rays, and curves backward to cross caudal peduncle. A large black oval ocellus on dorsal fin is included in the golden prolongation of the fourth band. Dorsal fin yellow, except for 2 silvery shafts corresponding to interspaces between body bands; tips of posterior dorsal and anal rays black, the rays between the black margin and the last cross-band pale blue, the membrane golden. Caudal and pectoral fins colourless. Ventrals white, with the two inner rays blackish. (After Ogilby.)

This fish is found in India, southern China, the Philippines, and the Indo-Australian Archipelago. In Australia it is known from Queensland and the Northern Territory and as a straggler in New South Wales. Grows to 7 inches.

Chaetodon

These beautiful fishes, most of which live among the coral reefs of the Indo-Pacific, are especially plentiful in the maze of coral growths on the Great Barrier Reef. When gazing down into the coral pools and deep chasms of the reef they are to be seen in dozens, milling about and flashing their brilliant colours among the coral growths. They are difficult to capture on account of not taking a baited line, and their quickness of movement protects them from enemies, which are unable to reach them in the coral. Many species are found on the reefs. Twenty-one species in Queensland waters.

KEY TO SPECIES IN QUEENSLAND
Based on McCulloch[32]

A.   Some or all of the scale rows below the lateral line run obliquely upward and backward.

      b. Scale rows oblique as above on both upper and lower parts of sides.

---

[32] *Rec. Austr. Mus.*, 14, p. 1, 1923.

c. Prɔfile convex, not concave, at base of snout, which is obtuse.

d. An oblique line on each row of scales on the sides; a broad black band before the ocular band covering the snout, and a narrow one behind it; Dorsal, anal, and caudal, each with a black stripe with light-coloured margins. .... *trifasciatus*

cc. Profile concave at base of snout, which is more or less produced.

e. Scale rows of upper anterior part of sides with dark lines running upward and backward and at *right angles* to those running downward and backward on lower posterior portion.

f. Dorsal with a produced setiform ray and a black ocellus. .... *auriga*

ff. Dorsal without a produced ray; a dark band from dorsal across peduncle to anal. .... *vagabundus*

ee. Scale rows with dark lines criss-crossing each other in a diamond pattern. .... *rafflesii*

eee. Scale rows either without dark lines, or, if they are present, they do not meet at right angles.

g. Ocular band mesially yellow with dark edges.

h. Body with 7 oblique dark stripes running upward and backward; a dark cross-bar on caudal; ventrals pale. .... *pelewensis*

gg. Ocular band black. .... *flavirostris*

i. Ventrals blackish, body dark-coloured. .... *flavirostris*

ii. Ventrals and body light-coloured with dark markings.

j. Ocular band much narrower than eye.

k. Each scale row with an oblique dark line running upward and backward; and other markings. .... *melannotus*

jj. Ocular band as broad as, or broader than, eye.

l. Body with subvertical dark lines descending through each scale row; scales very large and somewhat angular.

m. Two broad dark bands descending from dorsal fin on to upper half of sides, and a large spot on peduncle. .... *falcula* mm. A broad black band around base of dorsal, crossing peduncle to posterior base of anal. Black vertical lines down the scale rows. *lineolatus*

ll. No dark subvertical lines through scale-rows.

n. A broad black bar extending obliquely upward from shoulder to middle of spinous dorsal, and other markings. *lunula*

bb. Scale rows oblique on upper anterior part of side but more or less horizontal on lower portion.

o. Each scale with a round black spot forming oblique rows above and horizontal ones below. Anal broadly black-edged, the other fins plain. *citrinellus*

AA. Scale rows either horizontal or running somewhat downward and backward.

p. Scales large, in 35 or less series.

q. One or two produced setiform dorsal rays. Snout beak-like. Scales of sides not remarkably large.

r. A large patch covering greater part of second dorsal and part of back. *ephippium*

qq. No produced dorsal rays.

s. Anal fin deep and pointed, the third anal spine almost as long as head. Body with a series of curved vertical bands. *dixoni*

ss. Anal fin not so deep, rounded, the third anal spine much shorter than head.

t. A broad dark band from spinous dorsal to ventral and a much broader one from soft dorsal to anal. *kleinii*

tt. A very large elongate-oval blotch of violet-blue (black after death) on upper side of body; a large black spot on caudal peduncle, bordered below with white. *plebeius*

pp. Scales small, in 40 or more series.

u. Body and fins with 7 narrow equidistant dark cross-bars. Ocular band dark. *octofasciatus*

uu. Body either plain or with 3 broad cross-bands; ocular band yellow with dark edges.

v. Three broad cross-bands descending from dorsal fin, which are lilac-coloured in the middle portion, with orange-yellow borders. *rainfordi*

vv. Body largely brown or drab, without cross-bands descending from dorsal fin. *aureofasciatus*

AAA. Scale rows meeting in an angle in middle of body
depth, their direction marked by light or dark stripes.

    w. Body deep, nearly circular; dorsal spines 11; anal
       spines 3; soft dorsal rounded. Sides with angular,
       nearly vertical, lemon-yellow stripes.   *triangulum*

    ww. Body oblong-oval; dorsal spines 14; anal spines 4;
       soft dorsal pointed. Sides with about 20 dark
       lavender angular stripes bent to right angles.   *trifascialis*

261. THREAD-FIN BUTTERFLY-FISH *Chaetodon auriga* Forskål
[Colour-plate 36]

Chaetodon auriga Forskål, Descr. Anim., 1775, p. 60.
Illustration by G. Coates.

D. 12-13/23, 1, or 24; A. 3/20, 1, or 21, 1; L. l. 29-30; L. tr. 6-8/15-18. Colour
pearl-grey in front and below, including ventrals, with a faint tinge of violet,
changing abruptly to deep orange-yellow behind and on vertical and caudal
fins; on each side of body behind head is a series of 5 violet-grey lines running
upward and backward to base of dorsal spines; at right angles to these are
10 to 12 similar lines running from the last line downward and backward
towards anal; a broad, white-edged black vertical band, narrowing and sometimes with age, disappearing above, passes through eye and meets the opposite
one below; lips pinkish; soft dorsal is edged with black and has a large round
black spot near margin; anal is yellowish on its outer edge and has a narrow
submarginal band of black; caudal is bright yellow, broadly tipped with light
violet, and has 2 fine submarginal lines of blackish before which is a zone of
lemon-yellow; pectoral greyish. (After Herre and Montalban.)

A widely ranging species found on the Queensland coast from north to
south and straggling into northern New South Wales. Grows to 9 inches.

262. CRISS-CROSS BUTTERFLY-FISH *Chaetodon vagabundus* Linnaeus
[Colour-plate 36]

Chaetodon vagabundus Linnaeus, Syst. Nat., 10th ed., 1758, p. 276; 12th ed., 1766, p. 465.
Illustration by G. Coates.

D. 12-13/23, 1, or 24, 1; A. 3/20, 1; L. l. 29-30; L. tr. 7-8/14-15. Colour:
"In life the ground colour varies from straw-yellow to grey, the soft dorsal
and anal bright orange, the caudal golden or orange. From the base of the
spinous dorsal 6 black or purplish-brown lines run downward and forward.
At right angles to these 12 similar lines run obliquely toward the anal. A black
ocular band nearly as wide as the eye extends from the nape to the throat. A
black line beginning on the base of the spinous dorsal expands on the soft
dorsal to a broad band continuing across the caudal peduncle to the middle

of the anal base. Both dorsals are edged with black. On the caudal are two black cross-bands, the anterior one crescent-shaped. The anal has a sub-marginal black line." (Herre.)

In very young examples the soft dorsal fin bears a large black ocellus and there is a dusky stripe across the middle rays of both soft dorsal and anal fins.

A common Indo-Pacific species found in the waters of North Queensland. Grows to almost 8 inches.

263. LINED BUTTERFLY-FISH *Chaetodon lineolatus*
(Cuvier and Valenciennes) [Colour-plate 37]

Chaetodon lineolatus Cuvier and Valenciennes, Hist. Nat. Poiss., 7, 1831, p. 40.
Illustration by G. Coates.

D. 12/25, 1, to 28, 1; A. 3/20, 1, or 21, 1; L. l. 26-27; L. tr. 6-7/15-16. Colour: Body silvery-grey, darker above, and ruled with black vertical lines down the scale rows; a broad black stripe from nape through eye to throat and joined by its fellow across forehead by a horizontal stripe above eyes; another broad black stripe from middle of spinous dorsal along base of soft dorsal and down across caudal peduncle to base of anal, bordered anteriorly by a bright-yellow area; spinous dorsal yellow, the membranes bluish; soft dorsal divided median-ally by a narrow black line, the basal half yellow, with a broad orange longi-tudinal stripe, the outer half clear orange; anal clear yellow, with a narrow orange border; caudal orange basally, edged on each side with yellow, divided from the posterior third by a narrow black line, followed by a crescent-shaped zone of brown, hyaline terminally; pectorals and ventrals clear.

This fine species, which is one of the largest of all the chaetodonts, ranges from the Red Sea and the east coast of Africa through the Indo-Australian Archipelago to North Queensland, Polynesia northwards to Hawaii and southwards to the Society Islands. Apparently not common in Queensland. Grows to 12 inches.

264. RAINFORD'S BUTTERFLY-FISH *Chaetodon rainfordi* (McCulloch)
[Plate 40]

Chaetodon rainfordi McCulloch, Rec. Austr. Mus., 14, 1923, p. 4, pl. 2, fig. 1.

D. 11/21; A. 3/18; L. l. 45. Colour canary-yellow with darker orange cross-bands; a narrow dark-edged stripe with light lavender borders extends down median line of forehead to upper lip. The ocular band, which is much narrower than the eye, commences on nape and passes through eye and across cheek to breast; it is deep orange with narrow blackish edges, and has a light-lavender border on each side, which is broadest below. A narrow orange band curves forward from third dorsal spine to end of operculum and then backward over base of pectoral to behind ventral; its anterior edge is partly defined by a

blackish line, and it is preceded by a broad lavender stripe from above operculum to axil of ventral fin. A broad composite band curves forward from
sixth to ninth dorsal spines to region of vent; its middle portion is deep lilac,
which colour is darkest above, and bordered with rich orange on each side;
most of the scales bear dark basal spots, which tend to form dark edges to the
orange borders. Another similar band descends from anterior part of soft
dorsal to that of anal; a less defined orange band crosses from posterior part
of soft dorsal to anal and encloses a large rounded spot on caudal peduncle.
All fins are uniformly bright yellow, but the caudal has a broad pale-lavender
border.

A pretty little fish known only from the coast of Queensland. It is common
in the north. The most southerly range is Noosa Heads, South Queensland.
Grows to 5½ inches.

265. GOLDEN-STRIPED BUTTERFLY-FISH *Chaetodon aureofasciatus* Macleay [Colour-plate 37]

Chaetodon aureofasciatus Macleay, Proc. Linn. Soc. N.S.Wales, 2, 1878, p. 351.
Illustration by G. Coates.

D. 11-12/21-22; A. 3/16-18; L. l. 40. Colour: Body purple-drab, changing
into yellow on belly, soft dorsal and caudal base; a narrow orange stripe with
lilac edges extends down median line of forehead to upper lip; a bright cadium-
yellow ocular band, much narrower than eye, finely edged with black, exterior
to which are violet borders; an orange or cadium-yellow band commences
above shoulder and extends across end of operculum, across base of pectoral to
behind ventral fin; it is clearest above eye-level; its anterior edge is partly
defined by a dark line, preceded by a broad violet stripe; dorsal, anal, and
caudal fins bright orange-yellow, the latter with a broad violet border; ventrals
pale yellow, tinged with green.

A common species in the Northern Territory and North Queensland, extending down the coast to about the Whitsunday Passage, south of which it
is very rarely met with. Grows to 6 inches.

266. RIGHT-ANGLED BUTTERFLY-FISH *Chaetodon trifascialis* (Quoy and Gaimard) [Colour-plate 38]

Chaetodon trifascialis Quoy and Gaimard, Voy. Uranie, Zool., 1825, p. 379.
Illustration by G. Coates.

D. 14/15, 1, or 16, 1; A. 4/15, 1, or 16; L. l. 34-35; L. tr. 8/10-11. Colour
olive-brown above, paler to whitish below; 2 large elongate horizontal pale
blotches above median axis on middle of side; about 20 oblique dark-violet
stripes, bent to a right angle on side of body obliquely forward to median axis,
when all turn and run downward and backward; a broad blackish band,

bordered with a narrow pale-yellow stripe, from predorsal, occasionally meeting its fellow, runs through eye and over cheek to chest; spinous and soft dorsal orange, the latter with pale edge posteriorly and black submarginal band; anal canary-yellow, with narrow pale-blue edge; ventrals lemon-yellow; pectoral hyaline, with a narrow orange stripe at its base; caudal largely blackish-brown, upper and lower edges orange; narrowly white terminally, then narrow black submarginal line, followed by a broad vertical band of yellow narrowing to a point above and below.

A beautiful species known by its oblong-oval form, four anal spines, and right-angled stripes. Wide-ranging from the Red Sea to the East Indies, Micronesia, Polynesia and North Queensland. First recorded from North Queensland when George Coates obtained a specimen at Townsville in October 1946. Grows to 6 inches.

OTHER SPECIES

Lineated Butterfly-fish, *C. trifasciatus*. Although widespread in the Indo-Pacific region this fish is very rarely met with in Queensland waters. Grows to 6 inches.

Latticed Butterfly-fish, *C. rafflesi* Bennett. A common Indo-Pacific species which has been recorded from the Cardwell district, North Queensland. Grows to 6 inches.

Dot and Dash Butterfly-fish, *C. pelewensis*. A little-known fish from the South Seas which has been recorded from the waters of North Queensland. Grows to 5 inches.

Dusky Butterfly-fish, *C. flavirostris*. A species of the western Pacific, recorded also from the coasts of Queensland and northern New South Wales. Rare in Australian waters. Grows to 4 inches.

Black-backed Butterfly-fish, *C. melannotus*. A wide-ranging species found occasionally on the coral reefs of North Queensland. Grows to 7 inches.

Saddled Butterfly-fish, *C. falcula*. A large, wide-ranging fish found from the Red Sea across the Indian Ocean to the Indo-Pacific region. It is rare on Australian shores, being known only from Queensland. Two examples have been obtained from opposite ends of the State, namely Murray Island, Torres Strait, and in Moreton Bay. Grows to 8 inches.

Red-striped Butterfly-fish, *C. lunula*. A distinctively coloured fish occasionally captured in North Queensland. It is also found in the western Pacific, The East Indies, and Hawaii. Grows to 8 inches.

Speckled Butterfly-fish, *C. citrinellus*. A handsome little fish which ranges from the East Indies to the South Seas. In Australia it is known only from the coasts of Queensland and northern New South Wales. In the latter State and in South Queensland it is rarely seen, but it is quite common in the north. Grows to about 5 inches.

Black-blotched Butterfly-fish, *C. ephippium*. A large Indo-Pacific fish readily identified by the large black blotch. Known in Australian waters by a few examples taken in North Queensland. Grows to 12 inches.

Keel-finned Butterfly-fish, *C. dixoni*. A single specimen of this rare species has been recorded from Murray Island, Torres Strait. The only other locality from which it is known is the New Hebrides. Grows to almost 3½ inches.

White-spotted Butterfly-fish, *C. kleinii*. A wide-ranging species, very common in the Indo-Australian Archipelago but apparently rare in Australian waters, where it is known on the Queensland coast from a single example taken in Torres Strait. Grows to 5 inches.

Blue-blotched Butterfly-fish, *C. plebeius*. An Indo-Pacific species which is said to be somewhat rare elsewhere. Although recorded from Moreton Bay it is seldom seen south of the Capricorns, but north of that point it is quite common. Grows to 4½ inches.

Eight-banded Butterfly-fish, *C. octofasciatus*. A distinctively marked fish from the Indo-Australian Archipelago and the South Seas. It has been recorded from the Barrier Reef. Rare in Queensland. Grows to 4 inches.

Herring-bone Butterfly-fish, *C. triangulum*. A handsome fish which takes its name from the resemblance of its pattern to the traditional herringbone. Wide-ranging, common in the Indo-Pacific region and occasionally found in Queensland and New Guinea. Grows to almost 5 inches.

Microcanthus

Distinguished from *Chaetodon* by its small scales and shorter soft dorsal and anal fins, also horizontal blackish bands. A single species from China, Japan, and Australia.

267. STRIPEY *Microcanthus strigatus* (Cuvier and Valenciennes) [Plate 40]

Chaetodon strigatus Cuvier and Valenciennes, Hist. Nat. Poiss., 7, 1831, p. 25.
Microcanthus joyceae Whitley, Rec. Austr. Mus., 18, no. 3, 1931, p. 111, pl. 13, figs 4-5.

Footballer (Western Australia).

D. 11/16, 1, or 17; A. 3/13, 1, or 14; L. l. 42-45 + 2-3; L. tr. 12-13/22-27. Colour silvery-white, with 5 broad black bands sloping slightly downwards posteriorly from the horizontal; the upper ones are slightly broader than the interspace and all are obscurely edged with pale green; the two upper ones extend on to soft dorsal, and the two lower on to anal; spinous dorsal with a broad black band which extends on to soft dorsal; the fifth band runs from snout, through eye, crosses base of pectoral and extends on to soft anal anteriorly; there is a short black bar from beneath pectoral base to origin of anal; caudal silvery-white; ventrals pale.

A common little fish found in the waters of China, Japan, the Philippines, and Hawaii, as well as in Australia, where it is found in the waters of South Queensland, New South Wales, and Western Australia. It is common in the rock-pools along the coast. Grows to about 6 inches.

Heniochus

A small group of fishes with greatly compressed and elevated bodies and having bony projections or curved "horns" developed above the eyes, the number and size of which varies with age. In some of the species the fourth dorsal spine is greatly produced into a long filament. They are further characterized by their colours, which are composed of broad cross-bands on a whitish or yellowish ground colour.

The species are few in number and are found frequenting the coral reefs of the Indo-Pacific region, from Mauritius and India to the South Sea Islands, Hawaii, and Japan. Some are valued as market fishes. Three species are found in Queensland waters.

KEY TO SPECIES IN QUEENSLAND

Based on Weber and de Beaufort[33]

A. Nape of neck convex, without a median conical bony prominence. Above each eye, a small spine, sometimes bifid, stronger in adults, but shorter than pupil.

    b. Spinous dorsal as long as soft; fourth dorsal spine produced into a filament in adult at least as long as body. Two black transverse, somewhat inclined bands on body.   *acuminatus*

    bb. Spinous dorsal longer than soft; fourth dorsal spine rigid, longer than head, fifth shorter but much longer than remaining spines. Three strongly inclined transverse black bands, the first through head and eye.   *permutatus*

AA. Nape of neck with a conspicuous median conical bony prominence. Above each eye in the male is a strong curved, horn-like spine, sometimes bifid, small in the young and in the females.   *varius*

---

[33] *Fish. Indo-Austr. Archip.*, 7, 1936, p. 36.

268. FEATHER-FIN BULL-FISH *Heniochus acuminatus* (Linnaeus)

[Colour-plate 38]

Chaetodon acuminatus Linnaeus, Syst. Nat., 10th ed., 1758, p. 272.

Illustration by G. Coates.

Angel-fish, Coachman (South Africa).

D. 11-12/23-28; A. 3/15-19; L. l. about 45. Colour pearly-white or yellowish-white, the head somewhat greyish; 2 blackish-brown cross-bands on body, sloping obliquely backward, the anterior one from first four dorsal spines, reaching to and including ventrals, belly and tips of anterior half of anal; the second band is between sixth and tenth dorsal spines and posterior half of soft anal, covering behind a small part of caudal peduncle; dorsal rays, caudal, and free portion of pectoral lemon-yellow; bases of pectoral rays, the ventrals, interorbital space above eyes, upper surface of preorbital, and lips black. (After Herre and Montalban.)

A wide-ranging species recorded in Australian waters from the Northern Territory, Queensland, and New South Wales. It is very rare in the two latter localities and is only occasionally met with in the far north. Grows to 10 inches.

OTHER SPECIES

Three-banded Bull-fish, *H. permutatus*. An Indo-Pacific fish recorded from the reefs of Torres Strait. It is apparently rare in Queensland. Grows to 7 inches.

Horned Bull-fish, *H. varius*. Colour pattern varies somewhat. A common species in the East Indies, also occurring in the western Pacific, and in Australian waters it has been recorded from the Great Barrier Reef of Queensland. In localities other than the East Indies it is apparently rare. Grows to $7\frac{1}{2}$ inches.

Sub-family POMACANTHINAE: ANGEL-FISHES

The members of this sub-family are considered to be the most beautiful of all the coral-reef fishes. Their colours are unusually brilliant and exhibit extremes of contrast, with weird and intricate patterns. In some species great colour-changes take place with growth, the young being quite unlike the adults. They are readily distinguished from all other chaetodonts by the presence of the long, stout, and usually grooved preopercular spine.

The species abound among the coral reefs of most tropical seas. They are of small or moderate size and in some parts are valued as food. They seldom take a hook and are mostly secured by the natives with the aid of a spear.

KEY TO GENERA

Based on Fraser-Brunner[34]

A. Scales small or moderate (75 or more), not in regular series. Hind margin of preorbital not free; interoperculum large, without spines. Interorbital width greater than eye.

    b. Scales small or very small (85 or more), those of head and body subequal, not sharply differentiated. Lateral line terminating at end of soft dorsal, sometimes a separate portion on caudal peduncle. Posterior nostril the larger. Vertical fins not produced.   *Chaetodontoplus*

    bb. Scales moderate or small, more or less unequal, those of the head very minute, velvety, sharply differentiated from those of the body. Lateral line complete. Anterior nostril the larger. Vertical fins usually produced in adults. Young black with white markings.   *Pomacanthus*

AA. Scales large (50 or less), in regular series.

    c. Interoperculum large; interorbital width greater than eye. Scales on operculum in 6 or more rows.

    d. Lateral line complete. Scales on cheek irregular, unequal. Preorbital convex, its hind margin not free. Interoperculum without spines. Pelvics reaching well beyond origin of anal. Caudal rounded.   *Euxiphipops*

    cc. Interoperculum small. Lateral line terminating at end of soft dorsal.

    e. Interoperculum serrated or with spines posteriorly remote from suboperculum. Hind margin of preorbital free, serrated or with strong spines. Interorbital width equal to or less than eye. Scales on operculum in 5 or less rows.   *Centropyge*

Chaetodontoplus

For the principal characters of the genus see the preceding key. Three species occur in Queensland waters.

KEY TO SPECIES IN QUEENSLAND

Based on Fraser-Brunner[35]

A. Dorsal spines 11-12; scales with auxiliaries; ocular band present though sometimes diffused.

---

[34] *Proc. Zool. Soc. Lond.*, 1933, p. 548.

[35] *Ibid.*, p. 555.

b. Scales more than 100, most of them with one auxiliary; fifth dorsal spine shorter than soft rays; ocular band more or less distinct, sometimes diffused. A broad pale band from first dorsal spine to pelvics, bounded anteriorly by the ocular band, and one along base of soft dorsal. *duboulayi*

AA. Dorsal spines 13; scales without auxiliaries; no ocular band.

c. Body largely deep purplish-brown or black; teeth long, those in lower jaw rather longer than upper; scales numerous.

d. Head violet or purple, with large yellow spots; nape to snout and also breast, bright yellow; body jet black. *personifer*

dd. Head yellow, a dark line encircling eye; body rich coffee-brown; caudal yellow, the posterior third black. *conspicillatus*

269. SCRIBBLED ANGEL-FISH *Chaetodontoplus duboulayi* (Günther)
[Colour-plate 39]

Holacanthus duboulayi Günther, Ann. Mag. Nat. Hist. (3), 20, p. 67.
Illustration by G. Coates.

D. 11/21; A. 3/19-20. General colour of body purplish-brown or black; sides with or without many narrow, irregular wavy pale lines, either horizontal or vertical; a broad yellow band from below the 3 anterior dorsal spines across opercle and base of pectoral, to between origin of ventral and vent; a second band from about sixth dorsal spine along base of dorsal fins down on to caudal peduncle; this band is diffused anteriorly and brown-spotted posteriorly, the spots extending on to caudal peduncle; sides of head and breast lighter than body, uniform or with darker spots; lips and chin yellow, a black line surrounding mouth; dorsal and anal fins purplish, the former with irregular violet lines, the latter with longitudinal blue lines; pectorals hyaline; ventrals yellow; caudal yellow, with a broad whitish submarginal band; sometimes with fine black spots at the base of the fin.

A handsome species from northern Australian waters. It ranges from the north-west coast of Australia to Cape York and down the Queensland coast to Moreton Bay, becoming rare south of Gladstone. Found also in the Aru Islands. Grows to 11 inches.

OTHER SPECIES

Spotted-faced Angel-fish, *C. personifer*. A beautiful fish which so far has been recorded from Western Australia and South Queensland only. Grows to almost 12 inches.

Spectacled Angel-fish. *C. conspicillatus.* Found on the reefs of Queensland from Moreton Bay to the Capricorns, also at Lord Howe Island. Grows to 10 inches.

Pomacanthus

KEY TO SPECIES IN QUEENSLAND

Based on Fraser-Brunner[36]

A.   Adults brightly coloured deep brown or blue, with strong pattern of oblique yellow stripes on body. Young with the last broad white stripe strongly curved to form a ring before the tail.   *imperator*

AA. Adults dull brownish or greyish, with black spots; soft dorsal, anal, and caudal with white dots. Young specimens with whitish curved bands or lines arched but not circular.   *semicirculatus*

270. EMPEROR ANGEL-FISH *Pomacanthus imperator* (Bloch)   [Plate 41]

Chaetodon imperator Bloch, Nat. ausl. Fische, 3, 1787, p. 51.
Pomacanthus imperator Fraser-Brunner, Proc. Zool. Soc. Lond., 1933, p. 556, pl. 1 (showing pattern development).

D. 13-14/18-21; A. 3/19-21. Adults: Golden-brown or purplish-brown, with numerous narrow yellow or orange bands, those on upper half of body inclining upwards, on lower half horizontal or inclining downwards, but curved upwards again posteriorly on anal fin, those above concentrating on soft dorsal; broad dusky-brown ocular band arches back and down along hind preopercle edge, margined on edges with blue; a large black scapular blotch extends through pectoral base to breast, margined in front with pale blue; edge of spinous and soft dorsal pale blue; body lines which extend on to anal become light blue, the fin with a broad pale-blue border; ventrals with narrow blue anterior border, the rays greenish-yellow.

Young: Black, with several transverse white bands on head and sides with narrower, alternating bluish stripes in some stages of development. The posterior broad white band is very strongly curved, usually forming a ring on the tail, those nearest to it curving round it, those towards the head straighter; 2 white stripes between eyes; caudal yellowish. (Fraser-Brunner.)

A beautiful fish from the Indian and South Pacific oceans, occasionally found in North Queensland waters. Its flesh is said to be of good edible quality. Grows to 15 inches.

---

[36] *Ibid.,* p. 549.

271. ZEBRA ANGEL-FISH *Pomacanthus semicirculatus*
(Cuvier and Valenciennes) [Plate 41]

Holacanthus semicirculatus Cuvier and Valenciennes, Hist. Nat. Poiss., 7, 1831, p. 191.
Pomacanthus semicirculatus Fraser-Brunner, Proc. Zool. Soc. Lond., 1933, p. 563, text-fig. 10, (showing pattern development).

D. 13/21-22; A. 3/19-20. Colour: Young about 4 inches are very dark indigo or black with the ventral, dorsal, and anal margins deep blue; several transverse white bands, alternately narrow and broad, the anterior ones more or less straight and vertical, those posteriorly curved backwards; caudal hyaline on posterior half; adults are yellowish on anterior half of body including the head, and greyish or brownish on posterior half, the sides with blackish or blue spots, lighter on soft dorsal, anal, and caudal; pectorals and ventrals yellow, the latter margined anteriorly blue.

A variable species found on the reefs of North Queensland. The great colour-change it undergoes can be seen from the illustration. Ranges from the Red Sea to the Indo-Australian Archipelago and the South Seas. Grows to 15 inches.

Euxiphipops

For characters of the genus see the key on page 261. One species in Queensland.

272. SIX-BANDED ANGEL-FISH *Euxiphipops sexstriatus*
(Cuvier and Valenciennes) [Plate 42]

Holacanthus sexstriatus Cuvier and Valenciennes, Hist. Nat. Poiss., 7, 1831, p. 194.
Holacanthus sexstriatus Bleeker, Atlas Ichth., 9, 1877, p. 66, pl. 372, fig. 2.

D. 13/18-20; A. 3/18. Colour yellowish-brown or golden-green, each scale of the body with a dark-blue centre, head dark blue with a broad pearly-white vertical band from nape to base of opercular spine, passing between eye and posterior margin of preopercle; 6 dark-blue vertical bands across body; pre-opercular spine and dorsal spines blue; dorsal, anal, and caudal fins greenish-brown or yellowish-brown, with a blue margin and a narrow submarginal blue-black line; the 3 fins thick spotted with somewhat large bright-blue spots (excepting the spinous dorsal); pectorals and ventrals similar to other fins but without spots; the latter with a narrow blue border anteriorly.

A large and common fish of the North Queensland reefs, common also in the seas of the Malay Archipelago eastward to Papua, and found also in the Philippines. Used as food in the East Indies. Grows to 20 inches.

Centropyge

For characters of the genus see the key on page 261. Three species in Queensland.

A. Body yellow anteriorly, abruptly divided from the posterior half, which is black; a dark ocular band, diffused below the eye; caudal fin yellow. *bicolor*

AA. Body not particoloured as above.

    b. Uniform blackish-brown. *nox*

    bb. Pale yellowish, each scale with pale centre; a blue ring round eye; edge of operculum and edge of soft dorsal, anal, and caudal dark blue. *flavissimus*

273. BLACK AND GOLD ANGEL-FISH *Centropyge bicolor* (Bloch)
[Plate 42]

Chaetodon bicolor Bloch, Nat. ausl. Fische, 3, 1787, p. 94.
Holacanthus bicolor Bleeker, Atlas Ichth., 9, 1877, p. 61, pl. 369, fig. 3.

D. 15/15; A. 3/17-18. Colour: Anterior half of body from the vertical from sixth or seventh dorsal spine, pectorals, ventrals, caudal and upper edge of soft dorsal, is orange or lemon-yellow; the posterior half to a little before base of caudal, anal, and rest of dorsal violet-black, blue-black, or deep black; a broad blue-black supraocular band, horseshoe-shaped, descends on each side to eye; scales on black portion of body sometimes with transverse pearly or blue stripes; dorsal fin partly punctate with black; anal with spots and short irregular stripes of blue. (After Herre and Montalban.)

A small distinctively coloured fish which grows to about 5½ inches. It is found from the Malay Archipelago eastward to Samoa.

OTHER SPECIES

Dusky Angel-fish, *C. nox*. A sombre-coloured little fish known from North Queensland, the East Indies, China, Japan, and the Philippines. It is apparently rare everywhere and has been recorded from North Queensland reefs only once. Grows to 4 inches.

Yellow Angel-fish, *C. flavissimus*. A South Pacific fish found on the reefs of Queensland. It is not common and grows to only 4 inches. The young males have a large kidney-shaped blue-edged black spot on the side, becoming lost with age.

This is a handsome species found among the coral reefs of Melanesia, Micronesia, and Polynesia. It is rare in Queensland, one example only known from the coast.

---

[37] *Ibid.*, p. 589.

Sub-family DREPANINAE

Form strongly compressed, rhombic, very much elevated at dorsal fin. Scales medium-sized, finely ciliated, extending on to dorsal and anal fins, smaller on head and fins. Head shorter than high. Lower border of preoperculum denticulate, more especially in young. Mouth small, terminal, protractile downwards. Small setiform teeth in bands in jaws, palate toothless. Dorsal with 10 spines, the first procumbent, small, visible only in the juvenile, the following spines strong, with deeply notched membranes, the whole depressible into a high scaly basal sheath. Soft dorsal and anal high, rounded, the latter fin with 3 spines. Pectorals long, falcate. Caudal rounded. Ventrals with a strong spine and 5 rays, the first the longest.

A sub-family with a single genus and species, widely distributed in the Indo-Pacific, West Africa, and the eastern Atlantic.

274. SICKLE-FISH *Drepane punctata* (Bleeker)　　　　[Colour-plate 39]

Chaetodon punctatus Bleeker, Syst. Nat., 10th ed., 1758, p. 273; 12th ed., 1766, p. 461.
Illustration by G. Coates.

Peppercorn (Gladstone); Butter-fish (Ayr and Townsville); Sickle-fish, Concertina-fish (South Africa).

D. 8-9/20, 1, to 22, 1; A. 3/17, 1, to 19, 1; L. l. 46-50; L. tr. 14-15/33-35. Colour bright silvery, with purplish reflections on sides and also a golden tinge; uniform or with 4 to 11 vertical series of blackish spots on upper side of body, confluent and prominent in the young but obsolescent in the adult; fins pale or yellowish, soft dorsal sometimes with a longitudinal series of dark spots, one between each ray.

In Australian waters this fish ranges from Western Australia and north-western Australia across the northern waters of Torres Strait and down the Queensland coast to Moreton Bay. At Gladstone it is very common and numbers are forwarded to the Brisbane Fish Market, but south of Gladstone it is somewhat rare. It is a good food-fish, but the flesh is dry. Found in the sea and brackish estuaries. It has been trawled at Bowen, North Queensland, in 16 fathoms. Grows to 18 inches.

At Townsville it is common around islands and beaches, where it is usually taken in the fishermen's nets and traps.

Sub-family PLATACINAE: BATFISHES

Body compressed, much elevated, changing greatly with age and by variation. Scales small or moderate, ctenoid, minute on head, extending on to vertical fins. Head very high and short, the profile angular or semicircular. Mouth small, horizontal, not protractile, maxilla exposed distally. Teeth in jaws in a band, small, tricuspid, movable; teeth present or absent on vomer. A single dorsal fin, the spinous portion not differentiated from the rayed portion, its spines numbering 5 to 9 increasing in length posteriorly and more or less hidden by the scaly sheath. Anterior rays of dorsal and anal fins usually greatly prolonged in the young, but decreasing with advancing age; in adults the posterior rays are much shorter. Pectorals short. Caudal truncate or emarginate. Ventrals with a strong spine and 5 rays, the anterior ray prolonged, shorter with age.

A small family of marine fishes of moderate size living on coral reefs, in bays, and along rocky shores. Only one genus is known, occurring in the Indo-Pacific region. Many species have been named by authors, but perhaps only four are valid. The form of the body and fins undergoes remarkable changes with age. In the very young fish the soft dorsal, anal, and ventral fins are greatly produced or falcate, giving the fish an entirely different appearance to the adult (see Colour-plate 40). As the age of the fish advances these fins become shorter, until in the adult the dorsal and anal have an almost vertical hind border, rounded or pointed terminally. With age the dorsal spines are more or less hidden by the scaly covering of the dorsal.

One of the common names, that of Leaf-fish, is bestowed on account of the young fish's habit of floating motionless upon the surface of the water like a curled-up dead leaf, only to dart rapidly away when an attempt at capture is made.

From an edible standpoint the batfishes have flesh of excellent quality. A single genus comprises the sub-family.

Platax

For characters of the single genus see those given under the sub-family heading. Three species occur in Queensland waters.

KEY TO SPECIES IN QUEENSLAND

A. The 3 cusps of the teeth equal or almost so.

    b. 5 dorsal spines. Colour brownish, with 2 broad vertical bands from dorsal to ventral surface and sometimes a third indistinct one before the caudal peduncle, the second one commencing at the spinous dorsal.   *pinnatus*

    bb. 9 dorsal spines. Colour silvery, with 2 narrow bands from dorsal to ventral surface, the second one commencing on the nuchal region.   *novemaculeatus*

AA. On the 3 cusps of the teeth the middle one is the longer and stronger, the lateral ones being about one-third or one-quarter of it; posterior nostril remote from eye; 7 dorsal spines.   *batavianus*

275. BATFISH *Platax pinnatus* (Linnaeus)   [Colour-plates 40, 41]

Chaetodon pinnatus Linnaeus, Syst. Nat., 10th ed., 1, 1758, p. 272.
Illustrations by G. Coates.

Butterfly-fish, Turbot, Sunfish (Queensland); Leaf-fish (Queensland and the Philippines); Swallow Perch (Japan); Sea Bat, Angel-fish (South Africa).

D. 5/28-38, spines almost concealed; A. 3/24-29. Colour blackish-brown, tinged with purplish; in the young the colour is yellowish, reddish, or reddish-brown, with 3 diffused black bands similar to *P. batavianus*, which, as in that species, fade out with advancing age; pectorals yellowish, other fins blackish. In adults the bands are greyish or brownish and the pectorals and ventrals are yellowish. The caudal may also be yellowish.

A very common and wide-ranging species, the young occasionally being caught in the rivers and estuaries of Queensland. They may be commonly caught by hook and line, using ripe banana for bait, which they will frequently take in preference to fish-flesh or prawns.

Batfishes undergo great changes in both form and colour, especially with age. In the young fish the anterior dorsal and anal rays are greatly prolonged decreasing with growth in the adult (see Colour-plate 40).

In Australian waters the Batfish occurs from Western Australia, through the waters of North Australia to the coasts of Queensland and northern New South Wales. It grows to about 30 inches in length and has been said to attain to a weight of 50 pounds.

OTHER SPECIES

Short-finned Batfish, *P. novemaculeatus*. Seems to differ from other members of the genus in that during the juvenile stages of its growth (at least from 4 inches) it is very similar in form to the adult, lacking the greatly attenuated fins which are so characteristic in the other species. It has an apparently restricted range, being found only on the coast of Queensland, mainly in the northern portion.

Hump-headed Batfish, *P. batavianus*. A wide-ranging species, well known in the Indo-Australian Archipelago. It has been recorded from the waters of North Queensland. Old examples develop a large bony forehead, somewhat similar to that of an Old Man Snapper. The record for size is apparently a fish caught by George Coates off Cape Cleveland, near Townsville. It measured 21½ inches in total length and weighed 9 pounds 5 ounces.

Family **Enoplosidae**

Body and vertical fins greatly elevated. Pelvic fins large, with long and strong spines, placed below or slightly behind pectorals. Villiform teeth in jaws and on vomer and palatines; no canines. Two dorsals. Operculum without spine; preoperculum serrated and without spinous teeth at angle.

A single genus (*Enoplosus*) and species, inhabiting the coastal waters of the southern half of the Australian coastline from Moreton Bay in South Queensland to Western Australia. For characters of the genus see those of the family.

276. OLD WIFE *Enoplosus armatus* (White) [Plate 42]

Chaetodon armatus White, Voy. N.S.Wales, 1790, p. 254, fig. 1.
Enoplosus armatus Stead, Edib. Fish. N.S.Wales, 1908, p. 62, pl. 32.

Bastard Dory, Zebra-fish (Victoria).
D. 7, 1/14-15; A. 3/13, 1, to 15, 1; L. l. 66-73 + 6-8; L. tr. 15/30-32. Colour silvery-white, with 8 blackish or dark-brown vertical bands, the two broadest being one from first dorsal to belly and the other between soft dorsal and anal; spinous dorsal, ventrals, and elongate rays of soft dorsal and anal dark brown, rest of dorsal and anal rays white, the membranes bright red; caudal pink, bordered above and below with brown; pectorals pinkish-red.

This species occasionally straggles from southern waters into South Queensland. It frequents the coastline in rocky situations, and though usually found in shallow waters it has been trawled in 48 fathoms. It is a small fish and its flesh is sweet and delicious. It seldom takes a bait, and is seldom caught in fishermen's nets on account of its habit of frequenting rocky localities. Grows to 9 inches.

DIVISION *Amphiprioniformes*

Body short, deep, sometimes strongly orbicular, compressed. Only a single nostril on each side. Teeth small, conical or compressed.

A large group of small marine fishes, many of them brilliantly coloured, chiefly confined to abounding in great numbers in the reefs of tropical seas. Most masses of living corals contain shoals of them, milling about between the rich coral growths. Their habits are very similar to the butterfly-fishes (Chaetodontidae). Their alertness and quickness of movement, plus the protective environment in the form of holes and crevices in the coral masses, render them secure from enemies, despite their lack of protective coloration. In many species the juveniles are coloured quite differently from the adults, having the blue spots or ocelli on the fins; these spots disappear with age. In other species bold bands adorn the head and body.

A distinctive feature which serves to identify the members of this group is the presence of the single nostril on each side of the snout, a character shared by the Cichlidae, an exotic family with which they are said to have affinities.

Many of the species are carnivorous, feeding upon very small marine animals, crustaceans, etc. Others, which have incisor teeth, are herbivorous in habit.

A. Bases of spinous and soft dorsals about equal length. Fifty or more transverse series of scales. Dorsal spines 9 to 11. All opercles serrated.   AMPHIPRIONIDAE

AA. Base of spinous dorsal much longer than that of soft. Less than 50 transverse series of scales. Dorsal spines 12 or more (rarely 11).

     b. Teeth conical, villiform, or subcylindrical; not compressed.   CHROMIDAE

     bb. Teeth more or less compressed, at least anteriorly.   POMACENTRIDAE

     c. Lips normal.

       d. Preoperculum serrated.   POMACENTRINAE

       dd. Preoperculum smooth.

         e. Generally 30 or less transverse series of scales. Unpaired fins with small scales which do not form dense sheaths.   GLYPHISODONTINAE

         ee. Generally more than 30 transverse series of scales. Unpaired fins with dense scaly sheaths.   PARMINAE

       cc. Lips generally thickened, fimbriate, and curled back over the snout.   CHEILOPRIONINAE

Family **Amphiprionidae: Anemone- or Damsel-fishes**

Small, brightly coloured little fishes, living in and associated with the sea-anemones on the coral reefs of the Indo-Pacific region. The association of these handsome little fishes with certain species of the larger sea-anemones, especially the genus *Stoichactis*, is a most fascinating study. It is an instance of symbiosis, both partners deriving definite advantages from the curious partnership. One of the more interesting features of this fish's association with the anemone is its immunity from the powerful stinging tentacles which will destroy any other fish venturing near. Writers not familiar with these fishes in their natural environment have suggested that their immunity is probably due to their agility in avoiding the tentacles, a statement which, to anyone who has observed the fishes with their anemones, is utterly absurd. The little fish is perfectly at home with the creature, and when not swimming about above the anemone, dives in amongst the maze of tentacles, rubbing and burrowing its way in if the anemone is not fully expanded, causing it to "open the door" and make its entrance easier. In a few seconds its head will pop out from among the folds and survey the observer. If satisfied, it emerges from the tentacles and commences to

[38] *Mem. Qld Mus.*, 9, pt 3, 1929, p. 208.

swim about in close proximity to its host. Pausing, it curves the tail round towards the head, at the same time rapidly vibrating the vertical fins. It may remain poised thus for several seconds; then, turning round and swimming a few inches, it brings its tail round to the opposite side and repeats the process. After this curving of the tail and body, first to one side and then the other, it will suddenly turn on its side and rush at the anemone and brush along its tentacles; unless disturbed, the fish then repeats the whole process. On the approach of danger it dives between the tentacles out of sight, remaining there even if the anemone is removed from the water. According to Dr J. Verwey,[39] a scientist who has made very extensive studies of these fascinating fishes, some of the larger species will, when disturbed, "bite one's hands or flee ɩor fear and swim hither and thither, returning again and again to the spot in question". If returned to the sea without their anemones these fishes are quite lost and helpless, soon falling prey to any larger fish.

It can be seen that the anemone is this fish's natural protection from its enemies, providing a safe retreat in the event of danger. In what way does the little fish obtain immunity from a creature which ordinarily stings to death any other fish venturing near, and does the anemone itself derive any particular benefit from the presence of the fish? These two questions are naturally the first to interest a scientist. That the fishes do feed upon the tentacles of the anemone, in addition to other food which they obtain from the anemone, is a known fact, and it has been suggested, though not yet proved, that herein may lie the secret of their immunity.

Whilst it is apparently not possible for these fishes to survive in a state of nature without an anemone (they will live in an aquarium), the anemone is able to live without them, though the observations of Verwey tend to show that under certain conditions the anemone is much more active and healthy when tenanted by the fishes. Verwey states that "the anemones are probably more or less dependent on the fishes as they are fed and oxygenated by them". Of one species, *A. polymnus*, feeding its anemone, he writes: "It swims out to all parts of its tank, searching for food which sank down to the bottom; this food is taken up and rapidly conveyed to the anemone, after which the fish no less rapidly returns to the corner of the tank to fetch new food for its host." Farther on he states: "In fact the feeding instinct of this fish gives a most remarkable example of an organism which takes care of another organism in an apparently purposeful way. When *Amphiprion polymnus* is fed it only eats very small particles in the water between surface and bottom. It is the way in which *polymnus* is hunting for plankton in nature too. The larger particles of food, however, are not eaten, but grasped by the mouth and brought to the anemone. The fish swims to the latter and puts the food (prawn, piece of fish, etc.) on or between the tentacles. If there are large food particles only, too large to be

[39] *Treubia*, 12, 1930, pp. 305 *et seq.*

eaten by the fish, it brings all of them to the anemone, without eating anything itself."

In addition to feeding its host, the fish carries away or eats the waste matter and remnants of food rejected by the anemone.

That the anemone is oxygenated by these fishes is suggested by Dr Verwey. He states: "... the fishes are constantly removing the water from the neighbourhood of the anemone and rubbing the latter." According to him, though the anemones are able to do without the fishes they are under better conditions when helped by the fishes than when they are not. It even must be very probable that the constant moving about of the fishes is advantageous to them. Giving an instance of the treatment of the anemone by the fish he says: "If a newly collected anemone is brought into a basin with a host-less damsel-fish, the latter immediately begins thrusting its head between the tentacles and rubbing with its flanks against the upper-side or common wall of the latter. Even if the fish was already in possession of an anemone, it may leave its host to try and occupy itself with the new one. It swims up and down, to and fro, waving its great pectoral fins, diving head on or sideways in the anemone and does not stop till the condition of the anemone has improved and it is beginning to expand."

Apart from using the tentacles of the anemone as food, the fishes have a peculiar habit of eating the mucous coating on the tentacle itself, perhaps acting as cleansing agent at the same time. Writing of another species Verwey states: "... the fish started at once with a very remarkable behaviour. It took the tentacles of its newly obtained anemone in its mouth, the one after the other, without biting them off, however, but only to let them slip and take another and still another one. The whole proceeding suggested that it was eating the mucous covering the tentacles and nothing else; I counted the fish treating about 30 tips of tentacles in this way, but it thereafter continued its work for a long time and may have treated some hundreds of them. Such an observation makes one hesitate to assume that the fish can do quite well without its anemone."

Usually only two fishes occupy a single anemone, a male and a female, but in some of the smaller species, such as *A. percula*, as many as seven fish may be found in occupation of one anemone. In most species the female is the larger of the two, and in the case of *Premnas* she is as much as three times the size of her mate. According to Dr Verwey, who gives excellent notes on the breeding habits, the eggs are deposited at the foot of the anemone, the area having first been freed of all algae, other organisms, etc., by the male. He states: "Both parents take care of the brood, though the greater part of the work is done by the small male, the female being much more mobile; only every now and then it returns to its brood to wave its pectorals or clean the eggs."

The eggs, which average about two hundred, hatch in about seven days, the young larvae rising to the surface of the water and starting a planktonic life, which lasts a varying number of days, after which they swim to the bottom and search for anemones. Genera few, two in Queensland waters.

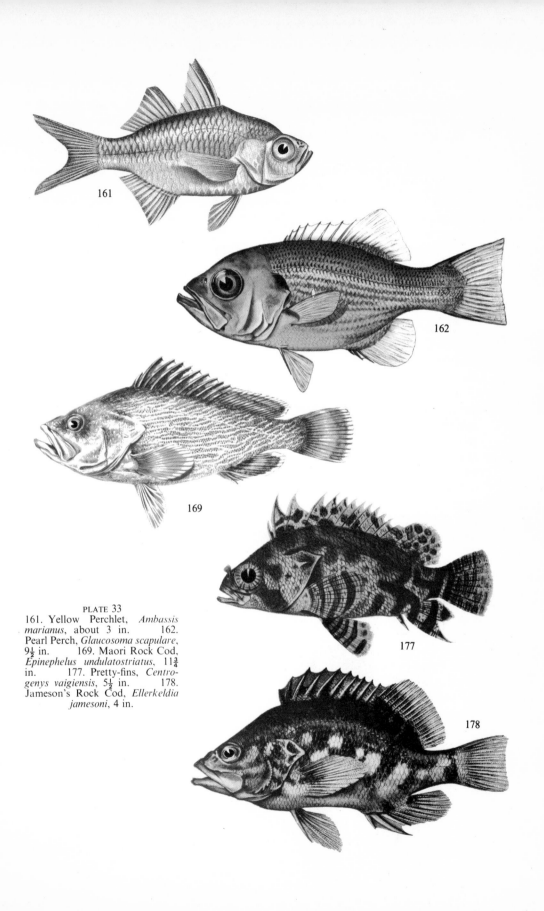

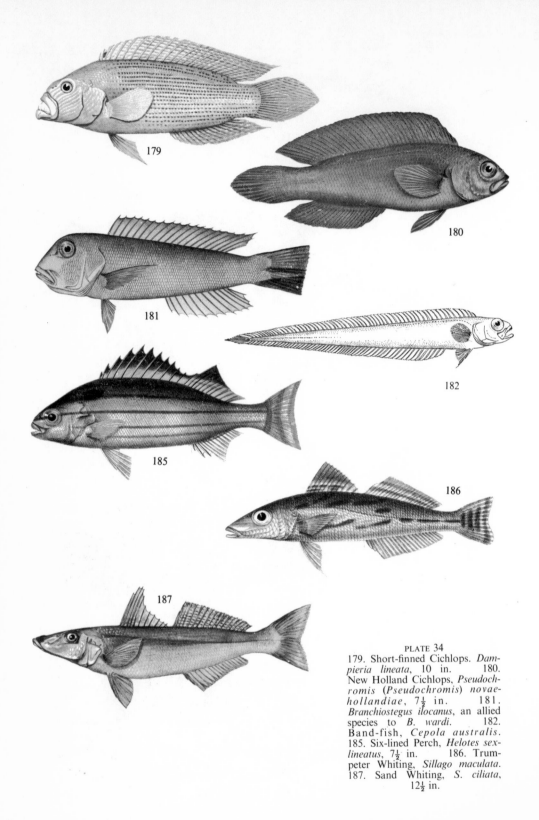

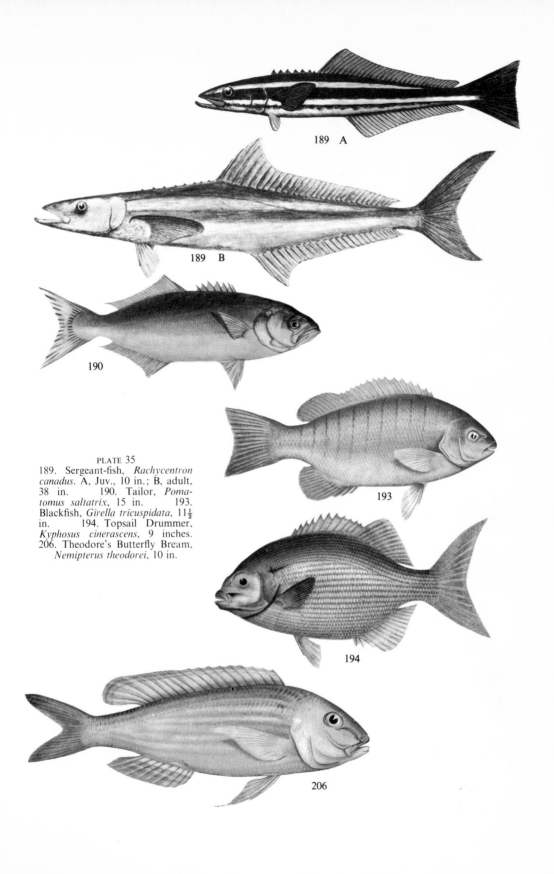

189 A

189 B

190

PLATE 35
189. Sergeant-fish, *Rachycentron
canadus*. A, Juv., 10 in.; B, adult,
38 in.   190. Tailor, *Pomatomus saltatrix*, 15 in.   193.
Blackfish, *Girella tricuspidata*, $11\frac{1}{2}$
in.   194. Topsail Drummer,
Kyphosus cinerascens, 9 inches.
206. Theodore's Butterfly Bream,
  Nemipterus theodorei, 10 in.

193

194

206

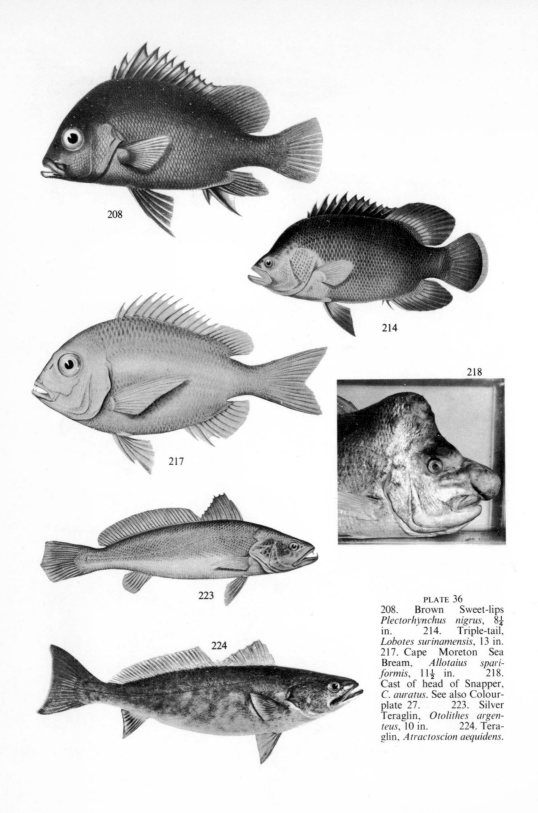

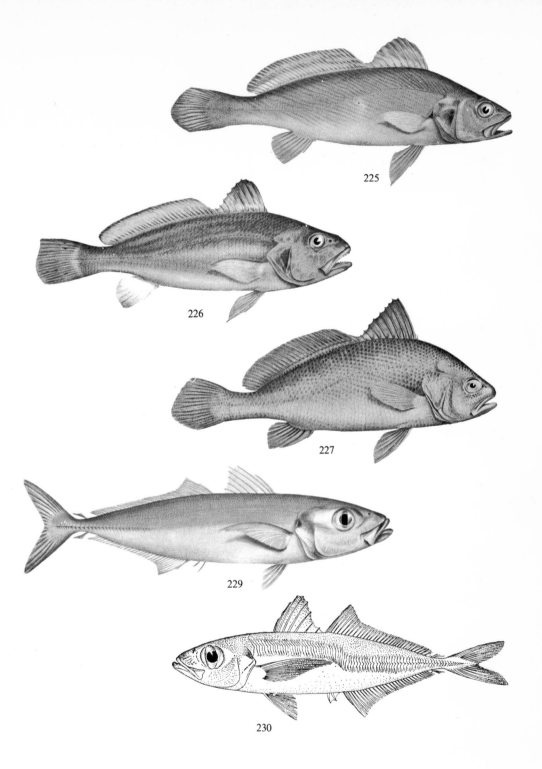

225. Jewfish or Mulloway, *Johnius antarctica*, juv., 11 in.   226. Little Jewfish, *J. australis*, 10 in.   227. Silver Jewfish, *J. soldado*, 14 in.   229. Northern Mackerel Scad, *Decapterus russellii*, $10\frac{1}{2}$ in.   230. Scad, *Trachurus declivis*, $8\frac{1}{2}$ in.

PLATE 38

231. White Trevally, *Caranx georgianus*, 10 in.   237. Cale-cale Trevally,
Ulua mandibularis, 12 in.   238. Diamond Trevally, *Alectis indica*, 14½ in.
240. Swallow-tail or Dart, *Trachinotus botla*, 10½ in.   243. Pilot-fish, *Nau-crates ductor*. A, 22.5 mm., B, 42 mm.

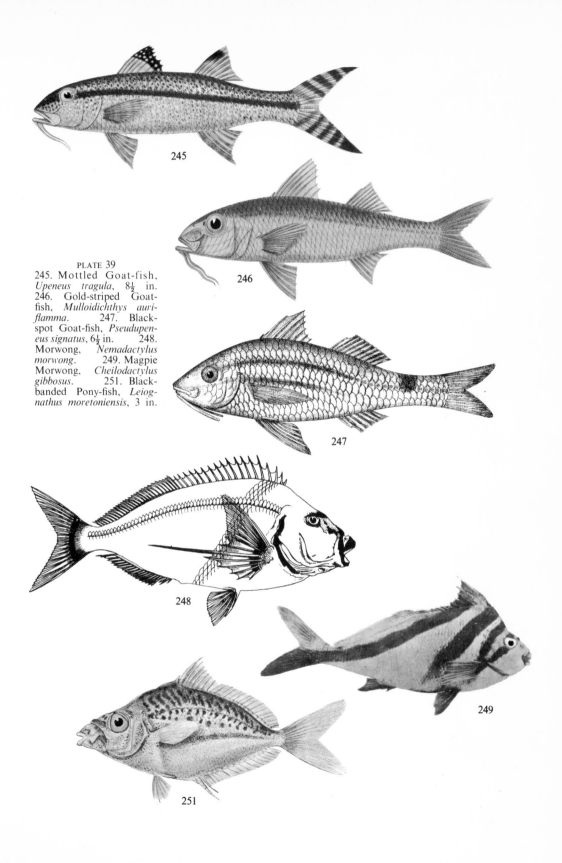

245

246

247

248

249

251

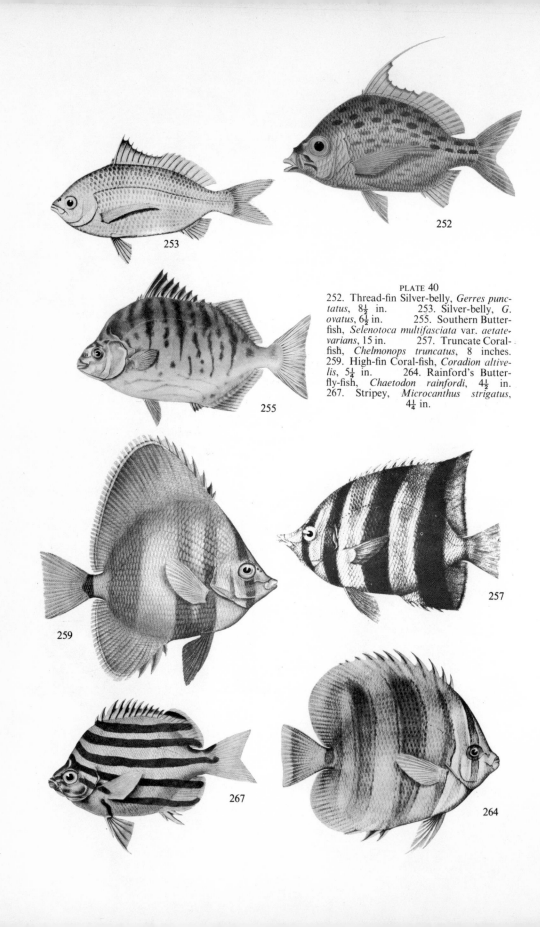

252. Thread-fin Silver-belly, *Gerres punctatus*, 8½ in.   253. Silver-belly, *G. ovatus*, 6½ in.   255. Southern Butterfish, *Selenotoca multifasciata* var. *aetatevarians*, 15 in.   257. Truncate Coralfish, *Chelmonops truncatus*, 8 inches. 259. High-fin Coral-fish, *Coradion altivelis*, 5¼ in.   264. Rainford's Butterfly-fish, *Chaetodon rainfordi*, 4½ in. 267. Stripey, *Microcanthus strigatus*, 4¼ in.

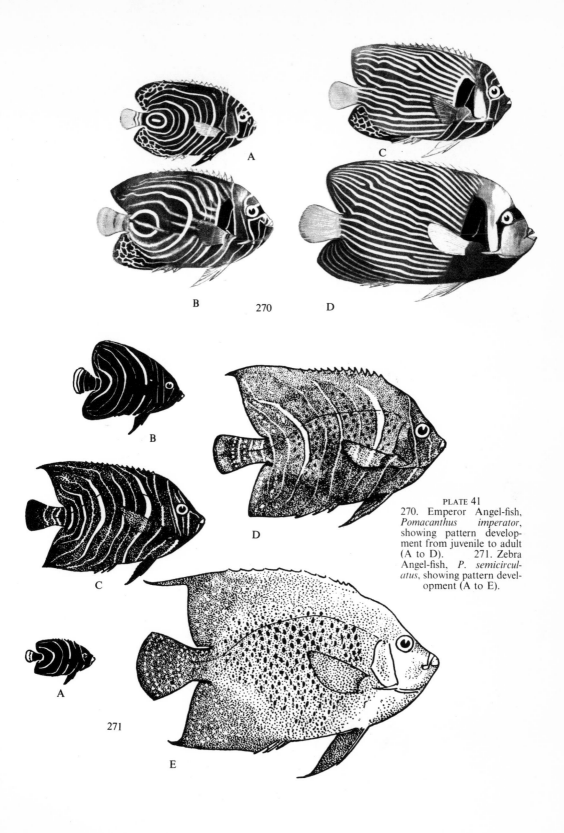

A

C

B   270   D

B

D

C

PLATE 41
270. Emperor Angel-fish, *Pomacanthus imperator*, showing pattern development from juvenile to adult (A to D).   271. Zebra Angel-fish, *P. semicirculatus*, showing pattern development (A to E).

A

271

E

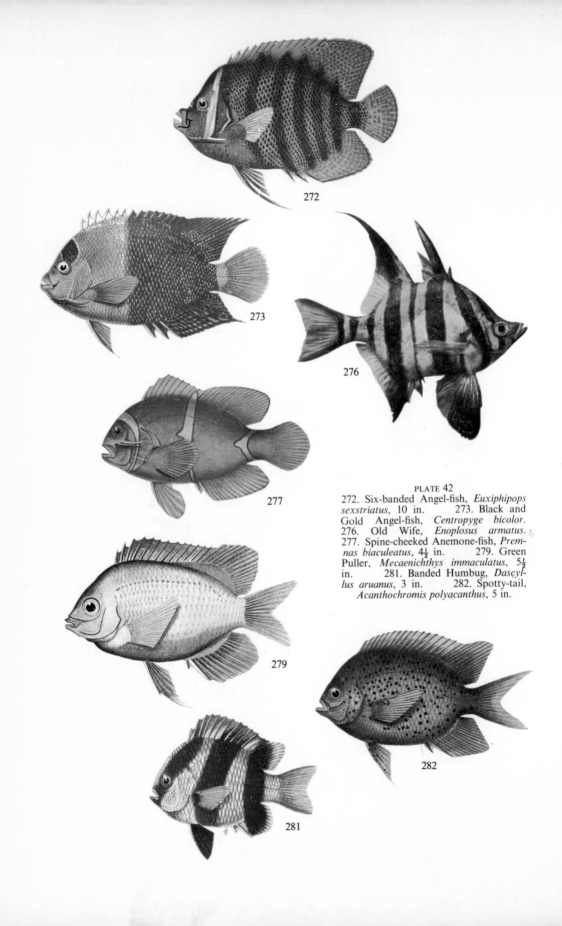

272

273

276

277

272. Six-banded Angel-fish, *Euxiphipops sexstriatus*, 10 in. 273. Black and Gold Angel-fish, *Centropyge bicolor*. 276. Old Wife, *Enoplosus armatus*. 277. Spine-cheeked Anemone-fish, *Premnas biaculeatus*, 4½ in. 279. Green Puller, *Mecaenichthys immaculatus*, 5½ in. 281. Banded Humbug, *Dascyllus aruanus*, 3 in. 282. Spotty-tail, *Acanthochromis polyacanthus*, 5 in.

279

282

281

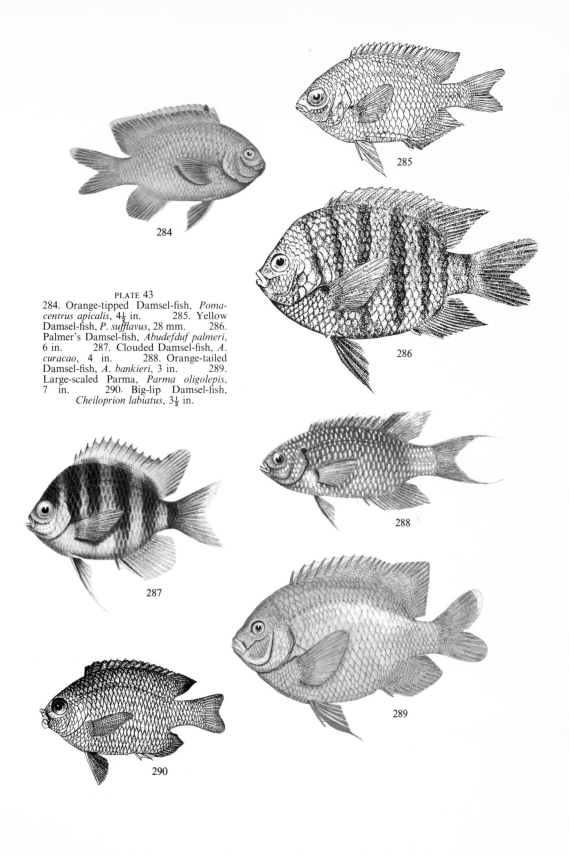

PLATE 43
284. Orange-tipped Damsel-fish, *Poma-centrus apicalis*, 4½ in.   285. Yellow Damsel-fish, *P. sufflavus*, 28 mm.   286. Palmer's Damsel-fish, *Abudefduf palmeri*, 6 in.   287. Clouded Damsel-fish, *A. curacao*, 4 in.   288. Orange-tailed Damsel-fish, *A. bankieri*, 3 in.   289. Large-scaled Parma, *Parma oligolepis*, 7 in.   290. Big-lip Damsel-fish, *Cheiloprion labiatus*, 3½ in.

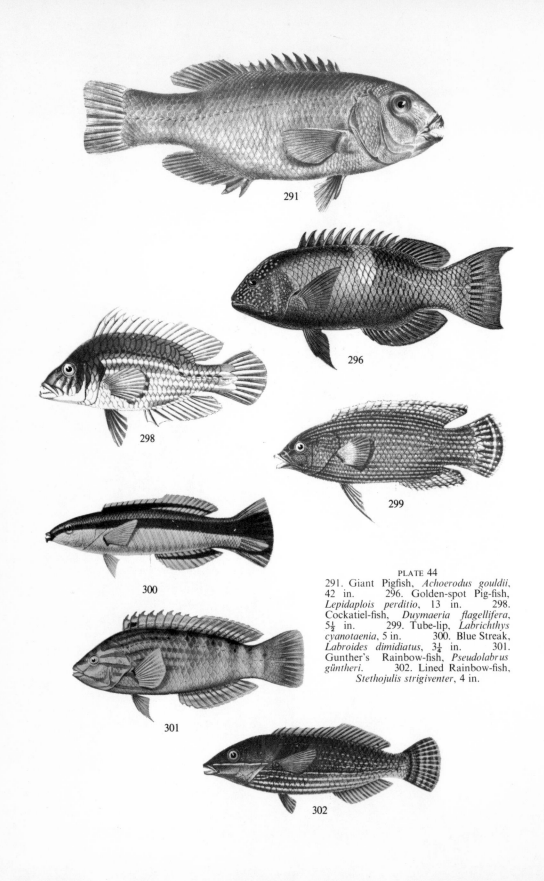

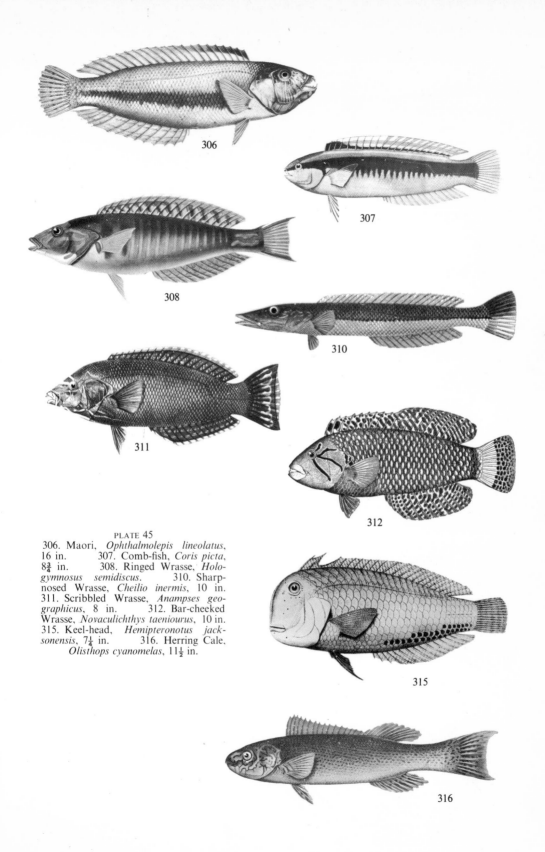

306. Maori, *Ophthalmolepis lineolatus*, 16 in. 307. Comb-fish, *Coris picta*, $8\frac{3}{4}$ in. 308. Ringed Wrasse, *Hologymnosus semidiscus*. 310. Sharp-nosed Wrasse, *Cheilio inermis*, 10 in. 311. Scribbled Wrasse, *Anampses geographicus*, 8 in. 312. Bar-cheeked Wrasse, *Novaculichthys taeniourus*, 10 in. 315. Keel-head, *Hemipteronotus jacksonensis*, $7\frac{1}{4}$ in. 316. Herring Cale, *Olisthops cyanomelas*, $11\frac{1}{2}$ in.

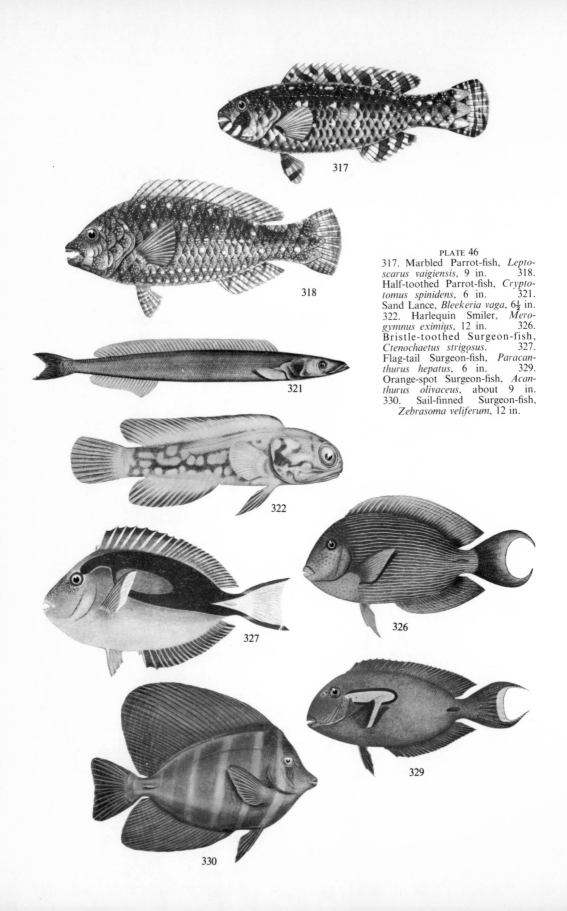

317

318

321

322

327

326

329

330

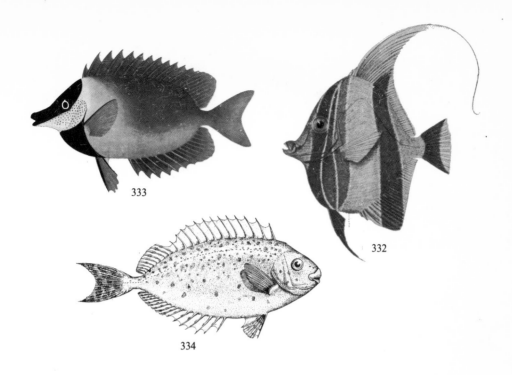

PLATE 47

332. Moorish Idol, *Zanclus canescens*, $2\frac{1}{2}$ in.   333. Fox-
face, *Lo vulpinus*.   334. Black Spinefoot, *Siganus rivulatus*, $8\frac{1}{2}$ in.   336. Cutlass-fish, *Trichiurus savala*, 12 in.
338. Southern Marlin, *Makaira australis*, 14 ft.

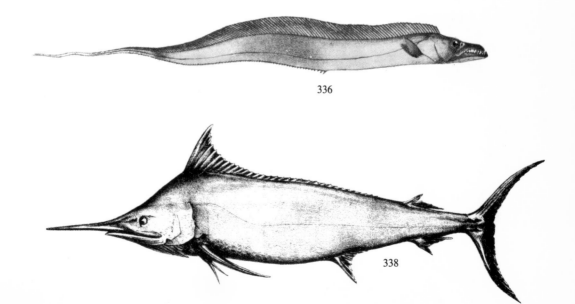

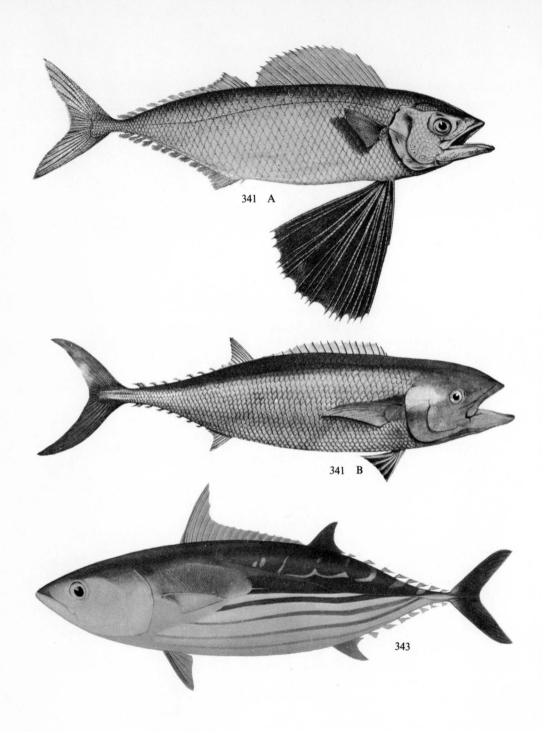

341 A

341 B

343

PLATE 48
341. Big-scaled Mackerel, *Gasterochisma melampus*. A, Juv., 8 in.; B, adult, 6 ft.
1 in.   343. Bonito, *Euthynnus pelamis*, 32 in.

A.   Preorbital with a strong spine, extended backward.   *Premnas*

AA. Preorbital without a strong spine.   *Amphiprion*

Premnas

Body oval. Head deep. Preorbital ending in a long, strong spine, directed backward. Distribution that of the single species known.

277. SPINE-CHEEKED ANEMONE-FISH *Premnas biaculeatus* (Bloch)
[Plate 42]

Chaetodon biaculeatus Bloch, Nat. ausl. Fische, 4, 1790, p. 11.
Premnas biaculeatus Bleeker, Atlas Ichth., 9, 1877, pl. 402, figs. 7-9.

D. 10/17, 1, or 18; A. 2/14, 1; L. l. tubes 44-45; pores in straight section 11-13 + 0-5; 5-6 scales above lateral line, 27-29 below. Colour dark or light cherry-red to brownish-red all over body and fins; 3 transverse pearl-white bands, wider above and narrowly edged with black (as seen in the illustration); fins narrowly edged with black. The white bands are very distinct in the males but may become quite indistinct or even wanting in the females. The males are much smaller than the females. Females mostly very dark red or even almost black. There is great individual variation.

A handsome species found in North Queensland. Also occurs in the East Indies, the Philippines, India, and Mauritius. According to Dr Verwey the males grow to almost 4½ inches and the females to 6¼ inches.

Amphiprion

Body ovoid or oblong. Scales fairly small. Lateral line incomplete. Suborbitals, opercle, preopercle strongly serrate. Teeth small, uniserial, conic or somewhat compressed.

Species few, all brilliant and easily distinguished, living in the coral seas of the Indo-Pacific.

KEY TO SPECIES

A.   Dorsal spines lower or subequal with the dorsal rays.

    b. Caudal emarginate or lunate, truncate in young; 3 white transverse bands.   *polymnus*

    bb. Caudal truncate.

      c. One white transverse predorsal band.   *melanopus*

      cc. Two white transverse bands, one predorsal, the other embracing posterior dorsal spines and a few anterior or most of soft dorsal rays, and extending across body to origin of anal; upper and lower edges of caudal light-coloured, united posteriorly.   *unimaculatus*

K

AA. Dorsal spines with the antero-median ones longest,
equal to or longer than dorsal rays; caudal rounded;
orange, with 3 bluish-white transverse bands. *percula*

278. ORANGE ANEMONE-FISH *Amphiprion percula* (Lacépède)
[Colour-plate 42]

Lutjanus percula Lacépède, Hist. Nat. Poiss., 4, 1802, p. 239.
Illustration by G. Coates.

D. 10/15-18 (normally 16); A. 2/12; L. l. tubes 29-38. General colour, including fins, orange or orange-brownish, cleaner on the head, becoming
more dusky dorsally and a brighter colour below, with a reddish tinge along
belly; 3 transverse bluish-white bands (as seen in the illustration) are usually
narrowly edged with black; eye clear light orange, stands out distinct from
colour of head; all fins, except spinous dorsal and ventrals, have a white
terminal and a black subterminal band; spinous dorsal and ventrals have
usually a black edge only, though sometimes there may be a very narrow
white edge.

This species is subject to great colour variation, mainly in the extent of
the white and black margins of the fins. It is a very common little fish and is
usually associated with the large sea-anemones, *Stoichactis*, on the coral
reefs of Queensland. Found also in Melanesia, Micronesia, Polynesia, and the
East Indies. Grows to about 3¼ inches, the females being larger than the males.

OTHER SPECIES

Yellow-finned Anemone-fish, *A. polymnus*. Has an emarginate or lunate
tail (truncate in the young) and three white transverse bands, the rest of the
body being black. It is wide-ranging, being found from the east coast of
Queensland, where it extends as far south as the Capricorns, through the
Indo-Malay Archipelago to China and Japan and also across to East Africa
and the Red Sea. Grows to 5½ inches, the sexes of about equal size.

Dusky Anemone-fish, *A. melanopus*. This species varies greatly in colour,
having one white transverse predorsal band on a background of light yellowish-
or reddish-orange to dusky-black. Found on the coasts of Queensland and
North Australia, and in the East Indies. Grows to 5 inches.

Yellow-faced Anemone-fish, *A. unimaculatus*. Has 2 white transverse bands,
one predorsal, the other embracing posterior dorsal spines. The colour is
usually chestnut-brown. It is a pretty little fish found on the east coast of
Queensland, the North Australia coast, and in the East Indies. Grows to
5 inches.

Family **Chromidae: Pullers**

Less than 50 transverse series of scales. Dorsal with 12 or more spines (rarely
11). Base of spinous dorsal much longer than that of the soft. Teeth conical,
villiform, or subcylindrical, not compressed.

Small fishes of the tropical waters of the Indo-Pacific. Their compact bodies are often brilliantly coloured. They abound in the coral reefs of tropical seas and are very active and difficult to capture. The species are numerous and vary considerably in form. Four genera are found in Queensland waters.

KEY TO GENERA IN QUEENSLAND

Based on Whitley[40]

A. Teeth subcylindrical.	*Mecaenichthys*
AA. Teeth conical or pointed, sometimes in bands.	
b. None of the opercles serrated.	*Chromis*
bb. Preoperculum, and sometimes suborbital, serrated.	
d. Dorsal spines 12-13.	*Dascyllus*
dd. Dorsal spines 16.	*Acanthochromis*

Mecaenichthys

Body deep, compressed, suborbicular. Eye large. All opercles entire. No preorbital spine or notch. A single series of slightly curved, fixed teeth in each jaw. Dorsal spines 13. Base of soft dorsal nearly half length of base of spinous dorsal.

A single species, inhabiting the waters of South Queensland and New South Wales.

279. GREEN PULLER *Mecaenichthys immaculatus* (Ogilby) [Plate 42]

Heliastes immaculatus Ogilby, Proc. Linn. Soc. N.S.Wales, 10, 3, 21st Dec. 1885, p. 446.
Heliases immaculatus Waite, Austr. Mus. Mem., 4, no. 1, 1899, p. 86, pl. 14.

D. 13/17; A. 2/14; V. 1/5; L. l. 28; L. tr. 4/12. Colour pale olive-green above, silvery-white below, the sides with a bronzy wash; scales on lateral line are darker, giving an appearance of a faint band; vertical fins with a violet tinge and narrowly edged with pale blue. (After Ogilby.)

A New South Wales species which has been recorded from Cape Moreton, South Queensland. Rarely seen, even in the south. Grows to 6 inches.

Chromis

Form oblong or oval. Teeth small, conic, villiform, often the outer row obtuse or little enlarged. None of the opercles serrated. Lateral line not developed on the tail.

Small fishes, compact of body and often brilliantly coloured. The species are numerous in tropical seas, mostly in the Indo-Pacific region. They are readily distinguished from *Pomacentrus* by their smooth preopercles. Five species are found in Queensland waters.

---

[40] *Mem. Qld Mus.*, 9, pt 3, June 1929, p. 209.

A. External teeth of mandible directed outwards. Colour
bluish or greenish.   *caeruleus*

AA. External teeth of mandible not directed outwards.

  b. Upper and lower edges of caudal dusky to blackish
  in contrast to rest of fin.

  c. Head yellow; sides silvery; a blackish stripe from
  snout, through eye to end of anterior dorsal rays.   *nitidus*

  cc. Colour dusky-greenish or olive, no blackish stripe
  from snout to dorsal rays.   *scotochilopterus*

  bb. No black stripe on caudal edges, though one may be
  present on middle caudal rays.

  d. Two longitudinal black bands.   *bitaeniatus*

  dd. Two broad vertical blackish bands.   *humbug*

280. BLUE PULLER *Chromis caeruleus* (Cuvier and Valenciennes)

[Colour-plate 42]

Heliases caeruleus Cuvier and Valenciennes, Hist. Nat. Poiss., 5, 1830, p. 497.
Illustration by G. Coates.

D. 12/9-10; A. 2/9-11; L. l. 26; L. tr. 2/1/7-9. Colour green, greenish-blue,
or blue, silvery or whitish below; each scale of head and sides with a blue
spot; a narrow blue line from eye to tip of snout; sometimes there are faint
bluish pencil lines along scale rows of sides; fins clear greyish, bluish or colourless, except caudal, which is greenish basally and has a green band along each
lobe; usually a large black spot at base of pectoral. In some examples there
is a bright golden-yellow spot on each scale and the soft dorsal and caudal
are bright orange. Varies greatly in colour.

A common fish on the Barrier Reef, living in schools of hundreds, milling
about among the mats of large branching corals. It is a wide-ranging species,
being found from the waters of Queensland, Melanesia, Micronesia, and
Polynesia, through the Indo-Australian Archipelago to the Red Sea. Grows
to 5 inches.

OTHER SPECIES

Shining Puller, *C. nitidus*. A common little fish on the coral reefs of Queensland. It has a yellow head with a blackish stripe from snout to anterior dorsal
rays. Grows to 2½ inches.

Striped-tail Puller, *C. scotochilopterus*. A species from the Philippines
recorded on the Australian coast from a single example collected on the outer
Barrier Reef between latitude 17° and 19°S. Grows to 4 inches.

Banded Puller, *C. bitaeniatus*. A handsome little fish, unique in its beautiful colour pattern of two blue-black longitudinal bands on the yellow body; it was known only from the Philippines until I took one at the Palm Islands, North Queensland. Grows to 2 inches.

Two-barred Puller, *C. humbug*. A pretty little fish so far found only in the waters of North Queensland, where it has been captured at Green Island near Cairns. In life it is creamy-white with two broad blackish bands. Known only from the unique holotype which is 18 mm. in standard length.

Dascyllus: Humbugs

Form orbicular. Head deeper than long. Mouth small, oblique. Conical teeth in several rows in each jaw, outer row somewhat enlarged. Preopercle, and sometimes preorbital, serrated. Scales rather large. Lateral line extends below soft dorsal.

Small fishes of the Indo-Pacific region found dwelling in the masses of branching corals on the reefs. They are exceedingly abundant on the Great Barrier Reef. Species few, four in Queensland.

KEY TO SPECIES IN QUEENSLAND

A. Colour generally uniform dark or dusky, no transverse black bands.

    b. Caudal very little emarginate; a whitish spot always present on each side of body below middle of spinous dorsal, and another on top of head in young examples.   *trimaculatus*

    bb. Caudal emarginate, colour greyish or yellowish, often a dark band from dorsal origin to pectoral.   *marginatus*

AA. Colour white, with 3 broad black transverse bands.

    c. Caudal white, the ocular band commencing from anterior dorsal spine.   *aruanus*

    cc. Caudal largely black; ocular band commencing on occiput.   *melanurus*

281. BANDED HUMBUG *Dascyllus aruanus* (Linnaeus)   [Plate 42]

Chaetodon aruanus Linnaeus, Syst. Nat., 10th ed., 1758, p. 275.
Tetradrachmum arcuatum Bleeker, Atlas Ichth., 9, 1877, pl. 409, fig. 6.

D. 12/12; A. 2/12, 1, or 13; about 25 series of scales and about 12 tubercles in L. l.; L. tr. 3/1/10. Colour pearly-white, with 3 broad black cross-bands which extend on to dorsals and, in the case of the posterior one, on to anal also; ventrals black; caudal white.

A handsome little fish seen in hundreds among the coral growths on the reefs of Queensland. A very widely distributed species. Grows to 3½ inches.

OTHER SPECIES

Three-spot Humbug, *D. trimaculatus*. Frequents the reefs from Queensland to Melanesia, Micronesia, and Polynesia, across the Indian Ocean to East Africa and the Red Sea. Grows to 6 inches.

Grey Humbug, *D. marginatus*. Found on the reefs of Cape York and Torres Strait, North Queensland. It ranges through the same waters as *D. trimaculatus* and also grows to 6 inches.

Black-tailed Humbug, *D. melanurus*. Found in Torres Strait, Melanesia, Micronesia, and the East Indies. Grows to 3 inches.

Acanthochromis

Oblong-oval. Head deeper than long. Upper jaw not protractile. Teeth biserial, conic, outer row not prominent. Preopercle serrate. Dorsal spines 17, rays 15 to 16. Anal rays 16 to 17. Caudal deeply forked. Probably only one species, found in Queensland, the East Indies, and Melanesia.

282. SPOTTY-TAIL *Acanthochromis polyacanthus* (Bleeker)   [Plate 42]

Dascyllus polyacanthus Bleeker, Nat. Tijdschr. Ned. Ind., 9, 1855, p. 503.
Acanthochromis polyacanthus Bleeker, Atlas Ichth., 9, 1877, pl. 410, fig. 7.

D. 17/15, 1, or 16; A. 2/16, 1, or 17; L. l. tubes 19-21; pores in straight section 13-15 + 1 or 2; L. tr. 4-5 above lateral line to spinous dorsal origin, 12-13 below. Colour dark purplish-brown over head and body as far back as a line from commencement of soft dorsal to anal spines; posterior to this line the soft dorsal, anal, and caudal are greyish, sometimes the ends of the fins with a yellowish tinge; spinous dorsal blackish; pectorals and ventrals pale greyish-brown; soft dorsal, anal, pectoral, and caudal more or less spotted with blackish spots; anus in a black area.

Another variety is deep reddish-brown to blackish-brown, a little paler on breast, and has head, trunk, and fins irregularly spotted with black.

This latter colour variety is known on the reefs from a single example only. The first variety, however, is extremely common everywhere among the coral growths. The species ranges from North Queensland through Melanesia to the East Indies. Grows to 7 inches.

Family **Pomacentridae**

Less than 50 transverse series of scales. Dorsal spines 12 or more (rarely 11). Base of spinous dorsal much longer than that of the soft. Teeth more or less compressed, at least anteriorly.

Fishes of small size found frequenting the coral pools and among coral growths on the reefs of tropical seas, being most plentiful in the East Indies and the South Seas. The four sub-families (Pomacentrinae, Glyphisodontinae, Parminae, and Cheiloprioninae) are separated by the characters shown in the key to the division Amphiprioniformes (p. 270).

Sub-family POMACENTRINAE

Members of this sub-family are characterized mainly by the serrated pre-operculums. Two genera occur in Queensland waters.

KEY TO GENERA IN QUEENSLAND

A. Spinous portion of dorsal and anal naked. Suboperculum
and interoperculum serrated. *Daya*

AA. Spinous portion of dorsal and anal scaly. Suboperculum
and interoperculum entire. *Pomacentrus*

Daya

Differs from *Pomacentrus* in having no scaly sheaths at bases of spinous dorsal and anal fins, and the membrane between the spines is naked instead of scaly.

Fishes of the East Indies region and Australia. Species few, one in Queensland.

283. JERDON'S DAMSEL-FISH *Daya jerdoni* (Day)　　[Colour-plate 42]

Pomacentrus jerdoni Day, Proc. Zool. Soc. Lond., 1873, p. 237.
Illustration by G. Coates.

D. 13/13; A. 2/14; P. 18; V. 1/5; C. 15; L. 1. 19; 30 scales between origin of lateral line and the hypural joint, 5 between origin of dorsal and the lateral line, and 10 more to anal origin. Colour olive or yellow, becoming lighter below; sides of head with several rows of light-blue spots; a row of light lines along centre of scales on sides; fins dark coloured, base of caudal and edges of dorsal and anal narrowly bordered white and, in the case of the two latter, followed by a very narrow dark line; there is a blackish spot between the anal spines; a large blackish spot at upper base of pectoral; a dark horizontal line extends along soft portion of both dorsal and anal medianally; caudal with irregular rows of dark-grey spots. Some examples are brown, each scale with a dark-blue basal spot.

This little fish has been trawled by the *Endeavour* at various points on the Queensland coast at depths ranging from 11 to 30 fathoms. The species has also been found in New South Wales, where two examples were found sheltering in a large *Dolium* shell at Port Jackson. They were doubtlessly stragglers from the warmer northern waters. Grows to 6 inches.

Pomacentrus

Form ovate or oblong, with somewhat large scales. Teeth in one or two close-set rows, compressed, immovable, truncate or conic at tips. Preorbital and infraorbitals more or less serrated, the former often with a pronounced notch. Preopercle more or less serrate. Dorsal spines 12 to 14. Two anal spines.

Species numerous, size small, often beautifully coloured. Very common in all tropical seas, where they frequent the coral patches. Ten species are found in Queensland waters.

KEY TO SPECIES IN QUEENSLAND

A. Snout scaled.

    b. Preorbital scaly; preorbital and infraorbital serrae large.

    c. Caudal deeply forked, the upper lobe the longer; broad margin of dorsal fins and tip of upper caudal lobe bright orange.   *apicalis*

    cc. Caudal emarginate; uniform brown, no orange on fins; a blue-black spot on upper scale of opercle.   *littoralis*

    bb. Preorbital scaleless.

    d. Cheeks with 2 rows of scales above preopercle ridge.

    e. Caudal emarginate; pectoral base with large black blotch; colour dusky brown.   *melanopterus*

    ee. Caudal deeply lunate; colour sapphire-blue, head spotted blue, fins yellow.   *pavo*

    dd. Cheeks with 3 rows of scales above preopercle ridge; yellow, with white spots on head; anus in a black area.   *amboinensis*

AA. Snout scaleless.

    f. Interorbital scales extending forward to nostrils; caudal forked or emarginate.

    g. Brownish. Caudal forked.   *tripunctatus*

    gg. Cadmium-yellow, caudal orange. Caudal forked.   *sufflavus*

    ggg. Head and body brown, caudal bright yellow. Caudal emarginate.   *flavicauda*

    ff. Interorbital region largely naked, scales not extending forward to nostrils; caudal emarginate.

    h. Brown, with 4 yellow cross-bands.   *fasciatus*

    hh. Yellowish-green; 2 straight lines from preopercle to angle of mouth, a line of spots below them.   *frenatus*

284. ORANGE-TIPPED DAMSEL-FISH *Pomacentrus apicalis* (De Vis)
[Plate 43]

Pomacentrus apicalis De Vis, Proc. Linn. Soc. N.S.Wales, 9, 1885, p. 874.
Pomacentrus apicalis Ogilby, Mem. Qld Mus., 6, 1918, p. 91, pl. 27.

D. 13/14-16; A. 2/13; P. 20; V. 1/5; L. 1. 26-28, L. tr. 3/11. General colour blackish-brown, including fins and caudal; spinous dorsal blackish-brown, the outer one-third bright orange, through which runs a bright-violet sub-marginal band; the first two spines and membranes are jet-black, the orange band being very narrow but suddenly deepening from the third membrane onwards; anal with the spine bright violet-blue; ventrals similar; tip of upper caudal lobe bright orange.

A somewhat uncommon species found on the reefs of North Queensland and Torres Strait. Grows to 4 inches.

285. YELLOW DAMSEL-FISH *Pomacentrus sufflavus* (Whitley) [Plate 43]

Pomacentrus sufflavus Whitley, Rec. Austr. Mus., 16, 1927, p. 18, pl. 1, fig. 3.

D. 13/15; A. 2/15; P. 17; V. 1/5; Sc. 26 to hypural; L. 1. with 17 tube-bearing scales. General colour cadmium-yellow, passing into strong orange colour on caudal, soft dorsal, and anal fins; dusky olive along back, from top of snout to about end of spinous dorsal; dorsal spines greenish-grey, a green blotch at tip of each one, membranes yellow; edge of anal fin with a narrow black border; pectorals and ventrals yellow; a small pale-blue or black spot is usually present at the commencement of the lateral line and a black one of similar size is always present in the axil of the pectoral.

A pretty little fish which swarms among the coral growths on the Great Barrier Reef. Grows to 3 inches.

OTHER SPECIES

Dusky Damsel-fish, *P. littoralis*. A very variable and common little fish found on the reefs and in the coastal waters of Queensland. Generally a uniform dusky-brown colour with a small blackish or bluish spot on upper scale of opercle. Outside Queensland it is wide-ranging through Oceania and the East Indies. Recognizable by the deep notch and large spine on the pre-orbital and the strongly serrated edges to the suborbital and preopercle. Grows to 4 inches.

Dark-finned Damsel-fish, *P. melanopterus*. Also a dusky-coloured fish, this is an East Indies species which frequents North Queensland waters. The pectoral base always has a large blackish blotch. Grows to 4 inches.

Peacock Damsel-fish, *P. pavo*. This species is a brilliant sapphire-blue, passing into bright lemon-yellow below with the fins yellow. Grows to 5 inches. Frequents the far northern waters of Queensland, also the East Indies, Africa, and the Red Sea.

Pallid Damsel-fish, *P. amboinensis*. An East Indies and South Seas species found on the reefs of Queensland. Grows to 4 inches. Colour clear yellow, with pearl-white spots on head and breast. A black spot covers the anus.

Three-spot Damsel-fish, *P. tripunctatus*. A little brownish fish with the body-scales bearing a narrow vertical blue bar at their bases. A black spot at origin of lateral line, another at pectoral origin, and a third one posteriorly on soft dorsal fin. It is very wide-ranging and in Australian waters is found in Queensland and North Australia. Grows to 6 inches.

Yellow-tailed Damsel-fish, *P. flavicauda*. A common fish on the reefs of Queensland, especially in the north of the State and in North Australia. It is dark brown with a bright-yellow tail and grows to $3\frac{1}{2}$ inches.

Banded Damsel-fish, *P. fasciatus*. A brown fish with four yellow cross-bands. It inhabits the waters of Queensland, North Australia, and the East Indies. Grows to almost 5 inches.

Bridled Damsel-fish, *P. frenatus*. A little-known species recorded from Cardwell in North Queensland. The unique holotype is 5 inches in length.

Sub-family GLYPHISODONTINAE

Less than 50 transverse series of scales. Spinous dorsal fin with 12 or more (rarely 11) spines, its base much longer than that of the soft. Preoperculum smooth. Gill-rakers less than 40.

Fishes of the coral reefs and tropical seas, the species numerous and included in the genus *Abudefduf*.

KEY TO SPECIES IN QUEENSLAND

A. Body banded with dark or light transverse bands.

  b. Body with dark transverse bands, usually more than 4 in number.

    c. Each caudal lobe edged with a blackish longitudinal stripe.

      d. Dark vertical bands 5, wide as pale interspaces. Form oblong-oval; 3-5 scales above end of upper section of lateral line.   *sexfasciatus*

      dd. Body with 6 broad dark transverse bands, usually indistinct or sometimes absent. Form orbicular; 1-2 rows of scales above end of upper section of lateral line.   *curacao*

    cc. Caudal uniform, no blackish edges.

      e. Dark vertical bands 5 (sometimes 6), but little narrower than pale interspaces.   *saxatilis*

      ee. Dark vertical bands 7, narrower than pale interspaces.   *palmeri* bb. Body with one light oblique transverse band and another at caudal base. Form oblong. Colour brown (blackish-grey in life). *amabilis*

AA. Body without transverse bands.

f. Body ovate.

g. Uniform blackish. Caudal emarginate, the lobes rounded. *melas*

gg. Green or brown. Caudal forked.

h. Dorsal spines highest posteriorly. Chocolate-brown, posterior part of soft dorsal and anal, and all of caudal bright yellow. *xanthurus*

hh. Dorsal spines highest medianally. Greenish, with caudal hyaline, a green stripe along upper and lower edges. *leucogaster*

ff. Body oblong.

i. Dorsal spines graduated up to the last, which is longest.

j. Caudal deeply forked, the outer rays attenuated. Colour brownish-black; posterior part of soft dorsal, anal, and whole caudal yellow. *bankieri*

jj. Caudal slightly forked, the lobes rounded.

k. 1-2 black, blue-edged ocelli on soft dorsal fin; 2 blue bands on each side of snout; caudal hyaline. *biocellatus*

kk. No ocelli on dorsal fin; a narrow sky-blue line may be present from nostrils to dorsal origin; caudal tinged orange. *glaucus*

ii. Dorsal spines highest medianally.

l. Caudal lobes rounded.

m. Blue above, orange-yellow below; caudal orange; a black blotch at base of last dorsal rays. *uniocellatus*

mm. Dark blue, caudal orange-red. *hedleyi*

ll. Caudal lobes pointed, colour yellowish. *melanopus*

286. PALMER'S DAMSEL-FISH *Abudefduf palmeri* (Ogilby)   [Plate 43]

Glyphisodon palmeri Ogilby, Mem. Qld Mus., 2, 1913, p. 87, pl. 22, fig. 2.

D. 13/14; A. 2/14; L. 1. 28; L. tr. 5/18 between dorsal base and vent. Colour greenish-grey, shading into silvery-grey on belly; with seven black cross-bands; head and throat like the back, with scattered silvery spots and bars; dorsal, anal, and ventral fins blackish.

A common fish on the Queensland coast, particularly in the Moreton Bay district. Grows to at least 7 inches.

287. CLOUDED DAMSEL-FISH *Abudefduf curacao* (Bloch) [Plate 43]

Chaetodon curacao Bloch, Nat. ausl. Fische, 3, 1787, p. 106.
Glyphisodon trifasciatus Bleeker, Atlas Ichth., 9, 1877, p. 410, fig. 3.

D. 13-14/12, 1, or 13, 1; A. 2/13, 1, or 14, 1; L. l. tubes 14-17; pores in straight section 10 + 2; L. tr. 3/1/9. Colour bright pale green above, silvery below; 5 vertical dusky bands about 3 scales wide, narrowing and becoming indistinct below; each scale within the dark bands narrowly pale-edged; spinous dorsal dusky; soft dorsal, anal, and caudal pale brown; ventrals whitish.

This little fish, recognized by its usually indistinct transverse bands and circular body, has been recorded from the Great Barrier Reef. It is also found in the East Indies and in Oceania. Grows to 5 inches.

288. ORANGE-TAILED DAMSEL-FISH *Abudefduf bankieri* (Richardson) [Plate 43]

Glyphisodon bankieri Richardson, Rept 15th Meet. Brit. Assn Adv. Sci., 1845 (1846), p. 253.
Parapomacentrus bankieri Bleeker, Atlas Ichth., 9, 1877, pl. 408, fig. 8.

D. 13/11, 1; A. 2/11, 1; L. l. 26-28; L. tr. 3/1/8; membrane of spinous dorsal incised and lobed; caudal well forked. General colour brownish-black, passing into grey on the belly; posterior portions of soft dorsal, anal, and whole of caudal cadmium-yellow; rest of fins similar to body, the spines and rays almost black; caudal terminating in long black rays; eye, pupil black, surrounded by a wide red ring, outside of which is grey; a small black spot at pectoral origin. Some examples have scattered bluish spots and a jet-black ocellus as large as eye just above and behind upper edge of opercle.

This very common little fish is seen in dozens playing among the coral growths on the reefs of North Queensland. It is also found in the East Indies, the Philippines, and China. Grows to 3 inches.

OTHER SPECIES

Stripe-tailed Damsel-fish, *A. sexfasciatus*. A very common fish in North Queensland and Torres Strait. It is also found in the East Indies, the Western Pacific, the Philippines, and Japan. Grows to 7 inches.

Five-banded Damsel-fish, *A. saxatilis*. A wide-ranging species occasionally found on the coasts of Queensland and New South Wales. Grows to 7 inches.

White-banded Damsel-fish, *A. amabilis*. Not generally met with on the Queensland coast, but fairly common in the Bunker and Capricorn groups. Grows to 3 inches.

Black Damsel-fish, *A. melas*. Very common among the corals on North Queensland reefs and widely distributed through the East Indies, Zanzibar, and the Red Sea. Distinguished by its black colour. Grows to 7 inches.

Scar-face Damsel-fish, *A. xanthurus.* Readily recognized by the two blackish vertical stripes on the opercles; the body is brown and the caudal yellow. Found in North Queensland and the East Indies. Grows to 8 inches.

Golden-scaled Damsel-fish, *A. leucogaster.* A very common reef species in North Queensland, also found through the East Indies, in Zanzibar, and in the Red Sea. In colour it is green, with each scale edged with gold. Grows to 5 inches.

Blue-banded Damsel-fish, *A. biocellatus.* A wide-ranging fish found in the northern waters of Queensland. Grows to 5 inches. Subject to great colour variation.

Sombre Damsel-fish, *A. glaucus.* Found in the Indo-Pacific region; has been recorded from North Queensland. Grows to $3\frac{1}{2}$ inches.

Blue Damsel-fish, *A. uniocellatus.* Occurs in Melanesia, Micronesia, Polynesia, and the East Indies, also found in North Queensland. Grows to $2\frac{1}{2}$ inches.

Hedley's Damsel-fish, *A. hedleyi.* A blue fish with orange-red tail, frequenting the reefs of North Queensland. Grows to 3 inches.

Blue and Gold Damsel-fish, *A. melanopus.* A brilliantly coloured and active fish found infrequently on North Queensland reefs. Grows to about $2\frac{1}{2}$ inches.

Sub-family PARMINAE

Usually more than 30 transverse series of scales. Unpaired fins with dense scaly sheaths. Preoperculum smooth.

Fishes of the Pacific. Genera few, one in Queensland.

Parma

Preoperculum not serrated. Teeth compressed, in a single series. Dorsal spines 12 to 13; Anal spines 2. Lateral line ceasing below posterior portion of dorsal fin.

Deep-bodied fishes, species few, one in Queensland.

289. LARGE-SCALED PARMA *Parma oligolepis* Whitley [Plate 43]

Parma oligolepis Whitley, Mem. Qld Mus., 9, pt 3, 1929, p. 230, pl. 28, fig. 1.

D. 13/19; A. 2/15; L. l. tubes 23 plus about 7 punctured scales; L. tr. 4/1/13. Colour uniform brownish; borders of fins and margins of scales of body somewhat darker.

A deep-bodied, large-scaled fish found in the coastal waters of South Queensland. Grows to at least $8\frac{3}{4}$ inches.

Sub-family CHEILOPRIONINAE

Lips greatly thickened, fimbriate, and curled back over the snout.

This sub-family consists of the genus *Cheiloprion* of the East Indian region and Australia.

Cheiloprion

Form ovoid, rather deep. Lips very wide and papillose. Teeth uniserial, fine and slender, compressed to form an even cutting edge. Preopercle entire. Dorsal spines 13, rays 12 to 13. Caudal little emarginate. A single species.

290. BIG-LIP DAMSEL-FISH *Cheiloprion labiatus* (Day)   [Plate 43]

Pomacentrus labiatus Day, Fish. India, pt 3, 1877, p. 384, pl. 81, fig. 2.
Cheiloprion labiatus de Beaufort, Fish. Indo-Austr. Archip., 8, 1940, p. 351, fig. 45.

D. 13/13; A. 2/12; L. l. 17-18 + 8-9; L. tr. $1\frac{1}{2}$-2/1/9. Colour uniform brownish, fins somewhat darker, the ventrals blackish; lips pale.

A sombre-coloured little fish, readily known by its swollen and curled lips. It is found on the reefs of North Queensland, in the East Indies, the Philippines, and the South Sea Islands. Grows to $3\frac{1}{2}$ inches.

DIVISION *Labriformes: Wrasses, Rainbow-fishes, Parrot-fishes*

Form oblong, sometimes elongate, compressed, covered with minute to large scales. Lateral line continuous or interrupted in posterior half. Teeth in jaws mostly caniniform. Characterized by the united pharyngeals, the lower ankylosed, the second upper pharyngeals being united with the third and fourth. One or more canines may be present in the jaws near the corner of the mouth. Only $3\frac{1}{2}$ gills. Spinous dorsal well developed, the spines rigid and pungent or feeble and flexible.

Three families form this group of brilliantly coloured percoid fishes. They are widely distributed throughout all temperate and tropical seas, and the genera and species are particularly numerous wherever large coral reef formations exist.

KEY TO FAMILIES

A.   Anterior teeth of jaws separate; lateral teeth usually separated from each other.   LABRIDAE

AA. Teeth of jaws more or less coalesced to form a parrot-like "beak".

     b. Dorsal fin with 15 to 24 spines. Ventrals with 4 rays.   NEOODACIDAE

     bb. Dorsal fin with 9 spines. Ventrals with 5 rays.   CALLYODONTIDAE

Family **Labridae: Wrasses, Rainbow-fishes, Pig-fishes, Tusk-fishes, etc.**

A large family of marine fishes inhabiting mainly tropical seas, though some are found in subtropical or temperate regions. Over sixty genera are known, containing nearly five hundred species. Wrasses are essentially reef-dwellers, inhabiting shallow waters among the coral reefs and rocks. Most of the species are brilliantly coloured and many of them grow to a large size and are valued food-fishes. They are subject to great variation in colour, and in some genera the species are difficult to determine. Most are carnivorous, feeding upon crabs, shellfish, etc., though they are also partly herbivorous. The lower pharyngeal bones, which are situated on the floor of the gullet, are completely fused together and form a broad, somewhat triangular plate which bears conical or tuberculate teeth, such an apparatus being admirably suited for crushing shells. The front teeth of the jaws are usually strong canines and the lateral teeth are more or less coalesced at their bases. In many species the teeth are green or bright blue in colour. The palate is without teeth. In certain species posterior or hind canines are frequently present. These are situated at the gape of the mouth on the upper or lower or both jaws and stand out at a right angle to the jaws. The lips are thick and fleshy, and usually with longitudinal folds—hence the popular German name of "Lippfisch". The scales of the body are cycloid and usually large in size. The dorsal and anal spines are not very strong. Some of the wrasses are known to construct nests for their eggs and young. In the European species such nests are constructed of algal growths, seaweeds, etc., the work being performed by both male and female. Almost all the larger species are valued food-fishes. Twenty-one genera occur in Queensland waters.

KEY TO GENERA IN QUEENSLAND

Based on Fowler and Bean[41]

A. Lateral line continuous, bent abruptly behind, but not interrupted.

   b. Dorsal spines 11-13.

     c. 45 or more scales on the lateral line. Lips thick and fleshy. Dorsal spines 11. Size large.   *Achoerodus*

     cc. 35 or less scales on the lateral line. Lips thin or moderate. 12-13 dorsal spines.

      d. Preorbital and cheek deep.

       e. Dorsal spines 11-13, rays 8-9. Maxillary longer, arched, reaches beyond front of eye. Cheek scales large, in but 3 rows. Size small.   *Choerodon*

---

[41] U.S. Nat. Mus. Bull. 100, 7, 1928, p. 188.

ee. Dorsal spines 13, rays 7. Maxillary shorter, scarcely arched, barely or not reaching eye. Cheek scales small, inconspicuous. Size large.

dd. Preorbital and cheek less deep. Dorsal spines 12, rays 10. Maxillary moderate, not or not quite reaching eye. Cheek scales all small. Size moderate or large. — *Lepidaplois*

bb. Dorsal spines 8-9.

f. Jaws exceedingly protractile, mandible greatly produced backward. Size rather large. — *Epibulus*

ff. Jaws normal, not produced backward.

g. Preopercle edge serrate. Cheeks and opercles with large scales; scales in lateral line 20. Front dorsal spines elevated, filamentous in males. — *Duymaeria*

gg. Preopercle entire.

h. Head more or less scaled, or only muzzle naked.

i. Body scales extending on to dorsal and anal fins.

j. Mouth rather large, lips moderate, forming a tube when mouth is closed. Head covered with small scales, much smaller than those on body. Scales in lateral line 25-27. — *Labrichthys*

ii. Body scales not extending on to dorsal and anal fins, or only partly so.

k. Scales small, 35-50 in lateral line. Head covered largely with small scales, scarcely smaller than those of body. Lips prominent, the lower divided into 2 lobes. — *Labroides*

kk. Scales large, 25-30 in lateral line. Cheeks and opercles scaly. Lower lip entire, not divided into lobes. — *Pseudolabrus*

hh. Head less scaly, opercles scaleless or with few scales only.

l. Body oblong, not cylindrical, depth less than 5 in length.

m. Dorsal spines 9.

n. Scales large, 25-30 in lateral line.

o. Thoracic scales as large as body scales, or larger. Mouth small. Upper canines very short, close-set, form terminal cutting edge; lower teeth similar, but longer. Dorsal spines short, pungent. — *Stethojulis*

oo. Thoracic scales not enlarged. Front canines normal.

p. Lips thick, with folds, lower pendant. Cheeks with small scales below. — *Hemigymus*

pp. Lips not enlarged. Cheeks usually naked. — *Halichoeres*

nn. Scales rather small or very small, 40-120 in lateral line.

q. Scales in lateral line 40-80.

r. A few small scales behind eye. Less than 60 scales in lateral line. — *Ophthalmolepis*

rr. No scales behind eye. More than 60 scales in lateral line. — *Coris*

qq. Scales very small, 90-120 in lateral line. — *Hologymnosus*

mm. Dorsal spines 8. No hind canines. Scales large, none on head. — *Thalassoma*

ll. Body elongate, subcylindrical. No hind canines. Scales small. Row of small scales on opercle. — *Cheilio*

hhh. Head scaleless.

s. Body deep, compressed. Dorsal spines 9. Two prominent canines in each jaw, flared forward, with cutting edges. — *Anampses*

AA. Lateral line interrupted behind, front section concurrent with profile of back, hind or lower section horizontally median along caudal peduncle.

t. First two dorsal spines not conspicuously removed from third.

u. Dorsal spines 9, rays 12. Anal spines 3, rays 12. Head compressed, upper edge obtuse. — *Novaculichthys*

uu. Dorsal spines 9-10, rays 8. Anal spines 3, rays 8. Snout large, often elongate. — *Cheilinus*

tt. First two dorsal spines more or less conspicuously removed, not entirely detached. Cheeks with small scales. — *Hemipteronotus*

Achoerodus

Body short, oblong-ovate, but little compressed. Lips thick and fleshy, the lower with a well-developed, rounded, lateral flap. Two pairs of strong canines in each jaw anteriorly; a lateral row of conical teeth, connected by an osseous ridge; posterior canine present or absent. Lateral line gently curved, continuous to caudal peduncle, the posterior tubes profusely branched.

A single species, inhabiting Australian waters only.

291. GIANT PIG-FISH *Achoerodus gouldii* (Richardson) [Plate 44]

Labrus gouldii Richardson, Ann. Mag. Nat. Hist., 1843, p. 353.

Platychoerops mulleri Klunzinger, Sitzb. Akad. Wiss. Wien, 80, 1879, p. 399, pl. 8, fig. 2.

Red Groper, Blue Groper, (South Queensland and New South Wales).

D. 11/10-11; A. 3/11; L. l. 39-45; L. tr. 8-10/14-17. Male (Blue Groper): "Above purplish-brown, sides and lower surface yellowish-brown, each scale with an orange spot or vertical bar; a narrow orange band encircles the eye; sides of snout with three similar bands, one of which crosses the cheek, separated by blue bands; fins purple, the membranes of the anterior rays of the dorsal and anal with orange spots; all these markings are most conspicuous in the young, but almost totally disappear in adult examples." (Ogilby.)

Female (Red Groper): "Uniform dull brick-red, a little lighter on the abdomen; cheeks, opercles, and lower surface of the head washed with gold; the spinous dorsal and the anal with a basal white band sparsely blotched with orange; remainder of the web hyaline; spines and other fins dusky; the ventrals pale red basally." (Ogilby.)

The Red Groper and the Blue Groper, at one time thought to be two distinct species, are merely the sexes of the Giant Pig-fish. This big fish is a lover of rocky situations, reefs, and projecting rocky headlands with caves and caverns, through which it swims leisurely in search of the molluscs and crustaceans upon which it feeds. With the ebb-tide it retires to the deep water, and on calm days may be seen slowly swimming below the rocky ledges. It takes a hook readily, but unless brought to the surface quickly it immediately makes for a cave or ledge in the rocks, from which, if it succeeds in getting there, it is a difficult matter to dislodge it, owing to the fish's great strength and tenacity. As a food-fish it is excellent eating when young, but old examples are very coarse.

The Giant Pig-fish is known only from Australian waters, being most commonly met with in New South Wales. The other localities from which it has been recorded are southern Queensland (as far north as Caloundra) and Western Australia. Grows to 4 feet and a weight of 40 pounds.

Lienardella

Head blunt, with snout rather abrupt. Scales on head large, in about 5 rows on cheek. Preopercle flange scaleless. A single species.

292. HARLEQUIN TUSK-FISH *Lienardella fasciatus* (Günther)
[Colour-plate 43]

Xiphocheilus fasciatus Günther, Proc. Zool. Soc. Lond., 1867, p. 101.
Illustration by G. Coates.

D. 12/8; A. 3/10; L. l. 29-30; L. tr. 4/10. General body colour blackish and pale green, the former darkest posteriorly where it descends the full depth of the body and nape, passing gradually into pale green on sides; breast, belly, and above anal fin pale green; head and body crossed with 6 to 9 vertical scarlet bands (as seen in the illustration), the broadest from origin of dorsal to ventral base; these bands are bordered with bright blue; dorsals with body colour and bands extending on to its base, above which is a longitudinal median blue stripe, followed by the scarlet upper half of the fin, which is edged blue; pectorals yellow, scarlet basally; ventrals scarlet, the spine dark blue and the fin edged pale blue posteriorly; anal scarlet, edged blue; caudal scarlet or pinkish, with an orb of orange or yellow basally.

A strikingly handsome fish known in Australia only from the reefs of Queensland, where it is fairly common from south to north. It has also been found in the Riu Kiu Islands, near Japan. Grows to 10 inches.

Choerodon: Tusk-fishes

Body oblong, compressed, covered with rather large scales. Head obtuse, a fatty hump forming with age. Cheeks deep, with small scales which may be imbricate though usually widely separated. Each jaw with 4 strong canines, the lateral teeth more or less confluent into a blunt osseous ridge; hind canine usually present in adult. Lateral line complete. Dorsal spines 11 to 13, rays about 7.

Brilliantly coloured labroids of medium and large size found on the off-shore reefs and rocky shores of the tropical parts of Australia and the South Seas, a few species occurring in the East Indies. They take the name of tusk-fishes from the tusk-like canines in the front of the jaws. Very often there is a posterior canine present in the adults. Ten species occur in Queensland.

KEY TO SPECIES IN QUEENSLAND

A.   Cheek scales imbricate or subimbricate.

    b. Cheek scales imbricate.

        c. Body slender, elliptical, its depth 3½ in the length; dorsal profile not greatly arched, much less than ventral.

            d. Rose-pink, each scale with pale-blue spot; 3-4 blue bands usually present on head.   *frenatus*

        cc. Body deeper, ovate; dorsal profile arched, as high as or higher than ventral profile.

e. A large blackish spot (purple or violet in life) present on spinous dorsal posteriorly.

 f. Yellow, each scale with a vertical blue bar, becoming round on belly where they form longitudinal lines.   *australis*

 ff. Rose-pink, a blue, yellow-edged band from eye to snout.   *monostigma*

ee. No blackish spot on spinous dorsal fin.

 g. Olive-green, darkest area under middle of dorsal, continued as stripe on the caudal peduncle, which has a pale blotch on its upper portion; head with small orange spots.   *anchorago*

bb. Cheek scales subimbricate, small, in 8 series.

 h. Colour pearly; usually a black band from eye to caudal or a large black spot at caudal base.   *vitta*

AA. Cheek scales not imbricate, widely separated.

 i. A large black spot at base of last 2-3 dorsal spines and a larger pale blotch below soft dorsal posteriorly.

 j. Colour olive-green; scales with dark-blue vertical bars; yellow stripe from upper lip to hind opercle edge; a black blotch below anterior dorsal rays.   *schoenleinii*

 ii. No black spot at base of last dorsal spines, though a large pale blotch may be present below soft dorsal.

 k. Several narrow orange transverse lines across snout and forehead.   *cephalotes*

 kk. No transverse lines on snout or forehead, though vermiculating lines may be present on snout only.

 l. Head and body with bright-blue spots; body colour varies, greenish or pinkish-red.   *venustus*

 ll. No blue spots on head and body.

 m. Colour bluish-green; a large pale blotch sometimes present below soft dorsal; vermiculating lines of orange on pale bluish-green snout.   *albigena*

 mm. Body crossed by 3-4 dark bands (sometimes indistinct or wanting) separated by shining silvery interspaces; caudal with pale transparent spots.   *cyanodus*

293. PURPLE TUSK-FISH *Choerodon cephalotes* (Castelnau)
[Colour-plate 43]

Choerops cephalotes Castelnau, Res. Fish. Austr. (Vict. Offic. Rec. Philad. Exhib.), 1875, p. 39.
Illustration by G. Coates.

Grass Parrot (Moreton Bay).

D. 14/7; A. 3/10; L. l. 28; L. tr. 3/1/10. Colour: Head dark olive-green down to a sharply defined semi-horizontal line from gape of mouth back a little beyond edge of opercle; forehead and snout bright purplish-green with 10 or 12 narrow transverse orange bands; a few short bright-blue bars around eye and other longer and narrower ones following down the scale rows on opercles, between which are circular and elongate-oval orange spots; chin and throat yellow-ochre, with 3 to 4 bright-blue vertical bars, the two posterior ones joined above; teeth blue; body olive-green with bright-blue vertical lines closely set anteriorly and becoming wider and more oval posteriorly and breaking into blue spots on caudal peduncle; the vertical blue lines also break up into spots on belly and extend on to breast; spinous dorsal blue-tipped, beneath which it has an alternate line of orange and blue; smoky colour medianally, followed basally by other horizontal lines of blue and orange; soft dorsal with orange and blue lines, almost vertical and following the rays; anal with an orange-red longitudinal stripe followed by a bright-blue one which fades into olive-yellow medianally, after which it passes into rich lavender with elongate orange spots; pectoral pale hyaline-green, with a blue-green and an orange bar across its base; ventrals with a longitudinal purplish-blue stripe anteriorly, bordered on each side by an orange one; fin hyaline posteriorly; caudal with alternate orange and blue vertical lines.

A handsome fish known only from Queensland where it is found along the whole coastline. Does not appear to be so commonly met with as *C. albigena*, though it is very common on weedy banks in Moreton Bay. Grows to at least 14 inches.

294. VENUS TUSK-FISH *Choerodon venustus* (De Vis)   [Colour-plate 44]

Choerops venustus De Vis, Proc. Roy. Soc. Qld, 1, 1884, p. 147.
Illustration by T. C. Marshall.

Blue Parrot, Parrot-fish, Pink-sided or Roseate Tusk-fish (Queensland); Blue-spotted Groper (New South Wales).

D. 13/7; A. 3/10; L. l. 29-30; L. tr. 4/9-10. Colour: Upper part of head green, becoming gradually more tinged with blue towards snout; cheeks and opercles olive, mandibular region violet; chin sky-blue; edge of maxillary lip with a narrow outer golden and inner blue stripe; anterior margin of preorbital very narrowly edged with blue; an oval sky-blue spot in front of orbit, and extending to about one-third of its diameter; body olive-brown above lateral line, rose-coloured below, most of the scales of the back and caudal peduncle with a medium-sized round blue spot; a broad dark band runs from the fifth scale of the lateral line forwards and downwards in an arcuate shape to the inferior margin of the opercle; dorsal fin golden, the spinous portion with a basal, median, and marginal band of blue, the two outer of which are exchanged on the rays for wavy anastomosing lines of the same shade; anal fin grey, with broad basal and marginal blue bands, bordered on the inner edge by a narrower golden stripe; ventrals bluish, the membranes between first and second rays golden; pectorals grey with 2 transverse golden bands in front of base, and the two outer rays and the basal third of the others blue; caudal brownish with outer rays blue, and bases of remainder green; irides golden and crimson, with sky-blue marginal spots; basal half of canines and lateral teeth light blue.

The Blue Parrot is common on the offshore reefs and rocky shores of northern New South Wales and Queensland as far north at least as Townsville. It is well known to the professional fishermen and at times forms a good percentage of their catch. With the sporting fishermen it is a great favourite on account of its edible qualities, many preferring it to a snapper or cod. The real home of these fishes is among the rich coral growths of the Capricorns and other northern reefs. They vary greatly in colour, some being green, others a bright brick-red. Most have the blue spots which are characteristic of the species. Said to reach a length of 4 feet, but the average size is about 16 inches, and in weight it reaches at least 16 pounds.

295. BLUE TUSK-FISH *Choerodon albigena* (De Vis)　　[Colour-plate 44]

Choerops albigena De Vis, Proc. Linn. Soc. N.S.Wales, 9, 1885, p. 876.
Illustration by T. C. Marshall.

Grey Tusk-fish (South Queensland); Blue-bone (Gladstone district); Blue Groper (Whitsunday Passage); Blue-fish (Thursday Island).

D. 13/7; A. 3/10; L. l. 28-29; L. tr. 4/1/8-9. General colour bluish-green, becoming more greyish on head above and between eyes; snout usually with vermiculating lines of dull orange and pale bluish-green; chin and throat coral pink, divided from the greyish-green cheeks by a smear or indistinct stripe of pale blue which stretches from beneath the salmon-pink lip of the lower jaw along lower edge of preopercle; dorsal fins with vermiculations of pale blue and orange, forming on spinous portion a longitudinal stripe at base and on soft dorsal in the form of small pale-orange spots on a pale-blue background; anal with alternate longitudinal stripes of salmon or yellow, and deep blue; both dorsals and anal edged with a narrow bright cornflower-blue line; pectorals similar to body, only paler terminally, the base darker than body; ventrals a shade darker than belly and edged in front with a narrow orange stripe; caudal a rich dark purplish-blue, the rays fawn colour and the whole fin with spots of fawn; teeth blue-green, pupil of eye black, encircled with short bars of scarlet, blue, yellow, and green.

One of the most common tusk-fishes on the reefs of Queensland and the Gulf of Carpentaria, but less frequently met with south of the Bunker and Capricorn groups. This fish is fairly easily speared when located lying on its side beneath the coral growths at low water. It is a good food-fish, growing to a length of at least 28 inches and a weight of 18 pounds.

OTHER SPECIES

Bridled Tusk-fish, *C. frenatus*. Known only from sixteen examples trawled by the *Endeavour* in 1910 in 33 fathoms near Double Island Point, South Queensland. Length 6½ inches.

Yellow-bellied Tusk-fish, *C. australis*. A very common little fish in South Queensland, where it inhabits the weedy banks. Grows to 6½ inches.

One-spot Tusk-fish, *C. monostigma*. This was also trawled by the *Endeavour* in 1910, in 26 fathoms, off Pine Peak, South Queensland, and off Cape Glouces-ter. Length 6½ inches. Other specimens have since been collected.

Orange-dotted Tusk-fish, *C. anchorago*. A handsome fish found on the reefs of North Queensland and North Australia, Micronesia, and the South Seas, also the East Indies. Grows to at least 12 inches.

Striped Tusk-fish, *C. vitta*. From the Aru Islands, this fish has been recorded from the reefs of Townsville, North Queensland. Grows to at least 8½ inches.

Black-spot Tusk-fish, *C. schoenleinii*. This fish frequents the reefs of Queensland and New South Wales. It is more commonly found in North Queensland, where it extends into New Guinea and through the East Indies. Grows to a length of 36 inches and a weight of at least 26 pounds.

Blue-toothed Tusk-fish, *C. cyanodus*. A common fish in the northern waters of Australia. Apparently it is not so frequently seen on the Queensland coast. Grows to 26 inches. Said to be a poor food-fish, the flesh deteriorating rapidly.

Lepidaplois

Form compressed, oblong. Scales large, 30 to 35 in lateral line. Snout pointed. Mouth large. Lateral teeth in both jaws in a single series, coalesced at base; four canine teeth in front; posterior canine present. Dorsal and anal scaly at base. Lateral line continuous. Dorsal spines usually 12, rays 10. Anal spines 3, rays 12. Caudal lunate.

Brightly coloured shore and reef fishes of moderate or large size found in the tropical waters of the Indo-Pacific.

KEY TO SPECIES IN QUEENSLAND

A. Preopercle limb scaly. A black band from pectoral axil
    to last dorsal spine and first dorsal ray; large black spot
    at pectoral base.   *mesothorax*

AA. Preopercle limb scaleless.

    b. Head sharply pointed; a strong posterior, forward-directed canine present.

      c. Scarlet-red becoming saffron-yellow or pink below; a larger blue-black, white-edged spot about centre of spinous dorsal.   *oxycephalus*

      cc. Red, very bright on head above; sides yellow, each scale with red spot and red edge, and with a red streak forming longitudinal lines; 3 rows of elongate crimson blotches on back and sides. *oxycephalus* var. *bellis*

    bb. Head blunt; no posterior canine.

      d. Red; head covered with yellow spots; first 3-6 dorsal spines black, each successive one bearing less black.   *perditio*

296. GOLDEN-SPOT PIG-FISH *Lepidaplois perditio* (Quoy and Gaimard)
[Plate 44]

Labrus perditio Quoy and Gaimard, Voy. Astrolabe, Zool., 3, Poiss., 1834, p. 702.
Lepidaplois perditio Jordan and Snyder, Proc. U.S. Nat. Mus., 24, 1902, p. 618, fig. 2.

D. 12-13/10, 1; A. 3/12, 1; L. l. 33; L. tr. 6/12. General colour of head and body bright red, brightest anteriorly, becoming suffused with dark orange, then with violet posteriorly; head and forepart of body thickly freckled with yellow spots; a bright-yellow patch or half-band above the lateral line, below 8th to 10th dorsal spines, broadly bordered posteriorly with black, or followed by a large blackish blotch; a second yellow spot is present on caudal peduncle; scales of posterior half of body edged with brownish-black; spinous dorsal with first 3 to 6 spines and membranes wholly black, each successive one bearing less black; soft dorsal scarlet basally and on rays; rest of fin golden-red; anal golden, red basally and edged blackish; pectoral pinkish, darkest on the membranes; caudal red or bright yellow; ventrals dusky pink.

A wide-ranging species caught on the reefs of Queensland and but rarely straggling into the waters of New South Wales. It is found in Melanesia, Japan, Mauritius, and Zanzibar. Grows to 21 inches.

OTHER SPECIES

Eclipse Pig-fish, *L. mesothorax*. An East Indian species which has been recorded from Queensland. Grows to 7½ inches.

Black-spot Pig-fish, *L. oxycephalus*. Inhabits the reefs along the coasts of South Queensland and New South Wales, Tasmania, and New Zealand. It also occurs in Hawaii and Japan. Grows to 18 inches and is an excellent food-fish.

Banded Pig-fish, *L. oxycephalus* var. *bellis*. It is likely that this is merely a colour variety of the previous species. Known in Queensland waters from a single example caught off Caloundra, South Queensland. The only other locality from which it is known is New South Wales. The largest recorded was 15 inches.

Epibulus

A single species from the Indo-Pacific region, unique among all fishes for its exceedingly protractile mouth and lower jaw, which is greatly produced backward.

297. SLING-JAW *Epibulus insidiator* (Pallas) [Colour-plate 45]

Sparus insidiator Pallas, Spic. Zool., 8, 1770, p. 41.
Illustration by G. Coates.

D. 9/10, 1; A. 3/8, 1; L. l. 13-15 + 6-8 + 2-3; L. tr. 2/1/6. General colour dark brown or dark olive-green, slightly paler below; before eye and part of cheek grape-green; dorsal similar to body, with flushes of brick-red between spines and rays; 2 bright-orange spots between first two membranes and spines of dorsal; scales of body outlined in black or dark red, clearest on upper half of body; eye with pupil black, surrounded with yellow line, then dark brown, outside of which is a bright violet-blue ring; cheeks whitish or paler than rest of head; throat, lips, and mouth-parts pinkish-white; pectorals olive-yellow on rays, the membranes hyaline; ventrals olive-brown, blackish posteriorly; anal similar to dorsal; caudal very dark reddish-olive.

The most common colour of this variable species is deep blackish-green, but some forms are light yellow. Another variety is brown, with pale-yellow cross-bands. Others are pale yellowish, with each scale edged with brilliant green.

This peculiar fish is recognized immediately by its extraordinary jaws. When captured and lying stranded it projects and retracts the jaws with lightning rapidity. Such a curious construction has no doubt been evolved through its environment as a coral-dweller. Common on the coral reefs of North Queensland. Ranges through the East Indies to East Africa and Mauritius. Grows to 13 inches.

Duymaeria

Body rather deep, oblong, compressed, covered with very large scales, 20 to 25 in lateral line, which is continuous. Cheeks and opercles with large scales. Preopercle serrated. Four strong canines in each jaw; posterior canines present; teeth in jaws uniserial. Dorsals with a narrow scaly sheath. Dorsal spines 9, rays 11 or 12; soft portion of fin rounded. Anal with 3 spines and 9 rays. Caudal rounded.

Fishes of rather small size and few species, found in Queensland, the East Indies, China, and Japan. The sexes are unlike, the males being more brilliantly and differently coloured and having the anterior dorsal spines elevated and sometimes filamentous. In the females these spines are only elevated, Species few, one in Queensland.

298. COCKATIEL-FISH *Duymaeria flagellifera* (Cuvier and Valenciennes)
[Plate 44]

Ctenolabrus flagellifera Cuvier and Valenciennes, Hist. Nat. Poiss., 13, 1839, p. 240.
Duymaeria amboinensis Bleeker, Atlas Ichth., 1, 1862, p. 78, pl. 23, fig. 7 (female).

D. 9-10/10, 1, or 11; A. 3/9, 1; L. l. 17-18, 5-6 + 2-3; L. tr. 2/1/6. The species is very variable in colour. The male is brightly adorned in life, being usually deep blue, with markings of gold, whilst the female may be brick-red of varying tones with blue lines on head and with blue-green spots on head and body.

Apart from the differences in colour, the sexes also differ in form; the male has a keeled hump in front of the dorsal, and the dorsal and anal spines have long filaments.

A small species seldom met with by casual observers, most examples obtained in Queensland having been taken by trawl. It ranges through the East Indies, the Philippines, Formosa, China, and Japan. Grows to 8 inches.

Labrichthys

Body oblong, compressed, the head pointed and totally covered with small scales, except on the lips. Body covered with large scales, which extend over bases of vertical fins followed by small scales almost to end of fins. Lateral line complete. Mouth very small, the lips produced to form a short rounded tube when mouth is closed. A single row of small teeth in jaws; 4 canines in front of upper jaw and 2 in lower. Dorsal with 9 spines and 11 rays. Anal with 3 spines and 11 rays. Caudal rounded. Distribution that of the single species known.

299. TUBE-LIP *Labrichthys cyanotaenia* (Bleeker) [Plate 44]

Labrichthys cyanotaenia Bleeker, Nat. Tijdschr. Ned. Indie, 6, 1854, p. 331; and Atlas Ichth., 1, 1862, p. 154, pl. 22, fig. 1.

D. 9/11, 1; A. 3/10, 1; L. l. 20, 5 + 0 or 1; L. tr. 5/1/11. Colour: "Dark brown, almost black, with obscure stripes of bronze and blue, very dark, and therefore faint; a black spot at base of pectoral; head with navy blue stripes, lips yellow; dorsal coloured like body, with blue edge; anal with blue edge and blue median stripe, elsewhere dark bronze; caudal like body at base, with blue curved streak, posterior part black, the edge pale; ventral blue, with black stripe; pectoral dusky greenish-yellow at base." (Jordan and Seale.)

A small fish remarkable for the peculiar shape of its mouth. The thickened elongate lips, which consist of deep, plicate folds of lamellae radiating outwardly, form a short truncate tube with a circular opening at its tip and which remains open when the mouth is closed.

Known from the reefs of North Queensland, and the South Seas, through the East Indies to Zanzibar. Grows to 6 inches.

Labroides

Body oblong, compressed. Snout pointed. Mouth very small. Lips prominent, the lower divided into 2 lobes. Teeth in jaws minute, in bands. Two more or less curved canines anteriorly in each jaw, the upper pair recurved in lower. A posterior canine each side. Lateral line complete. Opercles, cheeks, and bases of vertical fins scaly. Body scales small, 35 to 50 in lateral line. Dorsal with 9 spines and 9 to 11 rays. Anal with 2 to 3 spines and 9 to 10 rays. Caudal truncate or rounded.

Small fishes of the Indo-Pacific living in the coral reefs. Species few, one in Queensland.

300. BLUE STREAK *Labroides dimidiatus* (Cuvier and Valenciennes)
[Plate 44]

Cossyphus dimidiatus Cuvier and Valenciennes, Hist. Nat. Poiss., 13, 1839, p. 136.
Labroides paradiseus Bleeker, Atlas Ichth., 1, 1862, p. 155, pl. 44, fig. 2.

Paradise-fish, Sea Swallow (South Africa).

D. 9/11, 1; A. 3/10, 1; L. l. 52-53; L. tr. 3½-5/1/10-14. Colour brilliant blue, paler below, a black longitudinal band from snout through eye to end of caudal fin, narrow in front but gradually becoming broader posteriorly so as to occupy all of caudal fin, except upper and lower rays which are blue as the body; a blackish band runs along bases of dorsal and anal, where on the latter it is continued along lower surface of caudal peduncle and curved up on to caudal fin to join median lateral stripe. In some examples this anal band is entirely wanting, as is also a blackish bar across pectoral base.

Young examples are sometimes almost black, except for a light streak along the back and on upper and lower caudal rays. Other examples again may be yellow, with the black median longitudinal band.

An extremely active little fish which moves with great rapidity among the coral growths when startled. It ranges from Queensland and the South Seas through the East Indies to the Red Sea, Zanzibar, and Mauritius. Grows to 4 inches.

Pseudolabrus

Body compressed, oblong. Scales large, 25 to 30 in lateral line. Snout pointed. Cheeks and opercles scaly. Preopercle entire. Lateral line continuous. Dorsal fin not scaly at base. Teeth in single series in jaws. Posterior canine present. Dorsal with 9 spines and 10 rays. Anal with 3 spines and 10 rays.

A genus of fishes, mainly of small size, confined chiefly to the waters of Australia (including Tasmania) and New Zealand, a few species entering the South Seas. About fifteen species are known, two being found in Queensland.

KEY TO SPECIES IN QUEENSLAND

A. Four or more rows of scales on cheeks, extending forward to below middle of eye. Head and anterior portion of body with broad longitudinal bars; a black blotch usually present between 2nd and 3rd dorsal spines. *guntheri*

AA. One row of scales on cheeks, confined to posterior portions of cheek. Female brick-red, with cream-coloured spots; caudal and pectorals yellow; male purplish-brown, with a broad crimson band across body between soft dorsal and anal fins. *gymnogenis*

301. GÜNTHER'S RAINBOW-FISH *Pseudolabrus guntheri* (Bleeker)

[Plate 44]

Pseudolabrus guntheri Bleeker, Versl. Meded. K. Akad. Amsterdam, 14, 1862, p. 131.
Pseudolabrus guntheri McCulloch, Rec. Austr. Mus., 9, no. 3, 1913, p. 368, pl. 17.

D. 9/11; A. 3/10; L. l. 26-27; L. tr. 3-4/9. Life colours: General colour above chocolate-brown, which breaks into broad chocolate-brown stripes on sides, and which slope backwards and extend onto belly and anal fin where it becomes more reddish; pale apple-green between the bars; head rich apple-green with tan-red stripes radiating mainly from eye; lips reddish; eye with coppery ring surrounded by gold pupil; inside mouth pale bluish; teeth pale; dorsal tipped crimson, base of membrane behind first spine yellow and blackish blotch low on membranes between 2nd and 3rd and 3rd and 4th dorsal spines; rest of dorsal carries pattern of the body; anal similar to soft dorsal and has a blue margin; soft dorsal also has a blue margin; caudal reddish-chocolate distally and proximally with an E-shaped apple-green cross-band; upper and lower caudal rays reddish, with orange tips; pectorals pale orange with small blackish axillary spot; ventrals pink with the first rays red.

Young specimens have the same markings as adults, but the vertical bars on the body are much more pronounced and there are 4 to 6 pairs of dark-brown spots between the back and the lateral line, and one on the caudal peduncle. These are sometimes persistent in the full-grown fish.

A small fish from South Queensland and New South Wales. In the former locality it is found only as far north as the Capricorns and is fairly common, becoming rarer in New South Wales waters. Also found in Western Australia and at Lord Howe Island. Grows to 7 inches.

OTHER SPECIES

White-spotted Rainbow-fish, *P. gymnogenis*. A beautiful fish which inhabits the waters of South Queensland, New South Wales, Western Australia, and Lord Howe Island. It is seldom met with in Queensland, nor is it common in New South Wales. Grows to 15 inches.

Stethojulis

Body oblong or elongate, compressed. Head conic, scaleless. Mouth small. Scales on body large, those before dorsal somewhat smaller, but those on chest and breast usually enlarged. Lateral line complete. Jaws with small close-set canine-like teeth, upper short, lower as cutting edge; a large canine each side posteriorly. Dorsal spines 9, short and pungent, rays 11. Anal spines 3, rays 11. Caudal rounded or truncate.

Small brilliantly coloured fishes found on the reefs of the Indo-Pacific region. Species numerous, six in Queensland.

KEY TO SPECIES IN QUEENSLAND

A. Thoracic scales not or but slightly enlarged.

    b. A crescent of vivid scarlet above pectoral base and in axil.

        c. Lower flanks with each scale whitish on terminal half; pectoral base with a transverse blackish bar and a small scarlet dash in axil; caudal peduncle with a black ocellus.   *axillaris*

       cc. Lower flanks livid bluish-white; no dusky bar at pectoral base; a large scarlet crescent above and including pectoral base; no ocellus on caudal peduncle.   *casturi*

   bb. No scarlet patch above pectoral base.

        d. Lower flanks with many longitudinal olive or silvery lines; pectoral base without band or spot; small black ocellus on last dorsal rays and another at base of upper caudal rays.   *strigiventer*

       dd. Lower flanks with longitudinal rows of small dark spots; body above with spots and vermiculations; pectoral and caudal bases without band or spot.   *kalosoma*

AA. Thoracic scales greatly enlarged.

    e. Band below pectoral begins at gill-opening and
       reaches to opposite anal origin.   *renardi*

    ee. No band below pectoral; inferior body band extends
        from pectoral axil to caudal base.   *albovittata*

302. LINED RAINBOW-FISH *Stethojulis strigiventer* (Bennett)   [Plate 44]

Julis strigiventer Bennett, Proc. Zool. Soc. Lond., 1832, p. 184.
Stethojulis strigiventer Bleeker, Atlas Ichth., 1, 1862, p. 135, pl. 43, fig. 1.

D. 9/11, 1; A. 2/11, 1; L. l. 27; L. tr. 3/9. Colour: Upper half of head and body in a line from snout to caudal base sage-green; each scale of side of head and body with pale-olive lines; lower half of body with pale-olive lines longitudinally between scale rows, becoming silvery on belly; lower head and breast white; dark line from tip of snout under eye and across opercle; dorsal lemon-yellow towards edge, ray and spines dusky; anal hyaline; caudal olive-green, with 6 bluish-white bars basally; ventrals hyaline; pectorals pale creamy-yellow.

In some examples there is a small blue-black ocellus on the caudal at bases of upper median rays and another at base of penultimate dorsal ray.

A wide-ranging species found in North Queensland, Melanesia, Micronesia, Polynesia, the East Indies, Japan, Mauritius, and East Africa. Grows to 5 inches.

OTHER SPECIES

Dotted Rainbow-fish, *S. axillaris*. A wide-ranging fish found on the reefs of North Queensland. Grows to 5 inches.

Red-shouldered Rainbow-fish, *S. casturi*. A western Pacific species which has been recorded from Michaelmas Cay, North Queensland. Grows to 5 inches.

Spotted-bellied Rainbow-fish, *S. kalosoma*. Inhabits the reefs of Torres Strait, North Queensland; also occurs in Melanesia, the East Indies, Japan, Madagascar, South and East Africa, and the Red Sea. Grows to 5 inches.

Renard's Rainbow-fish, *S. renardi*. Frequents the reefs of North Queensland and is also found in Polynesia, Micronesia, the East Indies and Zanzibar. Grows to 5 inches.

Scarlet-banded Rainbow-fish, *S. albovittata*. A very pretty little fish common on North Queensland reefs, also wide-ranging outside Australia. Grows to 5 inches.

Hemigymnus

Body compressed, oblong. Lateral line complete, bent abruptly posteriorly. Scales rather large, 30 in lateral line. Head naked, except for a row of very small scales. Lips thick, pendant. Prominent conical front teeth; a canine in angle of mouth. Preopercle entire. Dorsal spines 7, rays 11. Anal spines 3, rays 11. Only two species, both wide-ranging, from Australia, through the East Indies; one in Queensland.

303. BLACK-EYED THICK-LIP *Hemigymnus melapterus* (Bloch)

[Colour-plate 45]

Labrus melapterus Bloch, Nat. ausl. Fische, 5, 1791, p. 137.
Illustrations by T. C. Marshall (adult) and G. Coates (juvenile).

D. 9/10-11; A. 3/11; L. l. about 28; L. tr. 5-6/11-13. The colour of this species is extremely variable with growth. In small examples up to about 5 inches, the anterior half of the body is light coloured, the posterior half dark coloured, the line of demarcation sharply defined and oblique. Top of head is greenish-grey, spotted with maroon-red, which colour passes into broad bands from eye to snout; cheeks and light-coloured anterior area of body somewhat greenish-white, thickly speckled with pale dusky dots and smudges; posterior half of body very dark brown, the scales edged with black, each scale with a greyish spot at its base; caudal yellow-ochre, merging gradually into the dark body-colour; dorsal and anal somewhat similar to body colour but with a reddish tinge; a submarginal blue band, a dark-red margin, and blue spots on both fins; pectorals hyaline; ventrals whitish.

In the adult the demarcation of the light and dark halves of colour disappears, the two colours merging into each other; the tail also becomes the same colour as the body; the maroon-red of the head becomes bright red and the greenish-grey bright light blue; the cheeks are apple-green and the lips emerald-green; nape of neck, down to level of pectoral base, grass-green; rest of body dark blue to caudal, where it gradually becomes somewhat dark greenish, and finally becomes salmon-pink posteriorly; this blue colour becomes bluish-grey on belly and grey on breast; whitish or bluish spots are scattered on upper sides of body and on tail; dorsal and anal with submarginal blue band and oblique blue stripes, edge of fin salmon-pink; pectorals and ventrals creamy, the latter with an orange-red border anteriorly.

After death, the red patch behind the eye turns rapidly to grey and finally to black. This is a very distinctive feature.

An Indo-Pacific species commonly seen on the coral reefs of Queensland. Its weird coloration reveals only half of a fish when it is seen swimming among the corals. Much more commonly seen north of the Capricorns. Grows to 36 inches.

Halichoeres

Body oblong or elongate, compressed. Head compressed, conic, usually naked, sometimes a few scales on cheeks behind eyes. Scales large. Lateral line not interrupted, bent abruptly behind. Large conical teeth in front of jaws; a canine usually present at corner of mouth. Fins low. Dorsal spines 9, rays 11. Anal spines 3, rays 11. First anal spine minute. Caudal lunate, truncate, or rounded.

Brilliantly coloured little fishes of the coral reefs of tropical seas, remarkable for the great variation of their colour patterns, especially of the markings of the head.

Species numerous, eleven in Queensland.

KEY TO SPECIES IN QUEENSLAND

A. One to 3 ocelli or a dusky blotch usually present on dorsal fins.

    b. A black ocellus usually present at base of caudal above; longitudinal orange stripes from head to tail, interspaces blue.   *hoevenii*

   bb. No ocellus at caudal base.

    c. A single large ocellus between 5th and 7th dorsal spine; caudal with broad blue transverse band; small blue-black triangular spot at pectoral origin.   *nigrescens*

   cc. Two ocelli or blotches on dorsal fin, one at anterior dorsal spines, and one at anterior dorsal rays.

    d. Anal fin with dark-brown spots, mainly on rays.   *miniatus*

   dd. No dark spots on anal fin; either with red ocelli, light spots or oblique or longitudinal lines.

    e. Bands on head comparatively straight, continuous with body bands.   *notopsis*

   ee. Bands on head curved beneath and behind eye, not continued on body.

    f. Black blotch at anterior spinous dorsal and another at anterior soft dorsal; colour olive-green; an ill-defined brownish median lateral band on side, with several blotches downward.   *nebulosus*

   ff. Black ocellus at anterior spinous dorsal and another at anterior soft dorsal; sometimes a third present at second last membrane of soft dorsal.

   g. Spinous and soft dorsals with black ocelli anteriorly; a broad bright purple-pink band at vent.   *margaritaceus*

   gg. Two black red-edged ocelli at anterior spinous and soft dorsals; a third frequently present on second last membrane; 5 broad indistinct dark cross-bands on upper half of body.   *binotopsis*

AA. No ocelli on the dorsal fins.

   h. One row of scales above lateral line. A small dusky blotch above end of pectoral and a blackish spot on upper caudal base.   *devisi*

   hh. 3-4 rows of scales above lateral line.

   i. A broad dark, somewhat zigzag, band medianally from snout to caudal base; no blotches above lateral line.   *scapularis*

   ii. No dark band medianally.

   j. Head somewhat scaly; 3 scales above lateral line. 2 black blotches above lateral line, second on caudal peduncle.   *trimaculatus*

   jj. Head entirely scaleless; 4 scales above lateral line. A black, blue-edged ocellus on upper caudal base.   *melanurus*

304. CLOUDED RAINBOW-FISH *Halichoeres nebulosus* (Cuvier and Valenciennes) [Colour-plate 46]

Julis nebulosus Cuvier and Valenciennes, Hist. Nat. Poiss., 13, 1839, p. 461.
Illustration by G. Coates.

D. 9/11; A. 3/10-11; L. l. 27-29; L. tr. 2-3/1/9. Colour olivaceous or yellowish; several violet or reddish bands on head, one on cheek being sometimes curved in a horseshoe shape or almost completed to form an irregular circle; opercular lobe violet; a dark-brownish obscurely defined median lateral band with several blotches downward on sides; a short dark bar close behind eye; spinous dorsal pale red, with marginal and basal row of pale red or yellow spots, margined with pale blue; a black blotch medianally on anterior dorsal rays and sometimes a smaller one at front of spinous dorsal; anal dusky red, with a blue-bordered red longitudinal band medianally and a row of spots similar to those on dorsal basally, the edge of the fin being narrowly pale blue as in dorsal; caudal pale reddish, crossed by 7 to 8 transverse narrow scarlet bars which may be broken up into a series of elongate blue-edged red spots.

A very handsome species, though variable in colour. Wide-ranging, known in Australia from the Queensland coast. Grows to 4 inches.

L

305. SADDLED RAINBOW-FISH *Halichoeres margaritaceus*
(Cuvier and Valenciennes) [Colour-plate 46]

Julis margaritaceus Cuvier and Valenciennes, Hist. Nat. Poiss., 13, 1839, p. 484.
Illustration by G. Coates.

D. 9/11, 1; A. 3/11/1; L. l. 28-30; L. tr. 2-3/1/9. Colour bright blue above, with a network of dark reddish-brown bordering the scales and extending down sides almost to a line with pectoral base and exceeding this line on caudal peduncle; belly and lower sides pale green, with a broad pale-pink vertical band at vent, joining its fellow below; head dark blue above, becoming paler greenish-blue on cheeks; streaks of maroon above, before and behind eye; a horizontal curved stripe below eye is pink, with a pale-blue border; lips yellow; dorsal blue, with vertical wavy streaks of maroon-red; a large and conspicuous yellow-edged black ocellus on front of soft dorsal, and a smaller black spot at front of spinous dorsal; anal orange, with about 9 vertical maroon stripes; pectoral pale yellow; ventrals pale blue, the anterior edge red; caudal yellow, with cross-rows of dark-red spots; a large pink spot at pectoral origin above. Sometimes a black ocellus is present on the opercle.

A common little fish among the coral growths on the Barrier Reef. Found also in the South Seas and the East Indies. Grows to $4\frac{1}{4}$ inches. Wide-ranging.

OTHER SPECIES

Orange-tipped Rainbow-fish, *H. hoevenii*. An East Indian and South Seas species recorded from the reefs of Torres Strait, North Queensland. Variable in its colour pattern; sometimes a small black spot is present at pectoral base, though this, together with the black ocelli on dorsals and caudal, may be absent. Grows to 4 inches.

Dusky Rainbow-fish, *H. nigrescens*. A wide-ranging fish found on the coasts of North Queensland and the Northern Territory. Very variable in colour. Grows to 6 inches.

Spotted-finned Rainbow-fish, *H. miniatus*. Readily recognized from most others by the spotted anal rays and the absence of a black caudal ocellus. It is an East Indian species found on the coral reefs of Queensland. Grows to 3 inches.

Another Rainbow-fish is *H. notopsis*, a small Indo-Pacific fish found on the Queensland coast. It reaches a length of 4 inches.

Banded Rainbow-fish, *H. binotopsis*. A pretty little fish which ranges from Torres Strait to Polynesia, Micronesia, and the East Indies. Grows to $3\frac{1}{2}$ inches.

De Vis' Rainbow-fish, *H. devisi*. Recognized by the absence of dorsal ocelli and by the single row of scales above the lateral line. It is known only from South Queensland, where the only recorded examples were trawled in 15 fathoms off Fraser Island. Length 3 inches.

Zigzag Rainbow-fish, *H. scapularis*. Known by the broad dark zigzag band along the side. It is wide-ranging and in Australian waters is found in Torres Strait, North Queensland. Grows to 7 inches.

Spot-tail Rainbow-fish, *H. trimaculatus*. A handsome and extremely active fish from the reefs of Queensland, the South Seas, Micronesia, and the East Indies. Grows to 6 inches.

Dusky-tailed Rainbow-fish, *H. melanurus*. Has been recorded from the waters of Torres Strait, North Queensland. Found also in the East Indies and Micronesia. Grows to 4 inches.

Ophthalmolepis

Body compressed, oblong. Scales less than 60 in lateral line. Head naked, except for a few small scales behind eye. Lateral line continuous, bent abruptly behind. Dorsal spines 9. A single species, inhabiting Australian waters.

306. MAORI *Ophthalmolepis lineolatus* (Cuvier and Valenciennes) [Plate 45]

Julis lineolatus Cuvier and Valenciennes, Hist. Nat. Poiss., 13, 1839, p. 436.
Ophthalmolepis lineolatus Kner, Novara Zool., 1, Fische, 1865, p. 258, pl. 11, fig. 1.

D. 9/13; A. 3/13; L. 1. 52-56; L. tr. 6/20. Colour: "Back red, with numerous small pale blue spots; sides traversed length-wise by a broad pink band superiorly, and a dark, frequently black, band inferiorly, which are usually separated by a narrow pinkish-white band; abdominal region pale yellow. Head olive-green; opercular region pale greenish-yellow; the whole traversed more or less vertically by numerous narrow pale blue bands, which frequently have darker blue edges. Rays of dorsal fin white, membrane reddish-orange with four narrow longitudinal blue bands, and scattered blue spots; rays of anal white, membrane yellow at base, reddish-orange at tips, the whole traversed by irregular and broken bands blue in colour; caudal pink, streaked with blue between the rays; pectorals yellow, streaked with red, a transverse blue band at base; ventrals immaculate. Irides crimson." (Roughley.)

The Maori inhabits the rocky headlands and coasts of New South Wales, Victoria, South Australia and Western Australia. Only odd stragglers reach the southernmost waters of Queensland, the species being most commonly met with in New South Wales. As a food-fish it is considered by some to be superior to the parrot-fishes. It takes its name from the Maori-like markings on its face. Grows to 16 inches.

Coris

Body oblong or elongate, compressed. Scales small or moderate, about 50 to 85 in lateral line, which is continuous but abruptly bent behind. Head scaleless, but sometimes a patch of scales behind eye. A single series of pointed conical teeth in jaws increase in size, the anterior ones being canines. A posterior canine present or absent. Dorsal spines 9, rays 12; anterior spines usually produced and flexible and sometimes distant from the following ones. Anal spines 3, rays 12. Caudal rounded or forked.

Brilliantly coloured fishes of the coral reefs of the Indo-Pacific. Species few, two in Queensland.

KEY TO SPECIES IN QUEENSLAND

A.   A black comb-like band from snout to tail; bright scarlet above and bright yellow below.   *picta*

AA. Pale yellow, with small black spots on head; a few indistinct dark transverse marks on sides; dorsals with a small black spot anteriorly.   *pallida*

307. COMB-FISH *Coris picta* (Bloch and Schneider)   [Plate 45]

Labrus pictus Bloch and Schneider, Syst. Ichth., 1801, p. 251.
Coris picta Waite, Rec. Austr. Mus., 5, 1903, p. 26, pl. 5, fig. 1.

D. 9/12; A. 3/12; L. l. 83; L. tr. 7/35. Colour: Upper part of snout greyish, followed by a wide red stripe which runs back along base of dorsal fin to caudal base; commencing below this, on snout is a dark chocolate band, which embraces the eye and runs back to the tail, widening to about one-third the depth of the fish; from its lower edge it gives off a number of short vertical bars, giving a comb-like appearance; these bars are less pronounced towards the tail; below this brown band, from mouth to tail, is clear lemon-yellow; dorsal with 3 zones of colour, the upper half deep yellow, followed by a somewhat narrower red band, beneath which is a dark-brown narrow band at the base of fin; pectoral, ventrals, anal, and caudal orange-yellow, the former with a dusky triangular patch at its tip.

A handsome and fairly common little fish known from South Queensland (Moreton Bay), New South Wales, and Lord Howe Island. Grows to 11 inches.

OTHER SPECIES

Pallid Wrasse, *C. pallida*. A small species from North Queensland and Torres Strait. Grows to about 4 inches.

Hologymnosus

Body elongate, compressed, covered with very small scales, 101 to 108 in lateral line. Head pointed, well compressed, naked. Lips fleshy. Front canines four in each jaw; no posterior canine. Lateral line complete, sharply deflected posteriorly.

Dorsal with 9 spines and 12 rays. Anal with 3 spines and 12 rays. Caudal truncate, the outer rays prolonged. Distribution that of the single known species.

308. RINGED WRASSE *Hologymnosus semidiscus* (Lacépède)　[Plate 45]

Labrus semidiscus (Commerson) Lacépède, Hist. Nat. Poiss., 3, 1802, pp. 429, 473.
Julis annulatus Cuvier and Valenciennes, Hist. Nat. Poiss., 13, 1839, p. 501, pl. 388.

D. 11/12, 1; A. 3/12, 1; L. l. 101-108; L. tr. 6/1/47-48. Colour: "Rosy, yellowish below, with numerous narrow yellow or dark brown, or blue edged with brown, vertical cross-bars; often a broad yellow or white cross-band behind the pectoral fin, bordered with brown or black in front and behind; yellowish or bluish irregular streaks on head; dorsal fin rosy or violaceous, usually with a semicircular white spot at base between each pair of spines and rays; anal yellowish or rosy; both dorsal and anal with blue or violet edging; caudal rosy or violaceous, with (typically) a crescent-shaped yellow band on hind margin." (Barnard.)

A handsome though very variable species ranging from Melanesia, the Society Islands, and the East Indies to Mauritius and East Africa. Recorded from Queensland on an example which was secured at Lady Musgrave Island by K. Kerr. Grows to 20 inches.

Thalassoma

Body oblong or elongate, compressed. Snout short, obtuse. Scales large, 27 to 30 in lateral line; those before dorsal and on thorax smaller than those of the body. Head scaleless. Prominent front canines; no hind canines; granular teeth inside mouth. Lateral line continuous, bent abruptly below soft dorsal. Dorsal with 8 slender spines and 12 to 13 rays. Anal spines 3, first very small, rays 11.

Fishes of small or moderate size with elongate compressed bodies, usually brilliant blue or green in colour. About twelve species are known, four being found in Queensland.

KEY TO SPECIES IN QUEENSLAND

A.　Body with black cross-bars or bands. Colour yellowish.

    b.　Head with red bands radiating from eye; 2 red longitudinal stripes on body; 5-7 black bars, not extending across body.　　　　　　　　　　*hardwicke*

    bb.　Head and body without red bands or stripes; two of the 5 black bands extend across body, one from dorsal to anal, the other across caudal base.　　　*jansenii*

AA. No black cross-bars on body. Colour green or blue.

    c. Body dark greenish-blue; head violet, green bands; pectoral dark blue, with broad reddish patch.   *lunare*

    cc. Body green, strongest in form of vertical band below first six dorsal spines; head orange, green bands; pectoral lemon-yellow, with broad blue border posteriorly.   *lutescens*

309. MOON WRASSE *Thalassoma lunare* (Linnaeus)   [Colour-plate 47]

Labrus lunaris Linnaeus, Syst. Nat., 10th ed., 1758, p. 283.
Illustration by G. Coates.

D. 8/13; A. 3/11; L. l. 27; L. tr. 3/1/9-11. Colour: Head rich violet, with several longitudinal arched bands of bright green; body dark greenish-blue, each scale with vertical red line or streak; base of dorsal fin body colour, passing into orange-red and bordered terminally with dark blue; anal similar; pectoral dark blue, with a broad reddish spatulate patch in its upper half; ventrals pale green; caudal yellow, the two pointed lobes orange-red, bordered above and below with dark blue.

Young examples have a black spot at base of second to fourth dorsal rays, and some light blotches along the back, also a black spot at root of caudal fin.

A wide-ranging and common species. It is very handsome, and is somewhat variable in colour. Studies of the living fishes will probably reveal this to be the male of the Green Moon Wrasse, *T. lutescens*. The two species are to be observed on the reefs in active companionship in the one school, and both are frequently caught together by line fishermen. In Australia it is known only from the coast of Queensland. Grows to 10 inches.

OTHER SPECIES

Six-barred Wrasse, *T. hardwicke*. A common and particularly striking species from the reefs of North Queensland. It is also found in Melanesia, Polynesia, through the East Indies to East Africa, China, and the Philippines. Grows to 8 inches.

Jansen's Wrasse, *T. jansenii*. Found on the reefs of Queensland; also occurs through the East Indies, Melanesia, Polynesia, and Micronesia. Grows to 7 inches.

Green Moon Wrasse, *T. lutescens*. Commonly found on the Great Barrier Reef swimming among the coral growths with *T. lunare*, of which it is most probably the female and not a distinct species as hitherto supposed.

Cheilio

Body elongate, somewhat compressed, covered with scales of moderate size, 45 to 50 in lateral line, which is continuous. Head long, pointed, almost entirely naked. Teeth small, uniserial. No hind canines. Two short stout curved canines in front of upper jaw. Dorsal with 9 (rarely 8) flexible spines and 13 (14) soft rays. Anal with 3 spines and 11 to 12 rays. Caudal slightly rounded. A single species, widely distributed in tropical waters.

310. SHARP-NOSED WRASSE *Cheilio inermis* (Forskål)   [Plate 45]

Labrus inermis Forskål, Descr. Anim., 1775, p. 34.
Cheilio inermis Bleeker, Atlas Ichth., 1, 1862, p. 82, pl. 31, fig. 4.

Scooper, Quaker (Queensland); Kupóupóu (Hawaiian Islands).

D. 10/13, 1; A. 3/12, 1; L. l. 46-48; L. tr. 5/1/13-14. Colour dark ivy-green above, lighter on sides and passing into nile-blue below; colours of back and sides are brightest in centres of each scale, the lighter edges forming a lattice pattern; a large zone on centre of sides, just beyond pectoral fin tip, is ochraceous-orange, anterior to which is a black spot which covers about 6 scales; head olive-green down to a pale and narrow orange line which extends horizontally back from gape to preopercle, below which it is deep sky-blue; dorsal with a pattern of reddish-pink vermiculated lines enclosing round whitish spots; anal similar in colour but with red and straw-coloured oblique lines, the red being wider than the straw colour; pectorals and ventrals hyaline, the latter with a greenish tinge; caudal with rays greenish, the membranes similar to dorsal; eye, pupil black, surrounded scarlet.

The species is subject to great colour variation. Although wide-ranging, being found from the South Pacific through the East Indies to the Red Sea, this elongate labrid is known in Australian waters only from Queensland, most examples having been taken in South Queensland (Moreton Bay), where it appears to be fairly common. Apparently rarely met with in the northern waters of the State. A good food-fish. Grows to 20 inches.

Anampses

Body oblong, rather deep, compressed, covered with moderate or large scales. Caudal peduncle compressed. Lateral line continuous. Head pointed, compressed, scaleless. Preopercle entire. Two prominent canines in each jaw, compressed and flared forward, with cutting edges. No posterior canines. Dorsal with 9 spines and 12 rays. Anal with 3 spines and 12 rays.

A genus of rather large dark-coloured fishes found in the Indo-Pacific. One species in Queensland.

311. SCRIBBLED WRASSE *Anampses geographicus* Cuvier and Valenciennes
[Plate 45]

Anampses geographicus Cuvier and Valenciennes, Hist. Nat. Poiss., 14, 1839, p. 10.
Anampses geographicus Bleeker, Atlas Ichth., 1, 1862, p. 102, pl. 25, fig. 3.

D. 9/12; A. 3/12; L. l. 51; L. tr. 10-11/1/19-21. "Head with many rather fine vermiculating lines, of which 2 or 3 sometimes continuous across snout, several also extend down across lower side of head, chest, and breast. . . .

"General shade olive with purplish tone anteriorly and blue posteriorly; vertical bar of scales bright blue with darker edges; dash of green above pectoral; on abdominal region vertical bars of scales changing to horizontal stripes, becoming dots along base of anal. Dorsal and anal with blue fronts and margins; body of dorsal olive below with reddish shade under marginal band, bright-blue line at its base throughout and two rows of small dots above, outer one fusing into an almost solid line. Anal body purplish, central band of blue breadth of pupil; basal line similar to that on dorsal but broader and a single row of more or less fusing dots between (the) central band. Caudal rays blue, membranes reddish becoming permanent colour to form two stripes to middle of lobes. Ventrals with blue fronts, line through rays more or less blue. Pectorals olive gray, rays more or less dusky, upper ray bright blue; blue bar across base, fleshy part below brownish; a second bar at base of fleshy part." (Fowler and Bean.)

A distinctively marked little fish found on the coral reefs of North Queensland. It is also found in Polynesia, the East Indies, Japan, and Mauritius. Grows to at least 6 inches.

Novaculichthys

Body oblong, compressed; scales large, about 26 to 28 in lateral line, which is interrupted below posterior end of soft dorsal and continued again on caudal peduncle. Head compressed, usually naked, the upper edge rather obtuse. Two front canines in each jaw curved; lateral teeth small, close-set, uniserial. Dorsal with 9 spines and 12 to 14 rays. Anal with 3 spines and 12 to 14 rays. Caudal rounded.

Fishes of the tropical waters of the Indo-Pacific and the Red Sea. Species few, one in Queensland.

312. BAR-CHEEKED WRASSE *Novaculichthys taeniourus* (Lacépède)
[Plate 45]

Labrus taeniourus Lacépède, Hist. Nat. Poiss., 3, 1802, pp. 448, 518.
Novaculichthys taeniourus Jordan and Evermann, Bull. U.S. Fish. Comm., 23, pt 1, 1903 (1905), p. 325, fig. 138.

D. 9/12-13; A. 3/12-14; L. l. 19-20 + 5-6; L. tr. 2-3/1/10. General body colour, with exception of belly, is dark olive-green, each scale with a light olive-green spot and broadly bordered dark green; belly bright russet, each scale edged with white; head a lighter green than body and passing into cadmium-yellow round the mouth-parts; 4 to 9 blackish bars radiating from eye; membranes of first two dorsal spines jet-black, with a bright lemon-chrome spot beneath; rest of dorsals with irregular bars and spots of similar colour to body; anal similar to soft dorsal; pectoral dusky olivaceous, and with a yellow sub-basal bar on fin-edge; axil black and inside of depressed fin is a black bar above and another below, both showing beyond the fin; ventrals dark reddish, the membranes black margined, the fin edged white posteriorly; caudal with a broad vertical yellow band at its base, rest of fin dark olive-green, with light greenish reticulations or spots. With age, the black bars on the head tend to disappear, leaving the head, in the adult, quite plain.

A handsome fish, readily recognized by its remarkable coloration, especially the "brick-wall" effect on the belly. Known in Australian waters from two examples caught on Hopkinson Reef, North Queensland, by G. Coates. Found also from Melanesia, Micronesia, and Polynesia to the East Indies, the Philippines, and Zanzibar. Grows to 10 inches.

Cheilinus

Body oblong or elongate, compressed, covered with large scales which form a more or less developed sheath at bases of dorsal and anal fins. Base of caudal covered by 3 very large scales. Snout large; lips thick. Teeth uniserial. Two canines in front of upper and also lower jaw. Lateral line interrupted. Dorsal spines 9 to 10, rays 9 to 11. Anal with 3 spines and 8 to 9 rays. Fins often filamentous.

A group of large or medium-sized deep-bodied fishes from the Indo-Pacific region, most of them adorned in colours of deep red and green, and with red Maori-like markings on the head, radiating from the eye. One of the species, *C. undulatus*, is the largest labroid in the Indo-Pacific region, reaching a length of over 7 feet. Seven species are found in Queensland waters.

KEY TO SPECIES IN QUEENSLAND

A. Dorsal spines, 9.

    b. Cheek scales cover, at least in part, lower preopercle flange; basal dorsal and anal scales usually elevated.

        c. Preopercle flange below entirely covered by cheek scales.

            d. Head pointed, colour olive-brown, head without spots or bands; size rather small.   *oxycephalus*

        cc. Preopercle flange only partly covered with scales of cheek; head obtuse, with spots and lines of red, but no lines on postocular; size rather large.   *trilobatus*

    bb. Preopercle flange naked; head with lines or vermiculations.

    e. Head and body deeper, more robust.

        f. Body with 6 broad dark transverse bands; no black lines from eye; size moderately large.   *fasciatus*

       ff. Body without transverse bands; each scale with one or more transverse or vertical red lines; 2 parallel black lines before eye and 2 shorter postocular; size very large.   *undulatus*

    ee. Head and body more slender, former pointed.

        g. Lower side of head with 8-9 blackish lines inclined backward.   *digrammus*

      gg. Grey or reddish lines, more or less radiating from eye.   *unifasciatus*

AA. Dorsal spines 10; olive-brown, each scale with one or more light dots or spots; fins spotted yellow.   *chlorourus*

313. SCARLET-BREASTED MAORI WRASSE *Cheilinus fasciatus* (Bloch)
[Colour-plate 47]

Sparus fasciatus Bloch, Nat. ausl. Fische, 5, 1791, p. 18.
Illustration by G. Coates.

    D. 9/10, 1; A. 3/8, 1; L. l. 20-21; L. tr. 2/1/5-7. Colour: Head dark green, with short scarlet bars radiating from eye, the anterior ones being longest; a broad vertical scarlet band extends from origin of spinous dorsal down to breast and anterior portion of belly, extending across opercles to behind eye; rest of body pinkish-red, with about 4 blackish vertical bands, the scales in their areas edged with black; one of the bands extends on to posterior portions of soft dorsal and anal fins for about half their depth; most of scales of body with small red spots; dorsals and anal fins scarlet, the membranes dusky-greyish, and with a narrow marginal border of blackish; red spots everywhere on both fins; pectorals and ventrals scarlet, without spots, the former with a black bar across its base; caudal scarlet, with red spots, a broad vertical black band medianally and a black border posteriorly.

    A very handsome fish found on the reefs of North Queensland, It is wide-ranging, being found also in Micronesia and the Gilbert Islands, the East Indies, Mauritius, East Africa, and the Red Sea. Grows to 14 inches.

314. HUMP-HEADED MAORI WRASSE *Cheilinus undulatus* Rüppell
[Colour-plate 47]

Cheilinus undulatus Rüppell, Neue Wirbelth., Fische, 1835, p. 20.
Illustration by G. Coates.

    Blue-tooth Groper (Queensland); Maori Cod (Gladstone); Giant Wrasse, Double-headed Parrot-fish (Townsville).

    D. 9/10, 1; A. 3/8, 1; L. l. 14-16 + 11; L. tr. 2/1/6. Colour: Top of head and along back rich dark purple, fading into green on upper sides and passing through light green into pale yellowish-green below; each scale of body with a broad basal vertical bar of dark violet, bordered on each side with parallel orange lines; these bars are more distinct above and posteriorly; scales of breast without the violet bar, being wanting altogether on scales of belly, which have about 10 narrow vermiculating orange-yellow vertical lines; these lines become much more numerous and wavy on scales of breast, finally becoming densely vermiculated towards isthmus; head purplish above, the cheeks and opercles pale green; lips greenish, passing into pale violet on throat; a pattern of wavy vermiculating lines over whole of head, those on upper parts of head and snout being purplish; similar vermiculating lines of bright orange over cheeks and opercles; those on branchiostegals and pectoral base indian-red; 2 dark-brown or blackish lines forward from eye to maxillary and 2 backward towards suprascapula separate the two colour-zones of vermiculating lines; dorsal purplish-grey, thickly spotted with orange-yellow spots on spinous portion but changing into vertical dark orange-yellow or sepia lines on soft dorsal; anal and caudal similar to soft dorsal, the latter edged posteriorly with orange-yellow; pectorals and ventrals very pale green, the former pencilled with very fine vertical orange lines.

One of the most beautiful labroids, and also the largest, in the Indo-Pacific region. Although its colours vary somewhat with age, the pattern remains very much the same. Large examples develop a big fleshy crest or hump on the head above and in advance of the eye, somewhat similar to that of the Snapper, *Chrysophrys auratus*. A large fish caught at Hayman Island, Whitsunday Group, North Queensland, and called a Blue-tooth Groper was probably this species. It measured 7 feet 6 inches in length and weighed 420 pounds.

On the Queensland coast north of Bundaberg the species is commonly caught in the deeper waters of the reefs along the edges of the coral shelf. Outside Australia it is wide-ranging being found from Oceania and the East Indies to the Red Sea and East Africa.

OTHER SPECIES

Plain-faced Maori Wrasse, *C. oxycephalus*. A small fish from the East Indies and Philippines found on the reefs of North Queensland. Grows to only $4\frac{1}{2}$ inches.

Trilobed Maori Wrasse, *C. trilobatus*. Another handsome fish found on the reefs of North Queensland. It also occurs in the South Seas, the East Indies and across to East Africa, and in Japan. Grows to 18 inches. Like many species of fishes in this family, the males have the caudal fin trilobate, the outer and middle rays being produced.

Violet-lined Maori Wrasse, *C. digrammus*. A beautiful wide-ranging fish known in Australian waters from the reefs of Queensland, more commonly north of the Capricorns. Grows to 15 inches.

Ring-tail Maori Wrasse, *C. unifasciatus*. Has been recorded from Lady Musgrave Island in the Bunker Group, off Bundaberg, and also occurs from the East Indies to Hawaii. Grows to 16 inches.

Yellow-dotted Maori Wrasse, *C. chlorourus*. Readily known by its ten dorsal spines and yellow-spotted body. Grows to 12 inches. Fairly common on the coral reefs of Queensland, and found also in the South Seas and the East Indies.

Hemipteronotus

Body oblong, rather deep, strongly compressed. Head deep, the dorsal profile with a sharp edge, strongly curved, sloping down almost vertically from before eyes to snout. Body with large scales, those on belly smaller; head naked, except for small scales on cheeks. Lateral line interrupted. Mouth moderate, low; no hind canines. Dorsal with 9 spines, the first two separated from the others; rays 12. Anal with 3 spines and 12 rays.

Fishes of the temperate tropical and subtropical coasts of the Indo-Pacific region, the Mediterranean, and the Red Sea. One species in Queensland.

315. KEEL-HEAD *Hemipteronotus jacksonensis* (Ramsay) [Plate 45]

Novacula jacksonensis Ramsay, Proc. Linn. Soc. N.S.Wales, 6, pt 2, 1881, p. 198.
Novaculichthys jacksonensis Waite, Mem. Austr. Mus., 4, 1899, p. 87, pl. 15.

D. 2, 7/12; A. 3/12; L. l. 22 + 6; L. tr. 3/11. Colour: "Opalescent, translucent salmon tint, with oblique blue hair-lines on the dorsal surface, one to each scale, lost about the lateral line. Two or three rows of scales bordering the ventral fin and extending along the lower side of the caudal peduncle were marked each with a large blue blotch at its base. All the fins orange, the dorsal and anal marked with oblique wavy blue lines and the tail with 5 bars of the same colour. Eye orange." (Waite.)

A rare southern species from New South Wales and Lord Howe Island, known in Queensland waters as a straggler. Grows to 7½ inches.

Family **Neoodacidae**

Form oblong or very elongate. Scales small or moderate. Lateral line continuous. Teeth in jaws coalescent, forming a sharp-edged plate. Dorsal spines numerous (16 to 24), flexible.

A small family of fishes found in the coastal waters of temperate Australia and New Zealand. One genus, *Olisthops*, with a single species is found in Queensland.

316. HERRING CALE *Olisthops cyanomelas* Richardson [Plate 45]

Olisthops cyanomelas Richardson, Proc. Zool. Soc. Lond., 12th Nov. 1850, p. 75.
Olisthops cyanomelas McCulloch, Rec. Austr. Mus., 13, no. 2, 20th July 1920, p. 69, pl. 14, fig. 3.

D. 18/9; A. 3/9; L. l. 52; L. tr. 7/15. Female: "Head and body olive-brown above, changing to rich orange on the sides and light salmon-colour on the belly, when in a fresh condition. Head with anastomosing dark blue lines and spots, which become pale green and less numerous on the upper surface. Each scale of the body with a large dark blue spot, which is often elongate and coalescent with its neighbours. Spinous dorsal transparent orange-brown, with a few pale green spots on the spines; soft dorsal, anal, and caudal orange like the body, with dark blue lines and spots between the rays. Pectoral olive-brown with blue lines and spots. Ventral orange and pink, mottled with olive. Eye light green and pale gold." (McCulloch.)

Male: "In the male the body is of a uniform bluish-black above; and a little lighter below. There is a bright blue band near the outer margin of each caudal lobe, and a similar one on each side near the upper margins of the pectoral fins." (Stead.)

This species exhibits an extraordinary range of variation in its colour, and Stead[42] records a male example which "possessed all the colours of the female"; but, as he remarks, "this is of very unusual occurrence".

This rock-dwelling fish, which mainly inhabits the cooler waters of the southern portions of the continent of Australia, occasionally straggles into Moreton Bay. Being of a herbivorous nature it is seldom taken by hook and line. Grows to 18 inches.

Family **Callyodontidae: Parrot-fishes**

Brilliantly coloured fishes, mostly of large size, inhabiting coral reefs and rocky formations in tropical seas, being especially numerous in the Indo-Pacific region.

Although very similar to the Labridae in general form, colour, and scales, they differ in having the teeth more or less fused into a parrot-like "beak", a character which varies in the different genera. Posterior or hind canines may be present or absent. The much enlarged lower pharyngeals are united in a spoon-shaped body on which their teeth are arranged in a mosaic. The dorsal and anal spines are not very strong, being very similar to and not clearly differentiated from the rays. In most of the species the points of the spines do not stand out from the fin as in most fishes, a condition no doubt readily understood when their actions are observed on the coral reefs. They have the curious habit of lying on their sides under the coral boulders and in shallow crevices or of forcing their way through horizontal cracks in the reefs. Such actions would

---

[42] Stead, *Fish. Austr.*, 1906, p. 147.

no doubt tend to check or impede their progress if naked and stiff spines were present.

Parrot-fishes feed mainly upon vegetable matter and invertebrates, their strong "beaks" readily crushing molluscs and corals alike. They may be observed on the Great Barrier Reef moving in schools in the shallows and tearing at and feeding upon the various coral growths. After such a meal large parrot-fishes frequently allow themselves to be cleaned by schools of wrasse. William Beebe, the well-known American marine biologist, gives an account in one of his fascinating books[43] of what he calls, "an interesting exchange of courtesy". He says: "Once I saw an interesting exchange of courtesy, one which I have observed many times when diving near shore. The giant caerulean parrot-fish browse on hard coral as a horse tears off mouthfuls of grass. After an interval of feeding, when the teeth and jaws and scales of the head are covered with debris, the fish upends in mid-water and holds itself motionless while a school of passing wrasse, all tiny in comparison with the big fish, rush from all sides and begin a systematic cleaning of the large fish's head. As in most relationships between different species of animals this is founded on mutual benefit, the parrot-fish getting a free cleaning, and the wrasse finding a supply of particles of food ready at hand".

Although of good edible quality, parrot-fishes are rarely seen in Queensland markets because their feeding habits preclude their capture by hook and line. A comparatively easy method of obtaining them is by means of a short-handled spear, with which they may be impaled as they attempt to hide beneath the coral growths in shallow water.

The family is composed of only a few genera, but the species are numerous. Three genera are found in Queensland waters.

KEY TO GENERA IN QUEENSLAND

A. A single series of scales on the cheek.

    b. Inner upper lip developed all round, separated from the outer lip. Teeth in upper jaw coalesced, those in lower jaw in overlapping rows.   *Leptoscarus*

    bb. Inner upper lip only developed posteriorly, its anterior end adnate to the outer lip. Mandibular teeth imbricate anteriorly.   *Cryptotomus*

AA. Two to four series of scales on the cheek. Inner upper lip only developed posteriorly. Teeth fused into plates, covering the jaw.   *Callyodon*

[43] *Half-mile Down*, 1935, p. 142.

Leptoscarus

Body elongate, compressed, covered with large scales. Large scales on cheeks and opercles. Upper lip double all round. Teeth separated, imbricate, in regular oblique rows in both jaws, entirely hiding dental plate; outer teeth form cutting edges to both jaws. Lateral line interrupted or bent down posteriorly. Dorsal spines 9, flexible. Anal with 3 spines and 9 rays.

Two species inhabit the tropical Pacific, both found in Queensland.

KEY TO SPECIES IN QUEENSLAND

A.   A row of canines anteriorly in the upper jaw.   *caeruleopunctatus*

AA. No canines in the upper jaw.   *vaigiensis*

317. MARBLED PARROT-FISH *Leptoscarus vaigiensis* (Quoy and Gaimard)
[Plate 46]
Scarus vaigiensis Quoy and Gaimard, Voy. Uranie, Zool., 18th Dec. 1824, p. 288.
Scarichthys auritus Bleeker, Atlas Ichth., 1, 1862, p. 15, pl. 1, fig. 3.

D. 9/10 (11); A. 3/9 (10); L. 1. 25; L. tr. 1½/1/6-7. Living colours: General colour olive-brown above passing into olive-green on sides and then into very pale greenish-cream below; back mottled with dark brown, sides mottled with brick-red, belly with flecks of yellowish; cheeks with flecks of brick-red and pinkish; eye, pupil black, surrounded by ring of orange, then pale green; lower lip dull orange; dorsal mainly hyaline, a few patches of brick-red on anterior half and with brick-red spots and blotches on all rays and spines which are olive-brown; pectorals very pale orange-yellow; ventrals pale orange, the rays mainly hyaline, with blotches of red; anal orange, with irregular blotches of dark red; caudal olive-yellow with spots of hyaline and blotches of darker olive, forming a reticulation.

A species found from Queensland and New Guinea through the East Indies and Indian seas to the east coast of Africa. Also recorded from Fiji in the South Seas. Known by its teeth and its unusual coloration. Not commonly met with. Grows to 16 inches.

OTHER SPECIES

Blue-spotted Parrot-fish, *L. caeruleopunctatus*. Has been recorded in Australian waters only from Dunwich, Stradbroke Island, South Queensland. It ranges through the East Indies to India, Mauritius, Zanzibar, and the Red Sea. Grows to 11 inches.

Cryptotomus

Body oblong, compressed, covered with large scales. Inner upper lip only developed at sides, not continued in middle and adnate to outer lip. Teeth coalesced but not to a smooth beak, each more or less visible individually. Lateral line scales with arborescent tubes, the line bent downwards or interrupted below end of dorsal. Dorsal with 9 flexible spines and 10 (11) branched rays. Anal with 3 flexible spines and 9 (10) rays.

Fishes of the tropical and subtropical waters of the Indo-Pacific and western Atlantic. Species few, one in Queensland.

318. HALF-TOOTHED PARROT-FISH *Cryptotomus spinidens* (Quoy and Gaimard) [Plate 46]

Scarus spinidens Quoy and Gaimard, Voy. Uranie, Zool., 28th Dec. 1824, p. 289.
Callyodon spinidens Bleeker, Atlas Ichth., Ned. Ind. 1, 1862, p. 13, pl. 2, fig. 2.

D. 9/10 (11); A. 3/9 (10); L. l. 24-25; L. tr. $1\frac{1}{2}/1/7$. Life colours: General colour above olive-brown, finely dotted with darker brown; sides very pale green, passing into whitish below; several incomplete fawn-coloured brownish-ringed ocelli on back and sides; dorsal hyaline-fawn, mottled with pale reddish-brown; pectorals hyaline, with pale yellowish tinge; ventrals whitish, with a few flecks of pale fawn; anal deep cream, with brick-red markings deepest basally; caudal pale olive, with fawnish markings and a series of darker spots along upper and lower edges.

This species has been recorded in Australian waters only from Moreton Bay, South Queensland. Found in the tropical waters of the Indo-Pacific and western Atlantic. Grows to about $11\frac{1}{2}$ inches.

Callyodon

Body robust, compressed, covered with large scales. Lower jaw included within upper. Lips variably cover or expose teeth. Teeth in jaws fully coalesced, surface like mosaic; edges of teeth mostly even; sometimes hind canines are present. Lateral line interrupted or bent down posteriorly. Dorsal with 9 flexible spines and 10 (11) soft rays. Caudal rounded, truncate or emarginate, the lobes often attenuated.

The members of this genus, which is the great central group of parrot-fishes, are brilliantly coloured herbivorous fishes of large or moderate size, especially plentiful in Polynesia and the East Indies, which is the centre of distribution, though several extend their range to Australia and the West Indies and some to Japan and the Red Sea. The larger species are good food-fishes. Their brilliant colours fade rapidly after death and it is often very difficult to identify the species. Eight species are found in Queensland.

A.   Preopercle flange below always scaleless.

    b. Cheek with 2 rows of scales.

       c. Lips cover teeth; 2 pale transverse bands at front of anal.   *mutabilis*

       cc. Lips narrow, usually cover basal half of teeth; no transverse bands before anal; a reddish-violet spot at pectoral base.   *cyanotaenia*

    bb. Cheek with 3 rows of scales.

       d. Head and trunk finely speckled or spotted above with rosy or reddish.   *pulchellus*

AA. Preopercle flange below with at least one scale, usually 2-4 (rarely preopercle flange entirely scaleless in *Callyodon dubius*).

    e. Cheek with 2 rows of scales.

       f. Dorsals with longitudinal median or partly median band.

          g. Female turquoise-blue, each scale edged with bright yellow; male bright light-green above, dull coral-red below, each scale with basal blotch of coral-red.   *fasciatus*

       ff. Dorsals without median longitudinal band, edges and bases sometimes narrowly blue or green.

       h. Snout and interorbitals without cross-bands or stripes.

          i. Olive-green above, pale violet below; 2-3 whitish longitudinal lines on side of abdomen.   *dubius*

       hh. Snout or interorbitals with one or more blue or green cross-bands or stripes.

          j. Profile of head markedly convex. Forehead bright violet; anterior part of back down to pectoral closely spotted with bright blue-green; 3 blue stripes on side of belly.   *globiceps*

          jj. Profile of head moderately convex. Greenish above, salmon-pink below, each scale with a vertical elongate reddish or dark area; belly salmon-pink; head similar.   *pyrrhostethus*

    ee. Cheek with 3 rows of scales.

       k. Lower portion of head, trunk, and tail dark grey, spotted in strong contrast with blackish; fins uniform, vertical ones edged narrowly with blue.   *bicolor*

322

319. SURF PARROT-FISH *Callyodon fasciatus* (Cuvier and Valenciennes)
[Colour-plate 48]

Scarus fasciatus Cuvier and Valenciennes, Hist. Nat. Poiss., 14, 1839, p. 222.
Illustrations by T. C. Marshall (male) and G. Coates (female).

D. 9/10, 1; A. 3/9, 1; L. l. 19-20, 5 or 6 + 2; L. tr. 2/1/6. Female: Turquoise-blue, each scale edged with bright yellow; head yellow, with 4 curved lines of blue around eye, one directed forward, 2 posteriorly, and one below; a similar line along edge of upper lip and 2 to 3 on chin and throat; dorsals and anal yellow, edged blue and a blue longitudinal line basally, the former with a row of blue spots medianally and a latter with orange marks medianally on membranes; pectorals and ventrals yellow, blue on edge anteriorly; caudal yellow, edged above and below with blue.

Male: Body light bright-green above, passing into dull coral-red or pinkish-red below; each scale with a basal blotch of coral-red, most distinct on back and upper sides; head salmon-orange with vermiculations of pale green; pupil of eye black, surrounded pale yellow, the lid above dark green; dorsal salmon-orange, with a row of pale-green spots medianally; a line which edges the full length of the fin is blue-green as is also the first spine; pectorals pale green, with a longitudinal mark of salmon-orange; ventrals wax-yellow, membranes almost hyaline, the spine blue-green; anal with the first spine and edge of fin blue-green, rest of fin coral-red, with a row of round pale-green spots basally; caudal salmon-orange, with elongate spots of pale green basally and short narrow bars of blue-green terminally, those on the upper and lower edge extending along the full edge of fin.

The Surf Parrot-fish is commonly seen on the Great Barrier Reef swimming in schools of thirty or forty, especially at low tide in the numerous coral pools. At the first sign of the rising tide they are to be observed in numbers fighting their way in over the edge of the reef to gain entrance to the lagoons, often swimming on their sides in water of only half their own depth or feeding upside down with tails out of the shallow water.

This species inhabits the waters of North Queensland, Melanesia, Polynesia, and the East Indies, also the Philippines and India. Grows to a length of 20 inches and a weight of at least 5 pounds. A good food-fish, with white, flaky flesh of excellent flavour.

OTHER SPECIES

Variable Parrot-fish, *C. mutabilis*. A beautiful fish found on the reefs of North Queensland. It ranges through Micronesia, Melanesia, and Polynesia to Japan, the Philippines, the East Indies, and Zanzibar. Grows to only 12 inches.

Red Parrot-fish, *C. cyanotaenia*. Previously known only from Java, but now recorded from Queensland at both ends of the State, namely Moreton Bay and Torres Strait. Grows to 17 inches.

Red-spotted Parrot-fish, *C. pulchellus*. A green fish with red spots, this is a wide-ranging species which inhabits North Queensland waters. Grows to 26 inches.

White-lined Parrot-fish, *C. dubius*. Most variable in its coloration, this fish is common on the reefs of North Queensland. Also found in Micronesia, Melanesia, and Polynesia, through the East Indies to Mauritius. Grows to 14 inches.

Violet-lined Parrot-fish, *C. globiceps*. A species from Micronesia and Polynesia which is fairly commonly found on the Great Barrier Reef in North Queensland. Readily recognized by its very convex forehead and blue-green scale-spots. Grows to 10 inches.

Flame-breasted Parrot-fish, *C. pyrrhostethus*. Commonly met with on the reefs of North Queensland, Torres Strait, and the Northern Territory. It is very variable in colour and grows to 21 inches.

Spotted Parrot-fish, *C. bicolor*. Readily recognized by its unique colour pattern. First recorded from Australian waters at Mackay. Grows to at least 20 inches.

DIVISION *Ammodytiformes*

Family **Ammodytidae: Sand Lances or Sand Eels**

A small family of slender silvery fishes found in both Arctic and tropical seas, living in shoals close inshore and with the habit of burying themselves in the sand in shallow water. In most of the tropical genera the body is covered with ordinary scales, but in those from northern Europe and other parts the body is scarcely scaly but has delicate, oblique cross-folds of skin. The many-rayed dorsal fin is without spines, and the ventral fins, when present, are jugular—that is, situated far forward at a point distinctly before the pectorals. Some of the species grow to at least 17 inches but are not valued as food. They are known in America as Sand Launce or Lant.

One genus with a single species (*Bleekeria vaga*) is found in Queensland.

Bleekeria

Body elongate, low, compressed, covered with scales of moderate size. No ventral fins. Vent remote from head. One long dorsal; anal of moderate length. Jaws and palate without teeth. Gill-openings very wide; gill-membranes not united. No free longitudinal fold of skin along each side of the ventral surface.

Small elongate fishes of the Indo-Pacific. Species few, one in Queensland.

320. Species number not allocated.

321. SAND LANCE *Bleekeria vaga* (McCulloch and Waite)   [Plate 46]
Bleekeria vaga McCulloch and Waite, Trans. Roy. Soc. Sth Austr., 40, 1916, p. 447, pl. 43, fig. 1.

D. 48; A. 22; L. l. 107 + 5; L. tr. 3/1/8. Colour in preservative uniform sandy-yellow, the opercles blackish. Probably silvery in life.

This interesting fish, originally described from Lord Howe Island and since

recorded from Shellharbour, New South Wales, has now been taken at Cowan
Cowan, Moreton Bay, South Queensland. Grows to at least 6½ inches.

DIVISION *Trachiniformes*

Family **Opisthognathidae: Smilers or Jaw-fishes**

A small but interesting family of carnivorous fishes of small or moderate size,
inhabiting rocky and coralline bottoms of tropical and temperate seas. Their
bodies are more or less covered with small cycloid scales, and the incomplete
lateral line, which ceases below the anterior dorsal rays, runs close to and
parallel with the dorsal contour. The distinctive feature is the large naked
head with its strongly curved anterior profile, and the big, deeply cleft, wide
mouth which has earned them the name of "smilers" or "jaw-fishes".

The eminent Australian ichthyologist, the late James Douglas Ogilby,[44]
writing of the family stated: "The Opisthognathidae, though weak in point of
numbers, forms a most interesting family of trachiniform percoids; it consists
of fishes of small or moderate size, inhabiting rocky and coralline bottoms
within the tropical and temperate zones. Its distribution is peculiar, no species
having so far been recorded from the Mediterranean nor the Eastern Atlantic,
nor from any of the Pacific Islands, nor the West Coast of the Americas, except
the Gulf of California, where an isolated colony, comprised of five species,
exists. The extreme limits of their polar range lie between lat. 40° N., where
Gnathypops hopkinsi has been taken off Misaki, Japan, and lat. 34° S., where
Merogymnus jacksoniensis is found.

"These fishes are everywhere of rare occurrence, many of the species being
only known from the single example described. The 'Smilers', to give them the
local vernacular name bestowed upon them, so a friend tells me, 'because of
their fine countenance', are essentially carnivorous and rock-loving fishes,
delighting in boulder-strewn shoals and coral reefs at a moderate depth. Hence
we find that in America as here many of the species are only known from offshore snapper grounds and similar localities, where they are occasionally taken
by hand-line in company with more valuable fishes or even from the latter
when captured disgorging them.

"The species vary greatly in coloration, some of them, such as my *Merogymnus eximius*, being arrayed in a livery of most gorgeous splendour, while
others, as my *Gnathypops inornata*, are soberly clad in uniform brown.

"One of our species, *G. maculata*, is said by the pearl-fishers to scoop holes
in the sand among the sea-fan forests of our tropic seas, from which it sallies
forth to pounce upon a passing prey, returning again to its lair after each
excursion."

---

[44] *Mem. Qld Mus.*, 7, pt 1, 1920, p. 22.

W. H. Longley[45] gives some interesting information from personal observation when "equipped with a diving hood in the unknown world of coral labyrinths at the bottom of the sea". He writes: "*Gnathypops aurifrons* prepares its own shelter in sandy places where the substratum is sufficiently compact to make successful tunnelling possible. Jaws and gaping mouth are its only entrenching tools, but meet its every need. It is found not uncommonly upon the open reef in little colonies, the formation of which is probably due in part to the discontinuous occurrence of suitable bottom rather than to the social instincts of the fishes themselves. During the day, if undisturbed, *Gnathypops* may be regularly observed resting nearly motionless in a semivertical position above its burrow. When alarmed it retreats into its hole tail foremost and conceals itself until the disturbance outside has ceased. Then it reappears cautiously, its beady black eyes being so situated that it is able to sweep the horizon with minimum exposure. If nothing happens to renew its alarm, it mounts a little further until its ventral fins are free, rests for a moment in the mouth of its burrow, and finally rises easily and gracefully to its original position.

"Still another of these fishes (as yet unidentified) shows a different variation of the tubiculous instinct. It lives in holes, quite possibly worm-tubes, which it discovers ready formed in pieces of dead coral upon the bottom. Its most striking structural feature is the immense dorsal fin, which when raised seems nearly as high as the fish is long. Its most interesting habit is that of protruding its body for about half its length from the chamber it occupies, and then elevating and depressing its great fin rapidly as if it were wigwagging in piscine code. This impression is heightened when two individuals separated by no great distance stand erect and repeat the performance in alternation."

Ogilby[46] further remarked on these curious creatures: "Nothing is known as to the breeding habits of these fishes, nor have I ever seen an example with ripe spawn, though all those which I have handled were fully adult. That the young are never found along the foreshore nor in the debris of the seine net seems to demonstrate the dermersal character of the ova. No data are available as to their edible qualities, unless it be that of an aquaintance, who took one home, and had it fried; he told me it was 'as good as any other rockfish'. On account of their scarcity and the difficulty of obtaining them all the species are greatly in request for museum collections, and every example should, therefore, be carefully preserved and forwarded, with as little delay as possible, to the nearest scientific institution."

About eight genera and thirty-two species are now recognized. Two genera are found in Queensland.

---

[45] *Amer. Mus. Journ.*, 18, Feb. 1918, p 81.
[46] Ogilby, *loc. cit.*

KEY TO GENERA IN QUEENSLAND

A. Dorsal spines 10-11. Jaws with bands of villiform
teeth, the outer row scarcely larger than the others. *Merogymnus*

AA. Dorsal spines 12. Teeth of outer row in jaws larger
than the others, except for an inner row of strong
teeth in lower jaw. *Tandya*

Merogymnus

Differs from *Tandya* in having the greater part of the body naked, the teeth
subequal in size, without any conspicuously enlarged ones, and the gill-rakers
more numerous, longer, and slender.

A genus of brightly coloured fishes of small size, inhabiting the eastern and
south-eastern coasts of Australia. Two species are known, both found in
Queensland.

KEY TO SPECIES

A. Scales very small, covering about half the sides and
belly; spines and rays of dorsal fin gradually increasing
in height. *eximius*

AA. Scales larger, but narrowly entering the trunk; belly
naked; spines of dorsal fin much lower than rayed
portion, the first ray of which is abruptly higher. *jacksoniensis*

322. HARLEQUIN SMILER *Merogymnus eximius* Ogilby [Plate 46]

Merogymnus eximius Ogilby, Proc. Roy. Soc. Qld, 21, 1908, p. 18; and Qld Mem. Mus., 7, pt 1, 1920,
p. 24, pl. 2.

D. 11/13; A. 1/12. Colour golden or golden-brown above; sides with two
series of large round or oval golden spots, separated by broad blue interlacing
bands; abdominal region and extremity of tail violet, with splashes of greenish-
gold; head lilaceous, with irregular violet spots and bars; a deep-blue blotch,
prolonged upwards as an uneven band on the opercle; branchiostegal region
blackish; outer part of spinous dorsal dark olive-green, narrowly bordered
above with purple, below with pale blue; the lower band is continued to the
end of the soft dorsal, the outer half of which is pale olive-green, with part
of the membrane blue, as also is the base. Anal blue, with a median and a
basal series of golden spots. Caudal rays olive-green or purple, the interradial
membrane blue. Pectoral pale yellowish-brown, the base with one or two
vertical blue bars. Ventral bluish-black.

A handsome fish known only from the waters of Queensland. It ranges as
far north as the Capricorns but is more frequently met with in South Queensland, where it is not uncommon. Said to be a good edible species. Grows to
14½ inches.

OTHER SPECIES

Southern Smiler, *M. jacksoniensis*. This species is confined, so far as is known, to the waters of Moreton Bay in South Queensland (where several have been taken) and to the waters of New South Wales; but the fish is rarely seen in the latter State, though originally found there at Port Jackson.

Tandya

Body wholly covered with scales. Maxillary extending well beyond hind margin of eye. Teeth of outer row in jaws larger than the others, except for an inner row of strong teeth in the lower jaw. Dorsal with 12 simple spines. Caudal rounded.

A genus of more or less sombre-coloured fishes found in the tropical waters of Australia and also in the Aru Islands. Of the four known species two are found in the waters of Queensland.

KEY TO SPECIES IN QUEENSLAND

Adapted from Whitley[47]

A. Teeth in several rows. Head spotted. Lateral line extending to below tenth dorsal ray. Depth about one-fourth of standard length. Body with many small spots.   *maculata*

AA. Teeth in a single row, except for a few supernumerary ones. Head not spotted. Lateral line extending to below fourth or fifth dorsal ray. Depth about one-third of standard length. Body with a few large dark blotches.   *latitabunda*

323. SPECKLED PUG *Tandya maculata* (Alleyne and Macleay)
[Colour-plate 48]

Opisthognathus maculatus Alleyne and Macleay, Proc. Linn. Soc. N.S.Wales, 1877, p. 280.
Illustration by G. Coates.

Speckled Smiler (Queensland).

Colour: "Pale rufous-brown, scarcely lighter below, everywhere spotted with dark blue or black, the spots largest on the upper part of the trunk and tail, smallest on the head; a large blackish or smoky-brown blotch beneath the appressed pectoral. Spinous dorsal sparsely, pectorals profusely spotted; the outer fins immaculate." (Ogilby.)

Occasionally captured in the waters of North Queensland and the Northern Territory. Found also in the Aru Islands. It is said to be a good edible fish. Grows to 17 inches.

---

[47] *Rec. Austr. Mus.*, 20, no. 1, 1937, p. 22.

OTHER SPECIES

Spotted Pug, *T. latitabunda*. Known only from the unique holotype caught at
Port Newry, north of Mackay, North Queensland. Measures 10¼ inches in
total length.

Family **Parapercidae**: Weevers

Body elongate, robust, cylindrical, covered with small scales. Lateral line
complete. One long dorsal fin with a few spines anteriorly. Anal long, with or
without spines anteriorly. Mouth large, with thick lips. Generally villiform
bands of teeth in the jaws with larger canines. Teeth present on vomer and
sometimes on palatines. Caudal rounded in the young, the lobes produced
in the adults.

A group of prettily coloured goby-like fishes of small or moderate size
inhabiting the middle Pacific. Like the true weevers, Trachinidae, which are
found on the coasts of Europe and West Africa, they are able to inflict very
painful wounds with the pungent dorsal and opercular spines. One genus in
Queensland waters.

Parapercis

Form elongate, body cylindrical. Head somewhat depressed. Dorsal with
4 to 5 spines and 19 to 23 rays, the soft portion much higher than the spinous.
Anal shorter than soft dorsal, with or without a weak spine and with 16 to 21
rays.

Fishes of the Red Sea and the tropical and subtropical waters of the Indo-
Pacific. Species few, four in Queensland waters.

KEY TO SPECIES IN QUEENSLAND

Adapted from McCulloch's key to the Australian species *Parapercis*[48]

A. Lateral line following the curve of the back; cheek scales
large. *cylindrica*

AA. Lateral line extending along middle of sides posteriorly;
cheek scales minute.

b. No blue lines crossing upper surface of head; outer
caudal rays not filiform.

c. Lower jaw much longer than the upper. *stricticeps*

cc. Jaws subequal. *hexophthalmus*

bb. Narrow blue lines between the eyes and crossing
the snout; outer caudal rays filiform. *nebulosus*

---

[48] *Biol. Res. Endeavour*, 2, pt 3, 1914, p. 154.

324. BAR-FACED WEEVER *Parapercis nebulosus* (Quoy and Gaimard)
[Colour-plate 49]

Percis nebulosus Quoy and Gaimard, Voy. Uranie, 1825, p. 349.
Illustration by G. Coates.

Sand Smelt (South Africa).

D. 5/22; A. 1/18-20; L. l. 78-85; L. tr. 6/20. Colour in life bright reddish-pink above, the scales outlined with darker edges; 6 to 7 red saddle-like bands across back extending down sides half-way, where they fade out into the clean white of the belly; head pink with 2 broad red bands across cheeks downwards, one from snout to chin, the other from behind eye to edge of preopercle; eye, pupil black, surrounded scarlet, the scarlet colour entering the black pupil above, causing it to look dented; a bright-yellow horizontal bar below; inter-orbital (eye to eye) with 3 bright-blue lines; 3 narrow blue lines from anterior edge of eye to lips, another curved one between these across snout; dorsals: spinous black on membranes, the spines creamy; soft dorsal almost hyaline, the outer half or almost half with faint pink spots; pectorals hyaline-pink; ventrals with their under-surface pale pinkish, upper surface dusky blackish on membranes, pinkish distally and with the rays whitish; anal white, the outer third dark red and with oblique pink bars and spots on its basal one-third; caudal pink, becoming dark red on its lower edge and orange-yellow on dorsal or upper edge; about 6 to 8 vertical reddish-brown bars over whole fin.

This fish, which is well known from South Queensland, New South Wales, and Western Australia, also occurs in South Africa. Fifteen examples were trawled in Queensland by the *Endeavour* in 1910. They were taken off Bustard Head, Fraser Island, and Double Island Point at depths ranging from 11 to 29 fathoms. The species does not appear to be well known in North Queensland.

In young examples the caudal is slightly emarginate, with the outer angles pointed, but in older fishes the outer rays are prolonged into filaments. Grows to 12 inches.

OTHER SPECIES

Sharp-nosed Weever, *P. cylindrica*. A small, well-marked species found in the waters of North Queensland. It occurs also in Micronesia, Polynesia, the East Indies, China, and the Philippines. Grows to 4 inches.

Black-barred Weever, *P. stricticeps*. A handsome fish known only from the waters of South Queensland. It is closely related to *P. hexophthalmus*, but is easily distinguished by its longer lower jaw and its coloration. Grows to 8½ inches.

Spotted Weever, *P. hexophthalmus*. Although perhaps common, this species is rarely seen or captured by the casual observer in Queensland. It has been recorded from each end of the State. Grows to 12 inches.

Family **Uranoscopidae: Star-gazers**

The star-gazers are bottom-dwelling carnivorous fishes inhabiting the mud and sand off the shores of most warm and tropical seas. They are characterized by the large cuboid head, which is bony, broad, and flat above and on which are situated the small eyes, looking upward as though gazing at the stars. Granular ossifications are developed on the roof and sides of the head, the mouth is almost vertical, the lower jaw being pushed well forward, and the lips are usually fringed. The body is naked or covered with small scales, and the spinous dorsal is short and may be wanting.

The common Star-gazer of the Mediterranean, *Uranoscopus scaber*, was well known to the ancient Greeks, who called it the Agnos or Holy Fish; they also knew it as the Ouranoscopos or Heavenward-looking Fish.

The Star-gazer is a very poor swimmer, so much so that as soon as it suspends its tail and fin movements it sinks to the bottom like a stone. It does not seem to be capable of the quiet floating practised by most other fishes. After sinking down onto the bottom and giving a few vigorous shovelling movements of the large pectoral fins it buries itself in the sand until only the mouth and eyes are exposed. Here it lies quietly, the only signs of its presence being a slight and regular disturbance of the sand as water is expelled from the gills or by a rapid movement of the eyes.

It obtains its prey in a somewhat similar manner to the angler-fishes, Antennariidae, insomuch as a lure is used to attract the victim within reach of its jaws. A delicate filament, which is attached to the floor of the mouth, projects through the mouth opening and is agitated by the creature. When a small fish, mistaking this filament for a worm in the sand, approaches within reach of the jaws there is a swirl of sand as the jaws open and close over the hitherto un-suspecting prey.

In one genus of star-gazers, *Astroscopus*, electric organs are present in the form of two oval areas of considerable size placed immediately behind the eyes and derived from portions of the eye-muscles. The fish is said to be capable of giving off a vigorous electric shock of painful intensity.

Eight genera and about twenty-five species of star-gazers are known, two genera (each with a single species) being found in Queensland waters.

KEY TO GENERA IN QUEENSLAND

A. One dorsal fin. No humeral spine. Humeral region
    with a fringed appendage.   *Ichthyscopus*

AA. Two dorsal fins. A strong humeral spine present. No
    fringed humeral appendage.   *Uranoscopus*

Ichthyscopus

Form robust. Covered with small scales regularly arranged in oblique cross-series. Head large, bony above. Cheeks naked, preopercle unarmed, covered with soft skin, fringed behind. Humeral projection fringed. Dorsal fin single; no spinous dorsal.

Fishes of the waters of India, Japan, and Australia. Species few, one in Queensland.

325. STAR-GAZER *Ichthyscopus lebeck* (Schneider) [Colour-plate 49]

Uranoscopus le Beck Schneider, in Bloch, Syst. Ichth., 1801, p. 47.
Illustration by G. Coates.

D. 4 + 16-18; A. 16-19. Colour: Upper surface of head, along back and upper sides brownish, enclosing pure white, round or oval spots, those on the head and nape being small and round, whilst those on the back and sides are elongate and large, forming 2 elongate irregular bars over the caudal peduncle and sometimes a long similar one on upper sides; a large dark-brown blotch on upper cheek; a broad dark diffused blotch across back anteriorly to origin of dorsal fin, extends down behind pectoral fins; pectoral dark, margined with creamy white; dorsal similar to back; ventrals and anal creamy white, the latter with the basal half dusky brown; caudal dusky brown with yellowish streaks.

Some examples are very pale and are without the round or oval white spots, having only 3 broad dark-brown blotches, one on the soft part of the preopercle, the second behind the operculum sometimes embracing the 4 anterior dorsal rays and the whole of the pectorals, or with a gap between, leaving the fin-rays jet-black; the third blotch is beneath the dorsal fin posteriorly.

The Star-gazer is not commonly met with on account of its habit of burying itself in mud and sand. It is found off the coasts of Queensland and New South Wales, where in the latter locality it is usually trawled in the deeper water, one example having been taken at an unusual depth of 63 to 75 fathoms.

Apart from the expert camouflage adopted by the Star-gazer in obtaining its food, the gastronomic powers of the fish are worthy of comment. Edgar R. Waite noted: "A large example, measuring 25 inches in length, contained a *Sillago ciliata*, 14 inches long; the capture of such lively fish indicates how admirably the sluggish *Ichthyscopus* must assimilate its surroundings."

Ogilby recorded a large example caught by J. Tait of Tewantin, South Queensland. It was a female over 21 inches in length and the ovaries contained eggs in an advanced stage of maturity. The whole mass of ova weighed exactly 7 ounces and after removing a portion and weighing and counting the eggs therein, Ogilby estimated that the fish contained about half a million eggs.

Uranoscopus

A genus with a single species in Queensland, namely the Armed Star-gazer, *U. terrae-reginae* Ogilby, known only from specimens trawled by the *Endeavour* in 1910 off the Capricorns and also Double Island Point. Grows to at least 6 inches.

Sub-order ACANTHUROIDEA

Oblong or deep, compressed, with thick leathery skin covered with minute shagreen-like scales. Mouth small, terminal, not or but slightly protractile, the teeth more or less compressed and incisor-like. A single dorsal fin, composed of a spinous and soft portion, the latter being much longer. Lateral line complete. One or more bony plates or spines at base of caudal on each side. Caudal truncate or lunate, the lobes sometimes elongate.

The juveniles are quite different from the adults, being usually without the rough scales, almost circular in shape and silvery or transparent.

Herbivorous shore fishes occurring in all tropical seas and living in and about coral reefs. The species are of small or moderate size. Two families, Acanthuridae a d Zanclidae, both found in Queensland.

Family **Acanthuridae: Surgeon-fishes and Unicorn-fishes**

Fishes of the tropical and subtropical seas, with more or less oblong or ovoid bodies, compressed and usually elevated, and with the skin covered with very small or minute scales, giving a more or less shagreen-like appearance. Their chief characteristic is the one or more movable spines or fixed knife-like bony plates with which the base of the tail is armed. Their mouths are small, each jaw having a single row of fixed or movable incisor-like teeth. All the species are edible and are of good flavour when properly cooked, the skin usually being removed first.

There are numerous species, most being dull-coloured, brown or blackish, though a few are quite gaudily striped and otherwise decorated. The family is represented in Queensland by six genera.

KEY TO GENERA IN QUEENSLAND

Based on Fowler[49]

A. Tail armed with a very sharp, antrorse, erectile, lancet-like spine, fitting into a groove.

    b. Teeth movable, rather long, bristle-like and expanded at the tips. Dorsal spines 8-9.   *Ctenochaetus*

    bb. Teeth immovable, lobate, broad. Spines 6-10.

      c. Ventral with 2-3 soft rays.   *Paracanthurus*

      cc. Ventral with 5 soft rays.

---

[49] U.S. Nat. Mus., Bull. 100, 8, 1929, p. 200.

    d. Body oblong or ovate to moderately ovate; dorsal
       spines 6-10. Soft dorsal and anal not elevated
       in front. Caudal usually lunate.   *Acanthurus*

    dd. Body deep, sub-rhomboid. Dorsal spines 4-5.
        Soft dorsal and anal high anteriorly. Caudal
        truncate.   *Zebrasoma*

AA. Tail armed with firmly immovable bony bucklers, each
    keeled or with a rigid spine.

    e. Two caudal bucklers.   *Naso*

    ee. More than 2 caudal bucklers.   *Prionurus*

Ctenochaetus

This genus, which contains only one species, is distinguished by the teeth,
which are movable, long and bristle-like, with the tips expanded and strongly
serrated on one side. There are also 8 to 9 dorsal spines.

326. BRISTLE-TOOTHED SURGEON-FISH *Ctenochaetus strigosus* Bennett
[Plate 46]

Ctenochaetus strigosus Bennett, Zool. Journ., 4, 1828, p. 41.
Ctenochaetus strigosus Herre, Phil. Journ. Sci., 34, no. 4, 1927, p. 438, pl. 15, figs 2-3.

    D. 8-9/26-29; A. 3/21-25. Colour reddish-brown or chocolate-brown, with
numerous longitudinal wavy narrow blue lines along sides; head and breast
with numerous small brownish-red or golden spots; dorsal with 2 or more
longitudinal blue lines; anal similar; eyes sapphire-blue.

    A common species on the coral reefs of Melanesia, Micronesia, and Poly-
nesia. Although common elsewhere it is not so frequently met with in Queensland. Grows to 11 inches. Wide-ranging.

Paracanthurus

A genus with a single species characterized by having only 2 to 3 rays in the
ventral fins. Found in the tropical waters of the Indo-Pacific regions.

327. FLAG-TAIL SURGEON-FISH   *Paracanthurus hepatus* (Linnaeus)
[Plate 46]

Teuthis hepatus Linnaeus, Syst. Nat., 12th ed., 1, 1766, p. 507 (part).
Paracanthurus lambdurus Herre, Phil. Journ. Sci., 34, no. 4, 1927, p. 435, pl. 13, fig. 3.

    D. 9/19-20; A. 3/18-20. Colour: "Brilliant ultramarine, becoming indigo
about base of pectoral and on basal half of dorsal and anal membranes, duller on
snout and paler on belly; from eye a black band goes up and back below base
of dorsal to tip of caudal, rapidly becoming much broader to posterior part of

dorsal, then narrowing again; beneath third dorsal spine a narrow black band curves downward and backward to tip of lower side of caudal; a broad black area below soft dorsal coalesces with upper and lower black bands, which have a blue island between them; a large brilliant yellow triangle on caudal, its apex extending forward of caudal spine; dorsal spines and rays yellow with a dusky marginal band, wider and becoming black posteriorly; anal like dorsal, but spines and rays brownish or black; basal half of two-thirds of pectoral deep blue, its upper margin black, its outer part lemon-yellow above, colourless below; ventral spine and rays blue, the membrane orange; eye deep black; the star-like scales on snout and cheek outlined with orange." (Herre.)

A very beautiful fish known in Australian waters only from Torres Strait, North Queensland. It is variable in colour, though the pattern remains unchanged. Some examples have the belly bright canary-yellow. Grows to 10 inches. Very common in New Guinea waters.

Acanthurus: Surgeon-fishes

Teeth fixed, strong, lobate, the edges finely serrated. Dorsal spines usually 9, variably 6 to 10. Ventral with a spine and 5 rays. Caudal spine erectile. Caudal truncate, emarginate, lunate or forked.

In this genus, as also in the two previous ones, the base of the tail is armed with a very sharp lancet-like movable spine which, when in use, is directed outwards and forwards, being retracted into a sheath in the skin when not required. With age it grows to a large size, and when using this murderous weapon the fish strikes sideways, the spine being held rigid and almost at right angles to the tail. They are dangerous fish to handle when alive. It is from this weapon that the names of Surgeon-fish, Lancet-fish, and Doctor-fish have been bestowed. In America they are also called Tangs, a name which means a point, lancet, or knife. These fishes swim in schools about coral reefs and feed mainly upon marine algae. There are many species, four being found on the Queensland reefs.

KEY TO SPECIES IN QUEENSLAND

A. Body with dark cross-bands.   *triostegus*

AA. Body without any cross-bands.

    b. An oblong, black-edged, orange shoulder blotch.   *olivaceus*
    bb. No shoulder blotch.
      c. Coloration nearly uniform brownish, without conspicuous markings; usually a white ring at caudal base.   *fuliginosus*
      cc. Body and head covered with wavy longitudinal lines on a blue background; a broad yellow band between the eyes.   *bariene*

328. FIVE-BANDED SURGEON-FISH *Acanthurus triostegus* (Linnaeus)
[Colour-plate 49]

Chaetodon triostegus Linnaeus, Syst. Nat., 10th ed., 1758, p. 274.
Illustration by G. Coates.

Kara-Hamoowah (India); Tagalog (Philippines); Dara Dara (New Guinea); Shimadai or Striped Perch (Japan).

D. 9/22 (23); A. 3/19-20. Colour pale greenish or light olive, sometimes tinged yellowish; chin, belly, throat, and a narrow stripe along base of anal, white; a black longitudinal line along middle of snout; dorsal greenish or yellowish, the spinous portion narrowly margined black; 6 black transverse bands on sides, in width about same as pupil, the first through eye to branchiostegals, the last in the form of 2 to 3 bars above each other on caudal peduncle; a dark-brown line, which becomes lost posteriorly, separates the white undersurface from the colour of the sides; pectorals, ventrals, anal, and caudal pale yellowish-green, the two former lightest; 1 to 2 black spots may be present on dorsals and caudal.

A widely distributed and common Indo-Pacific species. Large schools of the young frequent the shallow coral pools of the reefs, especially in North Queensland. It has also been recorded from New South Wales, Western Australia, New Zealand, and Japan. Grows to 10 inches.

329. ORANGE-SPOT SURGEON-FISH *Acanthurus olivaceus*
Bloch and Schneider [Plate 46]

Acanthurus olivaceus Bloch and Schneider, Syst. Ichth., 1801, p. 214.
Acanthurus olivaceus Herre, Phil. Journ. Sci., 34, no. 4, 1927, p. 413, pl. 12, fig. 1.

D. 9/24-25; A. 3/23 (24). Colour: Body and head dark olive-brown or olivaceous, with a broad, bright deep-yellow or orange longitudinal bar, broadly margined with black or very dark brown, beginning as a circular spot on opercle and running back to middle of body; dorsal, ventral, and anal fins same as body; pectorals very dark brown, the posterior part with a broad yellow margin; caudal brown, with a broad milk-white crescent on posterior margin, and narrowly edged black, the elongate lobes pale brown, spotted with dark brown; caudal spine in a dark-brown sheath, its groove edged blackish.

A wide-ranging species which has been recorded from the Capricorns and North Queensland. Grows to 16 inches.

OTHER SPECIES

Ring-tailed Surgeon-fish, *A. fuliginosus*. One of the most common species on the Great Barrier Reef. Schools of them are to be seen swimming everywhere over the reefs at low tide. They are a dark colour with a wide whitish band round the base of the tail. They grow to 25 inches and are wide-ranging outside Australia.

Pencilled Surgeon-fish, *A. bariene*. Another wide-ranging species which in Australian waters frequents the reefs of Queensland, stragglers being found in northern New South Wales. The species is subject to great variation in both form and colour. Grows to 19 inches.

Zebrasoma

Surgeon-fishes of the Indo-Pacific, with the dorsal and anal fins greatly elevated, the former with 3 to 5 flexible spines.

About five species are known, two being found in Queensland.

KEY TO SPECIES IN QUEENSLAND

A. Dorsal rays 30-32; body with transverse yellow bands. *veliferum*

AA. Dorsal rays 23; colour brown or yellow, no transverse bands. *flavescens*

330. SAIL-FINNED SURGEON-FISH *Zebrasoma veliferum* (Bloch) [Plate 46]

Acanthurus velifer Bloch, Nat. ausl. Fische, 9, 1795, p. 106.
Zebrasoma hypselopterum Ogilby, Mem. Qld Mus., 5, 1916, p. 174, pl. 23.

D. 4/30-33; A. 3/22-26. Colour dark brown or almost black; sides of snout and chin with yellow spots; 6 broad golden-yellow, lemon-yellow, or white bands on the sides, inclining diagonally forward; each of the broad brown interspaces posterior to the pectoral origin has 4 to 5 black lines running in the same direction; dorsal and anal purplish-black or violet, with numerous almost vertical pale-bluish cross-lines, more or less broken into rows of spots, plainer posteriorly; pectoral and caudal like body.

This handsome fish exhibits great variation of colour, but the pattern is constant. It is a wide-ranging species, found in Australian waters only from Torres Strait, North Queensland. Grows to 16 inches.

OTHER SPECIES

Sombre Surgeon-fish, *Z. flavescens*. Known in Australia only from the northern waters of Queensland. It is wide-ranging and grows to only 7 inches.

Naso

Herbivorous fishes of the tropical parts of the Indo-Pacific region, characterized by having 2, rarely 1 or 3, immovable bony plates on each side of the caudal peduncle. These plates are usually keeled into high knife-like blades which may be hooked forward, forming a dangerous weapon. They may be entirely

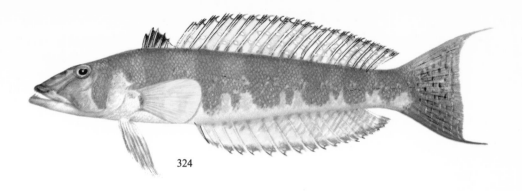

324

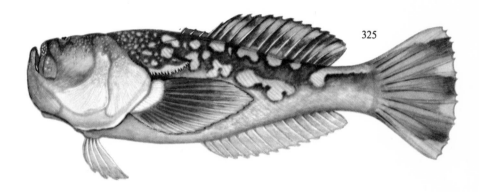

325

COLOUR-PLATE 49
324. Bar-faced Weaver, *Para-percis nebulosus*, 9 in.
325. Star-gazer, *Ichthyscopus lebeck*, 10 in. 328. Five-banded Surgeon-fish, *Acan-thurus triostegus*, 7 in.

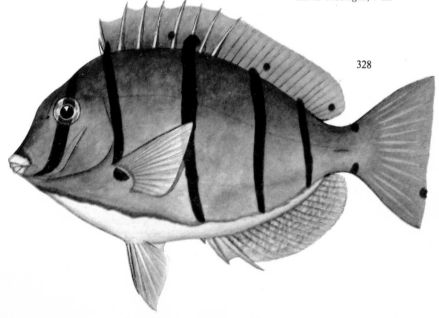

328

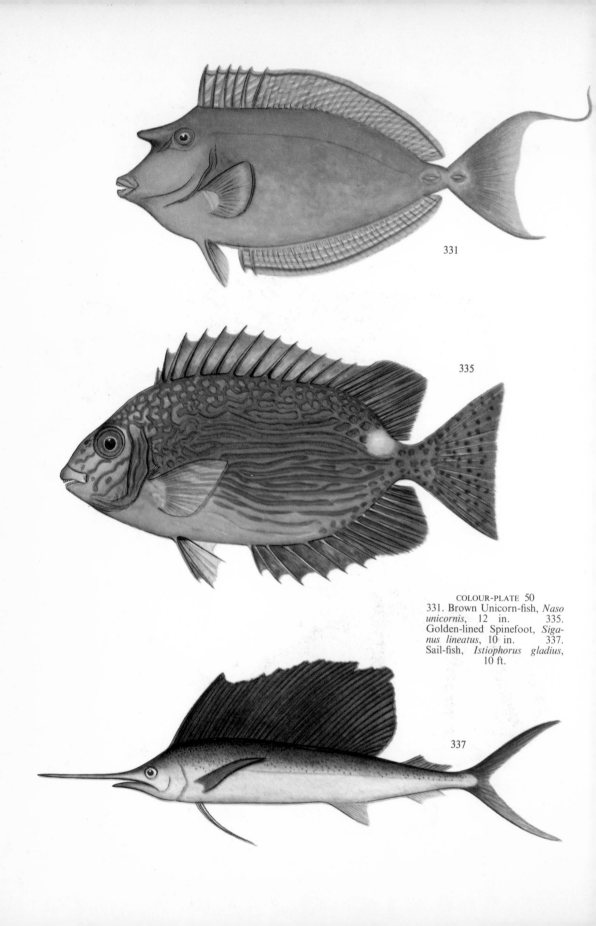

331

335

COLOUR-PLATE 50
331. Brown Unicorn-fish, *Naso unicornis*, 12 in. 335. Golden-lined Spinefoot, *Siganus lineatus*, 10 in. 337. Sail-fish, *Istiophorus gladius*, 10 ft.

337

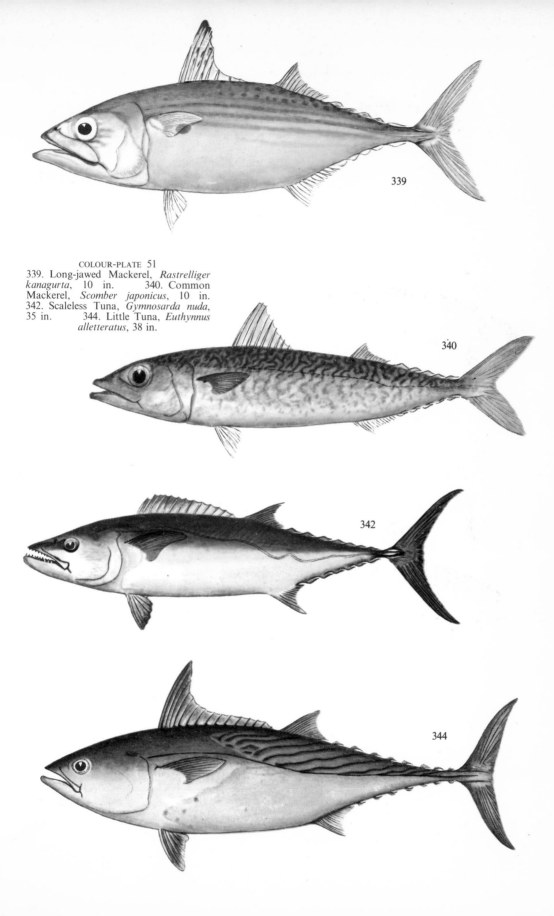

339

339. Long-jawed Mackerel, *Rastrelliger kanagurta*, 10 in.   340. Common Mackerel, *Scomber japonicus*, 10 in. 342. Scaleless Tuna, *Gymnosarda nuda*, 35 in.   344. Little Tuna, *Euthynnus alletteratus*, 38 in.

340

342

344

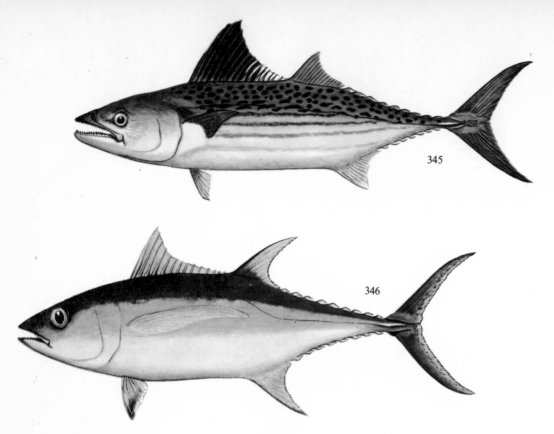

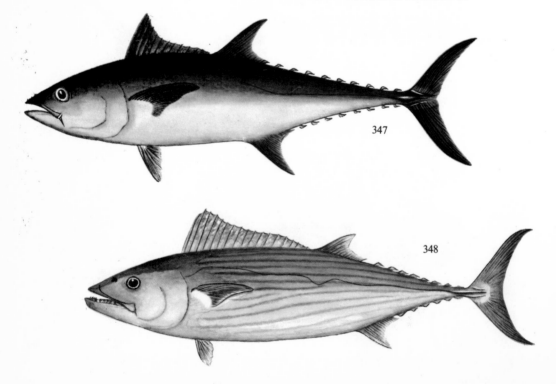

COLOUR-PLATE 52

345. Watson's Bonito, *Cybiosarda elegans*, 13 in.   346.
Pacific Yellowfin Tuna, *Neothunnus macropterus*, 38 in.
347. Northern Bluefin Tuna, *Kishinoella tonggol*, 45 in.
348. Little Bonito, *Sarda australis*, 9 in.

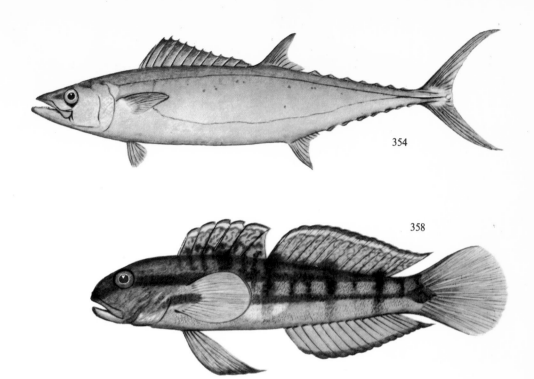

354

358

COLOUR-PLATE 53

354. Large-scaled Tunny, *Grammatorycnus bicarinatus*, 38 in.
358. Bynoe's Goby, *Amblygobius bynoensis*, 3⅜ in.
363. Fingered Dragonet, *Dactylopus dactylopus*, male, 6½ in.

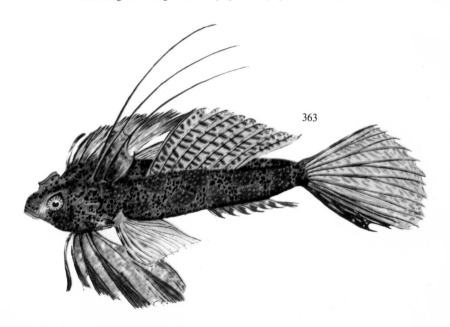

363

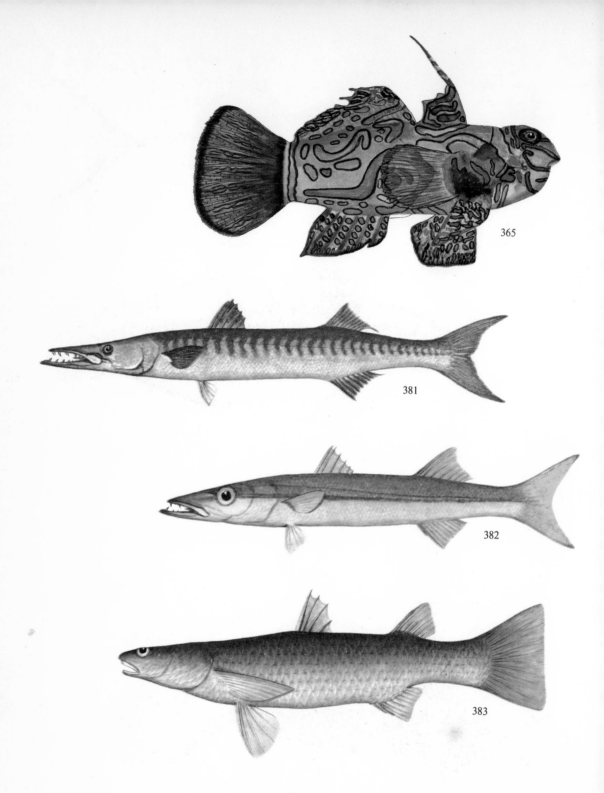

COLOUR-PLATE 54
365. Mandarin-fish, *Synchiropus splendidus*, $3\frac{1}{4}$ in.
381. Pick-handle Barracuda, *Sphyraena jello*, 30 in.
382. Striped Barracuda, *S. obtusata*, 10 in.
383. Shark Mullet, *Squalomugil nasutus*, 7 in.

COLOUR-PLATE 55

392. Diamond-scaled Mullet, *Mugil vaigiensis*, 12½ in.
393. Bluetail Mullet, *M. seheli*, 17 in.   400. Giant
Threadfin, *Eleutheronema tetradactylum*, 16 in.

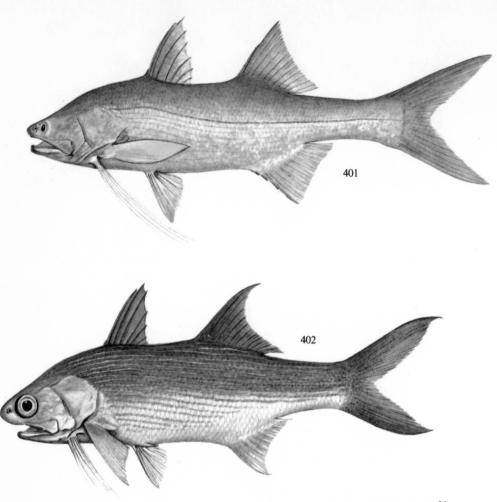

COLOUR-PLATE 56
401. Sheridan's Threadfin, *Poly-nemus sheridani*, 18 in.   402.
Striped Threadfin, *P. plebejus*,
19 in.   403. Flat Salmon,
P. multiradiatus, 8 in.

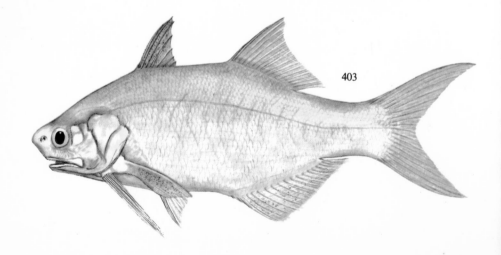

406

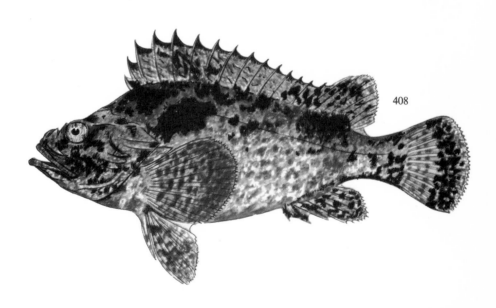

408

COLOUR-PLATE 57
406. Marbled Coral Cod, *Sebastapistes bynoensis*, 3 in.
408. Bullrout, *Notesthes robusta*, 10 in.

410

410. Red Fire-fish, *Pterois volitans*, 7 in.

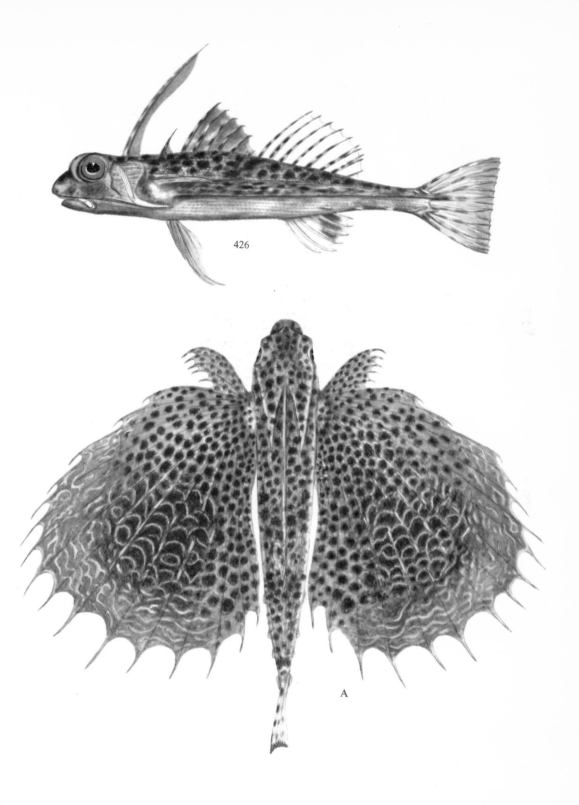

COLOUR-PLATE 59
426. Purple Flying Gurnard, *Dactyloptena orientalis*, 11 in.
A, Dorsal view with pectoral fins extended.

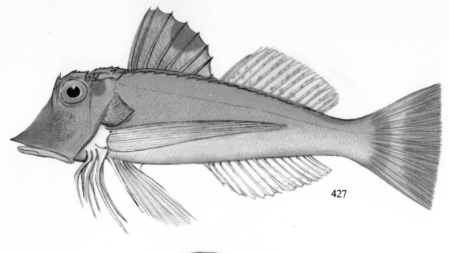

427

A

COLOUR-PLATE 60
426a. Rufous Flying Gurnard,
Dactyloptena papilio, 7 in.
427. Long-finned Gurnard,
Lepidotrigla calodactyla, 5¼ in.
A, Extended pectoral fin.

426a

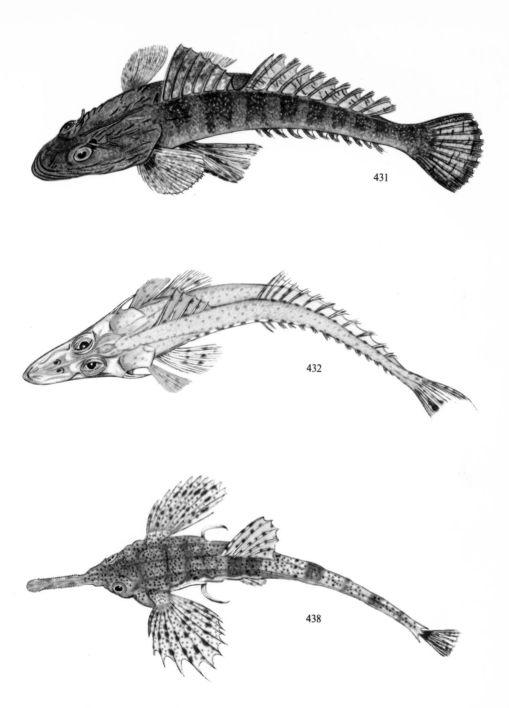

COLOUR-PLATE 61
431. Fringe-eyed Flathead, *Cymbacephalus nematophthalmus*,
10 in.   432. Dwarf Flathead, *Elates thompsoni*, 7¾ in.
438. Long-tailed Sea Dragon, *Parapegasus natans*, 4 in.

439

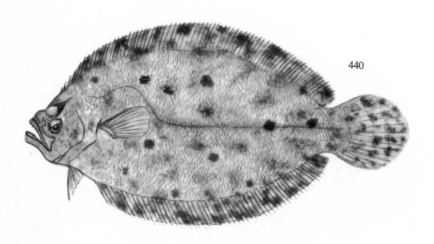

440

COLOUR-PLATE 62
439. Queensland Halibut or Adalah, *Psettodes erumei*, 15 in.
440. Large-toothed Flounder, *Pseudorhombus arsius*, 10¾ in.

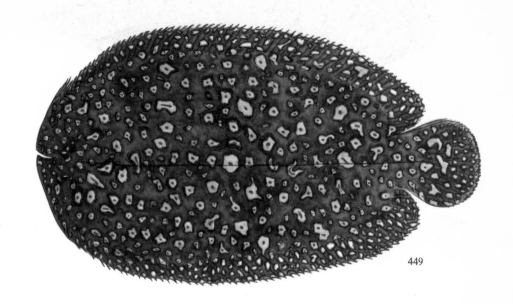

449

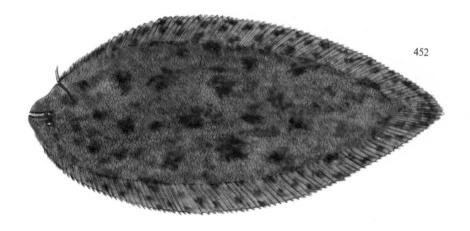

452

COLOUR-PLATE 63
449. Peacock Sole, *Pardachirus pavoninus*, 10 in.
452. Sharp-headed Sole, *Phyllichthys sclerolepis*, 5 in.

454

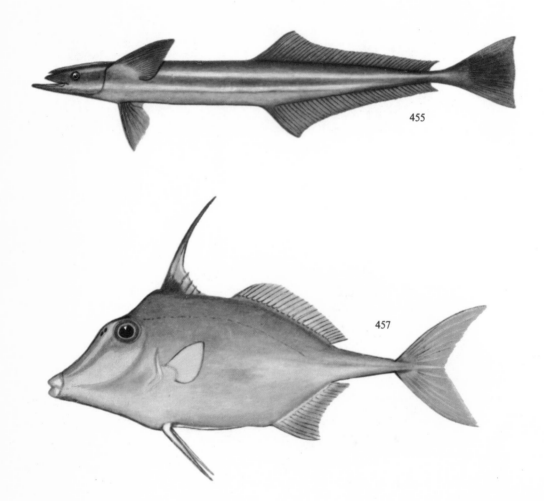

455

457

COLOUR-PLATE 64
454. Two-lined Tongue Sole, *Cynoglossus bilineatus*, 8 in.
455. Slender Sucking-fish, *Echeneis neucrates*, 23 in.   457.
Black-finned Triple-spine, *Triacanthus biaculeatus*, 7 in.

absent in the young, developing with age to a large size. In some species the adults develop a large compressed hump above the snout which often projects beyond the mouth. In other species an exceedingly long and conical horn develops on the forehead before the eyes, projecting far in front of the mouth.

There are many species of *Naso*, four being found in Queensland.

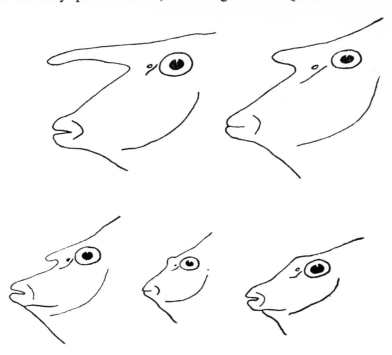

FIG. 9. Rostral development of *Naso unicornis* with age. AFTER FOWLER AND BEAN

KEY TO SPECIES IN QUEENSLAND

A. Forehead with elongated conic horn-like protuberance or crest-like hump above snout in adult.

    b. Forehead with conic rostral protuberance.

      c. Snout long or produced below rostral protuberance; pectoral uniform.

                                  unicornis
                                  (Fig. 9)

      cc. Snout moderately produced; pectoral with whitish edges. Juvenile examples with a white ring on caudal peduncle.

                                    annulatus
                                  (Fig. 10)

M

338

bb. A convex and compressed crest-like hump above
the snout, greatly developed with age.

tuberosus
(Fig. 11)

AA. Head without horn or hump at any age.

d. Yellow curved lines on face; soft dorsal and anal
dark basally, the outer half whitish; caudal bucklers
orange.

lituratus

331. BROWN UNICORN-FISH *Naso unicornis* (Forskål)

[Colour-plate 50; text-fig. 9]

Chaetodon unicornis Forskål, Descr. Anim., 1775, p. 63.
Illustration by G. Coates.

Tenguhagi or Long-nosed Scraper (Japan).

D. 5-6/28-31; A. 2/26-30. Colour dark olive, brownish, or greyish-black,
lighter below and on caudal; dorsal and anal clear brown or light orange, with
a dark-blue edge, and sometimes with light-bluish spots or longitudinal blue
lines; pectoral uniform olive; caudal sometimes with a wide band of yellow on
posterior margin.

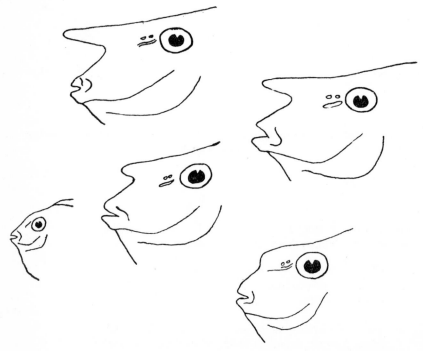

Fig. 10. Rostral development of *Naso annulatus* with age. AFTER
FOWLER AND BEAN.

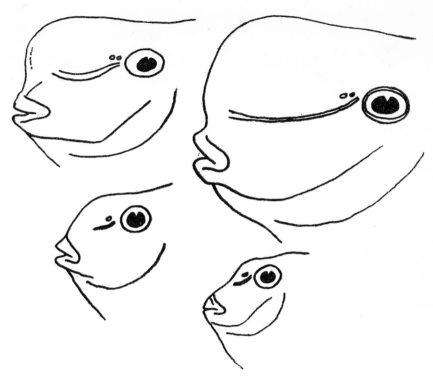

Fig. 11. Rostral development of *Naso tuberosus* with age. AFTER FOWLER AND BEAN.

This species is very variable in colour. It is a wide-ranging fish, recorded in Australian seas only from Queensland, where it has been taken at various localities from Moreton Bay to Torres Strait. Grows to 23 inches.

In old examples the horn grows to a remarkable degree, extending forward to a vertical line with the lips.

OTHER SPECIES

Short-horned Unicorn-fish, *N. annulatus*. (Fig. 10.) This species also varies considerably in colour. In Australia it has been taken only on the reefs of Queensland, where it ranges as far south as Mooloolaba. Grows to 20 inches. Wide-ranging.

Hump-headed Unicorn-fish, *N. tuberosus*. (Fig. 11.) One of the largest of the genus, attaining over 24 inches. It is a wide-ranging fish but known in Australia only from the waters north of Rockhampton, Queensland. It is readily recognized by the large rostral hump which, though scarcely developed in the juveniles, projects almost beyond the mouth in large examples.

Stripe-faced Unicorn-fish, *N. lituratus*. Yet another wide-ranging fish, inhabiting the waters of Torres Strait, North Queensland. It is very variable in colour but is easily recognized by the absence of a horn or hump at all stages of growth and by its facial markings. Grows to 16 inches.

Prionurus

Represented in Queensland by the Saw-tail, *P. microlepidotus*, a uniformly dusky-brown fish readily recognized by the many caudal bucklers. It grows to 18 inches and is found along the coasts of South Queensland and New South Wales, where it lives among the rocks and feeds upon seaweeds.

Family **Zanclidae: Moorish Idols**

Body elevated and much compressed. Scales minute, ciliated, almost invisible to the naked eye. Lateral line strongly arched, following dorsal profile. Head short, with greatly produced tubular snout. Mouth small, terminal, with produced jaws, not protractile. Teeth long, slender, brush-like and projecting. Bones of top of head thick and solid, developing with age a conspicuous median horn on forehead. Preopercle unarmed. Preorbital with or without a small re-curved spine near angle of mouth. A single dorsal fin with 7 spines, the two anterior ones very short and pungent, the five succeeding ones flexible and prolonged, the third into a very long filament. Anal with 3 spines, the long, soft-rayed portion with a nearly vertical hind border. Pectoral short, rounded. Ventrals pointed, the first ray somewhat produced. Caudal peduncle unarmed, the fin emarginate.

A family with a single genus, *Zanclus*, and probably but one species, distributed throughout the Indo-Pacific region and living about rocky islands and coral reefs.

332. MOORISH IDOL *Zanclus canescens* Linnaeus [Plate 47]

Zanclus canescens Linnaeus, Syst. Nat., 10th ed., 1758, p. 272; 12th ed., 1766, p. 460.
Zanclus canescens Bleeker, Atlas Ichth., 9, 1878, p. 78, pl. 366, fig. 3.

Toby (South Africa).

D. 7/40-41; A. 3/31-35. Colour: "Bright canary yellow (less often yellow shading into white, rarely pearly-white), with two wide black or dark brown cross-bands; the anterior one extends from first or second dorsal spine to supraorbital horns and down to breast and behind anus, including ventrals, its anterior margin bounded by a blue or pearly-white stripe; on lower half are two blue lines, one from origin of ventrals to gill opening and up behind eye to median line before first dorsal; the second blue line begins behind anus, goes up to base of pectoral, passes forward of this and up to origin of dorsal; the third line extends from upper margin of eye up to median line of head where it meets its fellow in a long acute angle; from upper anterior margin of eye a blue line curves up behind base of supraorbital horn and curves down to the middle of the space between the horn to meet its fellow; the posterior black band extends from tip of anterior dorsal rays across body to lower margin of greater part of anal, widest below, a blue line extending across its posterior part, a wide black band covers most of caudal, bounded posteriorly by a crescent-shaped blue or white band, the wide margin yellowish. A black or deep brown band extends from the interorbital space down snout to its tip; a stripe passes from it down side of snout and curves up back on tip of snout, enclosing a roughly triangular yellow area, the stripe margined below by the pearly-white or bluish line; a large black or deep brown spot on lower lip and jaw; pectorals pale yellowish; ventrals very dark brown or black; soft dorsal and anal edged black." (After Herre.)

This wide-ranging Indo-Pacific species has been recorded on the Australian coast from Queensland, where it very occasionally straggles south to Moreton Bay and New South Wales. Rare in Queensland. Grows to 7 inches. The horn above the eye increases with age.

Sub-order SIGANOIDEA

Body compressed, ovate, with slippery skin, covered with minute elongate concealed scales. Mouth small, with one series of incisors. A sharp antrorse spine before dorsal fin. Dorsal with 13 strongly heteracanth spines and 10 soft branched rays. Anal with 7 spines and 9 branched rays. Ventrals with an outer and inner spine and 3 soft rays between.

A single family with two genera of herbivorous fishes of the Indo-Pacific, easily distinguished by the number of anal and ventral spines.

Family Siganidae: Spinefeet or Rabbit-fishes

Small or moderate-sized fishes found in the tropical parts of the Indian and Pacific oceans. They are closely related to the surgeon-fishes, family Teuthididae, but are readily distinguished by the absence of bony bucklers or spines on the tail and by their increased number of dorsal and anal spines. With these strong spines they are able to inflict very painful wounds which cause distress for hours afterwards. This has earned them the name of Stinging Bream from Queensland fishermen. They frequent coral reefs and rocky localities, feeding in schools on the various marine algal growths. When frightened by an observer walking in the shallows on the reefs they become so frenzied in seeking cover that they endeavour to burrow beaneath one's feet. They are good food-fishes, having flesh which is firm and fiaky. Most of the species are dull in colour, though some are brightly coloured.

Of the two genera, one has only a single species, the other many.

342

A. Snout produced, elongate, muzzle as short tube. Colour
    yellow or orange; upper half of head, all breast and
    prepectoral edge black.   *Lo*

AA. Snout not produced or muzzle not protruded.   *Siganus*

Lo

A genus of few species characterized by the short tubular snout. They inhabit
the waters of the Indo-Pacific. One species in Queensland.

333. FOX-FACE *Lo vulpinus* (Schlegel and Müller)   [Plate 47]

Amphacanthus vulpinus Schlegel and Müller, Verhand. Nat. Ges. Neder. overz. bezitt., Zool. (Pisces),
    1844, p. 12.
Lo vulpinus Herre and Montalban, Phil. Journ. Sci., 35, no. 2, 1928, p. 182, pl. 6.

D. 8/10; A. 7/9. Colour: Upper part of body, the dorsals, anal, and caudal
brilliant orange, the remaining part of trunk clear yellow. A black or blackish-
brown band extends from dorsal origin diagonally downward and forward,
including snout, eyes, and tip of lower jaw, but leaving a paler median strip
from nape to tip of upper lip. Behind this dark band is a wide diagonal pearly-
white band thickly sprinkled with reddish or dark-red dots, which covers rest
of head below and behind eye and touches front end of breast. From the gill-
opening a black area extends to pectoral base and over breast to ventrals.
First ray of pectoral and both ventral spines are black or blackish-brown;
remaining portion of pectoral and ventrals is yellow to nearly colourless.

Some examples have a large round or irregular-shaped black blotch on
lateral line below posterior spines and anterior rays of dorsal fin.

This handsome fish, known from the East Indies, the Philippines, Samoa,
and the South Seas, has been recorded from the Queensland coast at Hayman
Island, North Queensland. Grows to 9 inches.

Siganus

There are nine species of this genus in Queensland. Care should be exercised
in the use of the following key to the species, for though, to quote Fowler and
Bean, it "expresses phylogeny more closely than structural characters", the
colours vary to a certain extent so that the species may sometimes be placed
equally well in either of two sections.

A. (1) Ground colour darker than markings which form
        whitish, golden, or bluish spots or vermiculated
        lines.

---

[50] U.S. Nat. Mus., Bull. 100, 8, 1929, p. 288.

b. Depth 1¾-2¼.

  c. Caudal slightly or moderately emarginate.

    d. Body marked with spots, at least on back.

      e. Back with pale round spots, oblong on middle of side, forming longitudinal streaks on belly; head uniform, also fins.   *javus*

    dd. Brownish, with vermiculated bluish lines on head and whole body except belly; caudal dotted all over with brown.   *vermiculatus*

  cc. Caudal deeply emarginate or forked.

    f. Olive-greenish or orange, with small sky-blue spots on body and bases of caudal and anal; spots very small, much smaller than interspaces between, but larger and more crowded on head and thorax.   *corallinus*

bb. Depth 2⅓-3.

  g. Caudal deeply emarginate or forked. Olive or chocolate-brown, with irregular lighter blotches; back and sides with numerous small close-set light-blue spots.   *rivulatus*

  gg. Caudal scarcely or but slightly emarginate. Greenish-yellow or brownish-olive, with numerous small scattered spots on back and sides; dark blotch on shoulder.   *canaliculatus*

A. (2) Ground colour blue, with golden hexagonal dots placed densely and covering head, body, and vertical fins; caudal deeply emarginate; depth 2⅛.   *punctatus*

A. (3) Markings darker than ground colour, chiefly formed as longitudinal streaks.

  h. Depth 2¼; slaty-blue, with brownish or dark-yellowish longitudinal streaks anastomosing with one another; head with some oblique bluish lines; yellowish or dusky blotch below soft dorsal dotted with black and edged red; caudal, anal, and hind part of tail with brown spots.   *lineatus*

  hh. Depth 2½-2⅔; greenish, with bluish or violet streaks, which are broader than interspaces between, longitudinal on sides, more vermiculated and reticulated on back; caudal with four or five dark cross-bands, very distinct on upper and lower margins.   *spinus*

A. (4) Very distinct transverse streaks; caudal moderately emarginate, or lunate; orange, with about 30 vertical bluish lines, last of which bend down and run longitudinally along posterior part of tail; those above pectoral oblique and those on opercle reticulated; caudal clear yellow.   *doliatus*

334. BLACK SPINEFOOT *Siganus rivulatus* (Forskål) [Plate 47]

Scarus rivulatus Forskål, Descr. Anim. 1775, pp. x, 25.
Siganus consobrinus Ogilby, Mem. Qld Mus., 1, 1912, p. 54, pl. 13.

Happy Moments, Black Trevally (Queensland and New South Wales); Stinging Bream (Queensland); Mi-Mi (Townsville); Rabbit-fish, Slimy, Spiny (South Africa).

D. 1 + 13/10; A. 7/9. Colour olive or chocolate-brown with irregular lighter blotches; back and sides with numerous small close-set light-blue spots as wide as or slightly narrower than the interspaces; entire body, or more usually its lower half only, with much larger scattered dark-brown or blackish spots; a round blackish shoulder spot about as large as the eye is usually present; head dark brown, blotched yellowish-green, the sides with or without blue spots; lips brown or lead blue; vertical fins hyaline, spinous portion with suffused dusky blotches, the rays of the soft portion more or less distinctly zoned with purplish brown and grey; caudal olive-green, the lobes glossed with yellow, outer ray above and below with alternate black and grey patches, sometimes as cross-bands. A most variable species rapidly undergoing great changes of colour whilst under observation.

A wide-ranging and very common fish found along the coasts of Queensland and New South Wales. Grows to 14 inches.

335. GOLDEN-LINED SPINEFOOT *Siganus lineatus*
(Cuvier and Valenciennes) [Colour-plate 50]

Amphacanthus lineatus Cuvier and Valenciennes, Hist. Nat. Poiss., 10, 1835, p. 310, pl. 286.
Illustration by G. Coates.

Mi-Mi (Townsville).

D. 13/10, 1; A. 7/9, 1. Colour slaty-blue, darkest above, with about 12 parallel longitudinal yellow lines as wide as the interspaces and broken below into spots; lines on face and cheeks bright blue, between which is yellow; spinous dorsal olive-yellow, soft dorsal with the membranes lighter; anal olive-yellow, spines lighter; pectorals and ventrals grey, the membranes hyaline; caudal dark slaty-grey, with black spots, changing to yellow ones on the caudal peduncle; a large dusky yellow blotch usually present below the last dorsal rays.

A common Queensland fish, especially plentiful on the northern reefs. Grows to 15 inches. Wide-ranging.

OTHER SPECIES

Blue-spotted Spinefoot, *S. javus*. Found on the Queensland coast, this species straggles into New South Wales and Victoria. It ranges to the East

Indies and India and is also found in the Philippines. It is known as Blue-spotted Trevally in Queensland. Grows to 13 inches.

Scribbled Spinefoot, *S. vermiculatus*. Easily recognizable by its vermiculated colour pattern. In Australian waters it is known only from Queensland. Grows to 15 inches. Wide-ranging.

Coral Spinefoot, *S. corallinus*. Another wide-ranging fish found in the waters of North Queensland. Grows to 12 inches. Not common in Queensland.

Pearly Spinefoot, *S. canaliculatus*. Wide-ranging outside Australia; has been recorded from the Queensland coast but is apparently not common in Queensland. Grows to 10 inches.

Yellow-spotted Spinefoot, *S. punctatus*. A large species which grows to 18 inches; very common everywhere on the reefs of North Queensland at low tide. Occasionally it is met with in the southern parts of the State. It ranges also to the East Indies and the western Pacific.

Blunt-nosed Spinefoot, *S. spinus*. Found on the reefs of North Queensland, also in the Pacific Islands, the East Indies, and the Philippines. Grows to about 9 inches.

Barred Spinefoot, *S. doliatus*. A very common species in North Queensland, where at low tide shoals of a dozen or more are to be seen feeding on the reefs. Found also in Melanesia, Micronesia, Polynesia, and the East Indies. Grows to 10 inches.

Sub-order TRICHIUROIDEA

This sub-order includes only a small number of carnivorous and predatory fishes, which are related to the mackerels and their allies. From them they are distinguished by the structure of the caudal fin. Some of the species are surface-dwellers, but others are found at considerable depths. Most of the species are not good food-fishes but a few are valued as such. The Snoek, *Thyrsites atun*—known in Australia as Barracouta—and the King Barracouta, *Jordanidia solandri* are two important food-fishes in southern Australia. To the sub-order also belongs the Scabbard-fish, *Lepidopus caudatus*, known in New Zealand as Frost-fish.

Family **Trichiuridae: Cutlass-fishes or Hair-tails**

Fishes found living at or near the surface of most warm and tropical seas, some inhabiting the coastal waters, others the open sea. Their bodies are extremely long and band-shaped, tapering to a slender point or in some species to a small caudal. The dorsal fin is usually continuous with the soft. There are no scales and the naked body is a brilliant silver in colour.

In other parts of the world these fishes are known as scabbard-fishes, silver-fishes, sable, savola, and frost-fishes. The family is represented in Queensland waters by one genus and a single species.

Trichiurus

Silvery fishes, very slender and band-like in form, their bodies tapering to a single hair-like point. The dorsal fin is continuous, the rays all similar. The wide mouth is armed with long, strongly compressed and barbed teeth, longest and strongest in the upper jaw. Species few, one in Queensland.

336. CUTLASS-FISH *Trichiurus savala* Cuvier [Plate 47]

Trichiurus savala Cuvier, Règne Anim., 2nd ed., ii, April 1829, p. 219.
Trichiurus savala Day, Fish. India, 1878-88, p. 201, pl. 47, fig. 4.

Hair-tail (Queensland and South Africa); White Girdle, White Tape (China).
Colour greyish along back, brilliant silvery on sides and below; fins pale yellow, the upper half of dorsal dusky, owing to numerous fine blackish dots.

A remarkable fish caught in the open seas and bays and also in the estuaries. It ranges from the seas of India to the Indo-Australian Archipelago, and in Australian waters is known from the Northern Territory down the coast of Queensland to New South Wales. Grows to 4 feet 4 inches.

Sub-order SCOMBROIDEA

This sub-order includes such fishes as the mackerels, tunnies, bonitos, and albacores, together with their allies the sword-fishes (Xiphiidae), the sail-fishes, and the spear-fishes or marlins (Istiophoridae). They are pelagic fishes, carnivorous in habit and especially abundant in all temperate and tropical seas. Two families are well represented in Queensland.

KEY TO FAMILIES IN QUEENSLAND

A.   Snout forming a long pointed rostrum or sword.   ISTIOPHORIDAE

AA. Snout not produced into a pointed rostrum or sword.   SCOMBRIDAE

Family **Istiophoridae: Sail-fishes, Spear-fishes, Marlins**

Giant mackerel-like fishes related to the Scombridae or mackerel family and found in most warm seas of the world. They are strong and rapid swimmers, living in the open ocean at or near the surface of the sea. These fishes are among the largest of the teleostean fishes and range in weight, when adult, from 20 pounds to over 1,000 pounds, with a length of 14 feet or more. Their bodies are long, tapering, and greatly compressed and are covered with narrow scales which are more or less embedded in the skin. Their chief characteristic is the sword or rostrum which is formed by the prolongation of the premaxillary and maxillary bones into a solid and extremly hard spear. Both jaws are provided with minute granular teeth, persistent with age. The middle spines of the dorsal fin are persistent through life. The ventral fins, which consist of one to three rays, are well developed. In the true Sword-fish, family Xiphiidae (not yet recorded from Queensland), the sword or spear is very long and broad, the teeth become lost with age, the ventral fins are wanting, the caudal peduncle has only one large keel, the middle dorsal spines become lost with age, and the body is scaleless.

Sail-fishes and marlin are capable of great speed, and Norman and Fraser give some interesting notes on them. They state:[51] "Indeed, they are held by many experts to be among the swiftest of exciting fishes, capable, not only of sudden rapid bursts of speed, during which they have been estimated to travel at 40 to 50 miles an hour, but of maintaining a high rate of progress for many hours on end. A torpedo fired from a battleship would soon be left behind by a large Spear-fish going 'all-out'. Professor Owen, when called upon to testify in a court of law as to the power of one of these fishes, stated that 'it strikes with the accumulated force of fifteen double-headed hammers; its velocity is equal to that of a swivel-shot, and is as dangerous in its effects as an artillery projectile'."

In shape these fishes show a perfect streamlined body. The spear forms an effective cut-water, and the fins of the back and belly fold down and fit neatly into deep grooves in the body as the fish gathers speed with its powerful tail. Numerous stories are on record of ships having been struck by "sword-fishes", but in many cases it is evident that the culprits have been either spear-fishes or sail-fishes. When hooked, they have been known to turn and charge a boat, but there are also many instances of unprovoked attack, seeming almost as though temporary insanity takes possession of the fish. They are known to frequently attack whales, repeatedly stabbing and thrusting at these helpless creatures. When travelling at a high speed these fishes can easily penetrate the sides of a wooden vessel, and definite evidence of such feats is to be seen in the Museum of the College of Surgeons in London. A section of timber from the bows of a South Sea whaler is exhibited and shows a spear 12 inches in length and 5 inches in circumference which has penetrated a thickness of $13\frac{1}{2}$ inches of solid timber. Another piece of ship's timber in the British Museum shows a transfixed "spear" through its 22 inches.

The food of the spear-fishes usually consists of the smaller scombroid fishes which are present in great shoals, sardines, flying-fishes, etc.

In many parts of the world game-fishing clubs have been formed to fish these giants of the sea and land them on light regulation tackle. The sport is thrilling and exhausting and certainly not without a certain element of risk. The method of capture is by trolling a bait or lure behind a fast-moving launch. When hooked, the fish rises to the surface and makes great leaps into the air in a frantic endeavour to throw the hook. Between such leaps it frequently "dances"

---

[51] *Giant Fishes, Whales and Dolphins*, 1937, p. 158.

along the surface of the ocean on its tail, sometimes for great distances, and often a battle royal will go on for hours before the great fish is finally exhausted and gaffed.

Most of the species are of commercial importance, being valued for their rich firm flesh, which, like that of the tunnies or tunas, is admirably suited for canning. In America, where so many of these large fishes are utilized, the livers of sword-fishes are processed for the valuable oil which they contain. This oil is usually rich in vitamins A and D and is said to be perhaps the most nearly ideal natural A and D concentrate yet investigated (1935). The commercial method of fishing these fishes in America is by means of the harpoon.

Many of these large fishes are captured on the Queensland coast from time to time, but owing to their large size are not preserved in museum collections. Rough notes or, at the most, poor photographs are kept, thus making positive identification difficult or impossible. Each season, fishing and game clubs record "Black Marlin", "Blue Marlin", and "Striped Marlin", but specimens are seldom brought under scientific notice.

The two genera which comprise the family are found in Queensland.

KEY TO GENERA

A. Dorsal fin greatly elevated; ventral fins very long, each of 3 rays, not fully united.   *Istiophorus*

AA. Dorsal fin low, elevated anteriorly into a high lobe, its anterior spines thickened, the others progressively shortened to the last. Ventral fins each of 1 slender ray.   *Makaira*

Istiophorus: Sail-fishes

Large fishes, similar in appearance to the spear-fishes and marlins but with a single and a very high sail-like dorsal fin. Pelvics each of 2 to 3 rays. They are fast-swimming fishes and in speed are said to rival the spear-fishes. At sea they are frequently to be seen on a calm day lazing on the surface with the sail-like fin fully erect above the water. Some authorities hold the opinion that the fish uses the fin as a sail to catch the wind, and the following quotation seems to bear this out: "The only amusing discovery which we have recently made is that of a sailing-fish, called by the natives 'Ikan layer', of about 10 or 12 feet long, which hoists a main-sail, and often sails in the manner of a native boat, and with considerable swiftness. . . . When a school of these are under sail together they are frequently mistaken for a fleet of native boats."[52]

As in the case of the spear-fishes many species have been made but it is doubtful if more than a quarter are valid. One species has been recorded from Queensland waters.

---

[52] *Memoir of the Life of Sir Stamford Raffles*, by his Widow, 1830.

337. SAIL-FISH *Istiophorus gladius* (Broussonet)   [Colour-plate 50]

Scomber gladius Broussonet, Mem. Acad. Sci., 1786, p. 484.
Illustration by G. Coates.

Peacock-fish (India).

D. 40-50 + 7; A. 10-12 + 6-7. Colour slaty to purplish-blue above, sides and below leaden-grey to whitish; body with light-grey cross-bands which increase from 10 to 20 with age and generally broken into variable spots; dorsal fin dark prussian-blue, with round greyish-black or black spots which increase in intensity and number with age; ventrals and caudal black; first anal bluish with darker tip.

This remarkable fish is often captured by the mackerel fishermen and occasionally exhibited in fishmongers' windows in Brisbane. It is commonly seen in the Indian Ocean and ranges through the East Indies into Australian waters. Stragglers are sometimes found along the coast of New South Wales. The species also occurs in the Pacific and in China. Grows to a length of 12 feet and a weight of several hundred pounds.

Makaira: Marlins and Spear-fishes

For characters of the genus see those given in the preceding key. The fishes of this genus are the largest, strongest, and most numerous of the family Istiophoridae. Like other genera of the family the species undergo considerable changes with growth. Many species have been made but it is doubtful if, as some authors suggest, more than half a dozen of them are valid. Two species are found on the Queensland coast.

KEY TO SPECIES IN QUEENSLAND

A. Spear long, its length from the eye double the rest of the head; height of dorsal lobe slightly less than length of pectoral. Colour steel-blue, with 13-17 pale-bluish vertical bars on sides.   *zelandica*

AA. Spear shorter, its length from the eye about 1⅔ the rest of the head; height of dorsal lobe much less than length of pectoral, about 1½ times in that fin. Colour deep blue-black, silvery on sides, white below. No bars.   *australis*

338. SOUTHERN MARLIN *Makaira australis* (Whitley)   [Plate 47]

Istiompax australis Whitley, Austr. Zool., 6, pt 4, 1931, p. 321.
Histiophorus gladius (not of Broussonet) Ramsay, Proc. Linn. Soc. N.S.Wales, 5, 1881, p. 295, pl. 8.

Black Marlin (South Queensland).

D. 35 + 7; A. 12-13 + 6. Colour uniformly dark grey or bluish-black on back, becoming lighter on sides and silvery or almost white on belly; fins blue-blackish, except the anal which is dark grey.

An eastern Australian and New Zealand species recorded in Australian waters from South Queensland and New South Wales. The ventrals are shorter than the pectorals, becoming much shorter with age. A large example, which measured 11 feet 2 inches, was found dying in shallow water at Scarborough, near Brisbane, in April 1937. The species reached a weight of at least 823 pounds and a length of at least 14 feet. This is the "Black Marlin" of the Brisbane fishermen.

OTHER SPECIES

New Zealand Marlin, *M. zelandica*. This is the Striped Marlin of the Queensland and New South Wales big-game clubs. It grows to at least 13 feet 6 inches in length and 820 pounds in weight and is frequently captured in the waters of South Queensland.

Family **Scombridae: Mackerels and Tunas or Tunnies**

Widely distributed fishes, pelagic in habit and living in great shoals in most warm seas of the world. They are powerful and swift swimmers, living at or near the surface of the sea, some growing to a very large size. They are mainly characterized by their spindle-shaped bodies, tapering back to a slender caudal peduncle, which is usually keeled on either side, and by the soft dorsal and anal fins, which consist of a short and pointed lobe on which the fin-rays are crowded together and followed by a series of detached finlets. The body is more or less covered with minute, closely adherent, smooth scales, which may be longer and thicker on the "shoulder" region, forming a kind of corselet, or the body may be largely naked. The head is sharply pointed and the mouth rather large. The jaws are armed with very strong and sharp teeth, subconical and but little compressed in the tunas, but compressed, subtriangular or knife-like in the Spanish mackerels, *Scomberomorus*.

Nearly all members of the family are valued food-fishes. Their flesh, which is firm, oily, and usually red in colour, is especially suited for canning.

The family includes some of the finest sporting fishes in the world, such as the well-known Bluefin or Leaping Tuna of the Mediterranean and Atlantic, *Thunnus thynnus*; the Atlantic Yellowfin Tuna, *Neothunnus argentivittatus*, various species of Albacore (*Germo*) and the Spanish mackerels, *Scomberomorus*. In Australia and various other parts of the world, especially America, sporting clubs have been formed to angle for these giants of the ocean, and they are often landed on the lightest of regulation tackle after fights of several hours' duration. The world's record for a tuna captured under club rules was for a fish captured off Los Angeles in 1938. It weighed 890 pounds and took five hours to bring to gaff.

These tunas or tunnies are the largest members of the family, or indeed, for that matter, of all the living fishes. The Common Tunny of the Mediterranean and Atlantic, a fish which was well known to the ancients, reaches a length of at least 12 feet and a weight of 1,500 pounds.

The tunas and their allies are unique among fishes in that their body temperature is several degrees above that of the surrounding water. They are warm-blooded fishes and their flesh receives a larger blood supply than ordinarily, so that it assumes a more or less distinctly "beefy" or red colour.

These tunas are among the swiftest and most powerful of all oceanic fishes, the form of their bodies being especially adapted for fast movement and offering a minimum of resistance to the water. The spinous dorsal, pectoral, and ventral fins fit snugly into grooves or depressions in the body, thus considerably lessoning drag or resistance and assisting in preserving a smooth body contour. The soft dorsal and anal, together with their finlets, act as stabilizers and keep the fish's balance, while the motive power is provided by the powerful tail, which is controlled by muscular movements of the whole body. There is a single keel on each side of the caudal peduncle and also a pair of lesser keels on the caudal base. These no doubt serve as additional stabilizers.

Tunas are lovers of the open ocean, moving in great shoals, leisurely or at high speeds, and travelling great distances in search of prey. They are carnivorous in habit, relentlessly pursuing and feeding upon other surface fishes such as herring, flying-fishes, and small mackerel. In Australian waters their presence may always be detected at great distances by the flocks of sea-birds which wheel and dive about over the fish. Closer observation often reveal the fishes feeding on shoals of herrings. The tunas lash the water into foam in their fierce orgy and frequently leap high over each other in their excited killing and maiming, which is always in excess of their wants. The dead and dying herrings float on the surface and thus attract the sea-birds to an easy meal.

The tunas are fishes of great commercial importance, and though their flesh is seldom consumed when fresh it is very rich in oils and is admirably suited for canning. The livers are rich in vitamins A and D; and various by-products, such as fish-glue, are obtained from the fish. Huge canneries have been established in California to deal with the enormous catches. Output from these canneries has grown to such an extent that the industry ranks second in importance to the salmon canneries of the Pacific coast. No doubt similar canneries will eventually be established along the Australian coastline to exploit the great shoals which visit Australian waters.

In fishing commercially for these valuable food-fishes, various methods are employed. In California and also in the Mediterranean huge purse-seine nets and other types such as trap and pound nets are used during the spawning season, when the adults do not feed. Another method is by means of harpoons, either thrown by hand or propelled by gun. Perhaps the most common methods are trolling a feather lure or spinner from a moving launch and pole-fishing with live bait. In the former method one or two unbaited hooks are attached to a feather lure and trolled behind a moving launch at a speed which varies according to the species sought. Other types of lures are also used, such as spoons and spinners of brightly polished metal, slotted down the centre to receive the hook. Even lily-stalks chopped into 12-inch lengths have been used successfully in North Queensland. A common practice in America is to rig the boat with two booms or outriggers, each of which carries as many as twelve trolling lines.

Pole-fishing with live bait is a method frequently used in California, and D. L. Serventy in his admirable report on the Australian tunas[53] gives some interesting notes on it. He states in reference to the fishing boats employed: ". . . these boats carry a small tank with live bait, and when, by trolling, a school is located, the bait is thrown out in scoopfuls, the boat is brought about, the engine stopped and fishing carried on with hand-poles and lines" He goes. on to say: "This method has been developed to a remarkable degree of efficiency in California. . . . An average modern tuna clipper evolved for this fishery, costing about £30,000 to build, about 120 feet in length and carrying a complement of 16 men, may fish three thousand miles from its home port; the cruises lasting up to six weeks. Pilchards and also anchovies caught by lampara nets on the way to the fishing grounds, are carried in large bait tanks, fed by circulating sea-water. When a school of tuna is located the fishing is done from racks over the side of the boat. Barbless hooks, either baited or fitted with a feather squid, are employed. For hauling in big fish two or more fishermen work together, linking their lines by a swivel to the one hook. Tuna over 30 lb. are regarded as 'two-pole fish' whilst those weighing 50 or 60 lb. are 'three-pole fish', needing three men to land the one tuna. Up to five-pole teams are known. The quantity of fish caught by this method is very great. In 1936 the Californian fleet of nearly 70 high seas tuna clippers, delivered about 35,000 tons of tuna to the canneries, the species comprising yellow-fin and striped tuna."

The names of "tunny" and "tuna" have been widely and very loosely applied to many species of the family Scombridae, the former name having been favoured by English peoples whilst the latter is used in the Americas. The names *Thunnus* and *Thynnus* are ancient names for the tunny, and such names as tunny, tuna, thon, etc., have been derived from them. The name of "albacore" has been erroneously applied to several species in this family. It should be reserved for the true Albacore, *Thunnus germo*, a wide-ranging species which so far has not been recorded from Queensland, though it frequents the waters of south-eastern Australia. Twelve genera represent the family in Queensland.

KEY TO GENERA IN QUEENSLAND

A. Caudal peduncle without a median keel on each side, though ridges may be present above and below.

b. Anterior dorsal rays highest. Scales small or minute.

---

[53] Serventy, *The Australian Tunas*, Div. Fish. Rep. no. 4, C.S.I.R., 1941, pamphlet 104, pp. 9-48 (with plates).

    c. Gill-rakers exceedingly long and numerous, visible from gape of mouth. Scales moderately small.   *Rastrelliger*

    cc. Gill-rakers not so long, not visible from gape of mouth. Scales minute.   *Scomber*

   bb. Median dorsal spines highest. Scales large.   *Gasterochisma*

AA. Caudal peduncle with a median keel on each side.

    d. A single lateral line on each side.

    e. Dorsal spines 10-20. Teeth entire.

     f. Body largely naked, except near the lateral line and corselet, or, along the top of back and on caudal peduncle.

      g. Scales of corselet concealed under the skin, forming wavy longitudinal streaks; spinous dorsal low, not forming a high lobe and not as high as soft dorsal. Lateral line undulating, forming a peak above anal origin. Colour uniform, without stripes.   *Gymnosarda*

      gg. Corselet well developed, scales visible. Spinous dorsal with a distinct high lobe, higher than soft dorsal. Lateral line comparatively straight; body usually with dark marks or oblique streaks.   *Euthynnus*

      ggg. Large scales embedded and partially hidden from an obscure corselet. Small scales present along top of back and on caudal peduncle. Dark, elongate spots on body dorsally and longitudinal dark lines below.   *Cybiosarda*

    ff. Body wholly covered with small scales.

     h. Teeth subconical, little compressed; gill-rakers numerous. Corselet distinct.

     i. Vomer and palatines with villiform teeth. Body robust, not compressed. Colour uniform.

      j. Air-bladder well developed. Second dorsal and anal much elongated, sometimes reaching caudal base. Pectoral long, reaching beyond origin of second dorsal.   *Neothunnus*

      jj. Air-bladder absent. Second dorsal and anal not so elongate, but little higher than first dorsal. Pectoral short, broad, not reaching to second dorsal.   *Kishinoella*

     ii. Vomer toothless, palatines with a row of conical teeth. Body elongate, slightly compressed. Dark longitudinal stripes present.   *Sarda*

    hh. Teeth compressed, subtriangular or knife-like. Gill-rakers comparatively few; corselet obscure.   *Scomberomorus*

354

ee. Dorsal spines 24-26. Teeth close-set, truncate,
sharp, edges finely serrate. Dark blue above,
silvery below, numerous silvery-green vertical
bands on body.   *Acanthocybium*
  dd. Two lateral lines on each side.   *Grammatorycnus*

Rastrelliger

Small mackerel distinguished chiefly by their numerous and long gill-rakers and
the long lower jaw. Two species in the Indo-Pacific, one being found in Queensland.

339. LONG-JAWED MACKEREL *Rastrelliger kanagurta* (Cuvier)
[Colour-plate 51]

Scomber kanagurta Cuvier, Règne Anim., 2nd ed., ii, April 1829, p. 197.
Illustration by G. Coates.

D. 9-10/11-12 + 5; A. 1-2/11-12 + 5; gill-rakers 25 to 35. Colour bluish
above, with a greenish tinge anteriorly; a row of greyish spots on each side of
spinous dorsal and usually one on base of origin of soft dorsal; 2 greenish-grey
longitudinal lines above lateral line and 2 golden ones from pectoral base;
cheeks and belly silvery; fins greyish, the finlets and anal tinged yellow.

This Indo-Pacific species visits the waters of North Queensland apparently
during the winter months. Grows to about 12 inches.

Scomber

Form elongate, body and cheeks covered by small thin scales. Eye with a well-
developed adipose eyelid. Small fine teeth in jaws and on vomer and palatines.
Two dorsals, the first of spines, the fin retracting into a sheath, the second of
soft rays. Two small keels on each side at caudal base. Five or six finlets behind
dorsal and anal. Caudal deeply forked, Pectorals short, the bases broad.

Pelagic fishes inhabiting most tropical and temperate seas. One species in
Queensland.

340. COMMON MACKEREL *Scomber japonicus* Houttouyn [Colour-plate 51]

Scomber japonicus Houttouyn, Nat. Verh. Holland, Maatsch. Haarlem, 20, 1780, p. 331.
Illustration by G. Coates.

D. 9-10/11-12 + 5-6; A. 1/11-12 + 5-6; gill-rakers 27-33. Colour: Back and
upper sides bright green, becoming dark blue after death, with numerous
irregular wavy transverse bars or streaks of dark green; sides paler green, with
numerous darker spots; lower surface pearly-white, with orange and pinkish
iridescence and with indistinct grey blotches and spots; fins pale greenish-
yellow.

A wide-ranging fish which inhabits the waters of the southern portions of Australia in great shoals, wandering into the waters of South Queensland, where during the winter months it is found as far north as the Caloundra Banks. The young are to be found in the bays and inlets, but the adults frequent the outside waters. The flesh is of good edible quality if eaten fresh. Grows to 20 inches. Average-sized specimens are from 12 to 14 inches. This species is possibly identical with the American Chub Mackerel and the so-called Spanish Mackerel of England (*S. colias*).

Gasterochisma

Body compressed. A deep groove along abdomen, in which the ventral fins can be completely concealed. Scales distinct, moderately large.

Large mackerel-like pelagic fishes inhabiting the temperate regions of the southern oceans. A single species.

341. BIG-SCALED MACKEREL *Gasterochisma melampus* Richardson
[Plate 48]

Gasterochisma melampus Richardson, Ann. Mag. Nat. Hist., 15, 1845, p. 346; and Ichth. Voy. Erebus and Terror, 1846, p. 60, pl. 37, figs 1-3 (young).
Gasterochisma melampus Waite, Trans. New Zeal. Inst., 45, 1913, p. 220, pl. 8 (adult).

Butterfly Mackerel.

D. 17/10-11 + 6-7; A. 2/10 + 6-7. Colour bluish-black above, silvery-white below; head steel-blue; ventral fins black; dorsal fin hyaline, the spines brown; pectorals silvery; caudal black; eye metallic-green and silver.

This rare oceanic species, originally recorded from New Zealand, has also been taken in Queensland, Tasmania, New South Wales, and South Africa. It is rarely seen, and its occurrence in Queensland is based on six examples which were seen in 1911 hanging in a Brisbane fish-shop window. The species has not been recorded from Queensland since. The fish undergoes great changes with growth, especially the ventral fins (as can be seen in the illustrations of the young and the adult). In the young examples up to about 15 inches these fins are very large, being one-third of the length of the whole fish. With age they become smaller, until in the adult they are of normal proportion. Grows to 6 feet.

Gymnosarda

Body robust, fusiform. Head large. Body naked except for corselet and lateral line. Dorsal fins continuous; margin of spinous dorsal straight.

Pelagic fishes of somewhat large size inhabiting the waters of tropical regions, mainly the Indo-Pacific. Species few, one in Queensland.

342. SCALELESS TUNA *Gymnosarda nuda* (Günther)　　[Colour-plate 51]

Pelamys nuda Günther, Cat. Fish. Brit. Mus., 2, 1830, p. 368.
Illustration by G. Coates.

White-flesh Tuna, Peg-tooth Tuna (Townsville); Dog-toothed Tuna (Tahiti).
D. 14/13, 7; A. 12/6; gill-rakers 2 + 10. Colour dark bluish to violaceous above, greyish-white below; top of head and lower jaw anteriorly greyish; fins black or greyish, the tip of soft dorsal and anal clear; dorsal finlets bluish; anal finlets yellowish.

This fish was originally recorded from the Red Sea and is known also from the tropical regions of the Indo-Pacific. In Australian seas it is known only from the waters of North Queensland. At Townsville it is well known, and examples of 50 and 90 pounds have been captured, though the average size is much smaller. It is usually caught over the outer reefs by the mackerel fishermen when they are trolling for mackerel. Said to grow to 8 feet, but the largest taken so far on the Queensland coast was 4 feet 6 inches.

Euthynnus: Little Tunas

Body robust. Small scales anteriorly only, forming a corselet in anterior half of body. Margin of spinous dorsal strongly concave.

Small tunas of the temperate and tropical seas. Three or four species are known, two being found in Queensland, both of which are destined to become of considerable commercial importance when canneries are established to deal with them and other members of the family which occur in Queensland waters, for they are present at times in great shoals. There are two species in Queensland.

KEY TO SPECIES IN QUEENSLAND

A.　Lateral line curved below second dorsal; 4 longitudinal
　　stripes on lower half of body.　　　　　　　　　　　　*pelamis*

AA.　Lateral line without distinct curve; no stripes on lower
　　half of body; pale wavy mackerel-like marks on upper
　　back.　　　　　　　　　　　　　　　　　　　　　*alletteratus*

343. BONITO *Euthynnus pelamis* (Linnaeus)　　　　　　[Plate 48]

Scomber pelamis Linnaeus, Syst. Nat., 10th ed., 1758, p. 297.
Katsuwonus pelamis Kishinouye, Journ. Coll. Agric. Tokyo, 8, no. 3, 1923, p. 453, pl. 30, fig. 53.

Oceanic Bonito (North America and South Africa); Lesser Tunny, Katonkel, Skipjack, Bonita, Watermelon (South Africa); Skipjack (California).
D. 12-17, 11-14 + 18; A. 11-15 + 7; gill-rakers 15-20 + 36-39. Colour deep bluish-black above; sides silvery, with 4 or more dark longitudinal bands on each lower side; dorsals, dorsal finlets, pectorals, and anal dusky.

In Australia this wide-ranging species is most commonly met with in the southern waters of the continent. In Queensland it has been recorded only from the south. Enormous shoals of these valuable fishes frequent the waters of Flinders Island, Tasmania and the vicinity, along the waters of Victoria to southern New South Wales. In California, where great numbers are caught and canned, it ranks next to the Yellowfin Tuna, *Neothunnus macropterus*, in commercial importance. Grows to about 36 inches in length and about 15 pounds in weight.

344. LITTLE TUNA *Euthynnus alletteratus* (Rafinesque) [Colour-plate 51]

Scomber alletteratus Rafinesque, Caratteri Alcuni Genere, etc., 1810, p. 46, (*fide* Sherborn).
Illustration by G. Coates.

Little Tunny, Bonito, Káwakána (Hawaii); Bonito (North Queensland); Mackerel Tuna (New South Wales); Bunny (Townsville); Mackerel Tuna, Merma (South Africa).

D. 15-16/11-13 + 8-10; A. 2-3/10-12 + 6-8. Colour dark bluish or green above, silvery on sides, white below; several greenish-blue wavy oblique streaks above lateral line, running backwards; a deep prussian-blue spindle-shaped mark above eye, from tip of snout to origin of second dorsal; fins dusky, the ventrals with a white margin; 4 to 6 round blackish spots on breast.

This small circumtropical fish is present on the Queensland coast in great numbers for most months of the year. G. Coates of Townsville states: "They do not appear to grow larger than 30 pounds and swim in very active shoals. They are along both coast and reefs." The Little Tuna is also found off the coast of northern New South Wales and in Western Australia.

The flesh is dark but of fair canning quality. Grows to about 4 feet.

Cybiosarda

Form mackerel-like, plump. Most of body naked, but small scales along top of back and on caudal peduncle, few on lateral line. Spinous dorsal fin high, the first spine longer than the second. A series of long, spaced, compressed teeth along each jaw.

A genus with a single species inhabiting the tropical and subtropical waters of Australia.

345. WATSON'S BONITO *Cybiosarda elegans* Whitley [Colour-plate 52]

Scomberomorus (Cybiosarda) elegans Whitley, Rec. Austr. Mus., 19, no. 4, 1935, p. 236.
Illustration by G. Coates.

Striped Bonito (South Queensland); Bonito (Queensland); Leaping Bonito, Watson's Mackerel (New South Wales).

D. 15-16/16 + 9-10 finlets; A. 15 + 8 finlets. Colour: Head sea-green above and down to a line about level with tip of snout, below which is yellowish-

white; back sea-greenish, becoming greyish-green on upper sides and passing
into whitish below; many small black spots on back near dorsals, becoming
larger, more elongate, and oblique on upper sides, those on sides transformed
into 3 to 4 black longitudinal stripes; spinous dorsal black anteriorly (or over
most of fin) and white on a few membranes posteriorly (sometimes also at
extreme base of anterior membranes). Soft dorsal, finlets, and caudal greyish;
pectoral dusky; ventrals greyish-white; anal and anal finlets greyish, the
former with yellowish anteriorly.

A small bonito found in the tropical and subtropical waters of Australia.
On the west coast it has been taken as far south as Fremantle and on the east
coast as far south as Shellharbour, New South Wales. Serventy states: "Shoals
of many hundreds are sometimes observed, and it can be trolled occasionally
in fair numbers north of Sydney. . . . This species is an excellent sporting fish
for its size, and is the one tuna whose flesh is appetizing in the fresh condition.
The meat is white and may be smoked quite well. No canning experiments
have yet been made."

The species grows to a length of 16 inches and a weight of 2 pounds.

Neothunnus: Yellow-finned Tunas

Large fishes ranking second in size to the great bluefin tunas, *Thunnus*. They are
recognized by the long pectoral fins, which are much longer than in the Bluefin
Tuna and which extend to the origin of the anal fin, but not beyond it as in the
true albacores. Another feature is the shape of the dorsal and anal fins, which
extend into long sickle-shaped lobes. These fins, which increase relatively
with age, are much higher than the first dorsal and in very large examples may
extend as far back as the tail-flukes. The dorsal and anal fins and finlets are
bright yellow, more especially in the young fish.

Three or four species are known, one being the Yellow-finned Tuna of the
Atlantic, *N. argentivittatus*, and another the Pacific Yellow-finned Tuna, *N.
macropterus*, which is described below. The Yellow-finned tunas are said to
reach a length of 9 feet and a weight of 400 pounds.

346. PACIFIC YELLOW-FINNED TUNA *Neothunnus macropterus* (Schlegel)
[Colour-plate 52]

Thynnus macropterus Schlegel, Fauna Japonica, Poiss., pts 5-6, 1844, p. 98.
Illustration by G. Coates.

Yellow-finned Albacore.

D. 13-14/14 + 9 finlets; A. 14-15 + 8-9. Colour black or deep prussian-blue
above, more intense towards the head; a bright-yellow patch round eye and
on top of opercle; sides opalescent-greyish with oblique alternating transverse
lines and series of spots anterior to anal; elongate light spots ventrally on tail;
dorsals, pectorals, and ventrals dusky, tinged with yellow which predominates

with age; anal and finlets of dorsal and anal intense brilliant yellow, with narrow and dark margins posteriorly.

This Pacific species is a well-known and highly important commercial fish. It roves the Indian and Pacific oceans and visits the waters of Queensland during the spring and summer months. A valuable canning species ranking second only to the Albacore, *Thunnus germo*, in California. Readily recognized by the long pectoral fin. Flesh red. About the largest example caught on the Queensland coast weighed 25 pounds. Grows to 5 feet.

Kishinoella

Near *Neothunnus* but differing mainly in the total absence of the air-bladder. The species are also smaller in size than the other known albacores or tunas. One species is found in Queensland.

347. NORTHERN BLUE-FINNED TUNA *Kishinoella tonggol* (Bleeker)
[Colour-plate 52]

Thynnus tonggol Bleeker, Nat. Tijdschr. Ned. Ind.,1, 1852, p. 356.
Illustration by G. Coates.

"Bonito" (Queensland).

D. 12-13/13-14 + 9; A. 13-14 + 8-9. Colour: Back greyish-blue, sides silvery-greyish, the colours sharply demarcated and separated posteriorly by a bright-blue stripe, colourless elongated spots in about five longitudinal rows are usually present; dorsal, pectorals, and ventrals blackish, the tip of the second dorsal and anal washed with yellow; anal fin silvery; dorsal and anal finlets yellow, with greyish margins; caudal blackish, with streaks of yellowish-green.

This fish is widely distributed in tropical and subtropical seas. On the east coast of Australia it has been taken as far south as Port Hacking, and in Western Australia almost to Busselton. It is also found in the East Indies, Ceylon, and Japan. Superficially it is like the Southern Blue-finned Tuna or Southern Tunny, *Thunnus maccoyi*, another common species found in the waters of the southern portion of Australia and with which it has been long confused.

The Northern Blue-finned Tuna differs from the southern species in that it is a longer or more attenuated fish, has an average of 9 finlets above and below, the spinous dorsal has a deeper concave margin, the total number of gill-rakers on the arch of the first gill is about 23, and, finally, the liver is pale brown and quite plain, without any dark lines on its surface (see Fig. 12).

The Southern Blue-finned Tuna is a stouter and heavier fish, has an average of eight finlets above and below, and 32 to 37 gill-rakers on the arch of the first gill. The liver is dark red with fine black parallel lines streaking its surface (see Fig. 12).

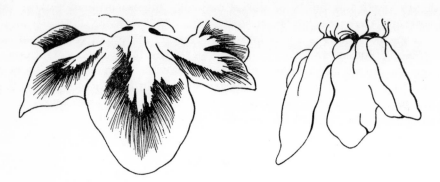

Fig. 12. Typical livers of tuna. That of the Southern Blue-fin (left) has parallel lines streaking the surface; the Northern Blue-fin has a pale and plain liver. F. OLSEN, AFTER SERVENTY.

The Northern Blue-finned Tuna is extremely common on the Queensland coast, usually being captured by the mackerel fishermen when they are trolling for those fish. It is a small tuna which does not appear to grow larger than about 4 feet in length and to a weight of 50 pounds, the average fish being 25 pounds. From an economic point of view it is a valuable species. Its flesh is pale in colour, rather soft but of good flavour, and it is highly regarded in Japan. The flesh is excellent eating when steamed and served with parsley sauce.

The Northern Blue-finned Tuna is present in Queensland at all times of the year and is commonly known as "Bonito".

Sarda

Body elongate, short and compressed in young. Scales minute; small corselet more or less distinct. Caudal keel thick, naked. Dark longitudinal stripes present.

Pelagic fishes of rather small size inhabiting subtropical and tropical waters of the Pacific and Atlantic oceans. Species few, one in Queensland.

348. LITTLE BONITO *Sarda australis* (Macleay) [Colour-plate 52]

Pelamys australis Macleay, Proc. Linn. Soc. N.S.Wales, 5, pt 4, 1881, p. 557.
Illustration by G. Coates.

"Bonito" (Queensland and New South Wales); Horse Mackerel (New South Wales and Victoria).

D. 19, 2-3 + 12 + 7-8 finlets; A. 2-3/ + 11-12 + 6 finlets. Colour blackish-green above, fading into silvery on sides and below; a broad dusky band covering upper surface of head and extending along dorsal surface; 5 to 11 dark longitudinal lines on sides, the lower ones faint; dorsal fins dusky, the upper third of the anterior spines darkest, of the rays yellowish, as also are the tips of the finlets; pectorals dusky, sometimes with a yellowish tinge; ventrals whitish; anal yellowish; caudal blackish, the tips tinged with greenish-yellow.

The Little Bonito is very common on the coasts of Queensland and New South Wales, being found in great shoals throughout the year. A likely place to capture them, like most other members of the family, is when trolling from a moving launch over the outside reefs. They are destined some day to be of economic importance in Australia. The flesh is light coloured, of delicate flavour and of good canning quality. The species grows to about 3 feet, but the average size met with is about 16 or 18 inches.

The Little Bonito is closely related to the Californian Bonito or "Skip-jack", *S. chiliensis.*

Scomberomorus

Large fishes, widely distributed in warm open seas. They are migratory in habit and visit the offshore waters of Queensland in great schools. Some of the species grow to a large size, and in Queensland are among the most important food-fishes.

The body is long, well compressed or more or less flattened on the sides, and the tail is usually much longer than the body. The head is small and pointed in front and the jaws are armed with strong, large teeth, compressed and with the edges trenchant. The body is covered with rudimentary scales, but there is no distinct corselet in the "shoulder" region. The dorsal fins are close together, the low spinous portion consisting of 12 to 22 spines. The short soft dorsal and anal fins have moderately high lobes in front and are followed by the usual "mackerel" finlets. The colour is usually more or less silvery, with a metallic bluish-black back and narrow vertical stripes or dark spots on the body. Some of the larger species grow to a length of 6 feet or more and a weight of over 100 pounds.

They are fast-swimming and predacious, pursuing and feeding upon fishes such as herrings, sardines, and other school fishes. When feeding on these schools they are easily caught by the fishermen because they will bite madly and blindly at anything which remotely resembles a fish. The usual method of capture in Australian waters is by means of trolling lines from a moving launch, a metal spinner or feather lure being used instead of a bait. When hooked, the fishes often leap high from the water, and jumps of at least 20 feet have been recorded. When gaffed and hauled aboard they quickly die, but while alive will snap viciously at anything within reach.

The flesh is of excellent flavour, though sometimes it is somewhat dry owing to the practice of fishmongers cutting the fish into rounds instead of longitudinal fillets. When treated in the latter manner the cells retain their moisture, and an altogether different flavour seems to be given to the flesh. No doubt, like the tunas, the flesh would be admirably suited for canning. Four species occur in Queensland waters.

362

Adapted from Munro[54]

A. Gill-rakers rudimentary, never more than $1 + 6$; teeth flat, compressed and minutely serrulate; 16-17 dorsal spines.

    b. Body marked with numerous narrow wavy bands on belly; lateral line with sharp inflection below second dorsal finlet.   *commerson*

    bb. Body marked with diffuse rounded blotches, each larger than diameter of eye and arranged in about 3 rows below lateral line; lateral line without a deep inflection.   *queenslandicus*

AA. Gill-rakers well developed, $2 + 8$-9; teeth slightly curved inwards but not serrulate.

    c. Body marked with anastomosing spots about the size of pupil of eye and confined to a band along middle of side; 20-22 dorsal spines.   *niphonius*

    cc. Body marked with a few broad straight vertical bands on its upper portion; spinous dorsal with only 13-15 dorsal spines; head very small.   *semifasciatus*

349. NARROW-BARRED MACKEREL *Scomberomorus commerson* (Lacépède) [Plate 49]

Scomber commerson Lacépède, Hist. Nat. Poiss., 2, 1800, pp. 598-603.

Scomberomorus (Cybium) commerson Munro, Mem. Qld Mus., 12, pt 2, 6th Nov. 1943, pp. 74-82, pl. 6, fig. B (adult) and pl. 8, fig. 3 (juvenile).

Narrow-barred Mackerel, Snook, Kingfish, Banded Tuna (North Queensland); Leaping Tuna (New South Wales); Albacore (Western Australia); Striped Sier (Ceylon); Kingfish, Bonita, Katonkel (South Africa); Barracouta, Kuda (Natal).

D. 14-17 + 16-19 + 9-11 finlets; A. 14-18 + 8-10 finlets. Colour: "The following colour notes apply to freshly caught specimens from the Queensland coast: Cranial regions and upper regions of back are mottled with iridescent blue and green with some purple and bronze colours giving a 'shot' appearance which rapidly changes to deep blue. Below the level of the lateral line from the snout to the caudal fork the sides are a pale silver grey with some iridescent shades and marked with transverse vertical bars of a darker grey, these extending upwards into the darker zone above the lateral line where they fade away. These bars are narrow and slightly wavy and often break up into spots in the belly region. This condition is most marked in the bars nearest the tail and in young fish. There are about 40 or 50 such bands in mature fish but there is

---

[54] *Mem. Qld Mus.*, 12, pt 2, 1943, p. 73.

usually less than 20 in fish up to 18 inches long. The cheeks, lower jaw and belly region are silvery white. Spinous dorsal fin is bright blue with white spines which rapidly fades to a blackish blue. The pectoral fin is a light grey which likewise turns to a blackish blue. The caudal flukes, soft dorsal, anal fins, and dorsal and anal finlets are a pale greyish white colour which quickly turn to dark grey with a tinge of blue-green or yellow. In younger specimens the membrane of the spinous dorsal fin is pure white with contrasting jet black areas anteriorly." (Munro.)

The Narrow-barred Mackerel is one of the most important food-fishes of Queensland. Tons of these valuable mackerel reach the Brisbane Fish Market each year from all ports, the busiest months being from about August to December when the fish school in their biggest numbers over the many outside reefs. Odd fish are present throughout the year but they move solitarily and not in the great schools seen in the above-mentioned months. Whilst they are doubtless migratory, limits to the distance they travel are apparent. It would seem that in the off-season the schools break up and the fishes move out into the open ocean away from the reefs over which they are usually caught. In the southern portions of the Great Barrier Reef, around such islands as the Bunkers and Capricorn groups, during the months of May and June they are to be found in immense numbers. They work northwards, and in the Whitsunday Passage are captured during September and October and at Townsville until the end of the year. Examples captured in the Moreton Bay district, South Queensland, during the early winter months are usually from 9 to 25 pounds in weight, larger ones being taken in the northern parts of the State. The record for size is said to be one which weighed 130 pounds and was 7 feet 6 inches in total length. According to G. Coates this specimen was taken off Townsville in 1948.

In Australian waters the range of the species is along the coasts of Queensland and New South Wales, especially the islands of the Great Barrier Reef, through Torres Strait and across the waters of North Australia to Western Australia. It also ranges through the Indo-Pacific to India, Ceylon, The Bay of Bengal, China, Japan, Africa, The Red Sea, etc.

From the point of view of edibility the flesh tastes better when boiled and served with a white sauce than cooked and served in any other way, though it is one of the best food-fishes when smoked.

350. QUEENSLAND SCHOOL MACKEREL *Scomberomorus queenslandicus* Munro [Plate 49]

Scomberomorus (Cybium) queenslandicus Munro, Mem. Qld Mus., 12, pt 2, 6th Nov. 1943, pp. 82-6, pl. 7, fig. B (adult) and pl. 8, fig. 1 (juvenile).

School Mackerel (Queensland); Doggie (Townsville district).

D. 15-17/16-20 + 9-10 finlets; A. 15-20 + 9-10 finlets. Colour: "In freshly caught specimens the colours are as follows: Crania regions and upper part of the back are an iridescent bluish green and the cheeks and belly are a silvery white. In adult fish the sides are marked with about three indefinite rows of bronze-grey indistinct blotches, each a little larger than the orbit. The membrane of the spinous dorsal fin is jet black with large contrasting areas of intense white between the sixth and last spines. The second dorsal fin and the finlets are pearly grey with darker margins. The caudal fin is of similar colour. The ventrals, anal fin and anal finlets are white. The pectoral fins are greyish, being darkest on their inner surface." (Munro.)

A small species of mackerel commonly found in the bays and in the waters along the whole of the Queensland coastline. Also found on the coast of Western Australia. Further investigation will probably show that it occurs in the waters of North Australia, though no examples have been taken to date.

The School Mackerel is commonly taken in Moreton Bay during the winter months by means of nets or of trolling lines. It reaches maturity at a small size, being the smallest of the Australian *Scomberomorus*. Average-sized fish are about 20 inches in length and weigh 3 to 4 pounds, but the largest are about 30 inches.

351. SPOTTED MACKEREL *Scomberomorus niphonius*
(Cuvier and Valenciennes) [Plate 50]

Cybium niphonium Cuvier and Valenciennes, Hist. Nat. Poiss., 8, 1831, pp. 180-1.
Scomberomorus (Sawara) niphonius Munro, Mem. Qld Mus., 12, pt 2, 6th Nov. 1943, pp. 86-90, pl. 7, fig. A.

Sawara (Tokyo); Sagoshi (Prov. Tosa); Japanese Spanish Mackerel.

D. 20-22/16-19 + 9-10 finlets; A. 15-18 + 9 finlets. Colour: "In freshly caught specimens the colours are as follows: Cranial regions and upper part of back are of darkish blue. The sides are a light silvery grey marked with three or four indefinite rows of dark grey spots along the region of the lateral line. These spots are rounded or irregular in shape and about the size of the pupil of the eye (ca. $\frac{3}{8}$-$\frac{1}{2}$ in. diameter). The cheek plates and belly are of silvery white. There is a pale but distinctive purplish sheen over most of the body of freshly caught fish and this is especially noticeable on the belly. The spinous dorsal is of a bright steely blue with a mottling of white throughout. There are white blotches on the membrane near the bases of the more posterior spines while there are areas of darker grey near the tips of the spines. The second dorsal fin and dorsal finlets are of a dull grey as also are the caudal flukes. Anal fin is light silvery grey with white near its tip. Anal finlets are silvery grey. Inner surface of pectoral fin is dark blue as on back and outer surface dark silver grey. Ventral fins silver white internally but greyish on the outside. The body colours lose their brilliance and fade to various shades of grey after death." (Munro.)

According to Munro this Japanese species is at present known in Australia only from the waters of the east coast of the continent. He states: "That this species occurs in Queensland waters has never before been appreciated nor put on record by ichthyologists. However it is quite well known from the seas of China and Japan. As far as records show the distribution in the Northern Hemisphere is roughly limited by the parallels of 25° N. and 45° N. along the coast of China, Korea, and both coasts of Japan. In Australian waters the known limits are 18° S. to 30° S. approximately and restricted to the east coast, i.e. from Cairns, N. Qld, to Coff's Harbour, N.S.W. It is caught principally in shallow waters over reefs close inshore but has also been caught along the Great Barrier Reef. It is fished in small numbers on North Queensland fishing grounds from October onwards but in large numbers in South Queensland and northern N.S.W. from December until April and May."

This species grows to over 40 inches in length and a weight of about 10 pounds.

352. BROAD-BARRED MACKEREL *Scomberomorus semifasciatus* (Macleay)
[Plate 50]

Cybium semifasciatus Macleay, Proc. Linn. Soc. N.S.Wales, 8, 1883, p. 205.

Scomberomorus (Indocybium) semifasciatus Munro, Mem. Qld Mus., 12, pt 2, 6th Nov. 1943, p. 91, pl. 6, fig. A (adult) and pl. 8, fig. 2 (juveniles), and text-fig. 4.

Striped School Mackerel, Tiger Mackerel, Brownie (Moreton Bay and Hervey Bay); Grey Mackerel, Broad-barred Spanish Mackerel (Queensland); School Mackerel (Whitsunday Passage).

D. 13-15/17-20 + 8-10 finlets; A. 20-22 + 8-10 finlets. Colour: "In immature specimens (i.e., less than 100 mm.) the colouration in life is as follows: Cranial regions and upper regions of the back are pale green with a bronze sheen and marked with about twelve to twenty broad vertical bands of a dark grey. These bars are confined to the region of the body above the lateral line and their number increases with age. The cheeks and belly are silvery white. The snout is a dark slate grey and there is a patch of green above the orbit. The spinous dorsal fin is jet black with contrasting areas of white in its central region. The second dorsal fin is cream with yellow anteriorly. The anal fin and all finlets are of a transparent white. The caudal flukes are creamy white at their margins and dusky or blackish near the hypural. The pectoral fins are dusky.

"As the species increases in size the bronze green colouration of the back turns to a greenish blue. The vertical bands on the back are most marked in specimens less than 500 mm. in length and in larger fish there is a tendency for these markings to become less distinct, break into spots or fade out more or less completely. Above 700 mm. dead fish assume a drab greyish-yellow blotchy appearance with little or no evidence of markings. This uniform grey colour apparently accounts for the vernacular 'Grey Mackerel' of Queensland fishermen as applied to older age groups of the species. The younger age groups caught in the Queensland estuaries principally Moreton Bay and Hervey Bay are called 'Brownies' or even 'Striped School Mackerel'." (Munro.)

A species which has commonly been confused with the Narrow-barred Mackerel, *S. commerson*. When the two are seen together the differences are quite evident, apart from colour. The large soft dorsal and anal fins and the caudal of *S. semifasciatus* together with the much larger keels on the peduncle, serve to at once distinguish it.

Known only from the tropical and subtropical coastal waters of Queensland, northern New South Wales, and also northern Australia. Grows to at least 40 inches. Common.

Acanthocybium

Form elongate, compressed, covered with minute narrow scales. Snout long. Mouth large; teeth large. Two dorsals, the first long, of 26 to 27 spines, the second short, of 10 to 13 rays. Distribution that of the single known species.

353. WAHOO or PETO *Acanthocybium solandri* (Cuvier and Valenciennes)
[Plate 50]

Cybium solandri Cuvier and Valenciennes, Hist. Nat. Poiss., 8, 1831, p. 192.
Acanthocybium solandri Kishinouye, Journ. Coll. Agric. Tokyo, 8, no. 3, 1923, p. 411, pl. 20, fig. 31.

Jack Mackerel, Pike Mackerel, Bastard Mackerel, Mongrel Mackerel (North Queensland).

D. 26-27/11-13 + 9 finlets; A. 11 + 8-9 finlets. Colour prussian blue on back, silvery on sides and below, the two colours separated by a broad or fairly broad sea-green stripe, the three colours fairly sharply defined; about 30 light silvery-green vertical bands on sides of body, many of them doubled by being joined below; cheeks silvery-blue, hind edge of preopercle with a black serration; spinous dorsal blue; soft dorsal blue-black; ventrals pale blue; pectorals and caudal blackish. Some examples are almost black, others are without the transverse bands which are most distinct in young examples.

The Wahoo is a fast-swimming fish and a lover of the open seas. It is seldom met with in numbers, being somewhat solitary in habit, and is not really common anywhere. Its food consists of pelagic fishes, cuttlefish, and squids. Of a vicious, greedy disposition, it can readily be attracted by either natural baits or artificial lures. In Australian waters it has been recorded from Queensland, northern New South Wales, and north-west Australia. In South Queensland it is frequently caught by game and professional fishermen, but becomes rare in the waters of North Queensland.

Grows to a weight of 136 pounds and reaches a length of at least 6 feet 8 inches. A good food-fish with white flesh of excellent quality but somewhat softer than that of the Spanish mackerels.

Grammatorycnus

Body elongate, compressed, covered with small deciduous scales. Two lateral lines on each side of body. Teeth elongated, trenchant. Two dorsals, the first with 11 to 12 strong spines, the second with a spine and 9 to 10 rays. Anal with 1 to 2 spines and 11 branched rays. Dorsal finlets 6 to 7; anal finlets 6. Distribution that of the single known species.

354. LARGE-SCALED TUNNY *Grammatorycnus bicarinatus* (Quoy and Gaimard) [Colour-plate 53]

Thynnus bicarinatus Quoy and Gaimard, Voy. Uranie Physic., 1825, p. 357.
Illustration by G. Coates.

Salmon Mackerel, Shark Mackerel (Queensland); Scaly Kingfish (North Queensland); 'Couta (northern New South Wales).

D. 11-12/1/9-10 + 7 finlets; A. 2/9-11 + 6-7 finlets. Colour: Back brilliant metallic green with a certain admixture of bright blue; upper sides yellowish-bronze-green; sides in the area between the two lateral lines silvery, with a longitudinal row of bright bronze blotches medianally; belly and lower parts of head, lower jaw, etc., creamy-white, with some yellow and marked with several rows of dark blackish blotches of irregular size; these belly spots are black, with yellowish areas round them; dorsal spines yellowish, the membranes dark grey, with a narrow border of dirty white; soft dorsal and its finlets and the caudal flukes all dark grey, with a yellowish tinge, the darkest areas being at base of dorsals and along posterior margin of caudal; anal and finlets lighter silver-grey, almost transparent, being whitish basally; tip of anal dark grey; outer surface of pectoral greyish, with some yellow as in the soft dorsal and caudal, the inner surface dusky; ventrals with the rays whitish, the membranes with blue-grey areas. (After Munro.)

This interesting fish, which until quite recently was thought to be rare, is well known to the Queensland mackerel fishermen. It is known from Australian seas only and has been recorded from Queensland, New South Wales, and Western Australia. As is the case with many other species it failed to come under the notice of scientific authorities as a common species until comparatively recently (1940), though apparently well known to the fishermen. It is received into the Brisbane Fish Market with the mackerel catch, and during the height of the season sometimes reaches as high as ten per cent of the mackerel catch handled there.

The name Salmon Mackerel is applied by the Moreton Bay fishermen. In North Queensland the name Shark Mackerel is bestowed on it because its flesh is said to have an odour similar to that of a shark. It is a good edible fish, and grows to 36 inches.

Sub-order GOBIOIDEA

Family Gobiidae: Gobies and Gudgeons

Body oblong or elongate. Scales and lateral line present or absent. Teeth of varying character, canines present or absent. Premaxillaries protractile. Eyes usually lateral, occasionally prominent and mostly without free orbital margins, the skin of the head being continued directly over their surface. Dorsal fins separate or united. Ventrals close together, separate or united to form a disc. Anal rather long, usually with a single weak spine, similar to soft dorsal. Caudal fin usually convex. Anal papillae prominent.

Carnivorous fishes, mostly of small size, living in warm regions on sandy and muddy bottoms close inshore. Many are found in rock-pools between tide-marks; others bury themselves in the muddy estuaries and mangrove flats; some inhabit the fresh water only, and some are equally at home in either fresh or salt water.

KEY TO SUB-FAMILIES

A. Pectoral base very muscular and mobile. Eyes erectile.   PERIOPHTHALMINAE

AA. Pectoral base not usually muscular or mobile. Eyes not erectile.

    b. Ventral fins more or less united, usually with an anterior membrane connecting the spines.   GOBIINAE

    bb. Ventral fins separate, no anterior membrane between spines.   ELEOTRINAE

Sub-family PERIOPHTHALMINAE: MUD-HOPPERS

Eyes close together, very prominent and erectile. Base of pectoral fin very muscular and mobile.

A small group of fishes inhabiting the estuaries and mud-flats of the waters of the Indian and Pacific oceans and Japan.

KEY TO GENERA

Adapted from McCulloch and Ogilby[55]

A. Soft dorsal with about 12 rays. Teeth vertical in both jaws, conical and subequal.

    b. Teeth uniserial in both jaws; scales small.   *Periophthalmus*

    bb. Teeth biserial in the premaxillaries; scales larger.   *Periophthalmodon*

---

[55] *Rec. Austr. Mus.*, 12, pt 10, 1919, p. 194.

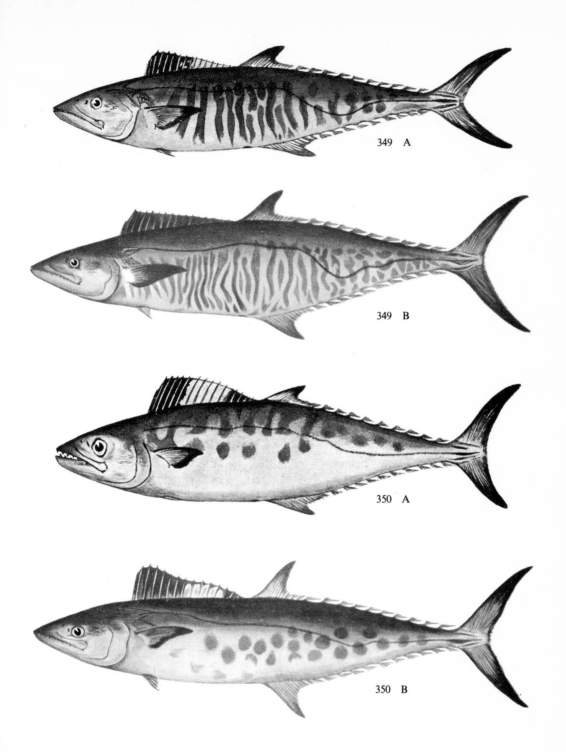

PLATE 49
349. Narrow-barred Mackerel *Scomberomorus commerson*. A, Juv., 16 in.; B,
adult, 41 in.   350. Queensland School Mackerel, *S. queenslandicus*. A, Juv.,
8 in.; B, adult, 24 in.

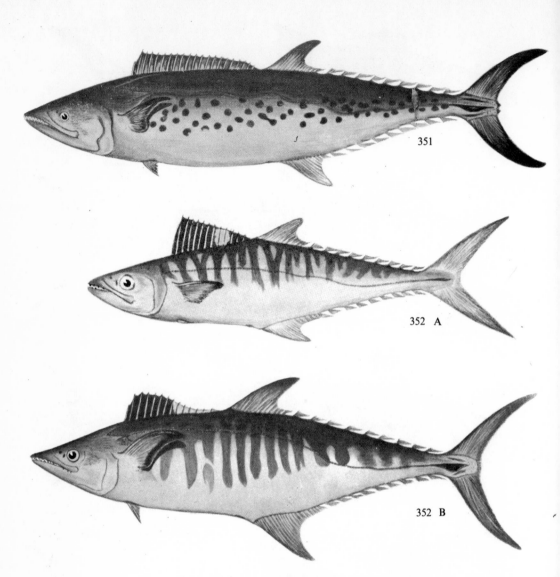

PLATE 50
351. Spotted Mackerel, *S. niphonius*, 33 in.   352. Broad-barred Mackerel, *S. semifasciatus*. A, Juv., 6½ in.; B, adult, 20 in.   353. Wahoo or Peto, *Acanthocybium solandri*, 44 in.

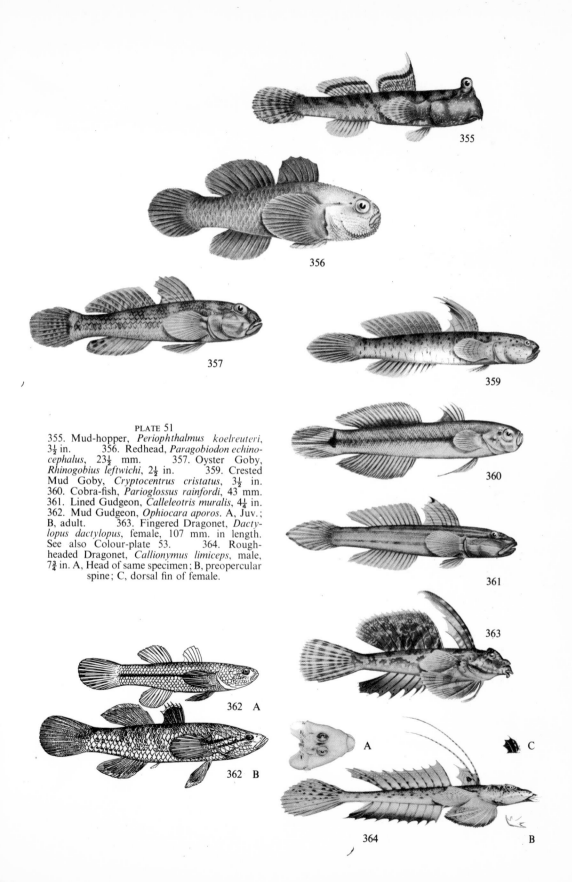

355

356

357

359

360

361

363

362 A

362 B

A

C

364

B

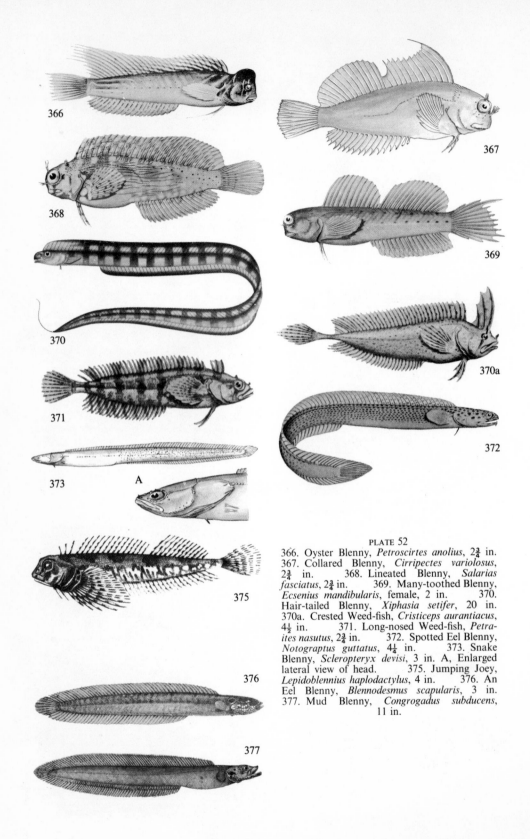

PLATE 52

366. Oyster Blenny, *Petroscirtes anolius*, 2¾ in. 367. Collared Blenny, *Cirripectes variolosus*, 2¾ in.   368. Lineated Blenny, *Salarias fasciatus*, 2¾ in.   369. Many-toothed Blenny, *Ecsenius mandibularis*, female, 2 in.   370. Hair-tailed Blenny, *Xiphasia setifer*, 20 in. 370a. Crested Weed-fish, *Cristiceps aurantiacus*, 4½ in.   371. Long-nosed Weed-fish, *Petraites nasutus*, 2¾ in.   372. Spotted Eel Blenny, *Notograptus guttatus*, 4¼ in.   373. Snake Blenny, *Scleropteryx devisi*, 3 in. A, Enlarged lateral view of head.   375. Jumping Joey, *Lepidoblennius haplodactylus*, 4 in.   376. An Eel Blenny, *Blennodesmus scapularis*, 3 in. 377. Mud Blenny, *Congrogadus subducens*, 11 in.

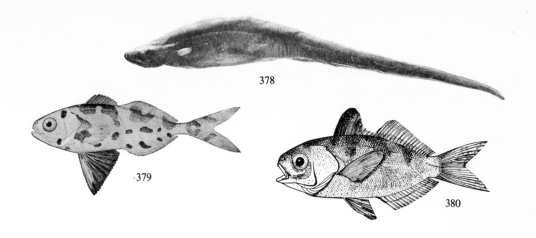

PLATE 53
378. Hump-back Messmate, *Carapus houlti*, 81 mm. 379. Portuguese Man-o'-war Fish, *Nomeus albula*, 3¼ in. 380. Whitelegge's Blubber-fish, *Psenes whiteleggii*, 2 in. 384. Tallegalane or Sand Mullet, *Myxus elongatus*. 385. Freshwater Mullet, *Trachystoma petardi*, 14 in.

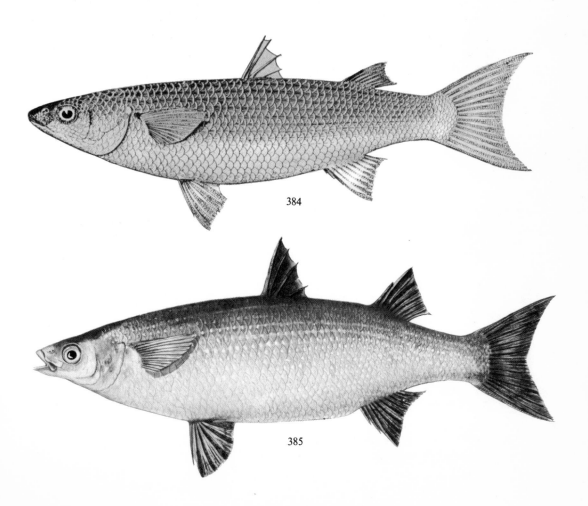

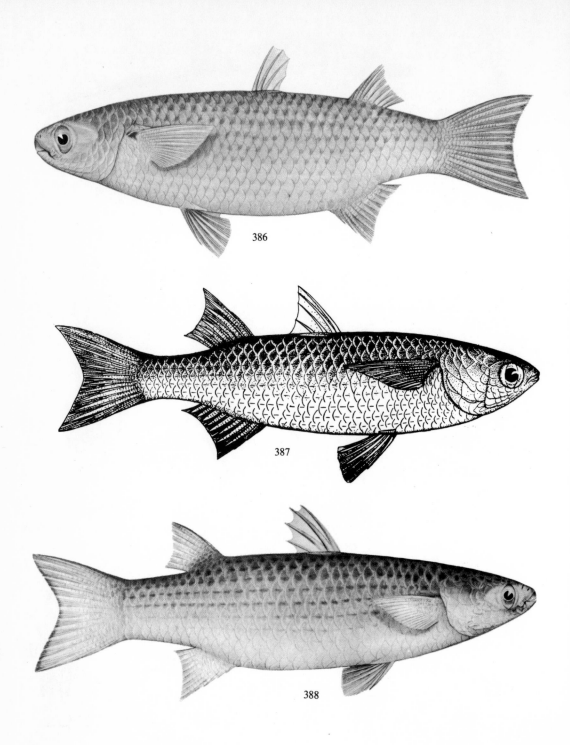

386

387

388

PLATE 54

386. Fantail Mullet, *Mugil georgii*, 9 in.   387. Long-finned Mullet, *M. strongylocephalus*, 9 in.   388. Flat-tail Mullet, *M. dussumieri*, 10½ in.

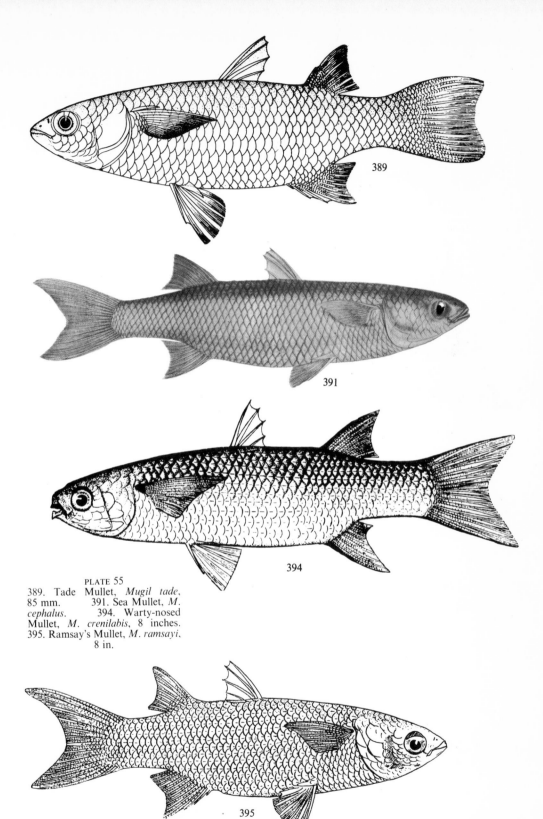

PLATE 55
389. Tade Mullet, *Mugil tade*,
85 mm. 391. Sea Mullet, *M.
cephalus*. 394. Warty-nosed
Mullet, *M. crenilabis*, 8 inches.
395. Ramsay's Mullet, *M. ramsayi*,
8 in.

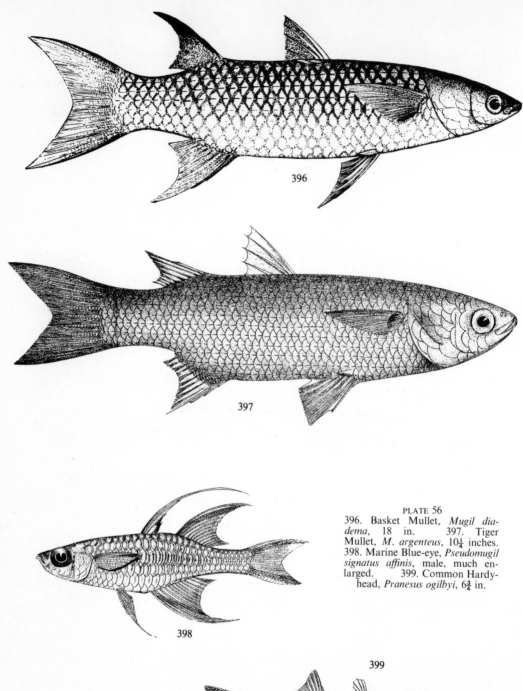

396

397

398

399

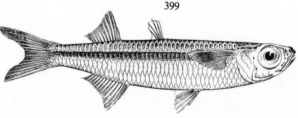

PLATE 56
396. Basket Mullet, *Mugil diadema*, 18 in. 397. Tiger Mullet, *M. argenteus*, 10½ inches. 398. Marine Blue-eye, *Pseudomugil signatus affinis*, male, much enlarged. 399. Common Hardyhead, *Pranesus ogilbyi*, 6¾ in.

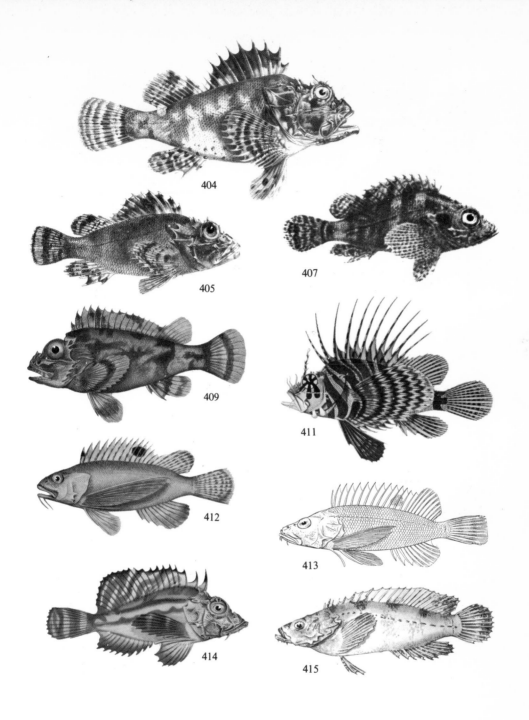

PLATE 57

404. Red Scorpion Cod, *Ruboralga cardinalis*, 18 in.   405. Little Scorpion Cod, *Oligoscorpaena bandanensis*, $4\frac{1}{4}$ in.   407. Guam Scorpion Cod, *Scorpaenodes guamensis*.   409. Marbled Fortesque, *Centropogon marmoratus*, 4 in. 411. Zebra Fire-fish, *Brachirus zebra*, 6 in.   412. Ocellated Wasp-fish, *Hypodytes carinatus*, $6\frac{1}{2}$ in.   413. Short-spined Wasp-fish, *Apistops caloundra*, $6\frac{1}{2}$ in.   414. Black-banded Wasp-fish, *Minous versicolor*, 4 in.   415. Brown Carpet-fish, *Peristrominous dolosus*, $3\frac{1}{4}$ in.

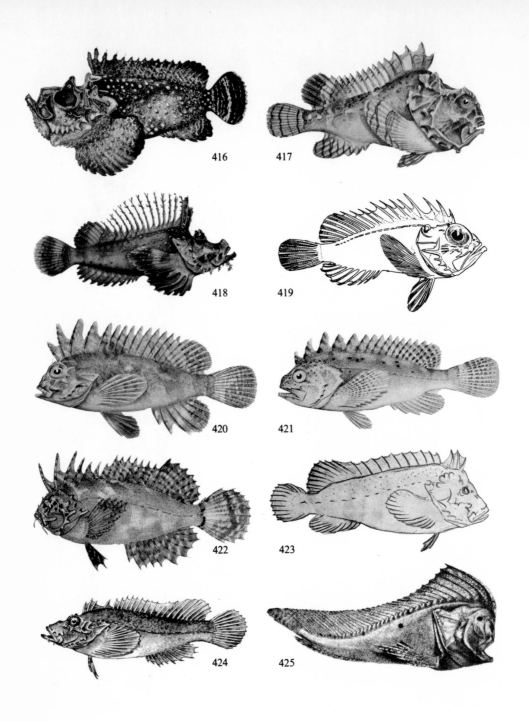

PLATE 58

416. Stone-fish, *Synanceja horrida*, 9 in.   417. Monkey-fish, *Erosa erosa*, 3 in.
418. Bearded Ghoul, *Inimicus barbatus*, 6½ in.   419. Rogue-fish, *Tetraroge leucogaster*, 2¼ in.   420. Freckled Wasp-fish, *Paracentropogon vespa*, 3½ in.
421. Yellow Wasp-fish, *Liocranium scorpio*, 3 in.   422. Port Curtis Mossback, *Bathyaploactis curtisensis*, 2¼ in. 423. Northern Mossback, *Paraploactis trachyderma*, 6 in.   424. Sandpaper-fish, *Adventor elongatus*, 4 in.   425. Red Indian Fish, *Pataecus fronto*, nearly 9 in.

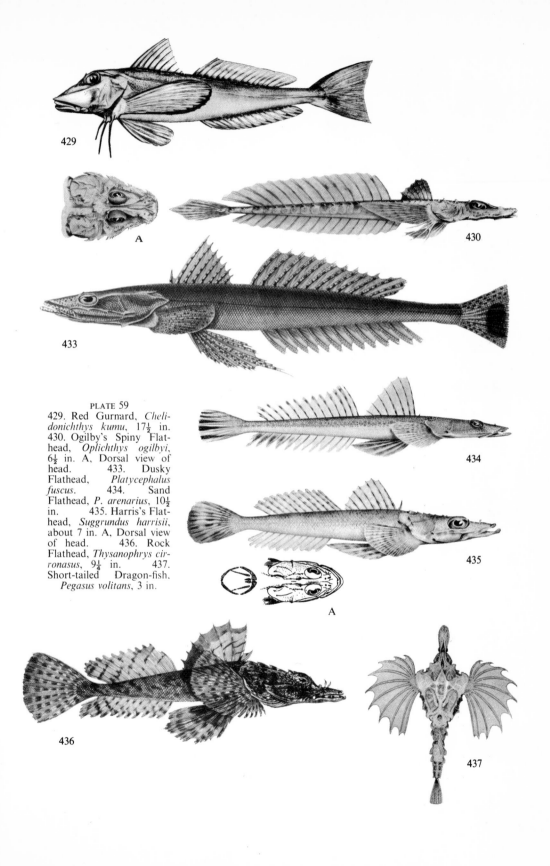

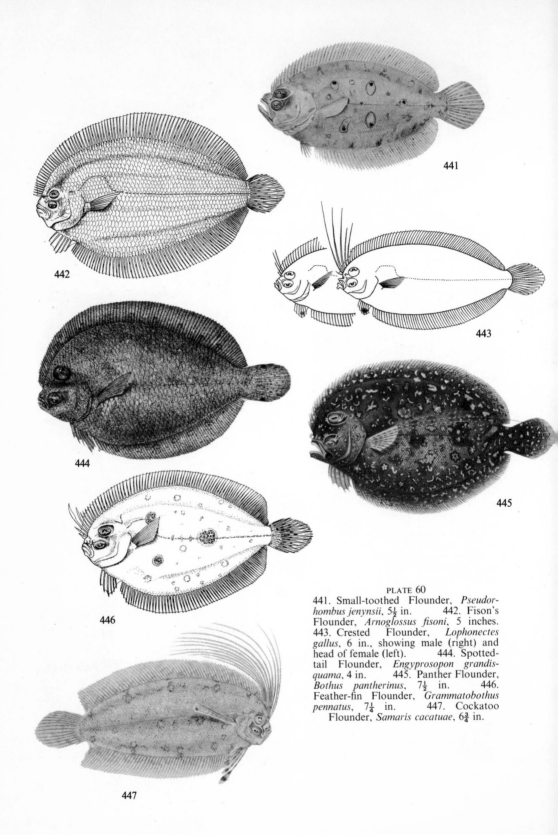

441. Small-toothed Flounder, *Pseudorhombus jenynsii*, 5½ in.   442. Fison's Flounder, *Arnoglossus fisoni*, 5 inches. 443. Crested Flounder, *Lophonectes gallus*, 6 in., showing male (right) and head of female (left).   444. Spotted-tail Flounder, *Engyprosopon grandisquama*, 4 in.   445. Panther Flounder, *Bothus pantherinus*, 7½ in.   446. Feather-fin Flounder, *Grammatobothus pennatus*, 7¼ in.   447. Cockatoo Flounder, *Samaris cacatuae*, 6¾ in.

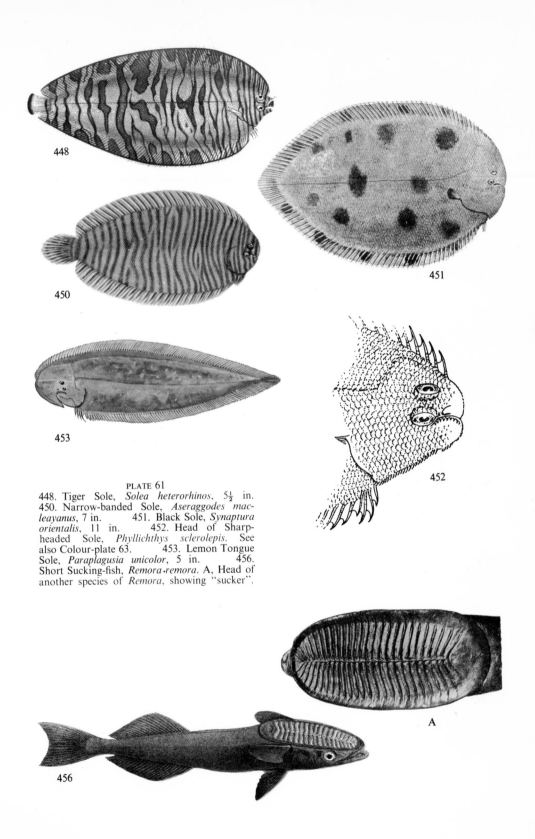

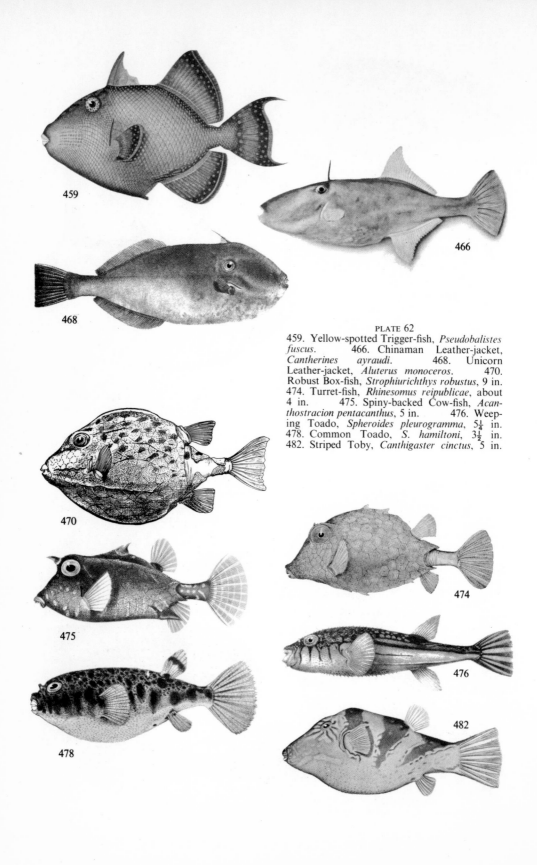

459. Yellow-spotted Trigger-fish, *Pseudobalistes fuscus*. 466. Chinaman Leather-jacket, *Cantherines ayraudi*. 468. Unicorn Leather-jacket, *Aluterus monoceros*. 470. Robust Box-fish, *Strophiurichthys robustus*, 9 in. 474. Turret-fish, *Rhinesomus reipublicae*, about 4 in. 475. Spiny-backed Cow-fish, *Acanthostracion pentacanthus*, 5 in. 476. Weeping Toado, *Spheroides pleurogramma*, $5\frac{1}{4}$ in. 478. Common Toado, *S. hamiltoni*, $3\frac{1}{2}$ in. 482. Striped Toby, *Canthigaster cinctus*, 5 in.

484. Long-spined Porcupine-fish, *Diodon holocanthus*, 12 in.   485. Myer's Porcupine-fish, *Dicotylichthys myersi*, 14½ in.   486. Ocean Sunfish, *Mola mola*, 10 ft.   487. Oblong Sunfish, *Ranzania laevis*, about 17 in.   488. Bridled Cling-fish, *Lepadichthys frenatus*, 2 in.   489. Frogfish, *Batrachomoeus dubius*, 4 in.   490. Banded Frogfish, *Halophryne diemensis*, 4½ in. A, Dorsal view of head.

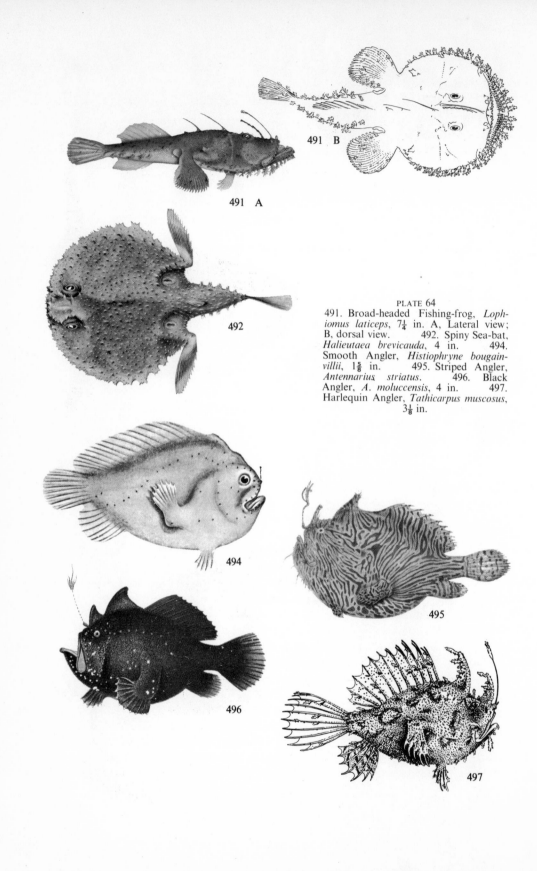

491 B

491 A

492

494

495

496

497

PLATE 64

491. Broad-headed Fishing-frog, *Lophiomus laticeps*, $7\frac{1}{4}$ in. A, Lateral view; B, dorsal view.   492. Spiny Sea-bat, *Halieutaea brevicauda*, 4 in.   494. Smooth Angler, *Histiophryne bougainvillii*, $1\frac{5}{8}$ in.   495. Striped Angler, *Antennarius striatus*.   496. Black Angler, *A. moluccensis*, 4 in.   497. Harlequin Angler, *Tathicarpus muscosus*, $3\frac{1}{8}$ in.

AA. Soft dorsal with about 25 rays. Mandibular teeth more or less horizontal; those of premaxillaries unequal, some subulate.

    c. Body scales small but distinct; mandibular teeth arranged in a row which does not curve inwards posteriorly.   *Boleophthalmus*

    cc. Body scales rudimentary; mandibular teeth in a row which curves inward posteriorly.   *Scartelaos*

Periophthalmus

355. MUD-HOPPER *Periophthalmus koelreuteri* (Günther)   [Plate 51]

Gobius koelreuteri (Pallas) Günther, Cat. Fish. Brit. Mus., 3, 1861, p. 97.
Periophthalmus koelreuteri var. *argentilineatus* McCulloch and Ogilby, Rec. Austr. Mus., 12, no. 10, 14th July 1919, p. 194, pl. 31, fig. 1.

Mud-hopper, Climbing-fish (North Queensland).

D. 12-16/12-13; A. 12. Colour: "Greyish-brown, with dark bars descending obliquely forward on to the sides; the lower portions of the sides with lighter spots and bars, the head dotted with white. Basal half of the dorsal fins grey, closely speckled with white; a broad, black, white-edged, submarginal band is present on each fin, the broader outer edge forming their white margins. Caudal with irregular bars of dark spots on the rays. Pectoral spotted like the caudal. Ventrals and anal white, with dusky markings." (McCulloch and Ogilby.)

In some examples, presumably the males, the edges of both dorsal fins are brilliant scarlet-red.

McCulloch (loc.cit.) stated: "The habits of *P. koelreuteri* have been observed by one of us (McCulloch) at several localities in Queensland. They move freely about on the mud, when the tide is out, in search of small crustaceans and insects, upon which they feed. When alarmed they skip rapidly away by means of their powerful pectoral, ventral and caudal fins, and retreat into a crab-burrow or some other crevice. At Cooktown, they were abundant around a narrow stream, a few yards in width, which enters Finche Bay; although many were driven towards the water, it was observed that none entered it, but skipped over its surface in a series of short quick leaps to the other side.

"At Port Curtis, it was noted that the rapid jumping movements usually seen when they are on land are only adopted as a means of escape. When undisturbed, they move in stages of two or three inches by raising the fore-part of the body on the pectorals, levering themselves forward; at the same time the ventrals are moved forward so that they act alternately with the pectorals, each fin of either pair moving in unison with its fellow. After each interval of walking, the fish looks around for prey by means of its elevated eyes, which are occasionally turned down into their sockets, apparently to moisten them.

N

The agility of these little fishes on the mud is so great that it is difficult to secure specimens without injuring them, and series could only be secured for study with a large cloth, which was spread over the mud, and suddenly lifted by strings when the fishes hopped over it. They are astonishingly fearless, and if driven from their feeding grounds, soon return, approaching to within a few inches on one if no movement alarms them.

"These fishes are very vicious towards one another, and the smaller examples were noticed to retreat before the approach of their larger fellows. From the fact that small crabs scurry into their burrows at the approach of a *Periophthalmus*, it would seem that they largely supply it with food, and one fish was observed to spring a distance of about six inches at a crab, which it secured and munched with evident relish.

"At Epi, in the New Hebrides, numbers of *Periophthalmus* were observed basking together in the hot sun on top of smooth basaltic rocks, about five feet above the level of the sea. It was also noted that specimens placed in glass jars could climb the smooth surface of the glass with ease, although their ventrals are not united into sucking discs as in the gobies."

This common and extremely interesting little fish is found along the coast of northern Australia from the west to Queensland. In Queensland it is very common as far south as Bundaberg but is seldom or rarely seen south of that district. It also ranges through Melanesia, Micronesia, Polynesia, the East Indies, across the Indian Ocean to West Africa and the Red Sea, etc. Grows to $5\frac{1}{2}$ inches.

Periophthalmodon

Represented in Queensland by the Great Mud-hopper, *P. barbarus*, a large, wide-ranging fish which grows to 11 inches and is commonly met with in North Queensland.

Boleophthalmus

Includes the Blue-spotted Mud-hopper, *B. pectinirostris*, a fish which frequents the mangrove-lined rivers of the Northern Territory and the Gulf of Carpentaria. Grows to $4\frac{1}{2}$ inches.

Scartelaos

This genus includes the Blue Mud-hopper, *S. viridis*, a wide-ranging little fish found in the littoral zone of the waters of North Australia. Grows to $5\frac{1}{2}$ inches.

Sub-family GOBIINAE

The genera and species of this large sub-family are so numerous that description must be limited. Nevertheless, an extensive key has been given, and mention is made of a few of the more common species.

McCulloch and Ogilby in their excellent paper on Australian Gobiidae[56] state: "The subfamilies Gobiinae and Eleotrinae have been regarded as well defined families by some authors, they being separated on the structure of their ventral fins. In the Gobiinae, the ventrals are juxtaposed and usually united into a complete disc, which is generally supplemented by an anterior membrane connecting the spines; further, the fifth rays are generally as long as the fourth. In the Eleotrinae the ventrals are separate; there is no anterior membrane, and the fifth ray is shorter than the fourth. Were these characters constant, the subdivision of the two groups would present no difficulties, but in some species the ventral structures are more or less intermediate between the two types.

"The highly specialised *Callogobius sclateri*, which has hitherto been regarded as an Eleotrid, is very similar in all its major characters to the other species of the genus, but has eleotrid ventrals as defined above though there is a membrane connecting the bases of the inner rays; in *C. hasseltii* the fourth ray is distinctly longer than the fifth, but the ventrals are otherwise of gobioid form. In *Zonogobius* the ventrals are completely united, but the fifth ray is shorter than the fourth; in the typical form *Z. semidoliatus*, there is no trace of an anterior membrane between the spines, but this structure is well developed in *Z. nuchifasciatus*. The ventrals of *Quisquilius eugenius* are similar to those of *Z. semidoliatus*, but it has been regarded as an Eleotrid by Jordan and his colleagues, though Weber associates it with the Gobies.

"These intermediate forms are few in number, however, and the greater mass of species of both groups are readily separable onto one or the other section. Under these circumstances, it seems unnecessary to maintain separate families for the Eleotrids and Gobies, though they can be conveniently classified as subfamilies, distinguished by the complete or partial junction (Gobiinae), or the complete separation of their ventral fins. (Eleotrinae.)"

KEY TO GENERA AND SOME SPECIES IN QUEENSLAND

Adapted from McCulloch and Ogilby[57]

A. Soft dorsal and anal long, partly or completely united with caudal. Body anguilliform.

    b. Soft dorsal and anal partly united with caudal. Body naked. Head with prominent raised papillose ridges. Eyes obsolete. Teeth long and curved.   *Leme*

    bb. Soft dorsal and anal completely united with caudal. Body covered with minute scales. Head without ridges. Eyes very minute. Teeth moderate, in bands.   *Trypauchen*

---

[56] *Rec. Austr. Mus.*, 12, pt 10, 14th July 1919, pp. 193-291.
[57] *Ibid.*, p. 203.

372

AA. Soft dorsal and anal shorter, free from caudal.

  c. Body naked.

    d. Caudal rounded.

      e. Body short, compressed and elevated. Teeth in a narrow band in each jaw, the outer row of which is largest. Ventrals small, cup-shaped.   *Gobiodon*

      ee. Body not so short or compressed. Teeth minute, conical, in broad bands in each jaw. Ventrals slender, separate.   *Austrolethops*

    dd. Caudal forked.   *Australaphia*

  cc. Body scaly.

    f. Chin and mandibles with barbels, cheeks, and opercles scaly.   *Parachaeturichthys*

    ff. Chin and mandibles without barbels.

      g. Head with very prominent raised papillose ridges.   *Callogobius*

      gg. Head with only microscopic papillae in rows.

        h. Opercles scaly, cheeks naked or scaly.

          i. Cheek scales large and distinct.   *Exyrias*

          ii. Cheek scales indistinct or wanting.

            j. 40 or more scales in a longitudinal row.

              k. Second dorsal with a black ocellus; body banded longitudinally.   *Koumansetta*

              kk. Body not banded; no black ocellus.   *Mugilogobius devisi*

            jj. Less than 40 scales in a longitudinal row.   *Parvigobius*

        hh. Opercles naked or nearly naked, cheeks naked.

          l. Upper pectoral rays free and silk-like.

            m. Tongue truncate or rounded anteriorly.   *Istigobius*

            mm. Tongue emarginate anteriorly.   *Bathygobius*

          ll. Upper pectoral rays not differentiated from the others.

            n. Tongue deeply notched anteriorly.   *Glossogobius*

            nn. Tongue not deeply notched.

              o. Head subspherical, bulbous, with small or large spines or papillae.

                p. Head with large papillae or setae.   *Paragobiodon*

                pp. Head with minute papillae in rows on slightly raised edges.   *Obtortiophagus*

              oo. Head longer, without spines or large papillae.

                q. Scales larger, 36 or less in a longitudinal row.

                  r. Nape and greater portion of neck naked.

s. Gill-openings extending well forward below, fifth ventral ray shorter than the fourth. — *Zonogobius*

ss. Gill-openings not extending forward below, fifth ventral ray as long as fourth.

    t. Caudal pointed, body longer. — *Arenigobius*

    tt. Caudal rounded, body shorter. — *Rhinogobius*

rr. Nape and neck scaly.

    u. Snout pointed, maxilla extending to below the orbital border. — *(Gobius) neophytus*

    uu. Snout obtuse, maxilla extending beyond orbital border. — *Favonigobius*

qq. Scales smaller, more than 36 in a longitudinal row.

    v. About 15 dorsal and anal rays, snout tumid, caudal rounded. — *Amblygobius*

    vv. 13 or less dorsal and anal rays, snout normal.

        w. Scales minute, about 90 in a longitudinal row. — *Cryptocentrus*

356. REDHEAD *Paragobiodon echinocephalus* (Rüppell) [Plate 51]

Gobius echinocephalus Rüppell, Atlas zu Rüppell, Reise (Senck. Nat. Ges.) Fische, 1830, *vel.* 1831, p. 136, pl. 34, fig. 3.

Paragobiodon echinocephalus McCulloch and Ogilby, Rec. Austr. Mus., 12, no. 10, 1919, p. 239, pl. 34, fig. 1.

D. 6/10; A. 10; P. 20; V. 1/5; A. 17. A little species which varies greatly in colour. Often the body and fins are blackish with the head fleshy-coloured or red. Others are golden-yellow or green, with the fins brownish-black and the head brownish. Sometimes the head is green.

Extremely common amongst coral growths and beneath coral clinker on the Great Barrier Reef. Grows to about 1½ inches in total length. Found in Queensland, Melanesia, Micronesia, Polynesia, the East Indies, China, the Nicobar Islands, the Andaman Islands, Madagascar, and the Red Sea.

357. OYSTER GOBY *Rhinogobius leftwichi* Ogilby [Plate 51]

Rhinogobius leftwichi Ogilby, Proc. Roy. Soc. Qld, 23, 7th Nov. 1910, p. 24.

Rhinogobius leftwitchi McCulloch and Ogilby, Rec. Austr. Mus., 12, no. 10, 1919, p. 248, pl. 34, fig. 3.

D. 6/10; A. 10; P. 17; V. 1/5; C. 13. Colour: "Pale yellowish brown, all the scales, except those along the ventral profile, edged with dark brown; in half grown examples there is a row of darker blotches along the middle of the sides, with sometimes a second row near the dorsal profile, the anterior spots often

meeting across the nape. Upper surface of head and nape spotted and vermiculated with brown; an indistinct violaceous band curves downward from the
eye to the angle of the mouth, behind which are two parallel bands, which
extend upon the base of the pectoral; opercles dull purplish. Fins hyaline,
closely powdered with dusky dots; dorsals with a basal row of dark spots;
last two dorsal and anal rays with alternate darker and lighter bars, sometimes
absent in the anal; caudal with a dark basal band." (Ogilby.)

Ogilby notes: "This pretty little goby abounds in the pools left by the receding
tide on the oyster banks in the Great Sandy Strait, and I have also seen specimens obtained in the vicinity of Woody Point, Moreton Bay. Along the edges of
these pools when undisturbed they lie motionless, basking in the shallow
water, but if alarmed by the approach of an enemy they dart away with great
rapidity, and seek refuge in the deeper water below or within the bunches of
oysters, adjusting their bodies with great nicety to the inequalities of the surface
on which they have found a haven. Here their colours assimilate so closely
with their surroundings that it requires a keen eye to locate their position
even though one may have been but a few feet from them when they sought
concealment; they are very quick in their movements, and even with a hand
net it is most difficult to catch them. I have never observed one of these fishes
to take refuge in a hole as is the usual habit of *Amblygobius gobioides*, which is
equally common on the oyster beds. The stomach of the example dissected was
packed with green weed regularly cut into lengths of about an inch, with which
also was a shrimp-like crustacean of about the same size."

The Oyster Goby, which attains to about 3 inches, is known only from the
coast of Queensland, where it ranges from south to north.

358. BYNOE'S GOBY *Amblygobius bynoensis* (Richardson)   [Colour-plate 53]

Gobius bynoensis Richardson, Zool. Voy. Erebus and Terror, Fish., 1844, p. 1, pl. 1, figs 1-2.
Illustration by G. Coates.

D. 6/15; A. 16; P. 18; V. 1/5; C. 15. Colour greenish; back with 4 to 5
brownish-violet cross-bands; on each side of the head 2 brownish-violet
blue-edged longitudinal bands, the lower of which terminates in a dark spot on
upper part of base of pectoral; neck with 2 series of brown blue-edged ocelli;
dorsal fins dotted with white; caudal with a brown spot on upper part of its
base; anal with violet margin; the other fins rose-coloured.

A handsome goby found in the northern waters of Queensland, Torres
Strait, the Northern Territory to Western Australia, also in the Malay Archipelago. Grows to 3¾ inches.

359. CRESTED MUD GOBY *Cryptocentrus cristatus* (Macleay) [Plate 51]

Gobius cristatus Macleay, Proc. Linn. Soc. N.S.Wales, 5, pt 4, 20th May, 1881, p. 610.
Cryptocentrus gobioides McCulloch and Ogilby, Rec. Austr. Mus., 12, no. 10, 14th July 1919, p. 255, pl. 36, fig. 1.

D. 6/13; A. 12; P. 16; V. 1/5; C. 15. Scales very small. Colour: "Purplish or reddish brown above, gradually fading into lilac below, the sides with from 40 to 50 alternate darker and lighter transverse bands, which in large examples are usually broken up into vertical bars. Upper surface and sides of head and nape with numerous round blackish spots. Fins vinous; anterior border of first dorsal white; sometimes a dark marginal spot between the fourth and fifth spines and some oblique dusky streaks basally; second dorsal with three series of dark spots; caudal sometimes with a few scattered spots. When newly caught, the lateral transverse bars are brilliant blue and gold." (Ogilby.)

J. D. Ogilby wrote many interesting notes on the habits of Australian fishes, and he gave the following information on this interesting goby, under the name of *Amblygobius gobioides*[58]: "This species is essentially a 'mud goby'. In the Wide Bay district I had many admirable opportunities of observing its habits on the vast flats left bare by each recurring tide. The fish either excavates for itself a burrow in the mud or takes possession of the deserted burrow of a worm or crab, and enlarges it to suit its own convenience. The burrow is invariably provided with two openings, which may be at the bottom of a small pool, but as often as not open upon the bare mud. Here, if one approaches cautiously, the little creature may be seen lying—regardless of or perhaps enjoying the fierce rays of a semi-tropical summer sun—close to the burrow, bent into a shape of a U with one of the sides shortened, its head turned towards the entrance, through which it disappears like a flash on any incautious movement of the spectator. If, however, perfect quiet be maintained, the head will shortly be seen to emerge from the other entrance, intently scrutinizing its surroundings to ascertain whether the danger be past. When they take refuge at the bottom of their retreat it is not an easy matter to dig them out."

Grows to 4 inches. Found in Queensland and New South Wales.

Sub-family ELEOTRINAE: GUDGEONS

The gudgeons are separated from the mud-hoppers (sub-family Periophthalminae) by the lack of an unusually muscular and mobile pectoral base and in the eyes not being erectile. They differ from the gobies (sub-family Gobiinae) in having their ventral fins separate and in the absence of a membrane between the anterior spines.

They are bottom-dwelling carnivorous fishes, inhabiting tropical seas and the tidal streams, many living in fresh water. Most of the species are of small

---

[58] *Proc. Roy. Soc. Qld*, 23, pt 1, 1911, p. 26.

or moderate size, though some, such as *Philypnus*, found in the rivers of tropical America, grow to a length of 36 inches.

A key to the seven genera is given, though mention can be made of only a few species.

KEY TO GENERA

A. Ventral rays 1/4.

> b. Body elongate. Scales minute. Dorsal rays 17 or more.
>
> c. Dorsal 5/17. Caudal rounded.   *Parioglossus*
>
> cc. Dorsal 6/29, the last spine widely separated from the fifth. Caudal emarginate.   *Ptereleotris*
>
> bb. Body short. Scales large. Dorsal rays about 6/9-10.   *Eviota*

AA. Ventral rays 1/5.

> d. Scales small, more than 50 in a longitudinal row.
>
> e. Sides of the head naked.   *Calleleotris*
>
> dd. Scales larger, less than 50 in a longitudinal row.
>
> f. Top of the head with bony crests.   *Butis*
>
> ff. Top of head without bony crests.
>
>> g. Preoperculum with 2-3 strong spines.   *Asterropterix*
>>
>> gg. Preoperculum without spines.
>>
>>> h. Snout broad, flat, and depressed. Enlarged scales on upper surface of head. First dorsal usually with 6 spines.   *Ophiocara*

Parioglossus

A small genus containing two species, one found in the Indian Ocean, the other in Queensland.

360. COBRA-FISH *Parioglossus rainfordi* McCulloch   [Plate 51]

Pariglossus [sic] *rainfordi* McCulloch, Proc. Linn. Soc. N.S.Wales, 46, pt 4, 30th Nov. 1921, p. 471, pl. 41, fig. 4.

D. 5/17; A. 16; P. 18; V. 1/4; C. 15. "General colour light green, with a dark bluish-black marking on the base of the caudal fin. A violet brown band usually extends along the middle of each side, but may be indistinct. A brown spot behind the eye and several pale blue ones on the cheek and operculum. First dorsal pinkish, its prolonged rays white, second dorsal dark violet basally, then yellow, with a broad pink border. Anal bright yellow, bordered with pink. Caudal with two broad oblique bars and the median rays pink, the intermediate colour yellow; the upper and lower edges white." (McCulloch.)

A very common little fish at Bowen, North Queensland, where it was first discovered in 1921 by E. H. Rainford, who found many examples dwelling in a log which was honeycombed by Cobra, *Calobates*, in the empty tunnels of which they were hiding.

So far recorded only from North Queensland. Grows to 2 inches.

Calleleotris

361. LINED GUDGEON *Calleleotris muralis* (Cuvier and Valenciennes]
[Plate 51)

Eleotris muralis Cuvier and Valenciennes, Hist. Nat. Poiss., 12, 1837, p. 253, pl. 357.
Valenciennea muralis McCulloch and Ogilby, Rec. Austr. Mus., 12, no. 10, 14th July 1919, p. 261, pl. 37, fig. 4.

D. 6/13; A. 13; P. 20; V. 1/5; C. 13. General colour pale green with pale-pink blue-edged bands running longitudinally; dorsal pale green, with several pink wavy bands; a large black spot behind the third spine at its tip.

Juveniles have a series of dusky spots on the back and sides which tend to form vertical bands.

A very handsome little fish found on the reefs of North Queensland, North Australia, Torres Strait, Melanesia, Micronesia, and Polynesia. It is also found in India, the East Indies, and Japan. Grows to $4\frac{1}{2}$ inches.

Ophiocara

Two species belonging to this genus are found in Queensland waters.

362. MUD GUDGEON *Ophiocara aporos* (Bleeker) [Plate 51]

Eleotris aporos Bleeker, Nat. Tijdschr. Ned. Ind., 6, 1854, p. 59.
Ophieleotris aporos Whitley, Austr. Mus. Mag., 11, no. 5, 1954, p. 154 (fig. unnumbered).

Mud Cod (Cairns).

D. 6/9; A. 10; L. l. 39. Colour dark above, orange below; scales of back and sides with dark spots; 2 to 3 dark stripes from eye to operculum; fin membranes dark, rays orange; dorsal fins, ventral and anal bordered with red; base of pectorals with dark transverse stripe, bordered with red; caudal spotted with yellow. (After Koumans.)

A large gudgeon found in the sea and rivers of North Queensland, also through the Indo-Australian Archipelago to India, the Philippines, and the Fiji Islands. In Queensland it has mostly been taken in the rivers of the northern half of the State and is very seldom seen in the sea. Grows to a weight of at least $1\frac{1}{2}$ pounds.

OTHER SPECIES

The other Queensland species, *O. porocephala*, is commonly found in the northern waters of Queensland and the Northern Territory. It grows to 14 inches and is said to have flesh of good edible quality.

DIVISION *Callionymiformes*

Family **Callionymidae: Dragonets**

Body elongate, almost cylindrical. No scales. Head more or less depressed. Mouth small, protractile, weak teeth in jaws in several rows, none on palate. Preopercle with a well-developed spine covered by skin, with or without a spine at base. Sometimes other spines at the extremity or along the upper edge. Gill-openings reduced to a rounded pore on each side. Two dorsal fins, usually elongate, the spines weak.

Small, beautifully coloured fishes living in shallow and moderately deep water in temperate and tropical seas, chiefly in the Old World. They are mainly shore-fishes, creeping about on the bottom in shallow bays, though some species have been dredged in deep water in the East Indies.

These fishes are noted for their strong sexual dimorphism, the males being much more brightly coloured than the females, especially during the breeding season when many of them are ornamented with yellow and blue bands. An exception to this rule is an Indian species in which the female is the more brightly coloured.

Further differences in the sexes is that the males are usually much larger in size than the females, have longer snouts, and higher and more filamentous fins, the membranes brightly ornamented.

The dragonets are one of the few groups of fishes in which the males of the species indulge in an elaborate courtship. Norman[59] states: "In the case of the Dragonet (*Callionymus lyra*), the male swims about in a state of great excitement at the time of courting, circling round the female, erecting his fins, and displaying for her benefit his intensified colours. She finally allows him to approach, and the male lifts his mate by placing his pelvic fin beneath hers; the two fishes then swim upwards towards the surface side by side, the eggs and milt being shed into the water at the same moment."

This family is represented in Queensland waters by three genera.

KEY TO GENERA IN QUEENSLAND

A. Outer ventral ray detached from rest of fin. Head triangular, not depressed. *Dactylopus*

AA. No detached ventral ray.

---

[59] *Guide to Fish Gallery*, Brit. Mus. Nat. Hist., 1937, p. 79.

b. Head and anterior part of body depressed. Gill-opening on upper surface of head. *Callionymus*

bb. Head and body not depressed. Gill-openings more on side of head. *Synchiropus*

Dactylopus

Head triangular, not depressed. Preopercular process strong, conical, no antrorse spine and with few small spines along upper border and larger ones along lower border. The ventral spine and first ventral ray detached from rest of the fin.

Fishes from the Molucca Seas to the east coast of Australia. A single species.

363. FINGERED DRAGONET *Dactylopus dactylopus*
(Cuvier and Valenciennes) [Colour-plate 53; Plate 51]

Callionymus dactylopus Cuvier and Valenciennes, Hist. Nat. Poiss., 12, 1837, p. 31.
Dactylopus dactylopus McCulloch, Biol. Res. Endeavour, 3, pt 3, 1915, p. 149, pl. 28 (female).
Colour illustration (male) by G. Coates.

D. 4/8; A. 7; P. 18. Colour: "Olive or violet-brown above, with six large blackish blotches across the back, the interspaces with darker freckles and sometimes with blue black-edged ocelli of variable size; sides with a similar number of somewhat stellate blotches, more or less corresponding to the spaces between the dorsal blotches, the interspaces chestnut or violet, with or without golden or pearly spots and reticulated lines; lower surface white, faintly tinged with bluish; under surface of head pale brown. Iris silvery, with an inner golden rim. Spinous dorsal and its filaments blackish, the membrane of the second ray with numerous small pearly spots on its outer half, that of the third with a wide lighter marginal band; second dorsal lilac, the ground colour well nigh obliterated by crowded oblique purplish bars; base of anal rufous-brown, deepening to purple at the margin; caudal fin golden, the rays brown, speckled with pale blue; posterior margin with wavy blue transverse streaks, the rest of the fin, except the two lower rays which are smoky-brown, with elongate blue lines, which are oblique above and horizontal below; pectorals hyaline, the basal half of the upper and middle rays with alternate lilac and rufous rings; free ventral ray with alternating rings of gold and purple, the united rays blackish or dark olive-green, with one or two large pearly basal spots.

"In the female the membrane of the spinous dorsal is golden-brown, with darker marblings and irregular light blue spots and short bands; basal two-thirds of soft dorsal with elongate dark brown blue-edged spots between the rays, the marginal third more faintly banded but profusely freckled with blue; inner third of anal golden-brown with elongate pearly spots, the rest of the fin smoky, with dark blue black-edged spots and lines." (Ogilby.)

This pretty little fish is known from the coast of Queensland to the East Indies. It has also been taken in Shark Bay, Western Australia. Grows to 8 inches.

Callionymus

Preopercular spine very large, hooked at tip and variously armed with recurved spines above, a small antrorse spine usually present at its base below. Gill-opening reduced to a small pore opening upward. Ventrals entire, the outer ray not detached. Sexual differences strongly marked.

Shore-fishes living mostly at the bottom in the temperate seas of the Old World and also throughout the warm seas of India and the Indo-Australian Archipelago and beyond. In Japanese waters they are numerous in all bays, living in the shallow water. Species numerous, seven in Australian waters.

KEY TO SPECIES IN AUSTRALIA

Adapted from McCulloch[60]

A. Preopercular spine almost straight and spear-like, with a row of spinules above and an antrorse barb below.

    b. All but the posterior dorsal rays simple; 9 dorsal and 8-9 anal rays.

       c. Snout but little longer than eye; upper lip projecting beyond preorbitals when mouth is closed.   *grossi*

       cc. Snout much longer than eye; preorbitals overhanging the upper lip when mouth is closed.   *nasutus*

    bb. All the dorsal rays bifurcate; 8 dorsal and 7 anal rays. Interorbital space concave; preopercular spine with fine denticulations above.   *rameus*

AA. Preopercular spine with its distal extremity curved upward, and having one or more large hooks above; lower antrorse barb present or absent.

    d. Preopercular spine with only 2 distal hooks.

       e. Eye smaller than snout.   *limiceps*

    dd. Preopercular spine with 3-5 recurved hooks above.

       f. First dorsal spine not longer than second.

          g. Spinous dorsal higher than soft portion; anal fin much higher posteriorly.   *calliste*

          gg. Spinous dorsal lower than soft portion; anal fin of about equal height throughout.   *calcaratus*

       ff. First dorsal spine longer than second.   *macdonaldi*

[60] *Biol. Res. Endeavour*, 5, pt 4, 1926, p. 195.

364. ROUGH-HEADED DRAGONET *Callionymus limiceps* Ogilby

[Plate 51]

Callionymus limiceps Ogilby, Ann. Qld Mus., no. 9, 1908, p. 35.
Callionymus limiceps McCulloch, Rec. Austr. Mus., 14, no. 1, 1923, p. 9, pl. 3, fig. 1.

D. 4/9; A. 9; C. 10; P. 18-19; V. 1/5. Colour: "Brown above, closely speckled with brown spots of varying sizes; these form short lines which extend obliquely forward below the eye and they are enlarged along the sides of the body. First dorsal with a large black spot on the third spine which is surrounded by angular grey stripes. The two filamentous spines with numerous grey annuli. Second dorsal with a narrow inframarginal white streak and numerous round spots; some larger dark brown spots on the lower half of the fin. Caudal ornamented with many small white spots between the rays and some darker ocellated spots. Anal with a broad dusky margin. Pectorals and ventrals with irregular rows of grey dots; the latter with a dusky border." (McCulloch.)

McCulloch in a note on sexual dimorphism states: "The females are readily distinguishable from the males by the size of the anal papilla and by the form of the first dorsal fin. In the females the anal papilla is small, whereas it is large in the males reaching backward almost to the origin of the anal fin. The two anterior dorsal spines are greatly elongated in the male, but in the female they are usually much shorter than the anterior dorsal ray; the black spot on the first dorsal fin is much smaller in males than in females, though its size varies considerably in the latter."

A species commonly taken by the prawn-trawlers in Moreton Bay, South Queensland. It has also been trawled between Hervey Bay and Port Denison, Queensland, at various depths between 13 and 26 fathoms. Found also in New South Wales waters. Grows to 10 inches.

OTHER SPECIES

Gross's Dragonet, *C. grossi*. A small species known only from the waters of Queensland, where it has been taken as far north as Townsville. Not commonly seen. Grows to 5 inches.

Long-nosed Dragonet, *C. nasutus*. This large dragonet is only occasionally caught in South Queensland by the prawn-trawlers. Grows to 9 inches.

Split-fin Dragonet, *C. rameus*. A little-known species from the waters of South Queensland, where it has been trawled at depths of 13 to 35 fathoms. Grows to about 8 inches.

Ornate Dragonet, *C. calliste*. A small Japanese species which has been recorded from North Queensland. Grows to 4 inches.

Stink-fish, *C. calcaratus*. A species found in South Queensland and New South Wales, also in Western Australia. Said to be remarkable for its power of producing an offensive odour. Not commonly seen in Queensland. Grows to 10 inches.

Grey-spotted Dragonet, *C. macdonaldi.* Another small fish known only from Queensland and New South Wales. In Queensland it is commonly taken in the otter-trawl nets of the prawners. Grows to 5 inches.

Synchiropus

Head and body not depressed. Gill-openings more on side of head. Small fishes of the Indo-Pacific region. Species few, two in Queensland.

KEY TO SPECIES IN QUEENSLAND

A. Eye large, equal to snout; body stout, 4 times in length. Orange, with broad green black-margined irregular bands. *splendidus*

AA. Eye small, shorter than snout; body more slender, 5 times in length. Dark brown, marbled grey and white; first dorsal black. *microps*

365. MANDARIN-FISH *Synchiropus splendidus* (Herre) [Colour-plate 54]

Gallionymus [*sic*] *splendidus* Herre, Phil. Journ. Sci., 32, 1927, p. 416.
Illustration by T. C. Marshall.

D. 4/9; A. 8; P. 29; V. 1/5; C. 10. General body colour bright orange, with several bright-green black-edged sinuous markings, the anterior one of which is in the form of a saddle across the nape, the posterior one as a ring round the caudal peduncle; between these bands are similarly coloured round and oval spots; head bright green above, passing into yellowish-green on throat and yellow on breast, with about 6 sinuous narrow blue black-edged bands; eye with the black pupil encircled by a narrow yellow line, outside of which it is scarlet, the whole surrounded with blue; gouts of orange before and beneath the green band on the nape, posteriorly to which a large area back to the pectoral and anal bases is deep violet; spinous dorsal orange, with about 3 sinuous dark-blue black-edged bands; soft dorsal somewhat similar, but with 1 or 2 green sinuous bands anteriorly and the edge of the fin dark blue; ventrals and anal pale orange with blue black-edged oval and round ocelli, mainly on the membranes; margins of fins purple; caudal dusky basally, passing into cerise on membranes and overlaid with lines of purple, the rays between being smoky-brown; a broad dark-purple border to the fin posteriorly; pectorals hyaline-orange, with a broad light-blue border.

This strikingly handsome little fish, which was first described from the Philippines in 1927, is so far known on the Australian coast from only two examples. The first was captured at Hayman Island Reef, North Queensland, in 1924, and I obtained the second one off West Molle Island, Whitsunday Passage, North Queensland, in 1937. It was taken in coral at a depth of 4 fathoms. The species grows to at least $3\frac{1}{4}$ inches.

OTHER SPECIES

Small-eyed Dragonet, *S. microps*. A common little species in the reef-pools of Queensland and the south-western Pacific. Grows to 3 inches.

Sub-order BLENNIOIDEA

A vast number of fishes of mainly small or moderate size living near the shore in tropical, temperate, and Arctic seas, though some species inhabit the deep water. In form they are mostly elongate, or some eel-like, with the ventral fins, when present, situated far forward in advance of the pectorals, sometimes even on the chin, and consisting of 1 spine and less than 5 soft rays, often reduced or even absent. The body is naked or scaly, the dorsal spines numerous; anal with or without spines; caudal usually rounded, rarely forked.

Most of the species are carnivorous. So far as is known the Clininae are ovoviviparous, the rest viviparous.

The giants of the sub-order are the wolf-fishes, Anarrhichadidae, some of which grow to a length of 5 feet. They are inhabitants of the North Atlantic, and one species, the Common Wolf-fish, *Anarrhichas lupus*, has been known to attack persons wading in the water.

Family **Blenniidae: Blennies**

Body elongate, smooth, no scales. Dorsal fin long, the spinous and rayed portions usually of equal length, sometimes separated by a notch, and the spines, if present, feeble. Anal long, usually of articulated rays, the spines absent or feeble. Pectorals present. Ventrals far forward, well before pectorals. Mouth small; teeth in jaws fixed and close-set with sometimes a canine on each side, in some species so large that the lower jaw has to be widely opened to reveal them. Caudal free or confluent with the dorsal and anal.

This great family of blennies contains over five hundred species and is represented in most waters of the world from the Arctic to the tropics. Like other members of the sub-order they are inhabitants of the tide-pools and rocky coasts; some species are commonly seen darting about from cover to cover in the shallow pools at low tide. Twelve genera are found in Queensland.

KEY TO GENERA IN QUEENSLAND

A.   One or two dorsal fins.

    b. Teeth slender and flattened, forming a comb-like row in each jaw. Lateral canines usually present.

      c. Dorsal and anal fins not united with caudal. Body shorter.

        d. Teeth immovable.

e. Gill-opening wide, separated by a narrow isthmus. *Blennius*

ee. Gill-opening reduced to a small foramen above pectoral. *Petroscirtes*

dd. Teeth movable.

f. A row of cirri crossing the neck to the opercular lobes. *Cirripectes*

ff. No such row of cirri crossing neck, but a single or branched tentacle may be present on each side of neck.

g. Each side of mandible either toothless or with a single canine. *Salarias*

gg. Each side of mandible with a row of about 6-7 small teeth; no canines. *Ecsenius*

cc. Dorsal and anal fins united with caudal. Body elongate. *Xiphasia*

bb. Jaws without either rows of comb-like teeth or large lateral canines.

h. 3 anterior dorsal spines, forming a separate fin above the head. Body shorter.

i. First dorsal spine over or in advance of eye. *Cristiceps*

ii. First dorsal spine behind vertical of eye. *Petraites*

hh. A single dorsal fin, united with anal to caudal.

j. Anal fin composed of numerous spines. Lateral line running high up along the back. *Notograptus*

jj. Anal fin composed of numerous rays. Lateral line running straight along middle of body. *Scleropteryx*

AA. 3 dorsal fins (Clininae).

k. Lateral line interrupted. *Tripterygion*

kk. Lateral line complete. *Lepidoblennius*

Blennius

Represented in Queensland by one species, *B. intermedius* Ogilby, a small fish known only from Torres Strait, North Queensland.

Petroscirtes

Small fishes of the tide-pools along the rocky coasts and coral pools and reefs of the Indo-Pacific region. They are characterized by the gill-openings being reduced to a small foramen situated above the base of the pectoral. Lower jaw with fairly large canines, those in the upper jaw small. Tentacles may be present on the head. Many species are known, eight being found in Queensland.

KEY TO SPECIES IN QUEENSLAND

A. Head with an elevated cutaneous crest, well developed in males, but rudimentary in females or absent in young; posterior rays of dorsal produced and filamentous.   *anolius*

AA. No cephalic crest or at most a low one; posterior dorsal rays not produced.

  b. Dorsals more or less notched.

    c. Anterior three dorsal spines elevated and separated from rays by a notch.   *mitratus*

    cc. Anterior dorsal spines not elevated; notch at twelfth dorsal spine.

      d. Dorsal 12/19; caudal sub-truncate; olive-brown, sides with a series of oblique brown bars; a black spot behind eye.   *obliquus*

      dd. Dorsal 12/22; caudal rounded; olive-green, 3-5 horizontal lines on body, clearest anteriorly. Male with a low crest.   *japonicus*

  bb. Dorsal continuous, not notched.

    e. Body elongate, its depth $10\frac{1}{2}$ times in the total length; a longitudinal violet-black band from snout to caudal base.   *tapeinosoma*

    ee. Body less elongate, its depth 6 times or less in the total length.

      f. Body with one or more dark longitudinal stripes. No tentacles.

      g. Depth of body about 5 in the total length; yellowish-white, with 3 equidistant longitudinal black stripes.   *grammistes*

      gg. Depth of body 6 in the total length; a broad bluish-black band from eye to caudal base, ending in a large black blotch; young examples have a row of blotches which with growth develop into the band.   *variabilis*

      ff. No longitudinal body stripes.

      h. A small tentacle over each eye and another on each side of nape; a series of large more or less confluent blotches on the back; belly plain.   *viperidens*

366. OYSTER BLENNY *Petroscirtes anolius* (Cuvier and Valenciennes)
[Plate 52]

Blennechis anolius Cuvier and Valenciennes, Hist. Nat. Poiss., 11, 1836, p. 288.
Petroscirtes anolius McCulloch, Austr. Zool., 1, pt. 4, 1917, p. 90, pl. 10, fig. 2.

Crested Blenny (Queensland).

D. 12/17-18; A. 1/20-21; C. 13; P. 13; V. 2. Colour: "Head and body chest-nut-brown or olive-green, the latter with numerous indistinct angulated transverse bars, which cease below the middle of the soft dorsal; rest of tail with three darker longitudinal bars and some scattered black spots. Head sometimes with one or two vertical silvery streaks and a dusky cheek-spot. Dorsal fin brownish-olive, darkest anteriorly, the spinous portion with three or four oblique darker bars, the soft immaculate; anal fin orange-brown, each ray with a basal, median, and terminal sky-blue spot; caudal orange; pectoral greenish-olive with a large round dusky spot on its muscular base; ventrals sky-blue." (Ogilby.)

Ogilby[61] notes: "The life history of this little creature, so far as it has been determined, is both curious and interesting. Apparently they mate at a very early age, since in no other way can we account for their presence in places which it is impossible for them to enter or leave in their adult state. Having paired, the young couple immediately proceed to the choice of a residence; this almost invariably takes the form of a dead oyster shell, between the valves of which they are able at this stage easily to insert their slim and delicate bodies. In the safe seclusion of this retreat they live out their peaceful lives, undisturbed by the strenuous and ceaseless war of nature, which rages over around and above them. Here they are dependent for food upon such small animals as may find their way between the valves of their prison and such flotsam as the tide may drift therein. Here too they breed, the female attaching her eggs by means of some glutinous substance to the upper wall of the shell, and it is remarkable that in all the cases which have come under my notice the ova were deposited not in a single mass but in scattered groups of some half-dozen eggs each; this arrangement may possibly be selected in order to ensure a freer play of water on each egg. The young, on their emergence from the ova are quickly driven out from the parents' domicile to make their own way in the great world beyond."

McCulloch notes: "This species undergoes considerable variation with growth. The elongate rays of the dorsal and caudal fins are only filamentous in larger specimens. The development of the cephalic crest varies greatly; it is absent in small specimens, and rudimentary in what I suppose to be females, but it increases in size in adult males until its height is equal to the length of the post-orbital portion of the head. When the crest is well developed, the

---

[61] *Proc. Roy. Soc. Qld*, 23, 1910, p. 52.

anterior cephalic profile is subvertical but it is more or less oblique in others, so that the snout appears pointed."

A common species on the coasts of South Queensland and New South Wales. Grows to 3 inches.

OTHER SPECIES

High-finned Blenny, *P. mitratus*. Wide-ranging outside Australia and recorded in North Queensland waters from Low Isles. Grows to 3 inches.

Zebra Blenny, *P. obliquus*. Has been recorded from North Queensland and the Northern Territory and also from the Fiji Islands. Grows to $3\frac{1}{2}$ inches.

Japanese Blenny, *P. japonicus*. Fairly common in the rock pools along the coast of South Queensland. Found also in Japan. Often makes its home in the *Teredo* burrows in submerged wood and is active and vicious. Grows to 4 inches.

Violet-banded Blenny, *P. tapeinosoma*. A wide-ranging species which frequents the waters of North Queensland. Grows to 4 inches.

Striped Blenny, *P. grammistes*. A distinctively marked blenny found in the coral pools on the Great Barrier Reef. Found also in the South Seas, the East Indies, and China, Grows to $2\frac{1}{2}$ inches.

Sabre-toothed Blenny, *P. variabilis*. Found along the coasts of Queensland and New South Wales. Wide-ranging outside Australia. Grows to $5\frac{1}{2}$ inches.

Viper Blenny, *P. viperidens*. A little-known though probably common blenny found in the waters of North Queensland. Grows to 2 inches.

Cirripectes

Blennies which have a row of cirri crossing the neck to the opercular lobes and with the upper lip fringed with short tentacles. A curved internal canine is present on each side of the mandible in addition to the single row of fine movable teeth planted in the skin of the lips in each jaw. Species few, one being found in Queensland.

367. COLLARED BLENNY *Cirripectes variolosus* (Cuvier and Valenciennes)
[Plate 52]

Salarias variolosus Cuvier and Valenciennes, Hist. Nat. Poiss., 11, 1836, p. 317.
Illustration by F. Olsen after McCulloch and McNeill.

D. 12/15; A. 2/16; P. 15; V. 1/3; C. 13. Colour almost uniform dark brown or blackish, with greyish spots nearly as large as the eye, forming vermiculations which are clearest on the posterior half; several dark-blue vertical bars on body; spinous dorsal brownish, the upper portion anteriorly abruptly pale in a line from about the tip of the last spine forward to the base of the first; other fins brownish, the caudal more or less pale on its upper portion; fringe of tentacles on nape black.

Some examples have the anterior spines produced and filamentous, decreasing backwards, a feature which is perhaps sexual.

A fish from the reefs of North Queensland and Torres Strait. Grows to 4 inches.

Salarias

A large genus of small fishes found in the rock-pools and coral reefs of tropical and subtropical countries. They are distinguished mainly by their wide gill-openings and movable fine teeth, set in a single comb-like row in the gums. Canine teeth may be present or absent. In some species an occipital crest is always present in the juveniles though it may be absent in the adults. In others it is present in both sexes or in the males only. The presence or absence of an orbital tentacle has been suggested by some authorities to be a mark of sexual distinction. Of the numerous species known, ten are found in Queensland.

KEY TO SPECIES IN QUEENSLAND

Based on McCulloch[62]

A. Dorsal fin not or scarcely notched between the spines and rays.

    b. Nuchal tentacles large, fringed; body and fins variegated. — *fasciatus*

    bb. No nuchal tentacles; body and fins nearly black. — *fuscus*

AA. Dorsal fin incised between the spines and rays.

    c. Mandibular canines large.

    d. 21 dorsal and 23 anal rays. — *chrysospilos*

    dd. 17 dorsal and 19 anal rays. — *guttatus*

    cc. Mandibular canines small or absent.

      e. Margin of upper lip crenulate.

      f. Ocular tentacles simple; about 18 dorsal and 19 anal rays; small mandibular canines present. — *sinuosus*

      ff. Ocular tentacles fringed; 19-20 dorsal and 19-20 anal rays; no mandibular canines. — *meleagris*

      ee. Margin of upper lip entire.

      g. Ocular tentacles simple; 19-20 dorsal rays. — *edentulus*

      gg. Ocular tentacles branched; 21-23 dorsal rays.

      h. Body with thin, dark, longitudinal lines; caudal plain. — *lineatus*

      hh. Body without longitudinal lines.

[62] *Rec. Austr. Mus.*, 14, pt. 2, 1923, p. 123.

i. No occipital crest; soft dorsal and caudal without
   dark borders.   *dussumieri*

ii. An occipital crest; soft dorsal and caudal with
    dark borders.   *geminatus*

368. LINEATED BLENNY *Salarias fasciatus* (Bloch)   [Plate 52]

Blennius fasciatus Bloch, Nat. ausl. Fische, 2, 1786, p. 110.
Salarias fasciatus McCulloch, Rec. Austr. Mus., 14, no. 2, 1923, p. 123, pl. 15, fig. 3.

Painted Blenny, Barred Blenny (Queensland).

D. 12-13/18-19; A. 2/20; P. 14; V. 2. Colour brownish or yellowish-brown, irregularly variegated, spotted and dotted with yellow and blue; region above opercles and along back thickly sprinkled with black "dots and dashes" which become thin undulating lines on the sides; about 2 rows of blue spots on upper half of side and some larger brown spots on caudal peduncle; about 8 broad dark cross-bands distinct in the young but becoming indistinct in large examples; head with brown dots above and a mark from eye to mouth; others on preopercular and opercular edges; each lip with spots on its edge; 2 broad bluish-brown cross-bands on throat; cross-bands of body continued on to dorsals in form of dark blotches basally, each of which divides and curves upwards and forwards in darker bands; these are crossed by narrow dark lines which end in dark marginal spots; on spinous portion of dorsal the broader bands are formed of anastomosing darker lines which enclose light round spots; anal dusky, with tips of rays blackish and with dark blotches basally; caudal and pectoral with cross-rows of dark spots; ventrals light-coloured with dark spots; large light spots at base of pectoral.

The species is subject to great variation of colour and in the relative length of the fin-rays and spines. In some examples the anterior anal rays may be greatly produced.

This rather large and handsome blenny, readily recognized by its deep body and distinctive colour pattern, is a very common fish on the coral reefs of Queensland north of the Capricorns. South of that locality it is seldom seen. It is wide-ranging and is found in the Pacific, the East Indies, East Africa, and in the Red Sea. Grows to 6 inches.

OTHER SPECIES

Dusky Blenny, *S. fuscus*. A species not commonly met with in Queensland. It ranges from the south-western Pacific to India. Grows to 4 inches.

Blue-spotted Blenny, *S. chrysospilos*. A North Queensland and South Sea Island species fairly common on the coral reefs of North Queensland. Grows to 6 inches.

Speckled Blenny, *S. guttatus*. A distinctively marked little species from North Queensland and the South Pacific. Grows to $2\frac{1}{2}$ inches.

Fringe-lip Blenny *S. sinuo, sus*. Found on the coral reefs of Queensland and also in the South Seas and the Indo-Australian Archipelago. Grows to 3 inches.

Peacock Blenny, *S. meleagris*. Common in the rock-pools on the reefs and mainland of Queensland, and in the Northern Territory, becoming rarer in the south and in northern New South Wales. Grows to 6 inches. An Indo-Pacific species.

Rippled Blenny, *S. edentulus*. A species from Queensland, Lord Howe Island, and the western Pacific. Grows to 6 inches.

Narrow-lined Blenny, *S. lineatus*. This wide-ranging blenny, which is found in Torres Strait, also occurs in Melanesia, Micronesia, Polynesia, and the East Indies across to the Red Sea. Grows to 4 inches.

Dussumier's Blenny, *S. dussumieri*. Another wide-ranging blenny found in Torres Strait. Grows to 4 inches.

Twin-banded Blenny, *S. geminatus*. A species from North Queensland and New Guinea. Wide-ranging. Grows to 4 inches.

Ecsenius

Blennies with the general form of *Salarias*, but differing in having a row of six or seven small cardiform teeth on each side of mandible, extending backward along the elevated ridge, in addition to the row of fine, curved, compressed and movable ones in each jaw anteriorly. There are no canines. The dorsal fin is deeply notched.

369. MANY-TOOTHED BLENNY *Ecsenius mandibularis* McCulloch
[Plate 52]

Ecsenius mandibularis McCulloch, Rec. Austr. Mus., 14, no. 2, 1923, p. 122, pl. 15, fig. 1 (male).

D. 12/14; A. 2/17; P. 13; V. 2; C. 13. Colour: "Light brown in formalin, with a bluish tinge on the sides. Two rows of brown spots which are round and spaced; the upper row near the back, the lower along the middle of the sides to the base of the tail. Fins almost without marking, but the thickened tips of the anal rays are distinctly lighter than the rest of the fin." (McCulloch.)

McCulloch further states: "The female differs from the male in the form of its fins and in having no occipital crest. The fin-rays are all shorter, and those of the anal lack the anterior dermal lobes."

This distinctive little blenny is so far known only from the coral reefs of the Capricorns and Bunker groups, Queensland. Grows to 2½ inches.

Xiphasia

A genus of attenuated snake-like blennies inhabiting the Indian Ocean and the Indo-Australian region. The tail is greatly elongated and laterally compressed, the eyes are large and the dorsal and anal fins are very long and united with the caudal. The maxillary and mandibular teeth are of uniform or almost uniform size and are placed close together. A pair of extraordinarily long and curved canines are situated far back in the lower jaw, and another smaller though still large pair are present in the upper jaw and placed farther back again than the lower pair. Palate toothless.

In commenting on these curious posterior canines, Herre (loc.cit.) states: "The function of the extraordinary canines, particularly the preposterous ones of the lower jaw, is not clear. It is difficult to believe that the fish could open its mouth sufficiently to use them in defending itself. They are so long and so curved that the points are out of sight even when the mouth is opened to its fullest extent. Of course it is possible that in life the jaws might open more widely. According to Jerdon, quoted by Day, it is said to be venomous."

Two or three species, one in Australian waters.

370. HAIR-TAILED BLENNY *Xiphasia setifer* Swainson [Plate 52]

Xiphasia setifer Swainson, Nat. Hist. Classif. Fish. Amphib. Rept., 2, July 1839, p. 259 (based on Russell, pl. 39).

Xiphasia setifer Herre, Phil. Journ. Sci., 31, no. 2, 1926, p. 224, pl. 1.

D. 120-129; A. 97-116; C. 3; P. 13. Colour bright yellow, with about 28 dusky bands on dorsal and body, almost as wide as the interspaces; the first band, which is just behind the head, does not extend on to the dorsal, which is clear yellow at its origin; dorsal and anal broadly edged with blackish; caudal filament black; head dusky-yellowish; pectorals and ventrals yellowish.

This rare pelagic fish is known in Queensland waters from a single example which was picked up in the surf at Stradbroke Island, South Queensland. A few specimens have been taken in New South Wales. The species is known also from Lord Howe Island in the South Pacific, and in India and Madagascar. Nowhere does it appear to be common. Grows to 20 inches.

Cristiceps

A small genus of fishes in which the first three anterior spines of the dorsal are usually entirely separated from those following, thus forming a separate fin above or in advance of the eye.

These are mainly fishes of the cooler waters of the southern half of the continent of Australia and also Tasmania. Of the nine known species found from New South Wales to Western Australia, one occurs in the waters of Moreton Bay, South Queensland.

370a. CRESTED WEED-FISH *Cristiceps aurantiacus* Castelnau [Plate 52]

Cristiceps aurantiacus Castelnau, Proc. Linn. Soc. N.S.Wales, 3, 1879, p. 386.
Cristiceps aurantiacus McCulloch, Rec. Austr. Mus., 7, no. 1, 1908, p. 38, pl. 10, fig. 1.

D. 3/28-30; 4-5 + 2; A. 2/23-25; V. 3. Colour a beautiful clear orange-yellow, with the fins yellow; there are 4 almost vertical hyaline patches on the second dorsal, the first about the seventh and eighth spines, another about the thirteenth and fourteenth, another about the twentieth and twenty-first and the last on the two last short rays. Some examples are reddish with the fins dark purple, with minute blackish dots and pectorals and ventral fins barred with yellow.

A fish commonly found among weeds in the estuaries of the streams of New South Wales. Its presence in Queensland is only as an occasional straggler into Moreton Bay. Grows to 10 inches.

Petraites

A genus of fishes separated from *Cristiceps* mainly by the position of the first dorsal fin, the first spine of which is placed behind the eye. Six species are known to inhabit the waters in the southern portion of Australia, one only of which enters into South Queensland.

371. LONG-NOSED WEED-FISH *Petraites nasutus* (Günther) [Plate 52]

Cristiceps nasutus Günther, Cat. Fish. Brit. Mus., 3, 1861, p. 273.
Petraites fasciatus McCulloch, Rec. Austr. Mus., 7, no. 1, 1908, p. 42, pl. 11, fig. 2.

D. 3/28-31, 1 + 1; A. 2/18-22; V. 2, rarely 3. Colour: "In colour it may be anything from dark green without markings to pale green with darker bands and silvery or transparent markings. Specimens living in the pink coraline sea-weed common on the coast are of a bright pink variegated with brown, throughout which, however, the typical bands and silver spots are maintained." (McCulloch.)

Queensland examples are usually raw sienna colour above, passing into bright olive-yellow below; dorsal hyaline, with yellowish tinge and with about 7 dark olive-green blotches, each covering about 3 rays. The olive-green blotch is darkest in its centre. These blotches extend on to the back where they have 2 white dots anteriorly and posteriorly. There are also 3 to 4 silvery-white marks along the sides, larger and more distinct anteriorly.

A very common species found living among seaweeds along the coast of New South Wales, and less commonly found in Queensland where its most northerly range to date is Caloundra. Grows to $2\frac{1}{2}$ inches.

Notograptus

Blennies with attenuated eel-like bodies covered with minute imbricate scales. Lateral line complete, running along base of dorsal fin. Teeth in a villiform band in both jaws. Pectorals and ventrals present. A short flat barbel at symphysis of lower jaw. Gill-membranes attached to the isthmus before the ventrals.

Two species, one found in the waters of North Queensland and Torres Strait, the other in those of Western Australia.

372. SPOTTED EEL BLENNY *Notograptus guttatus* Günther [Plate 52]

Notograptus guttatus Günther, Ann. Mag. Nat. Hist. (3), 20, 1st July 1867, p. 64.
Notograptus guttatus McCulloch, Mem. Qld Mus., 6, 1918, p. 94, pl. 29.

D. 62/1; A. 37/2; V. 1; P. 19; C. 10. Colour reddish or brownish, with numerous blue ocelli or spots on upper and lateral parts of body; the spots are largest and strongest on the head, nape, and lips; they are more numerous and plainest on the body anteriorly, becoming faint and more scattered posteriorly; dorsal with numerous less distinct blue spots.

This curious blenny frequents the waters of North Queensland, Torres Strait, and the Northern Territory. So far it is not known on the Queensland coast south of the Whitsunday Passage, where at Lindeman Island it was dredged in 9 fathoms by Mel Ward. Grows to 5 inches. Not commonly seen.

Scleropteryx

A genus of Queensland fishes with large eye, short and rounded snout. Teeth in upper jaw stout and conical, in 3 series anteriorly, in lower jaw in a stronger single series; a few scattered teeth on vomer. A single straight lateral line along the middle of the body. One species.

373. SNAKE BLENNY *Scleropteryx devisi* (Ogilby) [Plate 52]

Ophioclinus devisi Ogilby, Proc. Linn. Soc. N.S.Wales (2), 9, 2, 10th Dec. 1894, p. 373.
Illustration by F. Olsen after Whitley.

D. 70/3; A. 1/55; V. 1/2; C. 12. "Colours (in spirits)—Uniform reddish-brown, the occiput and opercles with a yellowish tinge." (Ogilby.)

A small and rare fish known only from Moreton Bay, South Queensland. Nothing is known regarding its habits. Grows to $3\frac{1}{4}$ inches.

Sub-family CLININAE

Tripterygion

Small fishes inhabiting the waters of New Zealand, through the Indo-Australian Archipelago to India and the Mediterranean. They are characterized mainly by having 3 dorsal fins (the first and second joined), a naked head, and with the lateral line interrupted. Two species occur in Queensland.

A. Eye large, longer than snout. D. 3/12/8; A. 14. Greyish,
with irregular bars of dark brown.   *atrogulare*

AA. Eye small, shorter than snout. D. 3/12/11; A. 1/18.
Colour from bright green to scarlet.   *annulatum*

374. BLACK TRIPLE-FINS *Tripterygion atrogulare* Günther

Tripterygion atrogulare Günther, Journ. Mus. Godef., 1, 1873, p. 267.

"Life colours: Ground colour greyish; body with very irregular bars of dark
brown and a few red dots on the sides; top of head flecked with red, a dark
bar on the snout. Eye green; pupil black, surrounded by a coppery ring. Dorsal
variegated with brownish; anal whitish with pink rays; pectorals whitish
proximally and pink distally; ventrals whitish; caudal whitish with a few short
brown bars on the rays." (Whitley.)

Günther gives the colours as clear brownish; ventral surface of body and
base of pectoral black; tail with a small black spot above and below.

A fairly common little fish found along the entire Great Barrier Reef. Grows
to 2 inches. Unfortunately no illustration exists of this small species.

OTHER SPECIES

Ringed Triple-fins, *T. annulatum*. A small and common fish of the rock-
pools of New South Wales, only occasionally straggling into Moreton Bay.
The colour varies from green to scarlet. Grows to 2 inches.

Lepidoblennius

A small genus of Australian shore-fishes found in Queensland, New South
Wales, and Western Australia. They are characterized by having 3 dorsal
fins (the first two joined but with the lateral line complete. Two species are
known, one being found in Queensland.

375. JUMPING JOEY *Lepidoblennius haplodactylus* Steindachner [Plate 52]

Lepidoblennius haplodactylus Steindachner, Sitzb. Akad. Wiss. Wien, 55, 1, 1867, p. 12, pl. 1, figs 1-1a.

Spangled Blenny (Queensland); Basking Blenny (New South Wales).

D. 17/12; A. 19; L. l. about 70. "Colour in spirits, yellowish, with a number
of rather faint reddish-brown spots and double vertical fasciae along the body;
fins of a more dusky yellow, with a brown spot at the extremity of the first
dorsal spine, and another on the membrane between the third and fourth; anal
margined with blackish." (Macleay.)

Although Steindachner's type is said to have been taken in the Fitzroy River at Rockhampton, Queensland, the species has since been recorded only from Moreton Bay. It extends into New South Wales and is very commonly met with there, usually in the rock-pools along the coast.

McCulloch notes that it "has the curious habit of leaving the water to bask in the sun on damp, weed-covered rocks. When approached, it skips rapidly into the water, and hides among the coralline sea-weeds, which it closely resembles in its colour marking. It is extremely active in the water, and is commonly known as Jumping Joey or the Basking Blenny". Grows to 5 inches.

Sub-order OPHIDIOIDEA

A large and varied group of fishes, widely distributed in all seas. They are closely related to the Blennioidea, agreeing with it in all respects except that no spines are present in any of the fins.

KEY TO FAMILIES

A.   Pseudobranchiae well developed, very rarely small or obsolete.

    b. Ventrals absent or rudimentary, when present, jugular.   CONGROGADIDAE

AA. Pseudobranchiae absent or rudimentary.

    c. Ventral fins entirely wanting. No scales. Vent at throat. Pectorals present or absent.   CARAPIDAE

    cc. Ventral fins well developed. Scales present. Vent posterior, normal. Pectorals present.   BROTULIDAE

Family **Congrogadidae**

Eel-like blennies inhabiting muddy areas in shallow waters in the Indo-Australian region. The teeth are closely set and in a single series. Pectoral fins are present but the ventrals are absent or rudimentary. Two genera are found in Queensland.

KEY TO GENERA IN QUEENSLAND

A.   Ventral fins reduced to 2 small and short filaments. D + C + A = 50 + 9 + 40. Size small.   *Blennodesmus*

AA. Ventral fins absent. D + C + A = 70 + 10 + 60 — 65. Size larger.   *Congrogadus*

Blennodesmus

Scales rudimentary. Lateral line indistinct. Head compressed, snout pointed. Ventrals reduced to 2 short filaments, jugular.

Small fishes of the tide-pools along the Australian coasts. One species.

376. AN EEL BLENNY *Blennodesmus scapularis* Günther [Plate 52]

Blennodesmus scapularis Günther, Proc. Zool. Soc. Lond., 1871 (May 1872), p. 667, pl. 67, fig. A.

D. + C + A = 50 + 9 + 40; V. 1. Colour: "Body brownish, marbled with darker, sides of the head with small round yellowish spots; a black yellow-edged ocellus in the scapular region; an undulated yellowish line along the middle of the nape and head; fins greyish." (Günther.)

A small fish very occasionally found in the coral pools and reefs of Queensland and west and north-western Australia. Grows to 3 inches.

Congrogadus

A small genus of fishes from the Australian and East Indian coasts, represented in Queensland by a single species. Pectorals present. No ventrals. Size large.

377. MUD BLENNY *Congrogadus subducens* (Richardson) [Plate 52]

Machaerium subducens Richardson, Ann. Mag. Nat. Hist., 12, 1st Sept. 1843, p. 175, pl. 6; and Voy. Erebus and Terror (Fish) 1844-8, p. 72, pl. 44, fig. 1.

Ambeetunbeet (Port Essington natives).

D. 71; C. 10; A. 60-65. Live colours: General colour olive, sprinkled thickly with rust-red blotches, those on belly, chin, and throat alternating with spots of very light bluish-white; dorsal and anal light olive with several rows of bright-red blotches. A large blue-black ocellus, surrounded white, is situated on the opercle; pectorals pinkish.

An eel-like fish which inhabits muddy areas in shallow water. It is fairly common in Torres Strait and ranges southward along the Queensland coast, the southerly record being Heron Island in the Capricorn Group. At Thursday Island it is occasionally disturbed in the mud when pearling luggers are being launched at the boat-slips. The species is also found in the Northern Territory, Western Australia, New Guinea, and the East Indies.

Whitley[63] records a specimen taken from a rock-pool at North-west Island, Capricorn Group. He states: "When alive, it was green with transparent fins. Head crossed by radiating silvery bars edged superiorly with blackish. Eye golden." Grows to 15½ inches.

Family **Carapidae: Pearl-fishes or Messmates**

Small shore-fishes of temperate and tropical seas, from Europe to the East Indian Archipelago and the coasts of Australia and New Zealand. They are remarkable for their habit of living in shells of molluscs, echinoderms (starfishes), tunicates, etc., and being frequently commensal with the pearl-oyster and with the large holothurians (sea-cucumbers).

[63] *Austr. Zool.*, 4, 1925-7, p. 236.

Their naked bodies are elongate and compressed, tapering into a long and slender tail. The vertical fins are very low, confluent and without spines. No caudal fin; pectoral fins present or absent; no ventral fins; mouth not protractile; lips weakly developed; teeth cardiform in jaws, on vomer and palatines; canines often present; gill-openings wide, the membranes free from isthmus; mucous canals of head and lateral line well developed; vent at the throat.

In writing on the fish's curious association with holothurians or other animals, Barnard[64] states: "They are not parasitic, but seek their food in a normal manner, merely returning to the Holothurian or other animal for protection and seclusion. They seem to be attracted to the Holothurian by the respiratory current and enter tail first. They are sometimes caught buried in sand or in crevices of coral reefs. The eggs are pelagic and are embedded in a mass of slime. The newly-hatched larva has been observed to float in a vertical position, head downwards. It possesses a remarkable elongate filament with foliate expansions, probably a modification of the 1st dorsal ray, which hangs down over the head and is evidently a sensory appendage, perhaps for the purpose of perceiving the respiratory currents of Holothurians, etc., and guiding it to a suitable retreat."

Two species from the one genus, *Carapus*, are known from the waters of Queensland.

KEY TO SPECIES IN QUEENSLAND

A. Body stiletto-shaped, tapering, becoming thinner gradually from head to tail; head thicker than body. *homei*

AA. Body deeper, the dorsal contour strongly gibbous; head thinner than body. *houlti*

378. HUMP-BACK MESSMATE *Carapus houlti* (Ogilby) [Plate 53]

Fierasfer houlti Ogilby, Mem. Qld Mus., 7, pt 4, 19th Dec. 1922, p. 301, pl. 19, fig. 1.

Colour: "Greyish-brown, dotted with darker, the dots even encroaching upon the basal half of the pectoral." (Ogilby.)

The species is known from only two examples, which are male and female and are presumably adults. They were trawled by Captain Hoult of the State trawler *Bar-ea-Mul* in 36 fathoms off Double Island Point in 1922. When caught, they were, according to his statement, enclosed in the eviscerated remains of a holothurian, and were very vicious when shaken out on the deck.

Type locality Double Island Point, South Queensland. Lengths 283 and 236 mm.

---

[64] *Ann. Sth Afr. Mus.*, 21, pt 2, Oct. 1927, p. 884.

OTHER SPECIES

Pearl-fish, *C. homei*. A small fish of 6½ inches ranging from North Queensland through Melanesia, Micronesia, and Polynesia to the East Indies.

Family **Brotulidae**

Form elongate, compressed, tail tapering. Body with small scales, sometimes naked. Caudal generally joined with dorsal and anal. Ventral usually present.

A large family of fishes with many genera and species found living in the depths of the sea, mainly in other parts of the world. In Cuba some of the species have degenerated into blind cave-fishes. Two genera are found in Queensland waters.

KEY TO GENERA IN QUEENSLAND

A.   Dorsal and anal fins united with caudal. *Sirembo*

AA. Dorsal and anal fins separate, not continuous with caudal. *Dinematichthys*

Sirembo

A small genus of fishes found in the seas of Japan and Queensland. Their elongate bodies are covered with very small scales, and the lateral line is simple and more or less indistinct. Eye of moderate size. Vertical fins united; each ventral reduced to a single filament, both close together but each with a distinct base. Bands of villiform teeth in the jaws, on the vomer and the palatines.

One species in Queensland, *S. everriculi* Whitley, a unique 6½-inch fish which was trawled in 10 fathoms in the Cumberland group, North Queensland, in 1935.

Dinematichthys

Fishes of the East Indian Archipelago and the coasts of California and Queensland. Body elongate, covered with very small scales. Eye small. One dorsal and anal fin, not continuous with caudal. Each ventral fin reduced to a single filament, both close together and inserted at throat but behind the isthmus. Jaws, vomer, and palatines with bands of teeth.

One species in Queensland, *D. mizolepis* Günther, a curious little fish inhabiting the coral reefs of North Queensland. It has not yet been recorded south of the Capricorns. Grows to 3 inches.

Sub-order STROMATEOIDEA

Family **Stromateidae: Pomfrets**

Form elongate to deep, sometimes compressed. Scales of moderate size, sometimes deciduous. Mouth small or moderate; teeth uniserial in jaws, present or absent on palatines. Dorsal and anal long, spines weak. Ventrals attached to body by membrane and recessed into belly groove; in some species the ventrals disappear or diminish with age.

Oceanic fishes of large and small size, pelagic or bathypelagic in habit and feeding upon pelagic jellyfishes, crustaceans, or the fry of other fishes. Two genera are found in Queensland waters.

KEY TO GENERA IN QUEENSLAND

A. Vomer and palatines with teeth.   *Nomeus*

AA. Palate toothless.   *Psenes*

Nomeus

Body oblong, elongate, somewhat compressed. Head moderate, slightly flat above. Snout conic. Eye anterior. Mouth small with small teeth uniserial in jaws, also on vomer and palatines. Nostrils together, high. Scales cycloid. Lateral line high. Ten to 11 dorsal spines. Anal with 3 strong spines, connected. Second dorsal and anal alike, with long bases and opposite. Caudal forked. Long, wide ventral, joined by membrane to belly and depressible into deep furrow.

Small pelagic fishes of tropical seas commonly found living under the large *Physalia* or Portuguese Man-o'-war. One species in Queensland.

379. PORTUGUESE MAN-O'-WAR FISH   *Nomeus albula*   (Meuschen)
[Plate 53]

Gobius albula Meuschen, Ind. Zoophylac. Gronov., pt 3, 1781, no. 278. Ex. Gronow, non-binom. (America).
Nomeus gronovii Goode and Bean, Oceanic Ichth., 1875, p. 220, pl. 63, fig. 227.

Pastor (Great Britain); Bluebottle-fish (South Africa).

D. 10-11 + 1/24-26; A. 3/24-27; L. l. about 65; L. tr. 5/20. Colour brownish or blackish above or sometimes blue, with large brown blotches and spots over body, dorsal, anal, and caudal fins; pectorals brown above, white below; ventrals with a broad black margin and with black along their inner edge, the rest white.

A widely distributed pelagic fish found in all temperate and tropical seas. It derives its name from its habit of swimming in small companies beneath the Portuguese Man-o'-war, *Physalia*, a large jellyfish. It is apparently immune to the powerful stinging tentacles and serves to lure other small fishes into the seemingly apparent protection and which thus serve as food to the jellyfish and its lodger. Grows to 6 inches.

Psenes

Body ovoid, compressed. Head of moderate size. Snout short, obtuse. Eye large, anterior. Mouth small, jaws even; maxillary oblique; teeth uniserial, none on palate or tongue. Nostrils together, small. Two dorsal fins, the first of 10 or 11 spines; second dorsal as high as first and similar to anal, which last has 2 to 3 spines. Ventrals inserted below pectorals. Lateral line unarmed.

Small pelagic fishes found in the warm ocean currents of tropical seas. The species are few, two being found in Queensland waters.

KEY TO SPECIES IN QUEENSLAND

A. Body elliptical, the dorsal and ventral contours evenly rounded and symmetrical; pectorals long, equal to the length of the head.   *hillii*

AA. Body compressed, the dorsal contour elevated and bulging above nostrils; ventral contour not so convex; pectorals short, equal to length of head, less the snout.   *whiteleggii*

380. WHITELEGGE'S BLUBBER-FISH *Psenes whiteleggii* Waite [Plate 53]

Psenes whiteleggii Waite, Proc. Linn. Soc. N.S.Wales (2), vol. 9, 1894, p. 218, pl. 17, fig. 1.
Psenes whiteleggii Smith, Sea Fish. Sthn Afr., 1949, p. 306, fig. 853.

D. 11. 1/19; A. 3/18; L. l. 55. Colour delicate salmon, with 3 brownish transverse bands, the first very broad; head brown above, silvery below, including opercles; fins brownish.

Known only from the waters of South Queensland (Moreton Bay) and New South Wales. Rarely met with. Grows to about 2 inches.

OTHER SPECIES

Hill's Blubber-fish, *P. hillii*. A rare fish so far known only from Moreton Bay in South Queensland. Length $4\frac{1}{2}$ inches.

Sub-order MUGILOIDEA:

BARRACUDAS, MULLETS, and ATHERINES

Two dorsal fins, the first with pungent or flexible spines, situated more or less distinct from the second. Opercles usually without spines. Three families constitute this sub-order.

KEY TO FAMILIES

A. Lateral line well developed. Mouth wide, teeth long and fang-like.   SPHYRAENIDAE

AA. No lateral line. Mouth moderate or small, teeth small or wanting.

b. First dorsal fin with only 4 stiff spines. Anal fin with 3 weak spines. MUGILIDAE

bb. First dorsal fin with 4-8 weak spines. Anal fin with a single weak spine. ATHERINIDAE

Family **Sphyraenidae: Barracudas or Sea-pikes**

Body elongate, subcylindrical, covered with small scales. Head very long, pointed, teeth in jaws and on palatines large, sharp, and of unequal size; none on vomer. Usually a very strong sharp canine near tip of lower jaw. Two short dorsal fins remote from each other, the first consisting of 5 rather stout spines. Anal similar to second dorsal and more or less opposite that fin. Ventrals of 1 spine and 5 rays, situated more or less opposite first dorsal. Caudal fin forked.

These pike-like, slender and fast-swimming powerful fishes inhabit most tropical and subtropical seas. They are extremely voracious and vicious in habit, and large examples, which reach a length of 8 feet, are known to be dangerous to man. They are known by the names of Barracuda, Sea-pike, Dingo-fish and Senuk or Snoek (now spelt and pronounced Snook). This last name is used by the Dutch colonists for different species of *Sphyraena*. The Barracuda must not be confused with the Barracouta, *Thyrsites*, of southern Australia, a fish which is quite unrelated, though somewhat similar in shape.

The barracudas are not much esteemed as food-fishes. Four species, all of the genus *Sphyraena*, are found in Queensland.

Sphyraena

For characters of the genus see those given under the family heading. Four species occur in Queensland waters.

KEY TO SPECIES IN QUEENSLAND

A. Angle of preoperculum rounded.

b. Eye small, 5 times in snout. *microps*

bb. Eye large, 2.4-4 times in snout.

c. Teeth in lower jaw vertical. Body with oblique dark cross-bars above lateral line. *barracuda*

cc. Teeth in lower jaw more or less directed backward. Dark cross-bars on body extending well below lateral line. *jello*

AA. Angle of preoperculum rectangular. *obtusata*

o

381. PICK-HANDLE BARRACUDA *Sphyraena jello*
Cuvier and Valenciennes [Colour-plate 54]

Sphyraena jello Cuvier and Valenciennes, Hist. Nat. Poiss., 3, 1829, p. 349.
Illustration by G. Coates.

Pike, Pick-handle Barracuda (Townsville); Dingo-fish, Sea Pike (Queensland, New South Wales, and South Africa).

D^1. 5; D^2. 2/8; A. 2/8; L. l. 123-130. Colour brownish or greenish above, silvery-white below, the colour of the back connecting to a number of cross-bars of the same colour; ventrals yellowish; pectorals yellowish basally, rest of fin hyaline; behind the pectoral a large blackish-brown spot; other fins dusky or blackish, the lower lobe of caudal yellowish. In some examples the cross-bars may be absent.

A wide-ranging species, common in North Queensland. Grows to at least 6 feet.

382. STRIPED BARRACUDA *Sphyraena obtusata* Cuvier and Valenciennes
[Colour-plate 54]

Sphyraena obtusata Cuvier and Valenciennes, Hist. Nat. Poiss., 3, 1829, p. 350.
Illustration by G. Coates.

Pike (Brisbane Fish Market); Sennit (Mackay); Striped Sea Pike (Queensland and New South Wales); Yellow-tail (Queensland).

D^1. 5; D^2. 1/9; A. 2-3/8-9; L. l. 82-85. Colour greyish-green or yellowish-green above, silvery-white below; the colour of the upper parts descends in a festooned edge below the lateral line; pectoral greyish-yellow, other fins yellowish, especially the soft dorsal; caudal bright yellow in the young; 1 or sometimes 2 longitudinal olive-yellow stripes, brightest and more yellowish before the eye, run from the snout through the eye to the caudal base; these may be very indistinct in some examples and in most are much more clearly indicated anteriorly.

A species which grows to about 20 inches. According to A. Raymond Jones this fish indulges in mimicry. He has noticed them, when in the vicinity of "dugong grass" and when danger threatens, up-end themselves, head downwards, and sway in unison with the grass as it moves with the current.

A wide-ranging fish, common on the Australian coast except in Victoria.

OTHER SPECIES

Small-eyed Barracuda, *S. microps*. A little-known fish occasionally caught by game-fishermen outside Cape Moreton, South Queensland. It grows to a length of 6 feet with a weight of at least 55 pounds.

Giant Barracuda, *S. barracuda*. Inhabits the waters of northern Australia and grows to a length of 6 feet with a weight of about 40 pounds.

Family **Mugilidae: Mullets**

Body oblong, somewhat compressed, covered with large cycloid scales, rarely ctenoid. Head large, convex, sometimes depressed, scaled above and on sides. No lateral line, but the furrows often deepened in the middle of each scale to form lateral streaks. Mouth small, the jaws with small teeth, or none, or with minute dermal ciliiform ones on lips. Premaxillaries usually protractile. Gill-openings wide.

Gills 4. Eyes lateral, with or without adipose lids. Opercles usually unarmed. Dorsal fins 2, well separated, the anterior with 4 stiff spines; second dorsal longer than the first and slightly shorter than the anal, which has 2 to 3 graduated spines. Ventrals abdominal, situated not far back and of 1 spine and 5 rays. Caudal forked.

Small or moderate-sized fishes living along the coasts and in the fresh waters of most temperate and tropical regions. All are valuable food-fishes and are to be seen in great numbers in all Australian fish markets at all times of the year. The method of capture is by netting, the grown fish only occasionally taking a bait and then mainly in the fresh waters.

The food of the mullet consists of organic matter contained in mud and sand and the minute organisms and algae floating on the surface of the water. The method of feeding was first noticed and described by Dr Günther,[65] who stated: "In order to prevent larger bodies from passing into the stomach, or substances from passing through the gill-openings, these fishes have the organs of the pharynx modified into a filtering apparatus. They take in a quantity of sand and mud, and, after having worked it for some time between the pharyngeal bones, they reject the roughest and indigestible portion."

In other parts of the world members of the family are referred to as grey mullets. The species are numerous, rather variable, and often somewhat difficult to determine. Four genera are found in Queensland.

KEY TO GENERA IN QUEENSLAND

A.   Head very depressed, broad and flat. Snout rounded, sharp and much produced. Mouth inferior. Eye small, situated level with top of head.   *Squalomugil*

AA. Head not so depressed, snout not produced. Mouth terminal or sub-inferior. Eye large, situated towards centre of head horizontally.

    b. A single row of well-developed teeth in upper jaw. Lower jaw fringed with minute cilia.   *Myxus*

    bb. Jaws toothless.

---

[65] *An Introduction to the Study of Fishes*, 1880, p. 502.

404

c. Teeth on vomer and palatines. No adipose eyelid.
Greenish-black in colour, fins black; eye orange-
yellow. Found in fresh water. *Trachystoma*

cc. No teeth on vomer or palatines. Adipose eyelid
well developed, rudimentary or absent. *Mugil*

Squalomugil

Head depressed, scaly, except tip of snout and lower jaw. Mouth moderate,
inferior, not protractile; upper lip thin; maxillary concealed. Jaws with
spatulate cilia. Soft dorsal and anal scaly, the former, with 1 spine and 7 rays,
the latter with 3 spines and 8 rays, originating in advance of the second dorsal.
Caudal feebly emarginate. Distribution that of the single known species.

383. SHARK MULLET *Squalomugil nasutus* (De Vis) [Colour-plate 54]

Mugil nasutus De Vis, Proc. Linn. Soc. N.S.Wales, 7, 1883, p. 621.
Illustration by G. Coates.

Sharp-nosed Mullet, Mud Mullet (Cardwell); Skip-jack (Rockhampton).
D. 4, 1/7; A. 2/8; L. l. 28. This peculiar mullet is readily recognized from all
other species by the pointed and flattened head with its long snout, and the
small eyes situated on top of the head. It is closely related to *Mugil corsula*, an
Indian species with similar habits, but differs in its much larger scales, longer
snout, and thin lips.

Little was known concerning it from the year it was discovered until Dr W.
E. J. Paradice collected it at Adam Bay in the Northern Territory. In July 1941
W. Watkins collected several at Cardwell, North Queensland, the type locality
of the species, and supplied the following interesting notes on them:

"There are plenty of them just about our area, but I have not noticed them
anywhere else; only on one occasion whilst on my return from Brisbane, some
three years ago. Whilst crossing what I should say is the Saint Lawrence River
I noticed some small ones coming up with the making tide. . . . I cannot say I
have seen them up to 12 inches. About 8 to 10 inches as far as I know would
be about the largest size I can call to memory. They are exactly as described by
you. Their eyes are really on top of their head, and they swim always with the
greater portion of the head and eyes out of water. When disturbed they dive
along just under water in short advances just a few yards and then to the
surface again. They frequent mud flats or banks and live entirely on mud.
They are always full of mud and thus we know them as Mud Mullet. Where a
mud bank say dips about 200 feet to the foot they can slide along till they are
right out of water, and after puddling with their snouts in the mud for a few
minutes slide back into water. They are never found in deep water at all, and
although they frequent our locality (a few miles either side of the town) you
never see them. They are very hard to catch with an ordinary bait net, for they

just slide over the cork line. A casting net is the only way outside shooting them. . . . They are rarely seen alone—mostly in small schools, about 6 to 12. They will swim slowly north or southwards till they find another small bunch, and so on, till they congregate into a school; then they apparently split up again and so on. There appears to be two kinds; whether male or female I do not know. Some have a more pointed nose than others. . . . They can jump along in small jumps of a foot or so, but most dive along in small advances, about 3 feet at a time, that is, when disturbed, but when not disturbed swim along with portion of head and eyes out of water. They have no windbag like other fish, and will drown very quickly if kept under water and cannot live out of water. . . ."

This very interesting mullet ranges from Rockhampton, Queensland, to the Northern Territory. Grows to about 12 inches.

Myxus

Snout pointed. Cleft of mouth extending on to the sides of the snout, but not reaching orbit; well-developed small teeth in a single series in the upper jaw, and sometimes in the lower; minute teeth on vomer and palatines. Upper lip not particularly thick; anterior margin of the mandible sharp.

Fishes living along the coats of eastern and Western Australia, Lord Howe Island and Norfolk Island, and in the Pacific Ocean, and the Red Sea. One species in Queensland.

384. TALLEGALANE or SAND MULLET *Myxus elongatus* Günther
[Plate 53]

Myxus elongatus Günther, Cat. Fish. Brit. Mus., 3, 1861, p. 466.
Myxus elongatus Waite, Trans. Roy. Soc. Sth Austr., 40, 1916, p. 454, pl. 44.

Wide Bay Mullet (Queensland); Sand Mullet, Tallegalane, Lano (New South Wales).

D. 4, 1/8-9; A. 3/9; L. l. 43-46; L. tr. 15-16. Colour reddish-brown or dark greenish above, sides pink or silvery, white below; a small distinct black axillary spot at upper base of pectoral fin, beneath which is a silvery-white zone basally; a diffused golden spot on upper posterior edge of operculum; fins and tail dull greenish-brown, the spinous dorsal paler.

A common fish along the coasts of northern New South Wales and South Queensland, and also found in Victoria, South Australia, Western Australia, and Lord Howe and Norfolk islands. In the latter place it is the staple article of food among the islanders. In South Australia it is frequently captured with hook and line. Grows to 16 inches.

Trachystoma

Six branchiostegals. Pseudobranchiae present. No adipose eyelids. Vomer and palate with distinct bands of villiform teeth; jaws toothless. Scales rather small, finely ctenoid.

Fishes found mainly in the brackish and freshwater streams and lagoons of South Queensland and New South Wales. A single species.

385. FRESHWATER MULLET *Trachystoma petardi* (Castelnau) [Plate 53]

Mugil petardi Castelnau, Res. Fish. Austr. (Vict. Offic. Rec. Philad. Exhib.), 1875, p. 32.
Illustration by M. Hall.

Richmond Mullet, River Mullet, Pink-eye (New South Wales); Freshwater Mullet (Queensland and New South Wales).

D. 4, 1/8; A. 3/9; L. l. 47-50; L. tr. 15-16. Colour greenish-black above, silvery below; fins black, the pectorals lighter at their bases; eye bright orange-yellow.

A freshwater species common in the streams and lagoons of the Moreton Bay district, South Queensland, and also in northern New South Wales. Grows to nearly 24 inches.

Mugil

Body oblong, somewhat compressed, the head rather large, convex or depressed, scaly above and on sides; cleft of mouth more or less transverse, its lateral extensions short and not reaching orbit; upper lip thick or thin, with or without papillae; lips sometimes with minute cilia-like flexible dermal teeth; no teeth on palate. Eye large, with or without an anterior and posterior adipose eyelid covering part of the iris.

Species numerous, living in great shoals in the sea along the shore-line and in brackish and freshwater rivers in all tropical and temperate countries, many of the species widely distributed. The genus is represented in Queensland waters by eleven species, all of which are valuable food-fishes, the most important being the Sea Mullet, *M. cephalus*.

KEY TO SPECIES IN QUEENSLAND

A. Eye partly covered by a gelatinous eyelid.

    b. Anal with 9 rays. Upper lip thick or fairly so.

        c. An enlarged axillary scale; pectorals about equal to head or longer; a dark axillary spot present; dorsal and anal rays scaly; upper lip very thick.

            d. Cheek-scales finely ctenoid; 30-32 scales between operculum and hypural joint, dorsal and anal rays not hidden by scales; first dorsal spine nearer to hypural joint than to the end of the snout.   *georgii*

      dd. Cheek-scales cycloid; 33-34 scales between operculum and hypural joint; dorsal and anal rays largely hidden by scales; first dorsal spine nearer end of snout than to hypural joint.   *strongylocephalus*

   cc. No enlarged axillary scale or at most a small one; pectorals shorter than head; no dark axillary spot; upper lip not particularly thick.

     e. First dorsal spine slightly nearer hypural joint than to end of snout or midway between; pectorals shorter than head.   *dussumieri*

     ee. First dorsal spine in adult much nearer to end of snout than to hypural joint; pectorals much shorter than head.   *tade*

  bb. Anal with 8 rays; lips thin; gelatinous eyelid well developed; about 40 scales in a longitudinal row.   *cephalus*

AA. Eye naked, without a gelatinous eyelid or at most very rudimentary.

   f. Anal with 8-9 rays.

    g. About 27-28 scales in a longitudinal row; pectorals much shorter than head; caudal truncate. Colour dark, with blackish longitudinal bands.   *vaigiensis*

    gg. About 37 scales in a longitudinal row; pectorals as long as or longer than head (shorter in adults). Colour silvery, fins blue; pectorals with a dark axillary spot.   *seheli*

   ff. Anal with 9-11 rays.

    h. Upper lip thick or very thick.

     i. Upper lip very thick, with 4 series of soft papillae; anal with 9 rays.   *crenilabis*

     ii. Upper lip moderately thick, finely ciliated, without papillae; anal with 11 rays.   *ramsayi*

    hh. Upper lip thin.

     j. Anal with 9 rays; ventrals yellow, above eye orange.   *diadema*

     jj. Anal with 10 rays; a large golden spot on opercle.   *argenteus*

386. FANTAIL MULLET *Mugil georgii* Ogilby   [Plate 54]

Mugil georgii Ogilby, Proc. Linn. Soc. N.S.Wales, 22, 1897, p. 77.
Mugil georgii McCulloch, Rec. Austr. Mus., 13, 1921, p. 129, pl. 22, fig. 1.

Fantail Mullet, Small Fantail Mullet (South Queensland); Tychuree (aborigines); Pink-eye (Southport and Mooloolaba); Flicker (Maryborough); Silver Mullet (New South Wales).

D. 4, 1/8; A. 3/9; P. 15; V. 1/5; C. 14. Colour pale olive-brown along back;

sides and below a beautiful clear silver with a golden tinge on belly; preorbital and preopercle golden; a deep black spot in axil of pectoral; borders of the soft dorsal and caudal dusky; anal, ventrals, and pectorals sometimes yellow, usually white, irides golden.

A handsome mullet known by its thick upper lip, by its caudal fin which is but little emarginate as compared with other fork-tailed species, and by its brilliant silvery colour. Found on the coasts and in the estuaries of the rivers of Queensland and New South Wales. It is a small species which does not grow more than about 10 inches. Large quantities are sold in the Brisbane Fish Market, but on account of the small size of the fish it is usually sold in the shops in the form of fillets.

387. LONG-FINNED MULLET *Mugil strongylocephalus* Richardson
[Plate 54]

Mugil strongylocephalus Richardson, Ichth. China Japan, 1846, p. 249.
Mugil strongylocephalus Smith, Sea Fish. Sthn Afr., 1949, p. 318, fig. 879.

Mud Mullet (Cairns).

D. 4, 1/8; A. 3/9; P. 16; L. l. 33-35; L. tr. 11-12. Colour greenish above, silvery below; caudal with dusky margin; base of the pectoral with a jet-black mark; upper surface of preopercle bright golden.

A small wide-ranging mullet known on the Australian coast from North Queensland and the Northern Territory. Grows to 10 inches.

388. FLAT-TAIL MULLET *Mugil dussumieri* (Cuvier and Valenciennes)
[Plate 54]

Mugil dussumieri Cuvier and Valenciennes, Hist. Nat. Poiss., 2, 1836, p. 147.
Mugil tadopsis McCulloch, Rec. Austr. Mus., 13, 1920-3, p. 127, pl. 22, fig. 2.

Green-backed Mullet (North Queensland); Brown-banded Mullet (Queensland); Flat-tailed Mullet (Moreton Bay district).

D. 4, 1/8; A. 3/9; L. l. 29-33; L. tr. 10-12. Colour: Back greyish-green posteriorly becoming brownish over head; sides silvery, washed with bronze, passing into white below and with about 5 longitudinal bands, formed by a golden-brown bar medially on scales of back and sides; dorsal fins greyish, ventrals off white; caudal dull greenish or bluish, black marginally; pectorals yellowish with an obscure blue-black axillary blotch; opercle with a dull brownish-golden spot; iris lead-blue with a narrow golden rim above.

An Indo-Australian species inhabiting the waters of Queensland from north to south. It is a fine food-fish and is especially common in Moreton Bay, South Queensland. Said to be the best of all the mullets, with flesh of delicate flavour. Grows to at least 15 inches.

389. TADE MULLET *Mudil tade* Forskål [Plate 55]

Mugil tade Forskål, Descr. Anim., 1775, p. 74.
Mugil tade Fowler, Fish. Oceania, Mem. Bern. P. Bishop Mus., 10, 1928, p. 122, fig. 26.

D. 4, 1/8; A. 3/9; L. l. 33-35; L. tr. 11. Colour pale olive, whitish below. Body with 5 to 7 indistinct dusky longitudinal lines along the scale rows. No dark spot at pectoral base.

A wide-ranging mullet which, in Australia, frequents North Queensland and Gulf waters. Grows to 18 inches.

390. This number was originally allocated to *Mugil tadopsis* but on further study that species was found to equal *M. dussumieri*. See, therefore, species 388.

391. SEA MULLET *Mugil cephalus* Linnaeus [Plate 55]

Mugil cephalus Linnaeus, Syst. Nat., 10th ed., 1758, p. 316 (based on Artedi).
Mugil dobula Günther, Cat. Fish. Brit. Mus., 3, 1861, p. 420; Fische de Sudsee, 1877, p. 214, pl. 120, fig. A.

Hardgut Mullet, Mangrove Mullet, River Mullet, Bully Mullet (New South Wales and Queensland); Sand Mullet (Victoria and Tasmania); Haarder, Springer, Flathead Mullet (South Africa).

D. 4, 1/8; A. 3/8; L. l. 38-42; L. tr. 14-15. Colour steel-blue, with a tinge of greenish or olive above; sides and below silvery; a small black axillary spot and a golden spot on upper angle of opercle; dorsal and pectoral fins dark bluish-grey; caudal and anal yellowish-green.

The young of the Sea Mullet spend the first few years of their lives far up freshwater rivers and creeks and are known as Hardgut and Mangrove Mullet. They feed and grow in these sheltered waters until mature, at about the age of three or four years, when they move out to sea for the purpose of ripening the ova, usually in the autumn months.

The fish "school up" outside the bays, awaiting the flood-tide and favourable currents before entering the rivers and bays in great shoals for the purpose of spawning along the sandbanks and inside the river mouths. This schooling commences in the month of May and it is then that the fishermen encircle the fish with their nets, taking toll often to the extent of hundreds of cases of fish in a single haul. Molested and frightened, the fish turn out to sea again and move on to the next river or creek, moving always in a northerly direction and again eagerly awaited by fishermen with their nets. So great have been the inroads made upon the mullet hordes that they are now showing definite depletion, and unless some protection is afforded them they will perhaps cease to be known as a food-fish. For many years now the percentage of mullet forwarded to the Brisbane market has been as high as 50 per cent of the total annual sales of fish, and in one year it was as much as 70 per cent.

The name of Hardgut Mullet is given by the fishermen to those fish taken during the November and December floodings of our rivers.

The Sea Mullet, which is almost of world-wide distribution, is found in Australian seas along the entire coastline and also in Tasmania. Grows to at least 30 inches in length and 10 to 12 pounds in weight.

392. DIAMOND-SCALED MULLET *Mugil vaigiensis* Quoy and Gaimard
[Colour-plate 55]

Mugil vaigiensis Quoy and Gaimard, Voy. Uranie Physic., Zool., 1825, p. 337.
Illustration by G. Coates.

Large-scaled Mullet (Queensland).

D. 4, 1/8; A. 3/8; L. l. 25-29; L. tr. 10-12. Colour dark greenish or blackish above, lighter on sides and silvery below; scales on upper sides with blackish borders; about 6 longitudinal blackish bands along the sides following scale rows; ventrals dirty white, streaked blackish; other fins and tail blackish, pectorals especially black.

A wide-ranging species found on the coasts of Queensland, New South Wales, and North and north-western Australia. It is far more common and grows to a larger size in localities north of and including Gladstone, where it reaches a length of at least 24 inches and a weight of 10 pounds or more.

393. BLUE-TAIL MULLET *Mugil seheli* Forskål [Colour-plate 55]

Mugil seheli Forskål, Descr. Anim., 1775, p. 73.
Illustration by G. Coates.

Long-finned Mullet (Queensland); Sand Mullet (Maryborough and Moreton Bay).

D. 4, 1/8; A. 3/9; L. l. 38-42; L. tr. 12-14. General colour in life greenish above, silvery below, each scale with a faint dusky mark centrally, forming indistinct longitudinal lines; soft dorsal and caudal bright light blue; ventrals white; anal silvery white; pectorals yellowish, with a prominent blue-black axillary spot.

The Blue-tail Mullet is an important food-fish in North Queensland waters, but it is only in recent years that it has been taken in really large numbers. It is common on the Queensland coast as far south as Rockhampton, but beyond that point is much more rarely met with. Stragglers have been taken as far south as Brisbane.

The species grows to a large size and is easily the largest mullet in Queensland waters. Average examples from Princess Charlotte Bay are in the vicinity of 18 or 19 inches, but they grow much larger. W. J. Kirkpatrick, a northern master fishermen, informs me that a large Blue-tail weighed in the north tipped the scales at $23\frac{1}{2}$ pounds.

The species is wide-ranging outside Australia.

394. WARTY-NOSED MULLET *Mugil crenilabis* Forskål [Plate 55]

Mugil crenilabis Forskål, Descr. Anim., 1775, p. 73.
Crenimugil crenilabis Smith, Sea Fish. Sthn Afr., 1949, p. 319, fig. 880.

D. 4, 1/8; A. 3/9; L. l. 38-40; L. tr. 13-14. Colour: Head, body, and tail greyish-green, silvery on sides and ventral surface; fins greyish, except pectorals which are pale yellowish with a bluish-black axillary spot.

A wide-ranging mullet which has been recorded in Australian waters from Queensland only. Common in North Queensland, where schools may be seen. Grows to 20 inches.

395. RAMSAY'S MULLET *Mugil ramsayi* Macleay [Plate 55]

Mugil ramsayi Macleay, Proc. Linn. Soc. N.S.Wales, 8, pt 2, 1883, p. 208.
Gracilimugil ramsayi Whitley, Austr. Zool., 10, pt 1, Dec. 1941, p. 18, fig. 14.

D. 4, 1/8-9; A. 3/10-11; L. l. 36-37; L. tr. 13-15. Colour silvery all over, with a bluish tinge on the upper surface.

A little-known North Queensland species from the Burdekin River district. It may be recognized by the thick upper lip, 11 anal rays, and the absence of adipose eyelids. Grows to 10¼ inches.

396. BASKET MULLET *Mugil diadema* Gilchrist and Thompson [Plate 56]

Mugil diadema Gilchrist and Thompson, Ann. Sth Afr. Mus., 11, 1911, p. 42.
Pteromugil diadema Smith, Sea Fish. Sthn Afr., 1949, p. 319, fig. 881.

D. 4, 1/8; A. 3/9; L. l. 30-31; L. tr. 11-21. Colour: The living fish is greyish above, silvery on sides and below, each scale with a horizontal whitish streak; spinous dorsal with the spines pale olive, the membranes hyaline; soft dorsal dark grey, somewhat dirty yellowish terminally; pectorals greyish; ventrals canary-yellow or bright orange, white basally; anal dirty yellowish or blackish, edged with orange; caudal dark greyish, blackish terminally and with traces of dirty yellow and orange along lower edge; eye with pupil black, surrounded straw-yellow and with bright orange above.

A northern mullet inhabiting the waters of the northern portions of Australia from the Gulf of Carpentaria to north-west Australia. Grows to 30 inches. It takes the name of Basket Mullet from the dark pattern formed by the edges of the scales.

397. TIGER MULLET *Mugil argenteus* Quoy and Gaimard [Plate 56]

Mugil argenteus Quoy and Gaimard, Voy. Uranie, 1825, p. 338.
Liza peronii Tosh, Rept Marine Dept Qld, 1902-3, p. 18. pl. 1, fig. 2.

Tygum (Queensland aborigines); Flat-tail, Tiger Mullet (Queensland); Gold-gill, Rockies, Rock Mullet (Moreton Bay); Jumping Mullet, Wankari (South Australia).

D. 4, 1/8; A. 3/9; L. l. 28; L. tr. 10. Colour steel-blue above, silvery on sides, white below; scales on back with a narrow median longitudinal streak forming bands, and often with golden reflections; a small black axillary spot preceded by a golden blotch; a large dark zone on inside of pectoral, at its base; soft dorsal, anal, and caudal fins tinged with gold on outer margins. There is also a large dark zone on the inside of the pectoral at its base.

A valuable food-fish commonly found in the estuaries and outside waters of northern New South Wales and South Queensland. It also occurs in Victoria, South Australia, North Australia, and Western Australia, and in Samoa. In habit it is very similar to the Sea Mullet in that it may be caught with a baited line, the bait used being either a worm or a piece of dough. Grows to 18 inches.

Family **Atherinidae: Silversides and Hardyheads**

Body more or less elongated, subcylindrical, covered with scales of moderate or small size. A silvery stripe along body. Lateral line indistinct or wanting. Teeth minute, on jaws and sometimes on vomer and palatines. Opercles unarmed. Dorsal fins 2, well separated, the first of 3 to 8 flexible spines, the second of soft rays. Anal with a weak spine, similar to the soft dorsal, but usually larger. Ventrals small, abdominal, with 1 spine and 5 rays. Pectorals moderate, inserted high.

A large family with many species of small carnivorous fishes living in shoals along the coasts of tropical and temperate seas, some entering the rivers, others living in fresh water permanently. The freshwater species make admirable little aquarium pets. Two genera in Queensland.

KEY TO GENERA IN QUEENSLAND

A.   Origin of anal fin at least before hind border of first
dorsal fin.   *Pseudomugil*

AA. Origin of anal fin far distant from first dorsal fin.   *Pranesus*

Pseudomugil: Blue-eyes

Small, elongate fishes, somewhat with the form of *Mugil*, living mainly in the fresh and brackish streams of Queensland, the Aru Islands, and southern New Guinea. Species few, two in Queensland, one marine, the other in freshwater streams.

398. MARINE BLUE-EYE *Pseudomugil signatus affinis* Whitley   [Plate 56]

Pseudomugil signatus affinis Whitley, Rec. Austr. Mus., 19, 1935, p. 228.
Pseudomugil signatus Whitley, Gt Barrier Reef Exped. Sci. Rept, 4, 9, 1932, p. 279, text-fig. 2 (male).

D. 5/13; A. 12. Colour: "Olivaceous above, each scale with a darker edge; becoming white on sides and belly. A brownish lateral band posteriorly and some blue spots on sides anteriorly. A median dark line along back. Head bluish-silvery with a red flush on operculum. Eye blue, with black pupil. First dorsal olivaceous, the spines darker. Second dorsal largely orange-yellow, with some anterior rays and their membranes blackish. Anal rays smoky, the fin with a white margin. Median portion of caudal yellow; some upper and lower rays blackish with the top and bottom of the tail white-edged. Upper pectoral rays blackish, remainder of fin white." (Whitley.)

This handsome little fish, which is a sub-species of the well-known Blue-eye of the mainland, *P. signatus*, is known only from Low Isles, North Queensland. Whitley, who collected numerous examples there, states: "In shallow water near mangrove roots were thousands of these little fishes, which could be netted as they swam in schools."

This sub-species differs from the mainland form by the greater number of fin-rays, the dorsal having 5/13 and the anal 12 rays. Its coloration is also different. Grows to about 2 inches.

Pranesus: Hardyheads

Small carnivorous fishes living in temperate and tropical seas and moving in shoals near the coast and in brackish streams, some species entering fresh water. Species numerous, three in Queensland waters.

KEY TO SPECIES IN QUEENSLAND

A. Pectorals long, about 4.8 in the length to median caudal ray. Colour grey; pectorals hyaline.   *endrachtensis*

AA. Pectorals shorter, five times or more in the length to median caudal rays. Colour green; pectorals black-tipped.

    b. Body stout, its depth 4.75 in the length; origin of spinous dorsal nearer to caudal base than to tip of snout; vent in advance of tips of ventrals.   *ogilbyi*

    bb. Body slender, its depth about 6 in the length; origin of spinous dorsal midway between caudal base and tip of snout; vent well behind tips of ventrals.   *lacunosa*

399. COMMON HARDYHEAD *Pranesus ogilbyi* Whitley   [Plate 56]

Pranesus ogilbyi Whitley, Mem. Qld Mus., 10, pt 1, Aug. 1930, p. 9.
Atherina pinguis Ogilby, Mem. Qld Mus., 1, 1912, p. 38, pl. 12, fig. 1 (not of Lacépède).

D. 5-6, 1/9-10; A. 1/13-14; L. l. 38-40; L. tr. 5. Colour: Upper parts pale green, each scale bordered and more or less dotted with black; pearly-white below, with a single or irregularly double series of black dots just below the lateral line; one or more rows along each side of base of anal, a single row along ventral ridge between anal and caudal fins, and a few dots irregularly distributed over sides of trunk and tail; a silvery lateral band from pectoral base to root of caudal; lips, upper surface of head and parietal region profusely covered with black dots, especially on snout; caudal narrowly, pectorals broadly, black-tipped, due to crowded black dots; caudal dusky tipped.

A very common little fish which swims in great shoals over the sandy flats in shallow bays and in estuaries. It inhabits the waters of Australia, New Guinea, New Zealand, and the Pacific Islands. Grows to 6¾ inches.

OTHER SPECIES

Grey Hardyhead, *P. endrachtensis*. Known by its grey colour and long pectorals. Found on the coasts of North Queensland, New Guinea, and south-west Australia, and in the Indo-Australian Archipelago. Grows to 4½ inches.

Slender Hardyhead, *P. lacunosa*. An Indo-Pacific species which enters the waters of Queensland. Grows to 5 inches.

Sub-order POLYNEMOIDEA

Family **Polynemidae: Threadfins or Tassel-fishes**

The threadfins are a single family which constitutes the sub-order Polynemoidea. They are carnivorous fishes of moderate or large size, inhabiting muddy shores and bays of tropical regions, some entering the estuaries and rivers. They are readily recognized by their pectoral fins, which are placed low down and are divided into two distinct portions. The lower part of the fin is detached from the upper and is composed of slender filamentous rays, which vary in number and length in the different species. These tassels or threads are provided with sensory organs and serve as feelers, assisting the fish to locate its food in muddy waters. Another feature is the prominent snout which is obtusely conical and overhangs the large mouth. The eyes are rather large and are covered by a gelatinous membrane.

Threadfins are highly esteemed as food-fishes and are considered to be among the finest of the edible fishes. A valuable isinglass may be made from the swim-bladders which in these fishes is exceptionally large and yields a high-class product in countries where they are collected and used. Two genera are found in Queensland.

KEY TO GENERA IN QUEENSLAND

A. Lower lip developed only at corner of mouth; teeth extending to exterior part of jaws; 3-4 free pectoral filaments.   *Eleutheronema*

AA. Lower lip well developed, but not to symphysis; teeth in jaws not extending to exterior; 5 or more pectoral filaments.   *Polynemus*

Eleutheronema

For characters of the genus see the preceding key. Fishes of the waters of India, the Malay Archipelago, and Australia. Species few, one in Queensland.

400. GIANT THREADFIN *Eleutheronema tetradactylum* (Shaw)
[Colour-plate 55]

Polynemus tetradactylus Shaw, Gen. Zool., 5, 1804, p. 155.
Illustration by G. Coates.

Burnett Salmon, Cooktown Salmon, Salmon, Blind Tassel-fish, Tassel-fish (Queensland); Kingfish (Rockhampton); Blue Salmon (Mackay).

D. 8 + 1-2/13-15; A. 2/15-17; P. 16-17 + 4 free filaments; L. l. 78-80; L. tr. 9-10/ 1/13-14. Colour bluish-dusky or somewhat greenish-dusky-black above, passing into silvery-white below, with very pale pinkish tinge on belly; dorsals and caudal greyish, with minute black dots and almost black at the edges; ventrals and anal with very pale orange tinge on their outer halves; pectorals dusky-blackish, the free rayed portions white; eye yellowish, pupil black.

A large and valuable food-fish, common on the coasts and in the bays and estuaries of Queensland and north and north-western Australia. It is also found in the East Indies, India, China, and the Philippines. In India it is said to reach a length of 6 feet and a weight of at least 320 pounds, but average fish taken in Queensland are about 23 inches in length and weight about 4 pounds.

It takes the names of "Cooktown Salmon" and "Salmon" from its external shape and the pink tint of its flesh when cooked.

Polynemus

For characters of the genus see the preceding key. Fishes of the tropical waters of the Indian, Pacific, and Atlantic oceans. Species numerous, three in Queensland waters.

KEY TO SPECIES IN QUEENSLAND

A. Five free pectoral rays.

    b. Eye small. Mouth slightly inferior. Snout slightly prominent. Caudal peduncle very long. Anus much nearer to end of snout than to end of middle caudal ray.   *sheridani*

    bb. Eye large. Mouth very inferior. Snout very prominent. Caudal peduncle short. Anus about midway between end of snout and end of middle caudal ray.   *plebejus*

AA. Usually 7 free pectoral rays, rarely 6.   *multiradiatus*

401. SHERIDAN'S THREADFIN *Polynemus sheridani* Macleay
[Colour-plate 56]

Polynemus sheridani Macleay, Proc. Linn. Soc. N.S.Wales, 9, 1, 23rd May 1884, p. 21.
Illustration by G. Coates.

King Salmon (Queensland); Kingfish (Maryborough and Bundaberg).

D. 8, 1/12-13; A. 3/11-12; P. 13 + 5 free filaments, the rays simple and undivided; L. l. 66-75; L. tr. 8-9/1/13-14. Colour light bluish-grey above, passing into silvery-white below, with faint, darker longitudinal lines along each row of scales from head to tail. Pectorals pale or bright yellow, thickly sprinkled with fine black dots which sometimes form a patch medianally. Ventrals pale yellow; rest of fins, including caudal, sprinkled with fine black dots. At certain seasons of the year these fishes have the whole of the belly region flushed with yellow.

An extremely common fish along the whole coastline of Queensland from Maryborough north to Cape York Peninsula and also down to the Gulf of Carpentaria. It is a valuable food-fish with flesh of very good flavour, and examples of 4 feet and over, weighing 40 pounds gutted, are common in the Fish Depot at Maryborough.

Although stated by Macleay to reach a weight of 100 pounds, such examples are not seen today. The record weight for one taken at Maryborough was 66 pounds.

402. STRIPED THREADFIN *Polynemus plebejus* Broussonet
[Colour-plate 56]

Polynemus plebejus Broussonet, Ichth., 1782 (unpaged), 8th plate.
Illustration by G. Coates.

Bastard Mullet (South Africa).

D. 8, 1/13; A. 2/11; P. 17-18 + 5 free filaments; L. l. 60-65; L. tr. 6-7/1/12. Colour golden, with a greyish tinge along the back and with dark-brown longitudinal lines running between the scale rows; anal greyish; ventrals whitish, externally greyish; pectorals dull yellowish; both dorsals, the caudal, and the pectorals grey-edged. The stripes are said to be more conspicuous in the older examples.

This wide-ranging species is known in Australian waters only from Queensland and New South Wales but is extremely rare in these States. Outside Australia it is common and is found throughout the Indo-Pacific and in the Philippines. It is a good food-fish and grows to about 24 inches.

403. FLAT SALMON *Polynemus multiradiatus* Günther [Colour-plate 56]

Polynemus multiradiatus Günther, Cat. Fish. Brit. Mus., 2, 1860, p. 324.
Illustration by G. Coates.

Flat Salmon (Townsville).

D. 8, 1/14-15; A. 3/17-18; P. 15 + 7 free filaments; L. l. 58-59. Colour golden on post abdomen, back, and head; silvery-pink on abdomen, the two colours sharply defined; anal and caudal fins greenish-yellow; pectorals yellowish, middle or whole of the fin densely speckled with black, spinous dorsal speckled to a lesser degree or not at all.

A small species found on the coast and in the rivers of Queensland from south to north. Very common. Grows to 11 inches.

Order CATAPHRACTI: MAIL-CHEEKED FISHES

This large and diversified group is characterized and easily recognized by the presence of a bony stay or ridge across the cheek from the suborbital bones to the preoperculum. This stay is present in most members of the order, but in some of the more specialized types it does not reach the preoperculum.

The head is generally armoured with bony plates, sometimes completely encased and with many or few spiny projections or with bony knobs. The body is naked or partially or wholly scaled.

Many of them can inflict severe wounds with their many spines, which in some species are poisonous, the glands on or at the foot of the spines containing venom of high toxicity. All the species should therefore be handled with great care. Some of the species, such as the fire-fishes, *Pterois*, are exceedingly beautiful. Most are of small or moderate size. Six families occur in Australian waters.

KEY TO FAMILIES REPRESENTED IN AUSTRALIA

A. Head not markedly depressed, deeper than broad.

    b. Head not completely encased in bony armature.

        c. Ventral fins present. SCORPAENIDAE

        cc. No ventral fins. PATAECIDAE

    bb. Head completely encased in bony armature.

        d. Two anterior dorsal spines separate. Pectoral reaching tail. CEPHALACANTHIDAE

        dd. No detached dorsal spines. Pectoral not reaching tail. TRIGLIDAE

AA. Head greatly depressed, much broader than deep.

    e. Body naked, with a row of large spiny bucklers along each side. OPLICHTHYIDAE

    ee. Body scaly, without large spiny bucklers on the sides. PLATYCEPHALIDAE

Family **Scorpaenidae**

A very large group of carnivorous marine fishes forming a most readily recognized family which includes a great variety of forms. They are mostly small fishes and are widely spread in all seas, being abundant round reefs and rocks in waters of shallow or moderate depths in tropical seas, though some are confined to cooler waters and a few occur in deep water at over 200 fathoms.

In all these fishes there is a bony stay or process below the eye which runs back across the cheek to the posterior margin of the preopercle. In most forms it is well developed and shows a prominent ridge, though in some it is small and concealed under the skin and is insignificant. The bones of the head are variously armed, especially the angle of the preopercle, and are characteristically spiny.

Most of the scorpion-fishes are brilliantly coloured, their marbled patterns blending into the coloured corals, sea-fans, etc., among which they live. Most of them have flesh which is white, firm and of good flavour.

There are many genera of scorpion-fishes in Australian waters and they can be distinguished by the following key. A few of the more common species in a few of the many genera will then be described in detail.

KEY TO GENERA IN AUSTRALIA

Adapted from Whitley[66]

A. Dorsal fin beginning far behind eye, usually at nape or not before level of proepercular limb.

  b. Body scaly, sometimes with fleshy flaps. V. 1/5.

  c. Lowermost pectoral ray not detached as a feeler.

    d. Dorsal spines not greatly produced with slender free tips. Pectorals moderate (Scorpaeninae).

    e. Dorsal spines normally 12.

      f. Scales on top of head ctenoid. Cranium moderately armed and without deep pits. Bony stay of cheek nearly smooth. Lower part of operculum scaly. Palatine teeth present.   *Helicolenus*

      ff. Scales on top of head cycloid or wanting. Cranium with many spines above, irregularly shaped. Cheek-stay with several spines. Lower part of operculum naked.

      g. No palatine teeth.   *Scorpaenopsis*

      gg. Palatine teeth present.

[66] *Rep. Internat. Convent. Life Saving Tech.*, 1960 B, 1963.

    h. Size large. Some pectoral rays branched.

Ruboralga and "*Scorpaena*" sp.

    hh. Size small. Pectoral rays simple. Head naked. Scales large. Large supraorbital tentacle.   *Oligoscorpaena*

    hhh. Size small. A spine before the eye. Pre-orbital strongly armed below. Two post-temporal spines on each side of head.   *Sebastapistes*

  ee. Dorsal spines 13.

    i. Maxilla with rib-like ridges.   *Maxillicosta*

    ii. Maxilla without rib-like ridges.

    j. Palatines toothless.   *Scorpaenodes*

    jj. Palatines toothed. Maxillary scaly.   *Neosebastes*

  eee. Dorsal spines at least 15.

    k. Nape deeply excavated.   *Glyptauchen*

    kk. Nape not deeply hollowed out.

    l. Back scaly anteriorly. Normally 15 dorsal spines, the first behind level of preopercular limb.   *Notesthes*

    ll. Back naked anteriorly. Normally 16 dorsal spines, the first over preopercular limb.   *Centropogon*

  dd. Dorsal spines produced with slender tips, 12-13 in number. Pectorals expansive (Pteroinae).

    m. Upper pectoral rays simple, elongated, with the membranes incised.   *Pterois*

    mm. Upper pectoral rays branched, shorter than the middle rays.   *Brachirus*

  cc. Pectoral elongate, its lowermost ray detached. Chin with barbels. Dorsal spines 15; anal 3. V. 1/5.

    n. Scales with 3 or more pointed marginal lobes. Three mandibular barbels. Pectoral reaching beyond anal rays. Antero-supraorbital bone coarsely carinate.   *Hypodytes*

    nn. Scales cycloid, with rounded margins. Five mandibular barbels. Pectoral not reaching anal rays. Antero-supraorbital bone nearly smooth.   *Apistops*

bb. Body scaleless, sometimes with warts or dermal flaps.

    o. Dorsal spines 12-13. Head normal, with strong preorbital and preopercular spines. Lower pectoral ray not free.   *Gymnapistes*

    oo. Dorsal spines 8-9 (up to 11 in extra-Australian species). Lower pectoral ray free.   *Minous*

    ooo. Dorsal spines less than 9. Lower pectoral ray not free.   *Peristrominous* oooo. Dorsal spines 13 or more. Head grotesquely formed, with deep depressions. (Synanceijinae).

p. Pectoral without free rays.

q. Skin warty. Cheeks hollowed out. V. 1/5.

  r. Eyes and orbits much elevated like two bony bosses which are fused together without a groove or crest between them. A deep saddle-like excavation at the occiput when viewed from the side, or the eyes separated by a broad sunken interspace and the occipital saddle almost obsolete.   *Synanceja*

  qq. Skin with small papillae or spines. V. 1/4. Upper profile of head convex.

       Dampierosa (Western Australia)

  qqq. Skin smooth. Cheeks not pit-like. V. 1/4. Upper profile of head not convex.   *Erosa*

pp. Pectorals with two lower rays not free. First 3 dorsal spines separate from others. Head fantastically depressed.   *Inimicus*

AA. Dorsal fin beginning farther forward, first spine inserted above eye. Pectoral without free rays. Scales small, rudimentary, or absent.

s. Body naked. V. 1/5. (Tetraroginae).   *Tetraroge*

ss. Skin with small scales or almost naked. V. 1/4.

  t. Palatines toothed.   *Paracentropogon*

  tt. Palatines toothless.   *Liocranium*

sss. Skin scaleless, covered with velvety prickles. No palatine teeth. V. 1, 1/2-3. (Aploactinae).

  u. Gill-openings reduced to small apertures near the opercular tips.   *Bathyaploactis*

  uu. Gill-membranes free.

    v. Interorbital has a small median depression surrounded by about six sunken areas bounded by ridges.   *Kanekonia*

    vv. Sunken portion of interorbital subtriangular.

    w. Sunken portion of interorbital forms a roughly triangular area, the base of the triangle being away from the dorsal fin.   *Aploactisoma*

    ww. Base of interorbital triangle facing dorsal fin. Snout and face longer, more deeply and elaborately sculptured.

      x. D. 10/11; A. 10; P. 12.   *Paraploactis*

      xx. D. 13/10; A. 11; P. 14.   *Adventor*

Sub-family SCORPAENINAE

Dorsal fin beginning far behind eye, usually at nape or not before level of preopercular limb. Body scaly, sometimes with fleshy flaps. Ventrals with 1 spine and 5 rays.

Twelve genera of this sub-family, with numerous species, are found in the waters of Queensland (see the preceding key).

Helicolenus

For characters of the genus see key to family. Fishes of wide distribution with one species found in Australia. Not yet recorded from Queensland waters.

Scorpaenopsis

Distinguished from *Scorpaena* in the lack of palatine teeth, larger size, and more peculiar appearance. Fishes of the tropical and temperate waters of the Indo-Pacific. Four species in Queensland, not commonly met with.

Ruboralga

For characters of the genus see key to family. Fishes of the tropical and temperate waters of the Indo-Pacific. Four species in Queensland, one described below.

404. RED SCORPION COD *Ruboralga cardinalis* (Richardson) [Plate 57]

Scorpaena cardinalis Richardson, Ann. Mag. Nat. Hist., 9, May 1842, p. 212.
Scorpaena jacksoniensis Steindachner, Sitzb. Akad. Wiss. Wien, 53, 1, 1866, p. 438, pl. 3, figs 2-2a.

D. 12/10; A. 3/5; P. 17; L. l. 20-21; L. tr. 8/15-17. General colour carmine-red above, passing into pearly-white below; a broad pink spot transversely on occiput immediately behind vertical groove; under-surface of head pale red, marbled with yellow, with which colour the lips are banded; lower part of sides with scattered dark-brown spots margined with carmine, strongest beneath pectorals; spinous dorsal bright red with silvery blotches and stripes and a black spot on outer half between the sixth and tenth spines present or absent; soft dorsal profusely marbled with silvery on its outer half; generally a small black spot at the base of the last two rays, behind which is a pink spot; caudal marbled red and yellow, with a row of black spots basally; pectoral somewhat similar and with blackish spots on the upper half; ventrals and anal yellow, spotted and blotched with carmine.

This is one of the most important of the scorpion cods on account of its high value as a food-fish, its flesh being white, very sweet, and tender. The range of the species is along the coasts of South Queensland, New South Wales, and Tasmania, where it inhabits rocky shoals off the coast and among rocks and weeds along the foreshores. In the latter localities only juvenile examples are taken, the adults preferring the outside reefs.

The Red Scorpion Cod feeds upon crustaceans, molluscs, and small fishes, and because of the situations it favours is only taken on hook and line. Grows to 18 inches.

Oligoscorpaena

For characters of the genus see key to family. A single species inhabiting the waters of Queensland, the South Pacific, and the East Indies.

405. LITTLE SCORPION COD *Oligoscorpaena bandanensis* (Bleeker)
[Plate 57]

Scorpaena bandanensis Bleeker, Nat. Tijdschr. Ned. Ind., 2, 1851, p. 237.
Scorpaena haplodactylus Day, Fish. India, 1878-88, p. 149, pl. 36, fig. 2.

D. 12/9-10; A. 3/5-6; scales L. l. 36, 6 or 7 above; Pectoral rays 15 to 16, all simple. Colour greenish above, below rosy-green to golden, clouded or variegated with brown; fins variegated with rosy-brown; soft dorsal, anal, caudal, and pectorals with transverse dark bands.

This little fish inhabits the waters of Queensland, the Southern Pacific, and the East Indies. Apparently it is uncommon in Queensland. Grows to $4\frac{1}{4}$ inches.

Sebastapistes

For characters of the genus see key to family. Species numerous among the coral reefs of the tropical waters of the Indo-Pacific. Small fishes with bright colours, very close to *Scorpaena* but much smaller in size and with a characteristic spine before the eye.

406. MARBLED CORAL COD *Sebastapistes bynoensis* (Richardson)
[Colour-plate 57]

Scorpaena bynoensis Richardson, Zool. Voy. Erebus and Terror, Fish, 1845, p. 22.
Illustration by G. Coates.

Marbled Scorpion-fish (Queensland).

D. 12/10; A. 3/5; P. 17; V. 1/5. Colour variable, from between greyish and blackish to bright brown and white, roseate on under-surface and on caudal peduncle; often dotted with black and with 3 to 4 irregular dusky transverse bands; usually a dark cross-bar at caudal base; fins pale, barred or mottled with reddish, brown, or dusky; lips and underside of head with white and brownish alternately.

A common little fish in the coral reefs of the tropical Indo-Pacific and western Pacific. In Australian waters it is found in Queensland, New South

Wales, and North Australia. It grows to a length of 5½ inches and for its size it is capable of inflicting a severe sting.

Maxillicosta

Maxillary naked, with 4 to 5 prominent rib-like ridges. Spines of the head numerous. Less than 40 scales on lateral line. Pectorals not evenly rounded.

Fishes of the southern parts of Australia. Species few. Not yet recorded from Queensland.

Scorpaenodes

For characters of the genus see key to family. Fishes of small size, widely distributed in the tropical parts of the Indo-Pacific. They frequent such places as beneath and around slabs of eroded and dead coral on the reefs, and are capable of violent and painful stings with their spines. Species few, one in Queensland.

407. GUAM SCORPION COD *Scorpaenodes guamensis* (Quoy and Gaimard)
[Plate 57]

Scorpaena guamensis Quoy and Gaimard, Voy. Uranie Physic., Zool., 1825, p. 326.
Scorpaena guamensis Günther, Journ. Mus. Godef., 2, 1873-5, p. 74, pl. 56, fig. B.

D. 13/8-9; A. 3/5-6. General colour rich reddish or dusky brown with striking darker bars and spots on the head, body, and fins; a more or less distinct black spot on the operculum.

A small stinging fish found beneath and around dead coral clinkers and rocks throughout the tropical Indo-Pacific. Grows to about 4 inches.

Neosebastes

Thirteen dorsal spines, very long and strong. A series of strong spines in a line from edge of preorbital across suborbital stay and preopercle. Palatine teeth in a long band. Vertical fins scaleless.

Fishes of the Indian and Australian seas. One species in Queensland, the Black-spot Gurnard Perch, *Neosebastes incisipinnis* Ogilby, known only from South Queensland, where most examples have been taken by trawl at depths down to 73 fathoms. Apparently it grows to a length of about 11 inches. In colour it is brick-red above and yellow below with a large black ocellus on the soft dorsal fin.

Glyptauchen

Head and body compressed. Crown of head with a deep saddle-like impression. Scales very small. Preorbital, preopercle, and opercle armed. Dorsal fin continuous, the spinous portion much more developed than the soft, with 17 spines. Anal with 3 spines.

Fishes of Australian waters, the species few and none yet recorded from Queensland. The Goblin-fish, *Glyptauchen panduratus* Richardson, a somewhat rare fish of grotesque appearance, inhabits the waters of the other States of Australia and will quite possibly sooner or later be recorded from South Queensland.

Notesthes

Outwardly resembling *Neosebastes* but differing from the latter in having the entire head naked of scales, the presence of an elongate defensive preorbital spine, a greater number of dorsal spines (15) and a fewer number of pectoral rays (12).

A single species, inhabiting the rivers and estuaries of eastern Australia.

408. BULLROUT *Notesthes robusta* (Günther) [Colour-plate 57]

Centropogon robustus Günther, Cat. Fish. Brit. Mus., 2, 1860, p. 128.
Illustration by G. Coates.

D. 15/9; A. 3/5; L. l. 85. Colour brown, irregularly marbled with black, which sometimes takes the form of broad vertical bands and frequently with yellow spots and blotches; a chestnut spot often present on the occiput; fins mottled with blue-grey, yellow, or black; a large black spot usually present in front of the middle of the spinous dorsal.

Although originally a marine form, this fish has taken to a brackish and even purely freshwater existence. It is commonly found in rivers far beyond the tidal influence and inhabits most of the rivers discharging into the seas of eastern Australia. In Queensland it is seldom met with north of the Mary River, though it has been recorded from Cape York Peninsula. In 1898 the *Thetis* trawled the species in Shaolhaven Bight, New South Wales, in 15 fathoms.

The Bullrout is capable of inflicting very severe pain with its many sharp and strong spines, and distinct symptoms of the direct effect of its venom are soon noticeable, the severe pain being out of all proportion to the insignificant nature of the injury. The temperature rapidly rises and falls, often below normal, when severe collapse occurs.

This is a good edible fish, its flesh being firm and of excellent flavour. When pulled from the water it emits a loud and harsh grunting noise. It is very tenacious of life, and one caught by me lived through the night lying in a dry pie-dish. Although it attains a length of 11 inches, such a size is rare, the average fish being about 7 or 8 inches.

Centropogon

Head rather large, entirely naked, as is also an area on the back and nape. Scales on body small, adherent, ctenoid. Preoccipital groove present. D. 16 (15) 8-9 (10) rays.

Small stinging fishes of the east coast of Australia. Two species, both found in Queensland.

A. Spinous dorsal high, $1\frac{1}{8}$-$1\frac{1}{3}$ in length of head. Pale yellowish or pale brownish with 6 irregular transverse dark-brownish bands.   *australis*

AA. Spinous dorsal low, the third spine only half the length of the head. Yellowish-brown, with indistinct mottlings of darker brown.   *marmoratus*

409. MARBLED FORTESQUE *Centropogon marmoratus* (Günther)

[Plate 57]

Centropogon marmoratus Günther, Ann. Mag. Nat. Hist., 11, 1st Feb. 1863, p. 136.
Illustration by G. Coates.

D. 16/9; A. 3/6; L. l. 68. Colour yellowish, marbled with brown.

A common little fish in Moreton Bay, Queensland, and in northern New South Wales, where it frequents weedy flats along the coasts. It can inflict very severe stings with its many sharp spines, particularly those on the pre-orbitals. Grows to $4\frac{1}{2}$ inches.

OTHER SPECIES

Fortesque, *C. australis*. This species is more commonly met with in New South Wales, though it has been recorded from South Queensland. It is much lighter in colour and more clearly banded than the Marbled Fortesque, and has a higher spinous dorsal fin. Grows to 6 inches.

Sub-family PTEROINAE: FIRE-FISHES

Pterois

Dorsal spines produced, with slender tips, 12 to 13 in number. All pectoral rays simple, elongate, the upper ones mainly free from membrane.

Beautifully coloured fishes of the shallow waters over the coral reefs of the Indo-Pacific. They are dreaded by fishermen on account of their venomous spines. Species few, two in Queensland.

A. Nape naked; scales small, in about 90-95 series above lateral line; soft dorsal, anal, and caudal spotted.   *volitans*

AA. Nape scaly; scales larger, in about 65-70 series above lateral line; soft dorsal and anal without spots.   *lunulata*

410. RED FIRE-FISH *Pterois volitans* (Linnaeus) [Colour-plate 58]

Gasterosteus volitans Linnaeus, Syst. Nat., 10th ed., 1758, p. 296.
Illustration by G. Coates.

Butterfly Cod, Zebra-fish, Feather-fins (Queensland and New South Wales).

D. 12, 1/11-12; A. 3/6-8; L. l. 90-95; about 12 scales between the median dorsal spines and the lateral line. Colour red or brownish-red, with numerous dark-red or blackish transverse bands or stripes bordered by white lines; soft dorsal, anal, and caudal fins with rows of black spots; pectorals and ventrals with larger spots; a black mark in the pectoral axilla has a vivid white spot in its centre.

A very colourful reef-dwelling fish of exquisite beauty and motion as it glides effortlessly through the corals on the Great Barrier Reef. In Australian waters it is found throughout the far northern waters, Queensland, and New South Wales; at Lord Howe Island, New Guinea, and outside Australia it is very wide-ranging.

The dorsal spines are long and needle-like and are charged with venom, the fish thus being able to inflict a painful wound. The Red Fire-fish grows to a length of 15 inches.

OTHER SPECIES

The other Queensland fire-fish is *P. lunulata*, a species not nearly so commonly met with as the previous one, and occurring also in Japan and in the Philippines. Grows to about 11 inches.

Brachirus

Like *Pterois*, but the pectoral fin is shorter and does not reach the caudal. Membrane between the rays not divided, or only at the tip. None of the rays free; some of the rays branched, only the lower 7 to 8 simple.

Beautiful fishes of the reefs of the tropical Indo-Pacific, all able to inflict very painful wounds with their venom-laden spines. Neither of the species found in Queensland is commonly met with.

KEY TO SPECIES IN QUEENSLAND

A. Interorbital region broad and shallow. A short inter-orbital tentacle. Central dorsal spines equal to height of body. *miles*

AA. Interorbital region narrow and deep. A long inter-orbital tentacle. Central dorsal spines much longer than body height. *zebra*

411. ZEBRA FIRE-FISH *Brachirus zebra* (Cuvier and Valenciennes)
[Plate 57]

Pterois zebra Cuvier and Valenciennes, Hist. Nat. Poiss., 4, Nov. 1829, p. 367.
Pseudomonopterus (Dendrochius) zebra Bleeker, Atlas Ichth., 9, 1878, pl. 411, fig. 1.

D. 13/10-11; A. 3/6-7; L. l. about 50; 8 scales between lateral line and median dorsal spines. Colour reddish, with dark reddish-black cross-bands; eye with radiating dark streaks, 3 of which are continued across cheek; dorsal spines annulated; soft dorsal, anal, and caudal with dark spots, rest of fins hyaline; pectorals with several rows of semilunate spots between the rays, a yellowish-white spot in the axil.

A beautiful but dangerous fish only occasionally met with in northern Queensland waters. Grows to a length of 7 inches. Wide-ranging in the central Indo-Pacific.

OTHER SPECIES

The other and less common zebra-fish, *B. miles*, is a spectacular species quite as venomous as *B. zebra*, and is a typical Indian Ocean form. Grows to 12 inches.

Hypodytes

For characters of the genus see key to family. Small stinging fishes ranging from the Indo-Australian Archipelago to Japan. Species few, one in Queensland.

412. OCELLATED WASP-FISH *Hypodytes carinatus* (Bloch and Schneider)
[Plate 57]

Scorpaena carinata Bloch and Schneider, Syst. Ichth., 1801, p. 193.
Apistus carinatus McCulloch, Biol. Res. Endeavour, 3, 1915, p. 160, pl. 31.

D. 15/9; A. 3/7; P. 11 + 1. Colour lilac above, lined and marbled with darker, shading through lavender and silver to white on belly; head darker than back, with a short black bar at end of interorbital groove, its sides and lower surface silvery; spinous dorsal hyaline, marbled with lilac; a small black spot on membranes of first spine and a still smaller one sometimes behind third; a large black broadly white-edged ocellus on ninth to eleventh spines, sometimes extending over 3 to 6 spines; soft dorsal and caudal lilac-spotted, the former with a wide submarginal band, the latter with a similar subterminal band; anal white, with a broad median lilac band and a few basal spots; upper pectoral ray white, the lower two and the detached ray soiled white, rest of fin lavender; ventrals white.

A species not usually met with except when taken by trawl, when it has been secured at various points along the Queensland coast at depths varying from 15 to 33 fathoms. Grows to 6½ inches. Inhabits the waters of Queensland, Western Australia, and India.

Apistops

Lateral line complete or incomplete. Orbital ridges smooth. A short but strong and acute humeral spine present. Dorsal fin but little notched, with 14 spines. Pectorals comparatively short, not reaching the soft anal rays. A single species, found only in Queensland.

413. SHORT-SPINED WASP-FISH *Apistops caloundra* (De Vis) [Plate 57]

Apistus caloundra De Vis, Proc. Roy. Soc. Qld, 2, 1886, p. 145.
Apistops caloundra McCulloch, Biol. Res. Endeavour, 3, 1915, p. 160, pl. 35, fig. 2.

D. 14/9; A. 3/7. A broad white-edged black blotch between the ninth and twelfth spines of the dorsal fin; top of the membranes between the first two spines also black; upper surface of the snout, a broad band across the occiput, a narrow curved band from the snout through eye to base of the opercular spine, 2 large blotches on upper part of the trunk connected and apparently traversed by 3 longitudinal bands, 2 horizontal bands on the soft dorsal, 3 vertical bands on the caudal, and the lower third of the pectoral black. (After De Vis.)

Until recently this little fish was known only from the type specimen. With the advent of the prawn-trawlers it has now been taken at several localities in South and North Queensland. It grows to 6½ inches. So far known only from Queensland.

Gymnapistes

For characters of the genus see key to family. Fishes of the seas of India across to Australia and the Philippines, one species entering fresh water. Not yet recorded from Queensland.

Minous

For characters of the genus see key to family. Small marine fishes of the waters of the Indo-Australian Archipelago and North Queensland. Species few, one in Queensland.

414. BLACK-BANDED WASP-FISH *Minous versicolor* (Ogilby) [Plate 57]

Minous versicolor Ogilby, New Fish. Qld Coast, 1911, p. 111 (a suppressed publication).
Minous versicolor McCulloch, Biol. Res. Endeavour, 3, 1915, p. 162, pl. 32.

D. 8-9/12-13; A. 10-11; P. 11 + 1. Colour: Body reddish-pink, strongest on breast and belly; upper half of body with irregularly shaped markings of blackish-brown which are continued on to spinous and soft dorsals; tips of spinous and dorsal rays black, which colour extends down the anterior spines to a depth of at least one-third of their height; head brownish-red, white on chin and throat; pectorals blackish, the lower free ray with its terminal half orange; ventrals blackish, tinged reddish basally; anal blackish; caudal pinkish with brownish mottlings in rough vertical form.

Not commonly met with unless taken by means of the prawn-trawl, when numerous examples have been captured in waters of varying depths down to 35 fathoms along the Queensland coast. Grows to $4\frac{1}{2}$ inches.

Peristrominous

Head armoured with rugose bones without sharp spines. Body scaleless, papillose. Less than 8 dorsal spines. All fin-rays simple. No free pectoral rays. V. 1/3. Dorsal fin begins well behind level of eyes. One species, from South Queensland.

415. BROWN CARPET-FISH *Peristrominous dolosus* (Whitley) [Plate 57]

Peristrominous dolosus Whitley, Rec. Austr. Mus., 23, no. 1, June 1952, p. 25, fig. 1.
Illustration by F. Olsen after Whitley.

D. 3, 4/17; A. 11; P. 13; V. 1/3; C. 13; L. l. tubes 16 to 17. Colour: Head and body with light brown, the darker marblings forming 4 obscure bars on back; belly lighter; fins variegated with smoky-grey and brownish; tips of anterior dorsal spines pale; pectorals and anal very dark.

A small fish known only from South Queensland, where it has been captured by the prawn-trawlers. Grows to $3\frac{1}{4}$ inches.

Sub-family SYNANCEIJINAE: STONE-FISHES

Synanceja

Head large, grotesque, with deep depressions. No scales, body and fins covered with warty tubercles, skinny flaps and tentacles. One dorsal fin, of 12 to 13 spines and 6 to 7 rays, the spines mostly enveloped in thick skin, the tips projecting or completely covered. Venom glands present. Pectorals large.

Particularly venomous fishes found in the waters of the tropical Indo-Pacific. Species few, two in Queensland.

KEY TO SPECIES IN QUEENSLAND

A. Teeth on vomer (rarely absent); orbits conspicuously elevated; no deep groove or ridges on interorbital; a deep saddle-shaped occipital groove; suborbital pit deep, more than twice eye width. — *horrida*

AA. No teeth on vomer; orbits but little elevated; interorbital deeply concave, no ridges; occipital depression shallow; suborbital pit less than twice eye width. — *verrucosa*

416. STONE-FISH *Synanceja horrida* (Linnaeus) [Plate 58]

Scorpaena horrida Linnaeus, Syst. Nat., 12th ed., 1766, p. 453.
Illustration by G. Coates.

D. 13/6-7; A. 3/6; P. 15-16. Colour brownish-fawn above, lighter below, with irregular blotches of greyish on body and fins; the marblings tend to form bars or reticulations on the fins, which are of a darker brownish along the margins. Inside the mouth may be white, greyish, or even yellow. Some examples are mottled in scarlet and grey with the head and back closely speckled with brown and red.

In Australian waters the deadly Stone-fish is found in Queensland, the Northern Territory, and Western Australia. In Queensland it is not only common on the shallow mud-flats and in the estuaries but also frequents the coral reefs and coral sand pools of the Great Barrier Reef.

Looking like an eroded piece of coral rock or stone, the creature exhibits no movement until poked with a stick or trodden upon, when it immediately raises the strong venom-laden dorsal spines. The venom is extremely virulent and causes the victim frightful agony which can and has caused death within one to four hours. Where death has not followed, wounds have developed gangrene, resulting in the loss of the limb, usually the leg.

The venom apparatus was studied by Duhig and Jones[67] and in an excellent paper they illustrate the dorsal spines and poison sacs in which the venom is secreted.

The Stone-fish grows to a length of 24 inches, though the average is about 10 inches. It is found throughout the waters of North Australia down the coastline of Queensland to at least as far south as Moreton Bay. Although a most repulsive-looking creature, its flesh is very white and of excellent quality and flavour.

OTHER SPECIES

The other Australian species of Stone-fish, *S. verrucosa*, inhabits the waters of North Queensland, New Guinea, the western Pacific, and the East Indies. It is seldom seen in Queensland.

Dampierosa

This genus is allied to *Erosa*, but the upper profile of the head is convex, the body papillated, and there are fewer dorsal spines and pectoral rays. One species, Western Australian.

Erosa

Body short, thick, covered with naked skin, on which are skinny flaps. Head large, with deep grooves and depressions. Mouth large, almost vertical. Eyes

---

[67] *Mem. Qld Mus.*, 9, pt 2, 16th June 1928, pp. 136-50.

small. Two strong spines on preorbital and 5 blunt spines on preopercle. Dorsal fin continuous, with 13 stout spines and 9 soft rays.

A single species, a little-known fish from the waters of Australia and Japan.

417. MONKEY-FISH *Erosa erosa* (Cuvier and Valenciennes)   [Plate 58]

Synanceia erosa Cuvier and Valenciennes, Hist. Nat. Poiss., 4, Nov. 1829, p. 459 (*ex* Langsdorff MS.).
Erosa erosa McCulloch, Mem. Qld Mus., 7, pt 3, Nov. 1921, p. 177, pl. 11 fig. 2.

D. 17/7; A. 3/6; lateral line with 11 pores. Colour brown, with a rosy tinge on shoulders; on the side, above and beneath the adpressed pectoral, there is a large patch which is roseate above and yellow below; roseate colour on nape of head, spinous dorsal, caudal, and pectorals; soft dorsal purple, anteriorly with a yellow spot covering the middle of the first three rays and a broad yellow tip, which, like the spot, is dotted with rose. (After Ogilby.)

A little-known fish which has been recorded from the coast of Queensland and also from Japan. In Queensland the only known examples were taken by trawlers at depths ranging down to 33 fathoms. Grows to about 5 inches.

Inimicus

Head depressed, fantastically formed. Skin of body smooth. Head and fins with skinny flaps. Pectoral fins large, the upper rays not filamentous, the two lower rays detached, connected by membrane at base. Dorsal spines slender, about 17 in number, the three anterior ones separate from the rest.

Ugly, misshapen fishes, sometimes highly coloured, feared by fishermen on account of their sharp and stinging spines. Species few, one in Queensland.

418. BEARDED GHOUL *Inimicus barbatus* (De Vis)   [Plate 58]

Pelor barbatus De Vis, Proc. Linn. Soc. N.S.Wales, 9, pt 3, 29th Nov. 1884, p. 547.
Pelor (Inimicus) barbatum McCulloch, Biol. Res. Endeavour, 4, pt 4, 31st Oct. 1916, p. 196, pl. 58.

D. 3, 13-14/8-9; A. 2/11-12; P. 10 + 2. General colour black or brown above, passing into dark brown or light brown on sides, usually densely freckled with blackish-brown; belly yellowish-brown; fins and caudal blackish or sometimes the soft dorsal with a pale blotch in the middle of its anterior half and the caudal may have a broad pale band across its centre flecked with dark brown. Pectoral sometimes with a pale central band. A white spot present in front of each orbit.

A grotesque fish commonly taken along the Queensland coast, mainly by the prawn-trawlers, though it is occasionally captured by line in the estuaries and rivers. Grows to at least 13 inches.

Tetraroge

Head and body compressed, the skin naked. Preorbital armed with a long backwardly directed spine, the preopercle with a still larger one. A single dorsal fin, with 13 spines, the second and third much elevated. Anal 3/5 or 6.

A genus of few species inhabiting the seas of North Australia, the East Indies, and the Philippines. One in Queensland.

419. ROGUE-FISH *Tetraroge leucogaster* (Richardson) [Plate 58]

Apistus leucogaster Richardson, Voy. Samarang, Fish., 1848, p. 5, pl. 5, figs 1-2.
Tetraroge leucogaster Whitley, Proc. Roy. Zool. Soc. N.S.Wales, 1950-1 (1952), p. 30, fig. 5.

D. 13/7-8; A. 3/6-7; P. 16; V. 1/5; about 15 tubes in lateral line. Colour brownish, marbled with brown, the spots extending on to dorsal fin; abdomen white.

A small stinging fish which is rarely met with and then only in North Queensland waters. It is found also in Western Australia. Grows to about 2½ inches.

Paracentropogon

Body oblong, laterally compressed, covered with small scales embedded in the skin. Head armed with spines, 2 on preorbital, 4 to 5 on hind margin of preopercle, and 2 on opercle. Dorsal undivided, beginning above eye, spines 12 to 15, the anterior ones strongly divergent, not elongate; 8 to 9 rays. Pectorals rounded, no free rays.

Brightly coloured stinging marine fishes found in Queensland, the East Indies, the Philippines, and China. Species few, one in Queensland.

420. FRECKLED WASP-FISH *Paracentropogon vespa* (Ogilby) [Plate 58]

Paracentropogon vespa Ogilby, New Fish. Qld Coast, 20th Dec. 1910, p. 116 (a suppressed publication).
Paracentropogon vespa McCulloch, Mem. Qld Mus., 7, pt 3, 4th Nov. 1921, p. 173, pl. 10, fig. 2.

D. 14/8; A. 3/5; P. 10; V. 1/4; C. 13. There are 22 tubular pores on the lateral line between its origin and the hypural joint and one on the caudal base. Colour chestnut above, freckled with lavender; lavender below, blotched with chestnut; head similar and with yellow on occiput and nape and with small dusky spots elsewhere; iris with alternate bars of orange and lavender; dorsal lavender, dotted black; anterior rays blotched with chestnut, the rest with numerous oblique wavy chestnut bars; caudal similar to soft dorsal; anal lavender, with broad, oblique rufous bands; pectorals chestnut, mottled with lilac and broadly tipped grey; ventrals blackish, membrane of inner ray white, from which a short band passes on to the two inner rays.

458

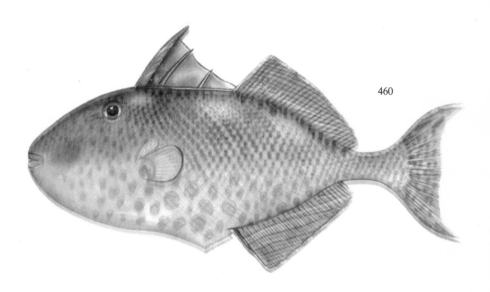

460

COLOUR-PLATE 65
458. Big-spotted Trigger-fish, *Balistes conspicillum*, 10¾ in.
460. Flat-tailed Trigger-fish, *Abalistes stellaris*, 10 in.

461

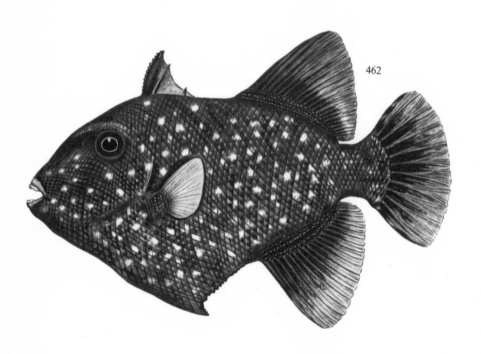

462

COLOUR-PLATE 66
461. Red-lined Trigger-fish, *Balistapus undulatus*, 14 in.
462. Spotted Trigger-fish, *Canthidermis rotundatus*, 4 in.

463

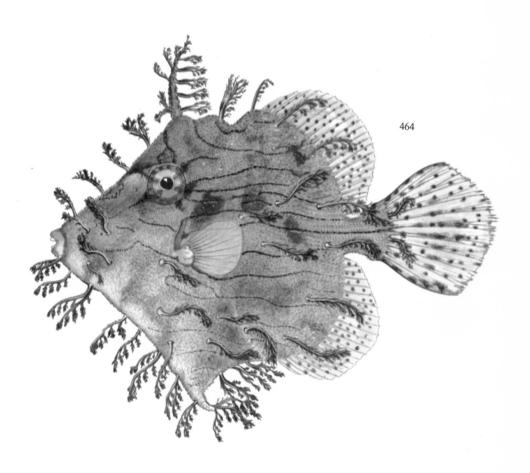

464

463. Beardie or Tape-fish, *Anacanthus barbatus*, 6½ in.
464. Prickly Leather-jacket, *Chaetoderma penicilligera*, 8 in.

465

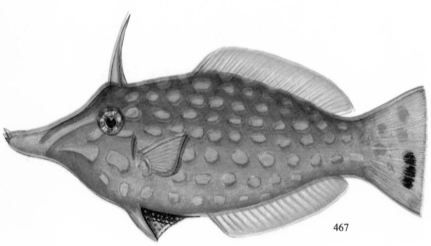

467

COLOUR-PLATE 68
465. Fan-bellied Leather-jacket, *Monacanthus chinensis*, 9 in.
467. Beaked Leather-jacket, *Oxymonacanthus longirostris*,
$4\frac{1}{2}$ in.

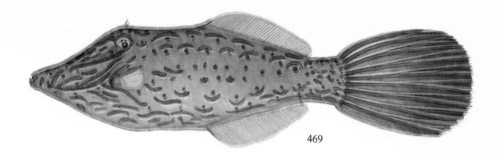

469. Figured Leather-jacket, *Osbeckia scripta*, 12½ in.
471. Long-nosed Box-fish, *Rhynchostracion nasus*, 14 in.
472. Blue-spotted Box-fish, *Ostracion tuberculatus*, 6 in.

COLOUR-PLATE 70
473. Cow-fish, *Lactoria cornutus*, 8 in.
477. Banded Toado, *Spheroides pleurostictus*, 4¾ in.
479. Stars and Stripes Toado, *Tetraodon hispidus*, 11½ in.

480. A Toado, *Tetraodon stellatus*, 22 in.   481. Marbled
Toado, *Chelonodon patoca*, 7 in.   483. Porcupine-fish,
Tragulichthys jaculiferus, $9\frac{1}{4}$ in.

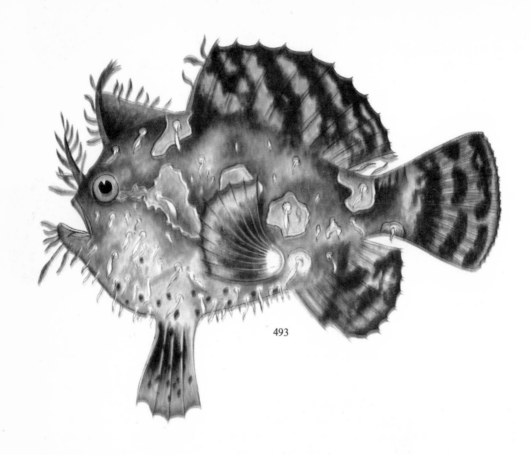

493

COLOUR-PLATE 72
493. Marbled Angler, *Histrio histrio*, $2\frac{1}{2}$ in.

A little-known fish which has been rarely taken in the waters of Queensland and North Australia by trawl, at depths from 7 to 13 fathoms. Grows to about 3½ inches.

Liocranium

Body ovate, strongly compressed, the back elevated in front. Scales minute. Head large, naked, no dermal appendages. Soft dorsal and anal fins without basal scaly sheath; last ray of each divided to the base. Dorsal of 13 spines and 7 rays, originating above anterior edge of eye.

Small Queensland fishes, the genus comprising two species.

KEY TO SPECIES

A. Diameter of eye much greater than width of interorbital
    space; gill-rakers of first arch short, thick, and rounded.   *praepositum*

AA. Diameter of eye much less than width of interorbital
    space; gill-rakers of first arch long, slender, and flattened.   *scorpio*

421. YELLOW WASP-FISH *Liocranium scorpio* (Ogilby)   [Plate 58]

Paracentropogon scorpio Ogilby, New Fish. Qld Coast, 1910, p. 115 (a suppressed publication).
Liocranium scorpio McCulloch, Mem. Qld Mus., 7, pt 3, 4th Nov. 1921, p. 175, pl. 11, fig. 1.

D. 14/6; A. 3/7; P. 6/8; 22-24 tubules on lateral line between shoulder and hypural joint. Colour brown, passing into lilac on sides and with a paler fuscous band along base of dorsal; some irregularly scattered black light-edged ocelli above lateral line and a few between that and the pectoral; breast and belly white, rest of body closely powdered with black spots; upper surface and sides of head lilac and grey vermiculations and a few larger violet light-edged ocelli; spinous dorsal lavender, the spines ringed with black; soft dorsal lavender, with numerous small white dark-edged ocelli; caudal barred black and white; anal golden, spotted with black; pectoral rays cross-banded black and white.

A little-known fish, all recorded examples having been taken by trawl at Bowen and Cape Capricorn, Queensland, in depths of 25 to 30 fathoms. Size 4 inches.

OTHER SPECIES

The only other known species of this genus is *L. praepositum* and it also is little known, the few captured having been taken by trawl on the Queensland coast. Grows to 5 inches.

P

Sub-family APLOACTINAE

Bathyaploactis

Body deep, compressed, without scales. Spaced villi present and weak spines along lateral line. Head armed with long knob-like preorbital and preopercular spines. Interorbital sunken. Four barbels. Gill-openings reduced to a small aperture near opercular flap. Villiform teeth on jaws and vomer, none on palatines. Dorsal fin twice notched, commencing over middle of eye, the anterior seven spines forming a distinct fin, though not separated from the other spines and rays.

Small fishes so far found only along the coasts of Queensland (north to south) and Western Australia. A single species.

422. PORT CURTIS MOSSBACK *Bathyaploactis curtisensis* (Whitley)

[Plate 58]

Bathyaploactis curtisensis Whitley, Rec. Austr. Mus., 19, no. 1, 2nd August 1933, p. 103, pl. 14, fig. 1.

D. 7, 7/8; A. 11; P. 11; V. 3; C. 12; L. l. 10. Colour brownish, with darker markings which are most strongly marked on the fins; some dark-brown bars with well-marked margins round the bluish eye. (After Whitley.)

This little fish is commonly taken in the nets of the prawn-trawlers in Moreton and Deception bays, South Queensland. It is also known from the Gulf of Carpentaria and at various points along the Queensland coast. A variant or sub-species has been recorded from Western Australia. The Mossback grows to a length of 2½ inches.

Kanekonia

For characters of the genus see key to family. Small fishes of the seas of North Australia and Japan. One species in Queensland, the Deep Velvet-fish, *K. queenslandica* Whitley, known from a single example caught at Albany Passage, North Queensland. Length 1¼ inches.

Aploactisoma

An Australian genus containing perhaps only a single species not yet recorded from Queensland but found in the waters of New South Wales, South Australia, and Western Australia.

Paraploactis

No teeth on vomer or palatines. Origin of dorsal fin over middle or posterior half of eye, twice notched. Profile of head steep. Body deep anteriorly. Eye small.

Small fishes of Australian waters, the species few in number and little known. One in Queensland.

423. NORTHERN MOSSBACK *Paraploactis trachyderma* (Bleeker)

[Plate 58]

Paraploactis trachyderma Bleeker, Ned. Tijdschr. Dierk., 2, 1864, p. 169.
Paraploactis trachyderma Whitley, Rec. Austr. Mus., 19, no. 1, 2nd Aug. 1933, p. 100, pl. 12, fig. 5.

D. 3 + 11/10; A. 10; P. 13; V. 1/3. Colour dark brown, with orange-yellow markings; snout orange, also lips; dorsal with orange patch over first three spines and membranes; posterior five rays and membranes of dorsal fin orange.

A small fish commonly taken by the prawn-trawlers in Moreton and Deception bays, Queensland. Also recorded from South Australia. Grows to 6 inches.

Adventor

Form elongate; compressed, scaleless, the skin covered with velvety papillae, which extend to head and around eye. Three anterior dorsal spines, elevated and forming a distinct but not separated fin, originating over middle of eye.

Small little-known fishes living well below low-water level along the Queensland coast. Distribution that of the single species known.

424. SANDPAPER-FISH *Adventor elongatus* (Whitley) [Plate 58]

Membracidichthys (Adventor) elongatus Whitley, Rec. Austr. Mus., 23, no. 1, 16th June 1952, p. 27, fig. 2.
Illustration by F. Olsen after Whitley.

D. 3, 10/10; A. 11; P. 14; V. 1/2; L. l. 12. Colour brownish-grey all over, somewhat lighter below; all fins somewhat darker than body, being blackish-grey, the dorsals and caudal mottled.

Very few specimens of this interesting little fish are known. Those captured were all taken by otter-trawl on the north and south coasts of Queensland (at Townsville and Moreton Bay); also known from Western Australia. The largest taken measured 4 inches.

Family **Pataecidae**

A small family of little-known marine fishes found in the waters of Australia. They are characterized by three features: the remarkably long dorsal fin which extends unbroken from head to tail, being either connected by membrane to the caudal (*Pataecus*) or free from that fin (*Neopataecus*); the naked body; and the absence of ventral fins. One genus is found in Queensland.

Pataecus

Body oblong, elevated anteriorly, very compressed and tapering to the tail. No scales. Dorsal fin long, continuous with caudal, some of the anterior spines strong. No ventrals. Species few, one in South Queensland.

425. RED INDIAN FISH *Pataecus fronto* (Richardson) [Plate 58]

Pataecus fronto Richardson, Ann. Mag. Nat. Hist., 14 (91), Oct. 1844, p. 280.
Pataecus fronto Waite, Fish. Sth Austr., 1923, p. 194, fig. 275.

Forehead-fish (South Australia).

D. 24/16; A. 11/5; P. 8; C. 10. Colour in life red, brick-red, or orange-red, with or without 4 black spots on upper part of body.

This remarkable fish, which bears a curious resemblance to a Red Indian with his trail of head-dress feathers, is occasionally met with in South Queensland waters. Nowhere does it appear to be commonly seen, either in Queensland, New South Wales, South Australia, or Western Australia, from which States it has been recorded. Grows to 9 inches.

Family **Cephalacanthidae: Flying Gurnards**

Body elongate, subquadrangular, tapering behind. Head blunt, its surface completely bony, with strong spines and keels. A bony ridge across cheek to preopercle. Jaws with granular teeth. Scales bony, strongly keeled. Two serrated knife-like appendages at base of tail. Pectoral fins enormous, wing-like.

In the young the body is small and soft, the pectorals are short, and the head is a huge bony shield with 2 very large spines on each side.

Fishes of the warm seas in both oceans. Genera and species few.

Dactyloptena

Occiput with an elongate ray-like free spine, followed by a detached finlet of one spine, before the spinous dorsal proper.

A genus with only a few species, inhabiting the waters of the tropical Indo-Pacific, Japan, and Hawaii. Two species in Queensland.

KEY TO SPECIES IN QUEENSLAND

A. Pectorals long, reaching tail, without an ocellus. *orientalis*

AA. Pectorals shorter, not reaching tail; a dark smudge or ocellus at its base. *papilio*

426. PURPLE FLYING GURNARD *Dactyloptena orientalis* (Cuvier)
[Colour-plate 59]

Dactylopterus orientalis Cuvier, Règne Anim., 2nd ed., April 1829, p. 162.
Illustrations by G. Coates.

D. 1, 1, 5, 1/8; A. 6; C. 3-7-3; P. 33-34; Sc. 49-28. Colour pale violet or purplish above, with 2 broad, darker cross-bands descending on sides to ventral edge; these bands are much clearer in the young, becoming indistinct with age and merging into the dark of the body colour in adults; back blotched and lined with dark violet and purple; belly pinkish-white or fawnish; head on sides and above pale yellowish-brown spotted with violet; second dorsal and caudal hyaline, the rays with alternate light and dark bands; anal and ventrals pinkish-white, the former with a dark basal blotch between fourth and sixth rays; pectorals violet, thickly spotted with purplish.

This interesting and most handsome fish occurs commonly along the whole coastline of Queensland though it is not often seen by the casual observer. The prawn-trawlers frequently take them with their catch in river, bay, and ocean. Its range extends into New South Wales, and outside Australia it is wide-ranging from New Guinea, Tahiti, and the East Indies across to India, Japan, and Africa. It grows to a length of at least 16 inches.

Actually these fishes do not fly, the beautiful pectoral fins being mainly for swimming and display purposes. However, the fish is known to leap high from the water and, at times, has landed on the decks of bay launches and other small craft. According to fishermen these fishes are able to glide short distances only.

OTHER SPECIES

Rufous Flying Gurnard, *D. papilio*. Known only from Queensland, and though originally described by Ogilby in 1910 the species was not encountered again until within the last few years (1952-5) when the prawn-trawlers began to collect them. Grows to at least 7 inches. [Species 426a—colour plate 60]

Family **Triglidae: Gurnards**

Body rather elongate, tapering, with scales or bony plates. Head large, more or less completely encased with rough bony plates, some of which are armed with spines. Preorbitals usually produced forward, with spines. Eyes high. Mouth terminal or subinferior. Spinous dorsal short. Soft dorsal and anal without spines. Pectorals large, with several lower rays detached, forming feelers and used chiefly in search of food. Ventrals thoracic, wide apart, separated by wide area.

Somewhat small, sluggish fishes found in all warm seas, mostly in the deeper waters where they live on the bottom, crawling about with the aid of their lower free pectoral rays and turning over stones in search of food. Most of the species are red in colour. Although common they are seldom seen unless taken by means of the otter-trawl, when they are found to be in great numbers. Many of them emit a croaking noise when removed from the water. Genera numerous, three in Queensland.

438

A. No palatine teeth. A series of spinigerous shields along base of dorsal fin.

    b. Scales rather large, in about 50-65 transverse series.

      c. Lateral line unarmed.   *Lepidotrigla*

      cc. Lateral line spinigerous.   *Paratrigla*

    bb. Scales small, in more than 100 transverse series. Lateral line unarmed.   *Chelidonichthys*

Lepidotrigla

Head parallelepiped, with the upper surface and sides entirely bony. Scales moderate, less than 70 along lateral line; lateral line scales not spiny. A row of bony plates along each side of dorsal base, each with one spine. Villiform teeth in jaws and usually on the vomer, none on palatines. Three free pectoral rays. Species numerous in all but the coldest seas. Three species occur in Queensland.

A. Pectoral long, extending far beyond tip of ventral and to vertical from nineth or tenth ray of soft dorsal; upper pectoral appendage reaching to or not quite to tip of ventral.   *calodactyla*

AA. Pectoral long, extending well beyond tip of ventral, and to vertical from eighth ray of soft dorsal; upper pectoral appendage not reaching tip of ventral.   *argus*

AAA. Pectoral short, extending a little beyond tip of ventral and to vertical from third ray of soft dorsal; upper pectoral appendage reaching beyond tip of ventral.   *grandis*

427. LONG-FINNED GURNARD *Lepidotrigla calodactyla* (Ogilby)

[Colour-plate 60]

Lepidotrigla calodactyla Ogilby, New Fish. Qld Coast, 20th Dec. 1910, p. 125 (a suppressed publication).

Illustrations by G. Coates.

D. 9/15-16; A. 15-16; P. 10 + 3; Sc. 54-56. Colour brick-red above, white below; spinous dorsal immaculate; pectoral with the base, the upper, and the 2 inner rays white, rest of the fin olive-brown at base, shading through greenish-yellow to grey, the whole crossed by wide umber-brown or blackish bars, some of which are angularly bent backward or broken up in spots on the lower rays.

A little-known species seldom captured and then only by trawl along the coast of Queensland, where it has been taken in 70 fathoms. Further trawling will, no doubt, reveal the species to be common in the deeper waters. Known only from Queensland. Grows to 7 inches.

OTHER SPECIES

Eyed Gurnard, *L. argus*; Great Butterfly Gurnard, *L. grandis*. These are also fishes of which little is known. Both species are known only from Queensland where they have been trawled at depths of 70 fathoms in the southern portions of the State. They grow to about 8 inches.

Paratrigla

Like *Lepidotrigla* but differing therefrom in the presence of a spinigerous lateral line.

Small gurnards of the coasts of Queensland and New South Wales and also the Indian Ocean. One species in Queensland.

428. BUTTERFLY GURNARD *Paratrigla papilio* (Cuvier and Valenciennes)

Trigla papilio Cuvier and Valenciennes, Hist. Nat. Poiss., 4, Nov. 1829, p. 80.
Trigla Pleuracanthica Richardson, Zool. Voy. Erebus and Terror, Fish. Mar. 1, 1845, p. 23, pl. 16, figs. 1-4.

D. 9/14; A. 14; L. l. 55. Colour brownish above, whitish below; head with yellowish tinge; spinous dorsal with yellow and with a large black spot, edged or streaked sometimes with white, between fourth and seventh spines; hinder surface of pectorals with the base, the inner rays, and a narrow tip white; the other rays black, either uniform or sparsely dotted with white.

A common and pretty little fish found offshore along the coasts of Queensland, New South Wales, and Tasmania, and in the Indian Ocean. In Queensland it has been trawled at depths of 12 to 26 fathoms. Seldom seen except when taken in the trawls. Grows to about 7 inches.

Chelidonichthys

Body covered with small or very small scales. Spinous and soft dorsal fins with a row of spiny plates along their bases. Lateral line unarmed, without elongated shields, the scales usually bifurcate at caudal base. Three free pectoral rays.

Gurnards of the Indo-Pacific waters and the Mediterranean. One species in Queensland.

440

429. RED GURNARD *Chelidonichthys kumu* (Lesson and Garnot) [Plate 59]

Trigla kumu Lesson and Garnot, Voy. Coquille, Poiss., 1826, p. 214, pl. 19.
Illustration by F. Olsen.

D. 9-10/14-16; A. 14-16; P. 10-11; V. 1/5; C. 12; L. l. 75-82. Colour red, reddish, grey or olivaceous above, sides reddish-yellow washed with pink; cheeks scarlet, mottled brownish; lower half of dorsal fins red, upper half greyish-yellow; caudal reddish-orange; ventrals pink or orange; inner half of anal grey, outer half pink; pectoral membrane deep bluish-grey externally, the rays orange, purple, or bluish-purple internally, with numerous bright-blue spots on its posterior half, and a large black blotch spotted with pale blue on lower third of fin; eye red, bordered with a narrow gold ring.

A very important food-fish in New South Wales and also in New Zealand where they are commonly seen in the markets. In Queensland the species is rather uncommon and is seldom seen or captured, except by outside fishermen.

Full-grown red gurnards weigh about 4 pounds and reach a length of about 21 inches. They can be captured by hook and line, though most examples are trawled. Adult fish are to be found in fairly deep water off the coasts, those in the inlets being usually immature. As a table fish it ranks high, the flesh being white and of good flavour, though perhaps somewhat dry.

In Australia the species occurs in the waters of all States and its range extends also to New Zealand, China, Japan, the Indo-Australian Archipelago, and South Africa.

Family **Oplichthyidae: Spiny Flatheads**

Body elongate, tapering, naked, a row of spiny scutes along each side. Head broad, depressed, somewhat spiny, with bony ridge across cheek to pre-opercle. Three to 4 of the lower rays of pectorals detached. Pelvics widely separated.

Curious fishes inhabiting the deeper waters of the Indo-Pacific; though abundant there, they are seldom caught by the average person. A single genus with few species.

Oplichthys

For characters of the genus see those of the family. Two species in Australian waters, one of them found in Queensland.

430. OGILBY'S SPINY FLATHEAD *Oplichthys ogilbyi* (McCulloch)
[Plate 59]

Oplichthys ogilbyi McCulloch, Biol. Res. Endeavour, 2, pt 3, 3rd July 1914, p. 133, pl. 28, figs 1-1a.

D. 6/15; A. 1/16; P. 12 + 4; V. 1/5; Lateral plates 27. Colour: "Apparently pink or yellow in life, with some very indefinite darker spots and lines; the back is crossed by six indistinct darker bands, of which the first is below the spinous dorsal, and the last on the base of the tail. The first dorsal is blackish, with several darker wavy cross-lines, and the pectorals have some irregular rows of dusky spots. Some very indefinite spots can also be traced on the second dorsal and the caudal." (McCulloch.)

Known only from two specimens which were trawled by the *Endeavour* off Cape Moreton, South Queensland, in 1910 at a depth of 73 fathoms. Lengths 150 and 197 mm. The species has not been taken since.

Family **Platycephalidae: Flatheads**

Body depressed anteriorly, subcylindrical posteriorly. Head depressed or flattened, more or less armed with spines and serratures. Body covered everywhere closely with ctenoid scales. Head scaly posteriorly. Lateral line present. Mouth large; bands of villiform teeth in jaws and on vomer and palatines, sometimes some teeth enlarged and more or less canine-like. No air-bladder. Two dorsal fins, the first preceded by a short isolated spine. Lower rays of pectorals more or less free at tips; no free rays. Ventrals with spine and 5 rays, thoracic, set wide apart and well behind the pectorals.

Carnivorous fishes living on the bottom of sandy and muddy areas along the coasts and in the estuaries of the Indo-Pacific and East Atlantic, some reaching rather a large size. They bury themselves on the bottom, often on a ridge overlooking the shallow water, only the eyes being exposed. From such a vantage point they will suddenly attack and devour any small fish which may inadvertently approach too near. Most flatheads are valuable foodfishes, with flesh of excellent appearance and flavour, thus finding a ready sale in all markets.

The genera and species are numerous and the flatheads are richly represented in the waters of Australia, at least thirty-nine species having been recorded.

Very severe stings or wounds can be inflicted by the preopercular spines, which vary in number, length, and strength in the many species. Professional fishermen usually paralyse the fish by laying it flat, and, holding down the body with one hand, they place the other hand under the head and force it upwards, thus breaking the spinal cord.

Five genera are found in Queensland waters.

KEY TO GENERA IN QUEENSLAND

A.   A large deep pit behind each eye.   *Cymbacephalus*

AA. No pit behind the eyes.

    b. Lower limb of preopercle sharp, terminating in a single long and slender spine.

    c. Spinous dorsal short, consisting of but 5 spines. Soft dorsal and anal rays (with the exception of the anterior 4-5) wholly free and unattached.   *Elates*

    bb. Preopercle with more than one spine.

d. Head largely scaly; no enlarged thickened scales on lateral line.

    e. Vomerine teeth forming a curved band across the bone. Cranial ridges not serrated or spinose.   *Platycephalus*

    ee. Vomerine teeth in 2 separate groups. Cranial ridges armed with spines and serratures.   *Suggrundus*

dd. Head almost naked. Scales of lateral line enlarged and thickened.   *Thysanophrys*

Cymbacephalus: Rock Flatheads

Form similar to *Suggrundus* but differing in the presence of a large deep pit behind each eye.

Fishes of the coastal waters of Queensland, the Northern Territory, New Guinea, and the East Indies. Species few, two in Queensland.

KEY TO SPECIES IN QUEENSLAND

A.   An orbital tentacle above eye; dorsal and caudal with blackish lines.   *nematophthalmus*

AA. No orbital tentacle; fins without blackish lines.   *parilis*

431. FRINGE-EYED FLATHEAD *Cymbacephalus nematophthalmus* (Günther)   [Colour-plate 61]

Platycephalus nematophthalmus Günther, Cat. Fish. Brit. Mus., 2, 1860, p. 184.
Illustration by G. Coates.

Sammy Dong (Tin Can Bay, Queensland); Rock Flathead (Queensland).

D. 8-9/11; A. 11; P. 19-20; V. 1/5; C. 11; L. 1. 54. Colour dark brown above with several blackish cross-bands which extend on to the sides where they break up into the brown in spots and speckles, ending in a sharp horizontal line against the pure white of the belly; several bars across throat; spinous dorsal greyish basally thickly speckled and marked all over with fine lines and spots of blackish, yellowish, and brownish; caudal, pectorals, and ventrals similar, the latter with some larger black spots; soft dorsal and anal greyish or whitish basally, yellow terminally, mottled with grey, black, and brown.

A common species in Queensland waters where it is taken in the nets of the prawn-trawlers. Otherwise met with only very occasionally. Found also in the Northern Territory, New Guinea, and the East Indies. Grows to 14 inches.

OTHER SPECIES

A closely allied species, *C. parilis*, frequents the northern waters of Queensland and the Northern Territory. Grows to at least 17 inches. Not commonly seen.

Elates

Differs from all the other platycephalids in having only a single preopercular spine, in the short spinous dorsal which has only 5 spines, in the length of the free interdorsal space, in the soft dorsal and anal rays (with the exception of the anterior four or five) being wholly free and unattached, and in the shape of the caudal.

Small and slender fishes so far known only from Queensland and the Philippines. A single species.

432. DWARF FLATHEAD *Elates thompsoni* (Jordan and Seale)
[Colour-plate 61]

Elates thompsoni Jordan and Seale, Bull. U.S. Fish. Bur., 26, 1906, 11th Jan. 1907, p. 39.
Illustration by G. Coates.

D. 1, 5/13; A. 13; P. 19-21; V. 1/5; C. 14-15; L. l. 90-99. Colour: Head and body pale sandy, with an irregular row of oval lilac spots along each side, below white; fins hyaline, the dorsals black-spotted; upper caudal lobe black-spotted, lower with 2 black horizontal subterminal bars, which are often coalescent. (Ogilby.)

This small and slender flathead is occasionally taken by the prawn-trawlers in North Queensland at Townsville; otherwise the fish has not been seen since 1910, when four specimens were trawled at Pine Peak and Cape Gloucester, Queensland. Grows to 8 inches.

Platycephalus: Flatheads

Head broad, more or less strongly depressed and more or less armed with spines. Body elongate, depressed anteriorly, subcylindrical posteriorly, covered with ctenoid scales. Lateral line present. Jaws, vomer, and palatine bones with bands of villiform teeth; enlarged canine teeth sometimes present. Spinous dorsal shorter than and separate from the soft dorsal. Anal with or without spines. Tips of lower pectoral rays more or less free. Ventrals widely separated.

An Indo-Pacific group of marine fishes living on the bottom in shallow and moderately deep water. Species numerous, seven in Queensland.

KEY TO SPECIES IN QUEENSLAND

A. Teeth not uniform, some on premaxillary symphysis, vomer, and palatines more or less enlarged.

   b. Interorbital space equal to or greater than transverse diameter of eye (except in young).

   c. Interorbital space nearly flat.

   d. 12 anal rays. *mortoni*

   dd. 13 anal rays.

e. Scales small, 130 in lateral series. Caudal whitish or yellowish, with 3 longitudinal black bands. *indicus*

ee. Scales larger, 100 in lateral series. Caudal with numerous dark spots on its upper half, the lower half uniformly dark brown; head and fins spotted brown. *fuscus*

cc. Interorbital space concave; head and body marbled with red and white; 6 indistinct broad dark-red bands across the body. *marmoratus*

bb. Interorbital space narrower than transverse diameter of eye.

f. 13 dorsal rays; eye diameter equal to about half its distance from end of mandible; 3 or more black longitudinal stripes along tail from base to tip. *arenarius*

ff. 14 dorsal rays; eye diameter greater than half its distance from end of mandible; black markings confined to posterior half of tail. *caeruleopunctatus*

AA. Teeth small and uniform, without larger ones on pre-maxillary symphysis, vomer, or palatines; lower pre-opercular spine very large. *longispinis*

433. DUSKY FLATHEAD *Platycephalus fuscus* (Cuvier and Valenciennes)
[Plate 59]

Platycephalus fuscus Cuvier and Valenciennes, Hist. Nat. Poiss., 4, Nov. 1829, p. 241.
Platycephalus fuscus Quoy and Gaimard, Zool. Astrolabe, 3, 1835, p. 681, pl. 10, fig. 1.

D. 2, 7, 1/13; A. 13; V. 1/5; P. 19-20; L. l. 100. Colour dark brownish on back, head, and sides, sometimes with a few lighter spots but more often without; sides of head pale olive-brown, with numerous darker spots; under-surface of head pale pink; dorsal fins straw colour, the spines and rays with a row of brown spots on each side; caudal with its upper half with numerous dark spots, the lower half dark brown; pectorals thickly spotted with brown; ventrals creamy, spotted with reddish-brown, the spots larger than those on the pectorals; anal whitish.

The Dusky or Mud Flathead is found along the coasts of Queensland, New South Wales, Victoria, South Australia, and northern Tasmania. As its name implies it is a lover of the estuaries and shallow flats, as a rule occurring only in the more open waters where deposits of silt have formed. It is extremely common in the above-mentioned localities, where it delights in burying itself in the mud and lying in wait for passing prey, its detection being rendered difficult by its dusky coloration as it lies with only the eyes exposed.

The diet of this species is varied and is composed of small fishes, molluscs, crustaceans, marine worms, and so on. Considerable numbers of Dusky

Flathead are caught annually by the fishermen and always command a ready sale in the markets. As a food-fish it ranks very high, the flesh being firm, white, and of excellent flavour. It is the largest of the Australian flatheads, reaching a length of 4 feet and a weight of at least 32 pounds. Most market fish would be about 20 to 25 inches in length.

434. SAND FLATHEAD *Platycephalus arenarius* (Ramsay and Ogilby)

[Plate 59]

Platycephalus arenarius Ramsay and Ogilby, Proc. Linn. Soc. N.S.Wales, 10, pt 4, 3rd April 1886, p. 577.

Platycephalus arenarius McCulloch, Biol. Res. Endeavour, 3, pt 3, 1915, p. 164, pl. 13, fig. 1 and text-fig. 3.

D. 8/13; A. 13; P. 20; V. 1/5; C. 13; L. 1. 74. Colour light yellowish-brown or sandy above, closely speckled with fine spots; spines and rays of dorsals with chestnut bands, the membranes hyaline; last five membranes of anal dark, remainder and rays white; ventrals and pectoral rays banded; caudal pure white, the upper half with 3 to 4 oblique parallel brown bands, the lower with 2 much broader black stripes.

The Sand Flathead is seldom found in the estuaries but is a lover of the sandy flats and bays along the coasts of Queensland, northern New South Wales, and the Northern Territory. It has been trawled at a depth of 29 fathoms twenty-two miles south-west of Double Island Point, South Queensland. Its flesh is considered by many to be of superior quality to that of the Dusky Flathead. In size it averages about 12 or 14 inches, but according to Ogilby it reaches a length of 18 inches.

OTHER SPECIES

Morton's Flathead, *P. mortoni*. A small and little-known fish found in the estuarine waters and shallow flats along the coast of Queensland. Grows to 16 inches.

Bar-tailed Flathead, *P. indicus*. Frequents mainly the waters of the northern portion of Australia from Queensland to Western Australia, thence through the East Indies to India, China, South Africa, and the Red Sea. Reaches 40 inches in length and is a good food-fish.

Marbled Flathead, *P. marmoratus*. From the coasts of South Queensland and northern New South Wales. This fish is very seldom met with; apparently it is a species which frequents moderately deep water. The few specimens so far taken have been captured at depths ranging from 35 to 40 fathoms. Grows to 20 inches.

Red-spotted Flathead, *P. caeruleopunctatus*. A common species on the trawling grounds along the coasts of South Queensland and New South Wales. It appears in goodly numbers in the catches of the prawn-trawlers operating off Point Danger, South Queensland. It is said to reach a length of 17 inches. Readily recognized by the profusion of rusty-red and milky-white spots everywhere.

Long-spined Flathead, *P. longispinis*. A small fish which grows to about 13 inches. It is occasionally caught by the prawn-trawlers operating in offshore waters of South Queensland and New South Wales. Known by the very long lower preopercular spine.

Suggrundus

Head broad, much depressed, armed with spines and serratures. Preoperculum with 2 or more spines; no antrorse spine on its lower face. Teeth usually villiform, sometimes cardiform, in bands on the jaws and palatines; teeth in 2 separate groups on the vomer, set lengthwise along the shaft of the bone. Scales large or small. Lateral line smooth or armed with spines, partially or for its full length.

Fishes of the waters of the Indo-Australian Archipelago, Japan, and the Philippines.

KEY TO SPECIES IN QUEENSLAND

Adapted from McCulloch[68]

A. Eyes smaller and round, the interorbital space about equal to their vertical diameter.

    b. Tail with 2 large dark blotches. Infraorbital ridge with 1 spine.   *bosschei*

    bb. Tail without dark blotches. Infraorbital ridge with 4 spines.   *malayanus*

AA. Eyes larger, elliptical, the interorbital space less than their vertical diameter.

    c. Anterior third of lateral line with distinct upstanding spines.

    d. Upper preopercular spine very large, about as long as the eye.   *macracanthus*

    dd. Upper preopercular spine much shorter than the eye.

    e. Infraorbital ridge expanded outwards posteriorly, overhanging the cheek.   *tuberculatus*

    ee. Infraorbital ridge not overhanging the cheek posteriorly.   *jugosus*

    cc. Anterior third of lateral line with indistinct prostrate spines.   *harrisii*

---

[68] *Biol. Res. Endeavour*, 2, 1914, p. 138.

435. HARRIS'S FLATHEAD *Suggrundus harrisii* (McCulloch) [Plate 59]

Insidiator harrisii McCulloch, Biol. Res. Endeavour, 2, pt 3, 3rd July 1914, p. 146, pl. 30, fig. 1 and text-fig. 12.

D. 9/11-12; A. 11-12; P. 20-25; V. 1/5; C. 11-13; L. l. 53. Colour light brown above, passing gradually into greyish-white below; spines and rays of dorsal fins with small brown spots; anal whitish; pectorals and ventrals brown-spotted; caudal dusky-greyish, with large, distinct, blackish-brown spots, brightest and largest on lower half of fin.

A small species seldom met with by the casual fisherman but extremely common in the nets of the prawn-trawlers along the whole Queensland coast-line. Sometimes hundreds are seen in a single haul. Grows to 9 inches.

OTHER SPECIES

Bossch's Flathead, *S. bosschei*. A species from northern Australia and the East Indies. Grows to about 12 inches.

Malay Flathead, *S. malayanus*. This small flathead ranges from Queensland to the East Indies. Within Queensland it has been recorded only from the far north. Length about 9 inches.

Long-spined Flathead, *S. macracanthus*. Met with in North Queensland only when taken by trawl. It is also found in the East Indies and the Philippines. Grows to 8 inches.

S. tuberculatus. Another flathead from the Indo-Australian Archipelago, this species has been trawled along the Queensland coastline in shallow waters of 7 to 9 fathoms. Grows to about 20 inches.

Rough-headed Flathead, *S. jugosus*. Known only from Queensland and New South Wales, where it has been trawled at various points between Bowen in North Queensland and Port Jackson in New South Wales. Length 8 inches.

Thysanophrys

Body rather short, stout, somewhat depressed. Scales rough, partly ciliated, partly cycloid. Head broad, much depressed, mostly naked. Scales of lateral line enlarged and thickened. Orbital tentacle present.

Fishes of the Indo-Australian Archipelago. Species few, one in Queensland.

436. ROCK FLATHEAD *Thysanophrys cirronasus* (Richardson) [Plate 59]

Platycephalus cirronasus Richardson, Zool. Voy. Erebus and Terror, 1848, p. 114, pl. 51, figs 7-10.

D. 8-9/11-12; A. 11-12; P. 20-21; V. 1/5; C. 10-11; L. l. 53-54. Colour: About 8 broad blackish-brown cross-bands on back, much wider than the narrow fawn-coloured interspaces; these narrow interspaces break up on the lower sides into yellowish vermiculations and irregular paler brown spots;

creamy-white below; pectorals reddish-brown with spots of black and vermiculations of yellow; ventrals similar; spinous dorsal dusky, with yellow and
black pencillings; soft dorsal similar, but the black pencilling more pronounced; anal similar, with tips of rays yellow; caudal similar to spinous
dorsal.

A handsome flathead variegated with many tints to harmonize and camouflage with the weed-covered rocks among which it lives. The species is only
a straggler into South Queensland, its real home being in the waters of New
South Wales. It occurs also in South Australia. Grows to 15 inches.

Order HYPOSTOMIDES: DRAGON-FISHES

Body covered with bony plates, firmly joined on body, movable on tail. Mouth
tiny, toothless, situated below a long flattened snout. Dorsal and anal short,
of soft rays only. Pectorals large, of elongate rays, sometimes spinous. Ventrals
abdominal, with spine and 1 to 3 rays.

A few fantastic little fishes of one family from the tropical Indo-Pacific.
Little is known of their habits, but they are said to speed along the surface
of the water with the large pectorals extended.

Family Pegasidae

Body broad, greatly depressed. A narrow gill-opening in front of base of pectoral
fin. Tail with 4 angles.

Genera few, three in Australian waters, two in Queensland.

KEY TO GENERA IN QUEENSLAND

A.   Tail short, quadrangular posteriorly.   *Pegasus*

AA. Tail long, flattened posteriorly.   *Parapegasus*

Pegasus

Trunk short, broad, greatly depressed. Tail short, not elongate or compressed,
but with 8 rings. Snout more or less extended. Pectoral rays all simple, slender,
not spine-like. Ventral with 1 to 2 rays, the outer longer. Species few, one in
Queensland.

437. SHORT-TAILED DRAGON-FISH *Pegasus volitans* Linnaeus [Plate 59]

Pegasus volitans Linnaeus, Syst. Nat., 10th ed., 1758, p. 338.
Zalistes umitengu Jordan and Snyder, Proc. U.S. Nat. Mus., 24, 1901, p. 2, pls 1-2.

Tail with 8 rings. Colour brownish, finely reticulated with darker brown;
snout and last two or three caudal rings black; pectoral rays with fine brown
dots and with a broad milky-white edge and sometimes a white band.

This curious little fish is not so frequently met with as the Long-tailed Sea
Dragon, *Parapegasus natans*, though the trawl may yet reveal them to be

more common than supposed. Found on the coasts of Queensland and New South Wales, also through the East Indies to India and Japan. Grows to 4 inches.

Parapegasus

Body slender. Ventrals composed of 2 separate rays, the first ray composite and large, and the second minute, the first consists of a spine-like process and 2 rays fused together. Tail much longer than trunk, flattened posteriorly. Species few, one in Queensland.

438. LONG-TAILED SEA DRAGON *Parapegasus natans* (Linnaeus)
[Colour-plate 61]

Pegasus natans Linnaeus, Syst. Nat., 12th ed., 1766, p. 418 (based on Gronow, Zoophylac, 357). Illustration by G. Coates.

Tail with 12 rings. Colour yellowish to tawny-olive above, with 5 indistinct transverse bands, the first at nape, the second above vent, and the others on tail; dorsal, pectoral, and caudal fins dotted with dusky above.

A common little fish along the whole Queensland coast, also New South Wales and North Australia, the East Indies, and China. Most specimens are collected along the beaches among after-storm litter. Grows to 7 inches.

Order **HETEROSOMATA: FLAT-FISHES, FLOUNDERS, SOLES**

Body asymmetrical, strongly compressed. Cranium normal behind, twisted in front to permit 2 eyes on the same side, either right or left, turned upwards. Teeth present, very small or obsolete, better developed on the blind side in many species. Paired fins often asymmetrical or wanting at one side. Eyed side pigmented, blind side usually without pigment. Dorsal and anal fins long, many-rayed. Ventrals with 6 rays or less, thoracic or jugular.

The great and important order Heterosomata, whose members are popularly called flat-fishes, is another group of bony fishes said to have descended from perch-like ancestors. They are among the most remarkable of living fishes in that they have both their eyes situated on the same side of the head, the skull being twisted anteriorly. Their bodies are compressed or flattened from side to side (not as in the rays, whose bodies are depressed or flattened from above downwards). Like the rays they are adapted for a life on the bottom.

One of the many interesting features regarding these fishes is that in the very early stages of their lives their two eyes are situated one on each side of the head as in other fishes. The little fishes are quite transparent and swim in a vertical position. At a very early stage one eye commences to migrate round the upper surface of the head to join its fellow on the opposite side, and at the same time the little fish begins to keel over on to one side or the other and to sink down and lie on the bottom, with the ocular side uppermost.

The eyed side, now turned constantly towards the light, becomes pigmented or coloured, whilst the underside or blind side remains colourless. As a general rule a particular species is either right-sided or left-sided: that is to say, the two eyes are on the right or left side and not, as might be supposed, sometimes right and sometimes left. However, exceptions occur in which a reversed example is found, a normally right-sided or dextral species becomes individually left-sided or sinistral, and vice versa.

After this migration of the eye has taken place, the greater part of their lives is spent on the bottom where they lie more or less covered with sand, gravel, or mud. They possess considerable powers of colour control and can readily adapt themselves to harmonize in colour with their surroundings. As mentioned, the young fishes in their early stages swim vertically, but this state ceases with the migration of the eye, and they now move and swim in a horizontal position, with undulating movements of the body and fins, as do the skates and rays.

In these fishes the dorsal and anal fins are long and, with the exception of *Psettodes*, without spines. In species such as the flounder they terminate in the region of the caudal peduncle, but in many of the soles they are continuous with the caudal fin. The scales of the body are cycloid or ctenoid, or absent. The lateral line may be single, double, treble, or absent altogether. The mouth is more or less protractile, the teeth often small or obsolete, in many cases more developed on the blind side.

Flat-fishes live and feed on the bottom. All the species are carnivorous, devouring any smaller fishes, crustaceans, worms, molluscs, etc., which they may find. They inhabit the seas and shores in all parts of the world, the majority leading a wholly marine life. Some species, however, prefer the muddy estuaries, whilst a few spend their entire existence in fresh water. Many species descend to great depths in offshore waters, where they are captured by the trawl-net or by a long hand-line. On the banks of Newfoundland one of the species, the halibut, is fished at 300 fathoms. Other species descend to greater depths, 500 fathoms and more, and one species trawled by the *Albatross* was brought up from 896 fathoms.

The flat-fishes are valuable food-fishes and are of great commercial importance to all maritime countries. This applies more especially to European countries, where great trawling industries are established for the fishing of these valuable food-fishes. The giant of the order is the halibut, a huge fish which grows to a length of 10 to 12 feet and attains a weight of at least 500 pounds. Although Queensland cannot boast of such fishes as the halibut, plaice, and turbot of British seas, nevertheless there are several genera and species of economic importance, and though small they have flesh of excellent quality.

The order is composed of five families, all of which have representatives in Australian waters.

A. Dorsal fin not extending forward on to the head, the anterior rays spinous. Each pelvic fin with 1 spine and 5 soft rays. Palatines toothed. Eyes on right or left side.   PSETTODIDAE

AA. Dorsal fin extending forward on to head at least above eye, none of the rays spinous. Pelvic fins without spines. No palatine teeth.

  b. Lower jaw generally prominent. Preoperculum with a free margin.

   c. Eyes on the left side (except in reversed examples).   BOTHIDAE

   cc. Eyes on the right side (except in reversed examples).   PLEURONECTIDAE

  bb. Lower jaw never prominent. Preopercular margin not free, hidden by the skin and scales of the head.

   d. Eyes on the right side.   SOLEIDAE

   dd. Eyes on the left side.   CYNOGLOSSIDAE

Family **Psettodidae**

Dorsal fin commencing on neck, not extending forward on to head. Anterior dorsal rays somewhat spinous. Ventrals composed of a spine and 5 rays, their form and position nearly symmetrical. Maxillary with a well-developed supramaxillary bone. Palatines toothed.

A single genus with two species, one from tropical West Africa, the other from the Indo-Pacific. Dextral and sinistral examples are equally numerous.

439. QUEENSLAND HALIBUT or ADALAH *Psettodes erumei* (Bloch and Schneider) [Colour-plate 62]

Pleuronectes erumei Bloch and Schneider, Syst. Ichth., 1801, p. 150.
Illustration by G. Coates.

D. 49-54; A. 36-44; P. 14-15; V. 1/5; L. l. 72-77; L. tr. 21-25/1/33-41. Colour brownish or greyish, sometimes with 4 broad dark transverse bars; body sometimes with small scattered white spots; dorsal, anal, and posterior part of caudal darker, the caudal sometimes with a distinct blackish band posteriorly; pectoral with small dark spots.

Juveniles are blackish, with 5 white transverse bands, narrower than their interspaces, the first on the upper part of the head only, the fifth across the tail-base; eye yellow.

This fine big fish, which attains a weight of 20 pounds, is the largest flat-fish in Australian seas. It is common on the Queensland coastline north of Bowen but is seldom taken by line-fishermen. During the investigations of the trawler *Endeavour* many years ago, examples were taken off Gloucester

Heads and Bowen at depths of 16 to 25 fathoms. No doubt when the species is fished systematically they will be seen in Australian markets more frequently.

In this fish the teeth are very strong and are barbed at their extremities. The species ranges into the Pacific and across to the Indo-Malay Archipelago, East Africa, and the Red Sea. Grows to 24 inches.

Family **Bothidae: Flounders**

Eyes normally on left side. Dorsal fin extending forward on head. No fin-rays spiniform. Ventrals short-based and symmetrical, or the base of that of the left side is longer than that of the right. Mouth large or moderate, the lower jaw somewhat prominent and often with a symphysial knob on chin. Teeth in both jaws more or less equal on both sides; caninoid teeth often present; no teeth on palate. Lateral line curved anteriorly.

Three sub-families are contained in this family, two of them being represented in Queensland waters by six genera.

KEY TO SUB-FAMILIES REPRESENTED IN QUEENSLAND

A. Ventral fins equal, short-based.   PARALICHTHINAE

AA. Ventral fins unequal, that of the blind side short-based,
    that of the ocular side much longer.   BOTHINAE

Sub-family PARALICHTHINAE

This sub-family contains many genera but only one of them occurs in Queensland.

Pseudorhombus

In this genus the eyes, which are on the left side, are separated by a bony ridge. There is a single lateral line developed on both sides of the body, with a strong curve anteriorly and with a supratemporal branch running upwards towards the anterior part of the dorsal fin.

Flounders of the Indo-Pacific region, eight species being found in Queensland. They are inclined to be small in size but are nevertheless valuable food-fishes. No trawling being engaged in on the coast (except for prawns) the flounders are seldom met in any great numbers. The little trawling done several years ago by the *Endeavour* proved them to be present in offshore waters, so there is no reason to doubt that some day they will be seen in the markets in numbers if trawling develops in Queensland.

KEY TO SPECIES IN QUEENSLAND

Based on Norman[69]

A. Origin of dorsal well in front of both nostrils of blind side; a line connecting base of first dorsal ray with posterior nostril, if continued, passes above hinder end of maxillary; dorsal profile of head markedly convex; gill-rakers palmate. *spinosus*

AA. Origin of dorsal behind, above, or a little in front of nostrils or blind side; a line connecting base of first dorsal ray with posterior nostril, if continued, crosses the maxillary; dorsal profile of head straight or notched in front of eyes.

    b. Scales of ocular side cycloid; no anterior canine teeth; gill-rakers longer than broad. *tenuirastrum*

    bb. Scales of ocular side ctenoid.

      c. Gill-rakers palmate; 3 or more double ocelli on body.

        d. Depth $2\frac{2}{5}$-$2\frac{2}{3}$ in the length; maxillary extending almost to below posterior border of eye or beyond, length 2-$2\frac{3}{4}$ in head; anterior teeth of both jaws forming strong canines, 4-8 teeth on blind side of lower jaw. *diplospilus*

        dd. Depth $2\frac{1}{10}$-$2\frac{2}{5}$ in the length; maxillary extending to below middle of eye or beyond, length 2-$2\frac{1}{2}$ in head; anterior teeth of jaws not greatly enlarged, 13-22 teeth on blind side of lower jaw. *dupliciocellatus*

      cc. Gill-rakers pointed, longer than broad; no conspicuous double ocelli.

        e. Origin of dorsal above or a little in front of nostrils of blind side, and well in advance of eye.

        f. Anterior teeth of both jaws enlarged and canine-like; 72-94 dorsal rays. *arsius*

        ff. Anterior teeth scarcely enlarged; 68-72 dorsal rays. *elevatus*

        ee. Origin of dorsal just behind posterior nostril of blind side, and above or very slightly in advance of anterior part of eye.

        g. 14-16 gill-rakers on lower part of anterior arch. *argus*

        gg. 7-10 gill-rakers on lower part of anterior arch. *jenynsii*

---

[69] *Biol. Res. Endeavour*, 5, pt 5, 1926, p. 223.

440. LARGE-TOOTHED FLOUNDER *Pseudorhombus arsius*
(Hamilton Buchanan) [Colour-plate 62]

Pleuronectes arsius Hamilton Buchanan, Acc. Fish. Ganges, 1822, p. 128 (*fide* Sherborn).
Illustration by G. Coates.

Tampar (East Indies).

D. 72-79; A. 54-62; C. 2/13/2; scales 70-80 in a longitudinal series, 24-30 between lateral line and highest point of dorsal profile. Colour brownish or greyish, generally with some darker spots and rings; usually a dark spot, sometimes surrounded by a ring of white dots, at junction of straight and curved parts of lateral line, and another on middle of straight portion; head and body sometimes with numerous scattered small dark spots, with or without bluish-white margins; median fins with brown spots and rings.

One of the most common of the Australian flat-fishes and a valuable food-fish, with flesh of good quality. A wide-ranging species found from the east coast of Africa to the Pacific. Grows to 15 inches.

441. SMALL-TOOTHED FLOUNDER *Pseudorhombus jenynsii* (Bleeker)
[Plate 60]

Platessa jenynsii Beeker, Verh. Akad. Wet. Amsterdam, 2, 1855, Viss. Van Diemen, p. 15, sp. 265 (*fide* Norman).
Pseudorhombus anomalus Whitley, Austr. Zool., 6, pt 4, 1931, p. 322, pl. 25.

D. 67-71; A. 50-56; C. 2/13/2; scales 64-74 in a longitudinal series, 26-30 between lateral line and highest point of dorsal profile. Colour brownish or greyish, with darker spots and markings, of which the five prominent ocelli are arranged as in *P. argus*; these ocelli usually with a number of small white dots and surrounded by a dark ring; fins with brown spots; a series of larger and more distinct dark spots on basal parts of dorsal and anal fins.

This fish ranges across the southern portion of the continent of Australia from Fremantle to Queensland, where it has been recorded from as far north as Townsville. A good food-fish. Grows to 16 inches.

OTHER SPECIES

Spined Flounder, *P. spinosus*. Recorded from southern Queensland and Western Australia. Queensland examples have been trawled by the *Endeavour* off Bustard Heads and Hervey Bay in 9 to 20 fathoms. Grows to 11 inches.

Deep-water or Slender Flounder, *P. tenuirastrum*. Ranges along the coast of south-eastern Australia, northwards to South Queensland (Double Island Point). In the south it is commonly taken by the trawlers in moderately deep waters. Although seldom seen in Queensland it is no doubt common, for several examples were trawled by the *Endeavour* in 33 fathoms. Grows to 11 inches.

Twin-spot Flounder, *P. diplospilus*. Recorded from Indo-China and the east coast of Queensland, all examples having been trawled by the *Endeavour* in 9 to 35 fathoms. Grows to 10½ inches.

Four-spot Flounder, *P. dupliciocellatus*. Ranges from the Nicobar Islands through the Malay Archipelago to the east coast of Australia, southwards to northern New South Wales. Also found in Japan. This species has been trawled by the *Endeavour* at various points along the Queensland coast at depths ranging from 19 to 33 fathoms. Grows to 15 inches.

Deep Flounder, *P. elevatus*. Ranges from Queensland through the Indo-Australian Archipelago to the Indian Ocean and the Persian Gulf. It has been trawled off Bowen and Hervey Bay at depths of 9 to 25 fathoms. Grows to 7 inches.

Ocellated Flounder, *P. argus*. A species so far known only from South Queensland and the Aru Islands. Specimens have been trawled three to seven miles north-west of Hervey Bay, South Queensland, in 9 to 11 fathoms. Grows to 7 inches.

Sub-family BOTHINAE

Ventral fins unequal, that of the blind side short-based, that of the ocular side much longer.

Thirteen genera constitute this sub-family, of which five are found in Australian waters. They are fishes mostly from tropical and temperate seas.

KEY TO GENERA IN QUEENSLAND
Based on Norman[70]

A. Lateral line absent or feebly developed on blind side.

    b. Eyes separated by a bony ridge or narrow concave space; interorbital region similar in both sexes.

        c. Male without rostral spines or tubercles.

            d. Scales of ocular side cycloid or rather feebly ctenoid. Maxillary 2-3¼ in head.   *Arnoglossus*

        cc. Male with bony tubercles on snout and at mandibular symphysis, which are feebly developed or absent in female; maxillary 3⅓ to nearly 4 in head. Anterior dorsal rays prolonged in male.   *Lophonectes*

    bb. Eyes separated by a more or less concave space (except in the very young), which is usually broad in the mature male. Male generally with one or more rostral spines.

---

[70] *Syst. Monog. Flatfish.*, 1, 1934, p. 171.

e. Less than 65 scales in lateral line. Gill-opening extending to lateral line, or ending a short distance above pectoral fin, in which case scaling of head and body is continuous below lateral line.

    f. Scales of ocular side rather feebly ctenoid. Maxillary $2\frac{1}{5}$-$3\frac{1}{2}$ in head.   *Engyprosopon*

ee. More than 74 scales in lateral line. Upper angle of gill-opening a short distance above pectoral fin or close to lateral line. Membrane joining operculum to pectoral arch scaleless.

    g. Eyes generally separated by a broad interspace (at least in male), the lower well in advance of the upper. Male nearly always with rostral and orbital spines. Teeth in 2 or more series (at least anteriorly).   *Bothus*

AA. Lateral line equally developed on both sides of body. Interorbital region narrow, concave, similar in both sexes. Scales small.   *Grammatobothus*

Arnoglossus

Eyes on left side, separated by a bony ridge or narrow concave space, the interorbital region similar in both sexes. Mouth small, jaws and dentition about equally developed on both sides. Pectoral fins unequal, that of the ocular side with longer base.

    This genus comprises several species from the eastern Atlantic, the Mediterranean, and the Indo-Pacific. Of the six species found in Australian waters three are present on the coast of Queensland.

KEY TO SPECIES IN QUEENSLAND

Based on Norman[71]

A.   Eyes separated by a ridge.

    b. About 50 scales in a longitudinal series; eye $3\frac{1}{3}$-$3\frac{3}{4}$ in head; 6-8 gill-rakers; pectoral fin with 12 rays.

    c. Dorsal profile of head not greatly arched, slightly notched in front of eyes; anal with 77-82 rays.   *waitei*

    bb. 52-56 scales in a longitudinal series; eye $4\frac{2}{3}$-5 in head; 9-10 gill-rakers; pectoral fin with 8-9 rays.   *fisoni*

AA. Interorbital region concave, its width $\frac{1}{4}$ or $\frac{1}{3}$ diameter of eye; 43-46 scales in a longitudinal series; gill-rakers "palmate".   *intermedius*

---

[71] *Biol. Res. Endeavour*, 5, pt 5, 1926, p. 240.

442. FISON'S FLOUNDER *Arnoglossus fisoni* Ogilby [Plate 60]

Arnoglossus fisoni Ogilby, Proc. Linn. Soc. N.S.Wales, 23, pt 3, 1898, p. 295.
Arnoglossus fisoni Norman, Biol. Res. Endeavour, 5, pt 5, 1926, p. 243, fig. 5.

D. 96-110; A. 77-80; C. 3-5/8-12/3-5. Colour: "Sandy grey with numerous small, faint, darker ocelli; a narrow yellowish band, parallel with the dorsal and anal profiles along the base of the interspinous rays; all the fins with smaller darker and lighter spots." (Ogilby.)

A small fish known from the coast of South Queensland and also from the Bismarck Archipelago. Only seen when taken by trawl at depths ranging from 5 to 25 fathoms. Grows to 5 inches.

OTHER SPECIES

Waite's Flounder, *A. waitei*. A species known from the east coast of Queensland and the Arafura Sea. Common in Moreton Bay. At various points along the Queensland coast it has been trawled at depths of 9 to 36 fathoms. Grows to 5 inches.

Intermediate Flounder, *A. intermedius*. A species from the Indo-Australian Archipelago and the Solomon Islands. It also has been trawled along the Queensland coast off Hervey Bay. Grows to 5 inches.

Lophonectes

Close to *Arnoglossus*, but the mouth is smaller, the length of the maxillary being $3\frac{1}{3}$ to almost 4 in that of the head. Male with bony tubercles on snout and at symphysis of lower jaw, these being smaller and more blunt in the female or absent altogether. In the males the anterior rays of the dorsal fin are greatly prolonged, whereas they are only slightly prolonged in the female. A single species from Australia and New Zealand.

443. CRESTED FLOUNDER *Lophonectes gallus* Günther [Plate 60]

Lophonectes gallus Günther, Rept Voy. Challenger, Zool., 1, 6, 1880, p. 29.
Lophonectes gallus Norman, Flatfishes (*Heterosomata*), 1934, p. 202, fig. 150.

D. 87-93; A. 71-77. Colour brownish or greyish, with or without darker markings, the most conspicuous of which are 3 blotches on the lateral line; fins with dark dots; ventrals of the ocular side generally blackish posteriorly, with a pale margin. (After Norman.)

A southern fish which ranges from off the mouth of the Murray River in South Australia northwards to Southern Queensland. Found also in Tasmania and New Zealand. Grows to 8 inches.

Engyprosopon

Eyes on left side, separated by a flat or concave space of varying width, which is usually broader in the males. Pectoral fins unequal, that of the ocular side longer. Male usually with one or more spines on the snout and orbital margins. Mouth small, teeth more or less equally developed on both sides.

A group of small flounders from the Indo-Pacific comprising about fifteen species, two being found in Queensland.

KEY TO SPECIES IN QUEENSLAND

A. Eyes close together, interorbital space a narrow groove, its width much less than ⅛ of eye diameter. No spots on caudal. *bleekeri*

AA. Eyes far apart, interorbital space concave, its width not less than ⅓ of eye diameter. Two black spots on caudal. *grandisquama*

444. SPOTTED-TAIL FLOUNDER *Engyprosopon grandisquama* (Temmick and Schlegel) [Plate 60]

Rhombus grandisquama Temmick and Schlegel, Fauna Japonica, Pisces, 1846, p. 183.
Rhomboidichthys spilurus Günther, Rept Voy. Challenger, Zool., 1, pt 6, 1880, pp. 47, 53, pl. 21, fig. A.

D. 79-89; A. 59-68. Colour light brownish, mottled with darker markings; dorsal, anal, and left ventral with small dark-brown spots; a pair of large blackish spots in middle of upper and lower edges of caudal.

Another small fish which ranges from East Africa through the Indian Ocean and Archipelago to Australia and Japan. It has been recorded from various parts of the Queensland coast, most specimens having been taken by the trawlers in depths ranging from 5 to 30 fathoms. Grows to 5½ inches.

OTHER SPECIES

Bleeker's Flounder, *E. bleekeri*. A small fish from Eastern Queensland, known only from the northern parts of the State, where several were trawled by the *Endeavour* twelve miles north-east of Bowen in 19 to 25 fathoms. Grows to 4 inches.

Bothus

Eyes on left side, separated by a flat or concave space of varying width, usually broader in the males. Pelvic of ocular side with longer base. Pectoral fins unequal, that of ocular side larger. Mouth moderate to small. Males with spines on snout and sometimes on orbital margins.

Flounders of the Mediterranean and the warmer parts of the Atlantic and Indo-Pacific regions. About fourteen species are known, one from Australia. In several of the species the males have the upper rays of the pectoral fin on the ocular side greatly prolonged.

445. PANTHER FLOUNDER *Bothus pantherinus* (Rüppell)   [Plate 60]

Rhombus pantherinus Rüppell, Atlas zu Rüppell, Reise (Senck. Nat. Ges.), Fische, 1830-1, p. 121.
Platophrys pantherinus Bleeker, Atlas Ichth., 6, 1870, p. 11, pl. 233, fig. 3.

Mottled Flounder (Sth Africa).

D. 85-95; A. 64-71. Colour brownish, with paler and darker spots, blotches, rings, or ocelli; usually a large dark blotch on middle of straight portion of lateral line; pectoral with brown spots, with or without irregular dark cross-bars.

This fish ranges from East Africa and the Red Sea through the Indian Ocean and Archipelago to Australia and the Pacific. In Australian waters it is known only from the far north of Queensland and in Torres Strait, where it is quite common. Grows to 9 inches in Queensland waters but is said to reach 18 inches in South Africa.

Grammatobothus

Interorbital region narrow, concave, similar in both sexes. Teeth uniserial in both jaws, slightly enlarged anteriorly. Anterior rays of dorsal fin somewhat prolonged in both sexes. Scales small, ctenoid on ocular side, cycloid on blind side. Lateral line equally developed on both sides.

Three species from the Indo-Pacific region, two of which are found in Queensland.

KEY TO SPECIES IN QUEENSLAND

A.   Depth about 1⅔ in the length; dorsal with 80-86 rays, second to fifth or sixth rays prolonged; anal with 64-67 rays.   *polyophthalmus*

AA. Depth 1⅘-2 in the length; dorsal with 88-91 rays, the third or third and fourth rays prolonged and pinniform; anal with 72-76 rays.   *pennatus*

446. FEATHER-FIN FLOUNDER *Grammatobothus pennatus* (Ogilby)
[Plate 60]

Platophrys pennata Ogilby, Mem. Qld Mus., 2, 1913, p. 83.
Grammatobothus pennatus Norman, Biol. Res. Endeavour, 5, pt 5, 1926, p. 255, fig. 7.

D. 88-91; A. 72-76. Colour brownish, with 3 prominent black ocelli, forming a triangle, the one on the middle of the straight portion of the lateral line being much darker and more prominent. A number of smaller and less distinct spots and markings on the head and body are arranged in more or less regular series.

A species known only from eastern Queensland, where several have been trawled at various points in depths ranging from 19 to 33 fathoms. Grows to 8 inches.

OTHER SPECIES

Three-spot Flounder, *G. polyophthalmus*. A somewhat similarly coloured fish, this is a small species from the Indo-Australian Archipelago which is also known from North Queensland. Grows to 6 inches.

Family **Pleuronectidae**

Eyes on right side, except in reversed examples in certain species. Dorsal fin extending on head, all fin-rays articulated. Mouth terminal, small or large. Lower jaw somewhat prominent. Teeth in jaws may be nearly equally developed on both sides, but often more so on the blind side. Preoperculum with free margin.

Of the five sub-families contained in the Pleuronectidae, one, Samarinae, is found in Queensland.

Sub-family SAMARINAE

Dorsal fin extending forward on the snout below the nasal organ on the blind side. Pelvic fins short-based or somewhat elongate. Lateral line rudimentary and scarcely apparent on the blind side of the body.

Four genera from the tropical Indo-Pacific, one genus being found in Queensland.

Samaris

Members of this genus are characterized by having the dorsal fin, which commences on the blind side in front of the eye, with its anterior rays greatly prolonged and filamentous. All the caudal rays are simple.

About five species from the Indo-Pacific, one of which is found in Queensland.

447. COCKATOO FLOUNDER *Samaris cacatuae* (Ogilby) [Plate 60]

Arnoglossus cacatuae Ogilby, New Fish. Qld Coast, 20th Dec. 1910, p. 130 (a suppressed publication).
Samaris cacatuae McCulloch and Whitley, Rec. Austr. Mus., 14, 1925, p. 348, pl. 49.

D. 13/73; A. 59. Colour lavender, dotted with black and with three series of rather obscure black spots more or less completely encircling a central lavender spot; blind side white; dorsal crest tawny-yellow; dorsal and anal fins lavender, with a series of obscure darker spots along their bases and a dusky basal blotch posteriorly; caudal with faint darker cross-bands; pectoral pale, the rays with alternate darker and lighter rings, the membrane of the first ray and a spot near the tip of the third blackish. (After Ogilby.)

A unique fish which was trawled by the *Endeavour* twenty miles north-east of Gloucester Head, Queensland, in 35 fathoms. Length 6¾ inches.

Family **Soleidae**: True Soles

Eyes on right or left side, according to genera. No spiny fin-rays. Ventrals small, one or both sometimes wanting. Caudal fin free or confluent with dorsal and anal. Pectoral fins small or wanting. Mouth small, terminal or inferior, much twisted towards the eyed side, lower jaw not prominent. Jaws with minute teeth on blind side and feebly developed or absent on eyed side. Lateral line, if present, is straight, or there may be 2 to 3 lateral lines developed.

A very large family of small or moderately sized fishes inhabiting all temperate and tropical seas, usually living on sandy or muddy bottoms at moderate depths. Some of the species enter the muddy estuaries; others, during the earlier stages of their existence, penetrate many miles up streams into fresh water, remaining there until mature, after which they move down to the sea to spawn. In Queensland there is a purely freshwater sole which, through natural barriers has been prevented from access to the sea for a very long period and has been compelled to adapt itself to an entirely freshwater existence.[72]

All the species are valued food-fishes, with flesh of excellent flavour. Unfortunately the supply to the markets is very small and erratic, the fishes seen there being mainly strays taken in the nets of fishermen when they are capturing other species. Many of the soles seldom or never take a hook. A popular method of capturing them in the southern States is by means of the spear. On calm, clear mornings, or at night with the aid of a torch, the fisherman floats slowly in a boat over the shallow flats where the soles abound. The disturbed fish endeavours to settle in the mud and in so doing raises a tell-tale cloud into which the fisherman plunges the spear, impaling the fish. In Queensland the art of fish-spearing appears to be practised only by the aborigines, who, needless to say, are experts. In British waters the sole is caught exclusively by means of the trawl in depths usually not less than 25 fathoms.

Five genera are found in Queensland waters.

KEY TO GENERA IN QUEENSLAND

A.   Dorsal and anal fins free from the caudal.

    b. Pectoral fins present.   *Solea*

    bb. Pectoral fins absent.

      c. A second lateral line on blind side along upper profile of neck. An open pore above base of each dorsal and anal ray. Right ventral with a long base, connected to anal.   *Pardachirus*

---

[72] *Synaptura selheimi* Macleay (*Proc. Linn. Soc. N.S.Wales*, 7, pt 1, 23rd May 1882, p. 71), Palmer River, North Queensland.

cc. No accessory lateral line on blind side. No open pores above base of each dorsal and anal ray. Ventrals short-based, symmetrical or almost so, free from anal. *Aseraggodes*

AA. Dorsal and anal fins united with caudal.

d. Ventral fins not united by membrane, right ventral free from anal. Pectorals present, well developed or rudimentary. *Synaptura*

dd. Ventral fins more or less united by membrane. Right ventral completely joined to first anal ray. *Phyllichthys*

Solea

Eyes on right side. One straight lateral line. Scales ctenoid on both sides. Dorsal and anal free from caudal. Pectorals present, well and equally developed. Dorsal originating on snout.

A genus of small fishes, few in species and of little value as food. One from Queensland waters.

448. TIGER SOLE *Solea heterorhinos* Bleeker [Plate 61]

Solea heterorhinos Bleeker, Act. Soc. Sci. Indo-Neerl., 1, 1856, p. 64; and Atlas Ichth., 6, 1866-72, p. 17, pl. 240, fig. 2.

D. 88-98; A. 80-87; L. l. 110-120. Colour rich brownish-olive, with irregular vertical bands, blotches, and spots edged with black, continued on to the vertical fins, which are often bordered with black or have a submargined band of black.

An Indo-Pacific fish recorded in Australian waters from Torres Strait. Grows to 5½ inches.

Pardachirus

Eyes on right side. Dorsal and anal rays separate from caudal. Scales feebly ctenoid, those along vertical fins smaller and cycloid. A straight lateral line on both sides, in addition to which there is a second one on the blind side along the upper profile of the neck, commencing on snout. Mouth strongly contorted. Each dorsal and anal ray with a pore at its base. Pectorals wanting. Ventrals unsymmetrical.

Small soles, thick-set in form, inhabiting the littoral waters of the Indian and western Pacific oceans. About four species, two of which are found in Queensland.

A. Scales of head and sometimes of anterior trunk ctenoid, ocelli of coloured side each with a dark central spot; back without black blotches.   *pavoninus*

AA. Scales everywhere ctenoid; ocelli of coloured side usually without central spot; back with three series of black blotches.   *hedleyi*

449. PEACOCK SOLE *Pardachirus pavoninus* Lacépède.   [Colour-plate 63]

Achirus pavoninus Lacépède, Hist. Nat. Poiss., 4, 1802, pp. 658, 660.
Illustration by G. Coates.

D. 63-68; A. 49-52; L. l. 85-90. Colour yellowish-brown or rich coffee-brown, the head and body with numerous larger and smaller rounded or irregularly shaped white spots, edged and minutely dotted with dark brown, and with a round black dot in the centre; vertical fins with numerous whitish ocelli.

A species from the waters of North Queensland and found also in the Malay Archipelago, the Andaman Islands, the Pacific, and southern Japan. Grows to at least $8\frac{1}{2}$ inches.

OTHER SPECIES

Southern Peacock Sole, *P. hedleyi*. Ranges from Moreton Bay, South Queensland, southwards to Port Jackson, New South Wales. In this species there are 3 series of black blotches on the back, and the ocelli are usually without the black central spots. Grows to 8 inches.

Aseraggodes

Eyes on right side. Dorsal and anal separate from caudal. One straight lateral line on each side. Ventrals short-based, symmetrical or nearly so. Dorsal beginning on snout. Scales ctenoid on both sides. Pectoral fins absent. Head small, snout without hook. Head everywhere scaly, except the snout of the eyed side and a narrow stripe on the blind side, from the snout to the apex of the branchial aperture, which is densely clothed with skinny filaments.

A genus of flat-fishes distributed from the Arabian Sea and the Indian Ocean to Japan and Australia and to Bougainville Island in the South Seas. Most of the species are found in deep waters, and one is known from fresh water. Several species are known, and four are found in Australian seas, two of them in Queensland.

464

A. 96-104 scales in a longitudinal series; body with dark
    cross-bars.   *macleayanus*

AA. 68-75 scales in a longitudinal series; body with small
    dark spots; no cross-bars.   *melanostictus*

450. NARROW-BANDED SOLE *Aseraggodes macleayanus* (Ramsay)

[Plate 61]

Solea macleayana Ramsay, Proc. Linn. Soc. N.S.Wales, 5, pt 4, 1881, p. 462.
Aseraggodes macleayanus Ogilby, Mem. Qld Mus., 5, 1916, p. 137, pl. 15.

D. 62-66; A. 48-52; L. l. 90-100. Colour lavender-grey, with 32 to 36 narrow irregular brown cross-bars on head and body; membranous parts of all fins darker than the rays.

J. D. Ogilby, writing on this species,[73] stated that these soles are "occasionally found in considerable numbers, especially during the spring months, when they come in apparently from the open sea in shoals, all being of large size and about the same length; these school fish are very thick and firm and of delicious flavour, but are without rudiments of spawn."

Ogilby stated that this shoreward movement is preparatory to spawning and is most noticeable off the mouths of such considerable rivers as the Shoalhaven and Hunter, where the trawler *Thetis* took spawning fishes at not less than three stations.

He concluded by stating: "In the spring of the year the fishes, which have spent the winter months in moderately deep water, begin to draw inshore, and this movement doubtless continues with more or less regularity throughout the summer, during which time the ova is gradually ripening, that of the individuals which make their way shorewards earliest coming to maturity sooner than that of the later arrivals. As the time for shedding the spawn approaches, the fishes collect in the vicinity of river mouths, where they shed their pelagic ova, after which operation they retire once more to deeper water to recoup. The young fishes, as soon as the yolk-sac is absorbed, make their way into the estuaries, and gradually work up these even to far beyond the limit of the tide."

This sole is found on the coasts of New South Wales and South Queensland, its range being from Shoalhaven Bight in the south to Moreton Bay in the north. Grows to 11 inches.

OTHER SPECIES

Dotted Sole, *A. melanostictus*. A small species which has been recorded from Queensland on an example captured off Gladstone. It is found also in the Solomon Islands. Grows to $5\frac{1}{2}$ inches.

---

[73] *Edib. Fish. Crust. N.S.Wales*, 1893, p. 159.

Synaptura

Eyes on right side. One straight lateral line on both sides. Scales ctenoid on ocular side, cycloid or ctenoid on blind side. Lower lip fringed. Dorsal and anal united with caudal. Pectorals short, well developed or rudimentary. Ventrals short, broad-based, free from each other and from the anal.

Soles from the Indian and western Pacific oceans. Five species are found in Queensland.

KEY TO SPECIES IN QUEENSLAND

A. Interorbital region distinct, scaly.

   b. Right pectoral fin longer than diameter of eye. Colour blackish, no cross-bars.

     c. Body deep, its depth 2½ in the total length; eye smaller, 8.6 in head, the upper well in advance of the lower.   *setifer*

     cc. Body more elongate, its depth 2⅓-2⅛ in the total length; eye larger, 6-6.8 in head, the upper slightly in advance of the lower.   *orientalis*

   bb. Right pectoral fin shorter than diameter of eye. Body with numerous dark cross-bars.   *fasciata*

AA. Interorbital region naked, or the eyes contiguous.

   d. 70-81 scales in a longitudinal series; head 4¾-5 in the length. Colour brownish, with groups of black dermal filaments.   *muelleri*

   dd. 90-130 scales in a longitudinal series; head 6¼-6½ in the length. Colour light brown, with 20-24 dark cross-bands.   *craticula*

451. BLACK SOLE *Synaptura orientalis* (Bloch and Schneider) [Plate 61]

Pleuronectes orientalis Bloch and Schneider, Syst. Ichth., 1801, p. 157.
Synaptura nigra Waite, Mem. Austr. Mus., 4, pt 1, 1899, p. 125, pl. 30.

D. 61-65; A. 44-48; P. dextr. 7-8; P. sin. 5; L. l. 75-85. Colour blackish or olive-brown, sometimes with small yellowish or creamy-white spots; blind side whitish, clouded with pale yellowish-brown, the vertical fins broadly stained straw-colour or bright orange.

The Black Sole is a lover of muddy estuaries and bays rather than of sandy areas. It rarely if ever takes a bait, and those seen in the Queensland fish market have been caught by the net fishermen. One of the favourite methods in the south of securing these valuable food-fishes is by means of the spear. The species is wide-ranging: in Australian waters it is found on the coasts of Queensland and New South Wales, where it is common; from North

Q

Queensland it ranges to the Northern Territory, the Malay Archipelago, the Indian Ocean and the China Seas. Grows to 14 inches. A good food-fish.

OTHER SPECIES

Tufted Sole, *S. setifer*. Ranges from North Queensland and the Northern Territory to the East Indies and Singapore. It is frequently captured in seine nets in shallow water over the mud-flats. Grows to 8 inches.

Many-banded Sole, *S. fasciata*. This species frequents the waters of Moreton Bay and northern New South Wales. In the latter locality it has been trawled in 28 fathoms off the Richmond River. Not commonly met with in Queensland except when taken by trawl. Grows to 8 inches.

Mueller's Sole, *S. muelleri*. A species from the Arafura Sea and the east coast of Queensland, where it ranges as far south as the Cumberland Group. Little is known of it. Grows to 9 inches.

Zebra Sole, *S. craticula*. A handsome fish known only from two examples captured off Bowen, North Queensland. Grows to at least 6 inches.

Phyllichthys

Australian soles allied to *Synaptura* but differing in having the ventral fins more or less united by membrane, and the right ventral completely joined to the first anal ray. The vent is placed in front of the anal fin, but slightly to the left of the median line. One species in Queensland.

452. SHARP-HEADED SOLE *Phyllichthys sclerolepis* (Macleay)
[Colour-plate 63; Plate 61]

Synaptura sclerolepis Macleay, Proc. Linn. Soc. N.S.Wales, 2, 1878, p. 363.
Phyllichthys sclerolepis McCulloch, Mem. Qld. Mus., 5, 1916, p. 66, pl. 9, fig. 2, text-fig. 4.
Colour illustration by G. Coates.

D. 84; A. 71; V. 4; L. l. 93; L. tr. 30/35. Colour dark olive-green or dark brown, the fins lighter edged, being orange or pinkish in life; numerous spots and blotches over both body and fins.

Found in the waters of the Northern Territory and Queensland as far south as Moreton Bay. Grows to 11 inches.

Family **Cynoglossidae: Tongue Soles**

The tongue soles are distinguished from the true soles (Soleidae) chiefly by having their eyes on the left side of the body. The eyes are very small and usually close or nearly in contact, not separated by a ridge. The lips are fringed or entire. The mouth is unsymmetrical, strongly curved, the snout being hooked and overhanging the mouth-opening. The scales are usually ctenoid. Lateral lines 1 to 3 on the ocular side, sometimes absent; none, 1, or 2 may be present on the blind side. The dorsal and anal fins are confluent with the pointed caudal. Pectorals absent, and only the left ventral is present, it being free or connected with the anal.

A large family of mainly tropical fishes inhabiting the Indian Ocean and the Indo-Australian Archipelago to Australia and the Western Pacific. They are usually found on sandy bottoms in shallow waters or at moderate depths.

The name Tongue Sole has been bestowed on account of the fish's resemblance to an animal's tongue.

Tongue Soles are divided into several genera, two being found in Queensland.

KEY TO GENERA IN QUEENSLAND

A.   Lips on the ocular side with a row of fringed tentacles.   *Paraplagusia*

AA. Lips not fringed.   *Cynoglossus*

Paraplagusia: Fringe-lip Tongue Soles

Eyes on left side. Scales ctenoid on both sides. Two or three lateral lines on ocular side, none on blind side or one without pores. Mouth unsymmetrical, strongly curved, the snout hooked and overhanging the mouth-opening. Lips of ocular side with fringed tentacles. Pectorals absent. Only the left ventral developed. Dorsal, anal, and caudal confluent.

This genus is readily recognized by the fringed lips. There are two species in Queensland waters.

KEY TO SPECIES IN QUEENSLAND

A.   Two lateral lines on the ocular side; fringes on the lower
     lip generally branched.   *unicolor*

AA. Three lateral lines on ocular side; fringes on lower
     lip short and generally unbranched.   *guttata*

453. LEMON TONGUE SOLE *Paraplagusia unicolor* (Macleay)   [Plate 61]

Plagusia unicolor Macleay, Proc. Linn. Soc. N.S.Wales, 6, 1882, p. 138.
Illustration by F. Olsen after McCulloch and Whitley.

D. 113; A. 87; C. 8. Colour pale yellowish-brown, with round spots of an even lighter shade; fins profusely ornamented with brown and milk-white spots; bluish-white below.

A common sole on sandy bottoms in shallow waters. It ranges from the Wide Bay district in South Queensland down the coast of New South Wales, but is more common in the former locality. Found also at Lord Howe Island. Grows to 13 inches.

OTHER SPECIES

Spotted Tongue Sole, *P. guttata*. A fairly common fish on the mud-flats along the coasts of the Northern Territory and Queensland as far south as Moreton Bay. It is closely related to *P. unicolor*. Grows to 11 inches.

Cynoglossus

Gill-openings very narrow. Eyes on left side. Anterior portion of snout prolonged into a hook; mouth unsymmetrical. Lips not fringed. Teeth minute, on right side only. Vertical fins confluent. Pectorals absent. Scales ctenoid or cycloid. Two or three lateral lines on ocular side.

Of the numerous species of this genus, inhabitants of the waters of most warm seas, four are found in Queensland.

KEY TO SPECIES IN QUEENSLAND

A. Two lateral lines on both sides of body.

    b. 14-15 interlinear scales on the ocular side.   *bilineatus*

AA. Two or three lateral lines on the ocular side, none on the blind side.

    c. Two nostrils; rostral hook not extending to below eye; 7-13 interlinear scales.

    d. Scales ctenoid on both sides of body; 9-13 interlinear scales; 3 lateral lines on the ocular side.   *maccullochi*

    dd. Scales cycloid on the blind side; 7-8 interlinear scales; 2 lateral lines on the ocular side.   *ogilbyi*

    cc. A single nostril in front of lower eye; rostral hook extending to below eye; 17-18 interlinear scales.   *macrophthalmus*

454. TWO-LINED TONGUE SOLE *Cynoglossus bilineatus* (Lacépède)
[Colour-plate 64]

Achirus bilineatus (not of Bloch) Lacépède, Hist. Nat. Poiss., 4, 1802, pp. 659, 663.
Illustration by G. Coates.

D. 102-112; A. 82-97; L. 1. 86-98. Colour uniform brownish, the fins lighter.

A large and very common species found in the waters of the east coast of North Queensland. George Coates of Townsville states that it is very common along the mainland beaches and is usually taken in the fishermen's nets. Found also in the Indo-Pacific, the Philippines, Japan, and the Indian Ocean to the Red Sea. Grows to 16 inches.

OTHER SPECIES

McCulloch's Tongue Sole, *C. maccullochi*. A species known only from Lindeman and Hummocky islands, Queensland. In the latter locality the holotype was dredged by the *Endeavour* in 14 to 16 fathoms. Grows to 7½ inches.

Ogilby's Tongue Sole, *C. ogilbyi*. A rare fish so far known only from the unique holotype from southern Queensland. Total length 7¼ inches.

Long-nosed Tongue Sole, *C. macrophthalmus*. Another unique fish, known only from the holotype which was trawled by the *Endeavour* in 20 fathoms. off Bustard Head Light, Queensland. Total length 10¾ inches.

Order **DISCOCEPHALI: SUCKING-FISHES** or **REMORAS**

Body elongate. Head flattened, on which is a powerful sucking-disc which occupies the whole of the top of the head; this disc has been formed by the modification of the spinous dorsal fin, which, instead of standing erect, has its spines much modified and deflected to right and left into a horizontal position, forming flat plates and surrounded by a continuous edge, which forms the margin of the disc (see Plate 61).

By means of such structure the fish is able to attach itself to any flat surface, a slight raising of the plates creating a series of vacuum chambers and enabling the fish to take a strong hold on the object. To dislodge the disc it is necessary to push the fish forward, thus lowering the plates and breaking the vacuum. The greater the pull backwards the firmer will the disc adhere, until it is possible to pull the fish asunder, the disc still remaining fast. This has been observed with a fresh dead fish; the living fish would of course let go when the strain became too great.

Sucking-fishes have the habit of attaching themselves to sharks, rays, large fishes, and turtles, or to ships and other floating objects, thus transporting themselves with a minimum of effort. They do not always attach themselves externally to the bodies of their hosts—sometimes they have been found beneath the gill-covers of swordfishes, sunfishes, and other large fishes, and even inside the mouths of giant devil rays.

Besides being a very good means of transport, the association with its host very likely provides a haven of shelter for the sucking-fish from its enemies and also ensures its presence at its companion's meals.

No doubt they are able to obtain a plentiful supply of food from the fragments of their host's meal, for they themselves are carnivorous. They do no harm to their host, nor do the fishes or other creatures to which they attach themselves show any signs of resentment at their presence.

Sucking-fishes are powerful swimmers and may frequently be seen to leave their host and to change their position whilst travelling. All the species are tropical and, though in some instances very common, are seldom seen by the casual observer. The flesh is quite edible. A single family.

Family **Echeneidae**

The single family, Echeneidae, is a small one of only about six genera and about eight species. Four of the genera are found in Queensland.

A. Pectoral rays stiff and ossified.   *Rhombochirus*

AA. Pectoral rays soft and flexible.

      b. Body and tail slender. Pectorals long and pointed.

      c. 21-28 laminae in disc. Caudal with the median rays produced in the young, emarginated in the adult.   *Echeneis*

      bb. Body and tail short and robust. Pectorals short and rounded.

      d. 29-32 rays in soft dorsal fin. Caudal slightly double concave.   *Remoropsis*

      dd. 22-25 rays in soft dorsal fin. Caudal deeply concave.   *Remora*

Echeneis

455. SLENDER SUCKING-FISH *Echeneis neucrates* Linnaeus

[Colour-plate 64]

Echeneis neucrates Linnaeus, Syst. Nat., 10th ed., 1758, p. 261; 12th ed., 1766, p. 446.
Illustration by G. Coates.

Remora, Shark-sucker, Sucker-fish (South Africa); Pilot-fish (North Queensland).

Laminae in disc 21-28; disc is more than twice as long as broad; soft D. 32-40; A. 32-37. Colour brownish above and below (as is usual in this family); sides with broad darker stripe edged with whitish and extending through eye to snout; pectorals and ventrals black; dorsal and anal edged white anteriorly; caudal blackish with whitish edges.

A very common fish found almost exclusively on the sharks. It grows to a length of 38 inches and is found in all warm seas.

These fishes were commonly used in Torres Strait by the natives when turtle-hunting. A strong rope was attached to the tail of a large sucking-fish and the fish was carried in the canoe. When a turtle was sighted asleep on the surface the sucking-fish was released as close as possible to the quarry. It would fasten itself firmly upon the luckless creature, and the native was then able to swim along the rope and secure the creature, the hold of the sucking-fish being sufficient to retard its progress.

Remora

456. SHORT SUCKING-FISH *Remora remora* (Linnaeus)   [Plate 61]

Echeneis remora Linnaeus, Syst. Nat., 10th ed., 1758, p. 260; 12th ed., 1766, p. 446.
Echeneis remora Day, Fish. Gt Brit. and Irel., 1, 1880-4, p. 108, pl. 39, fig. 2.

Remora, Shark-sucker, Lootsman, Sucker-fish (South Africa).

Laminae in disc 16-20; soft D. 22-25; A. 23-25; disc about half as wide as long. Colour blackish or brownish, nearly uniform above and below.

A short, thick-set sucking-fish not so commonly seen as *E. neucrates*. Found in all warm and temperate seas. It is usually attached to large sharks or sea turtles. Grows to about 18 inches.

Rhombochirus

Represented in Queensland waters by the Bony-finned Sucking-fish, *R. osteochir* (Cuvier), a wide-ranging fish found in all seas. It may be distinguished by the very long and large sucking-disc which extends well beyond the short, broad, and bony-like pectoral fins. Found chiefly attached to the marlins and swordfishes. Grows to 16 inches.

Remoropsis

One species in Queensland, *R. pallidus* (Schlegel), a small pale-coloured fish of a yellowish-buff colour. To date the known Queensland specimens have been taken from marlins in North Queensland by G. Coates. Grows to 8 inches.

Order **PLECTOGNATHI:**
TRIGGER-FISHES, FILE-FISHES, LEATHER-JACKETS, BOX-FISHES, SUNFISHES, TOADOS, PORCUPINE-FISHES, TRIPLE-SPINES, COW-FISHES, TURRET-FISHES

Opercular bones more or less reduced. Gill-openings very restricted at sides. Premaxillaries and maxillaries often firmly united. Pectoral arch suspended from cranium. Pelvic bones, if present, more or less completely co-ossified. No ribs. Spinous dorsal small or absent. Ventrals reduced or wanting. Jaws strong; teeth separate or united into a "beak". Skin usually with scales reduced, as spines, rough shields, or bony plates.

Fishes mainly inhabiting tropical waters, most species inactive and depending upon their rough skin or bony or spinous armature for their protection.

The Plectognathi is composed of the sub-orders Balistoidea, Ostraciontoidea, and Tetraodontoidea.

472

A.   Jaws with distinct teeth, not united. Scales absent or modified, either as small spines or frequently enlarged as bony plates, coalesced to form a hard covering.   BALISTOIDEA

AA. Jaws with distinct teeth, not united. Body encased in large juxtaposed bony plates, mostly hexagonal and immovably united, the jaws, fins, and tail only free.   OSTRACIONTOIDEA

AAA. Each of the jaws modified into a sort of beak, with median suture, each with an enamel-like covering and without distinct teeth; scales rhomboid or spiniform, with or without root-like insertions, or skin may be naked; spinous dorsal wanting.   TETRAODONTOIDEA

Sub-order BALISTOIDEA: Triple-spines, Trigger-fishes, File-fishes, and Leather-jackets

Plectognathus fishes with bodies of normal fish-like shape, fairly deep and mostly compressed. Scales may be absent or rough or spinigerous or frequently enlarged and coalesced to form hard plates. Teeth normal, not united. Gill-opening much reduced. Fin-spines may be rudimentary or reduced, but there is usually a separate anterior dorsal fin of 1 to 6 spines, the first much the longest, usually with a special arrangement of the bones which enables the fish to lock the fin in an erect position.

Fishes mostly of the tropical and sub-tropical seas, some inhabiting shallow bays and estuaries.

Five families comprise this sub-order, all being represented in Queensland waters.

KEY TO FAMILIES

A.   Ventral fin represented each by a large spine. First dorsal fin with 3-6 strong spines.   TRIACANTHIDAE

AA. Ventral fins obsolete, or the pair represented by a single spine at the end of the long pelvic bone.

    b. Body covered with large bony rough plates, forming a coat of mail.   BALISTIDAE

    bb. Body covered with minute scales, their edges spinescent, forming a smooth, rough, or velvety surface.

    c. Gill-openings before the eyes. A long barbel on chin.   ANACANTHIDAE

    cc. Gill-openings beneath or behind the eyes. No barbel on chin.

    d. Pelvics united to one spiny process.   MONACANTHIDAE

    dd. Pelvics absent (in adult).   ALUTERIDAE

Family **Triacanthidae**: Triple-Spines or Horn-Fishes

A small family of tropical shore-fishes of few genera and species, their distribution being chiefly Indo-Pacific, one of them American.

Their bodies are compressed laterally, with a similarly flattened, somewhat elongate snout, and covered with small or minute scales more or less spinigerous. Their small mouths, which open only slightly, have the teeth separate and conical or incisor-like, and in one or two series in each jaw. The spinous dorsal fin is composed of 3 to 6 strong spines, the first one by far the largest. The soft dorsal is rather long and low and similar to the anal. The ventral fins are reduced to a strong spine which is attached to the pelvic bone and in length is nearly as long, or as long, as the first dorsal spine.

The triple-spines are fishes of no economic value. Herre,[74] writing upon them in the Philippine Islands, states: "They are all small and unimportant fishes, excessively abundant at times but rejected as food in most regions. However, the one peculiar to Japan is highly prized in the region about Nagasaki. In the members of this group the percentage of waste is so high that even if their flesh is not positively harmful it is so scanty and unpalatable that it is rejected. In the provinces I have seen fishermen throw away hundreds at a time, taken from their fish corrals. In Manila where the struggle for food is much more severe they are sometimes seen in the markets, mixed with other small fishes. Poor people sometimes seine them in considerable numbers in the bay along the sea wall beside Dewey Boulevard and prepare them in the following manner: The still flopping fish is grasped in both hands and given a quick hard transverse pull, which tears the fish in two directly behind the dorsal and ventral spines. The anterior half is thrown away and the skin is removed by a single jerk from the posterior half, thus yielding about two bites of meat."

The family is represented by one genus and a single species in Queensland.

457. BLACK-FINNED TRIPLE-SPINE *Triacanthus biaculeatus* (Bloch)
[Colour-plate 64]

Balistes biaculeatus Bloch, Nat. ausl. Fische, 2, 1786, p. 17.
Illustration by G. Coates.

Silver Leather-jacket (Nth Qld); Queensland Triple-spine (Qld).

D. 5-6/22-23; A. 18; P. 16. Colour pale lettuce-green above, passing gradually into greenish-white below; spinous dorsal with a large black spot which extends well on the base of the first large spine, all but the edge of the first membrane, all the second spine, and over most of the second membrane; other spines and membranes greyish; edge of first membrane yellow; first spine with its upper half black and a white area between it and basal spot; soft dorsal

---

[74] *Phil. Journ. Sci.*, 25, no. 4, Oct. 1924, p. 417.

pale grey, tinged with yellow terminally; pectoral yellow; anal similar to soft dorsal; caudal yellow, dusky basally; eye, pupil black, surrounded brownish-red.

A common species along the whole coastline of Queensland and the Northern Territory. Stragglers are occasionally taken in New South Wales. In writing on the occurrence of the fish in the Northern Territory, Paradice and Whitley[75] note that in the Sir Edward Pellew Islands and at Darwin it is "a common species caught by net on sandy beaches. In the living fish the dorsal spine is produced as a fine filament almost the length of the fish. This filament is very brittle and specimens seldom reach an institution with it intact."

The species is also found in the East Indies, India, and China. Grows to $9\frac{1}{2}$ inches.

Family **Balistidae: Trigger-fishes**

Body oblong or ovate, moderately compressed. Eye near occiput. Mouth small, terminal, low; jaws short, one series of separate incisor-like teeth in each. Preorbital very deep. Chin without barbel. Lateral line obscure or wanting. Gill-openings small and slit-like, above or in front of pectorals, and not before eyes. Body covered with large bony rough plates or scutes of various forms, but not forming an immovable carapace. In some species there are rows of spines or tubercles on the sides of the tail. Two dorsal fins, the spinous of 2 to 3 spines, the first spine highest and very strong, the second locking it when erected. Second dorsal remote from first and composed of many soft rays. Anal similar. Ventrals composed of a single stout thick spine at the end of the very long and usually movable pelvic bone.

Carnivorous or partly herbivorous shore-fishes of the tropical seas, rather large in size but seldom used as food on account of the fact that the flesh of many is always more or less poisonous. Day[76] states: "Eating the flesh of these fishes occasions in places symptoms of most virulent poisoning. Dr Meunier, at the Mauritius, considers that the poisonous flesh acts primarily on the nervous tissue of the stomach, occasioning violent spasms of that organ, and shortly afterwards of all the muscles of the body. The frame becomes racked with spasms, the tongue thickened, the eye fixed, the breathing laborious, and the patient expires in a paroxysm of extreme suffering. The first remedy to be given is a strong emetic and subsequently oils and demulcents to allay irritability."

The name Trigger-fish is bestowed on account of the peculiar locking mechanism of the dorsal spines. Trigger-fishes feed upon crustaceans and molluscs, crushing the shells of the latter with their powerful teeth. They are said to create great havoc on the beds of pearl-oysters.

[75] *Mem. Qld Mus.*, 9, pt 1, April 1927, p. 94.
[76] In *Fish. India*, 1878, p. 686.

KEY TO GENERA

A. Gill-opening with a number of enlarged bony plates or scutes behind it. Pelvic spine freely movable.

   b. A deep groove before the eye, below the nostril.

     c. Caudal peduncle compressed.

       d. Cheeks normally scaly.   *Balistes*

       dd. Cheeks naked anteriorly, with small scales in separate elevated rows.   *Pseudobalistes*

     cc. Caudal peduncle depressed.   *Abalistes*

   bb. Eye without preocular groove.   *Balistapus*

AA. Gill-opening with only ordinary scales behind it, no enlarged bony plates or scutes. Pelvic spine scarcely movable, its surface scaled.   *Canthidermis*

Balistes

A groove before the eye. Enlarged rounded plates behind the gill-opening. Soft dorsal and anal fins elevated in front. Caudal lobes more or less produced; caudal peduncle compressed. Four species occur in Queensland waters.

KEY TO SPECIES IN QUEENSLAND

A. Sides of tail without spines or tubercles.

   b. Colour brownish or blackish, with yellowish or whitish fins; soft dorsal and anal narrowly edged with blackish.   *vidua*

   bb. Sides of tail with several spines or tubercles, more or less set in rows.

     c. 2-3 rows of large, pale-yellow spots on lower half of body.   *conspicillum*

     cc. No large spots present, though a small dark spot may be present on each scale.

       d. A "bridle" mark, consisting of a yellow stripe, bordered below by a white one, from gape of mouth backward towards base of pectoral, joined to its fellow on opposite side by a white throat-bar.   *capistratus*

       dd. No "bridle" mark from mouth to pectoral base.

         e. Brownish or blackish; soft dorsal and anal yellow or white; a yellow ring behind lips; caudal fin with pale-yellowish crescent terminally.   *chrysopterus*

458. BIG-SPOTTED TRIGGER-FISH *Balistes conspicillum*
Bloch and Schneider [Colour-plate 65]

Balistes conspicillum Bloch and Schneider, Syst. Ichth., 1801, p. 474.
Illustration by G. Coates.

Mongara Kawahagi or Spotted Skin Peeler, and Komoniuwo or Blotched-fish (Japan).

D. 3/25-26; A. 22-23. Colour blackish or brownish, with very large round yellow spots on lower half of body; a lighter greyish patch on back between dorsals, in which there are numerous dark spots; a greyish-white band across snout from eye to eye; mouth with the black lips set in an orange patch followed by a black line and then one of orange-yellow; spinous dorsal black with a yellow patch at its base anteriorly; soft dorsal and anal dirty-white with a line basally; caudal peduncle orange; caudal with a black band at its base and terminally separated by a broad green band medianally; pectoral with a narrow scarlet line across its base.

This strikingly handsome species, which frequents rocky situations on the coast of Queensland, is not commonly met with in these waters. It ranges through the Indo-Pacific region and attains to a length of 13 inches.

OTHER SPECIES

White-tailed Trigger-fish, *B. vidua*. Apparently rarely seen in Queensland waters; has been recorded from Torres Strait, North Queensland. It ranges to the East Indies, Polynesia, Micronesia, and Hawaii. Grows to 12 inches.

Bridled Trigger-fish, *B. capistratus*. A common, dull-coloured species found everywhere along the Queensland coast. Wide-ranging, being found throughout the Indo-Pacific region to the east coast of Africa. Grows to 15 inches.

Black Trigger-fish, *B. chrysopterus*. Occasionally found on the Queensland coast from north to south. It ranges through the Indo-Pacific region to the Red Sea. Grows to 12 inches.

Pseudobalistes

A groove before the eye. Enlarged plates behind gill-openings. Soft dorsal and anal elevated in front. Cheeks naked anteriorly, posteriorly with scales in horizontal lines. Species few, one in Queensland.

459. YELLOW-SPOTTED TRIGGER-FISH *Pseudobalistes fuscus*
(Bloch and Schneider) [Plate 62]

Balistes fuscus Bloch and Schneider, Syst. Ichth., 1801, p. 471.
Balistes fuscus Günther, Journ. Mus. Godef., 9, pt 17, 1910, p. 442, pl. 168.

D. 3/24-27; A. 22-24. General colour bright bluish-purple, each scale with a yellow spot; snout, chin, and throat violet, the upper lip with 2 yellow lines, the anterior one ceasing at gape of mouth, the posterior one extending down on sides to level of chin; spinous dorsal with membranes bluish and with yellow spots; soft dorsal purplish-blue with yellow spots and with a wide pale-blue border; 2 yellow lines basally; anal and caudal similar, but the latter without yellow lines basally; pectorals blue and yellow with wide pale-blue borders.

An example of this Indo-Pacific species has been captured off Caloundra, South Queensland. Apparently somewhat rare in Queensland waters. Grows to 20 inches.

Abalistes

This well-marked genus differs from all other balistids by the peculiar shape of the caudal peduncle, which is thick and strongly flattened above and below, so that its depth is much less than the breadth. The first dorsal is also longer, more slender, and more pointed than in others of the Balistidae. A single species, wide-ranging.

460. FLAT-TAILED TRIGGER-FISH *Abalistes stellaris*
(Bloch and Schneider)   [Colour-plate 65]

Balistes stellaris Bloch and Schneider, Syst. Ichth., 1801, p. 476.
Illustration by G. Coates.

Varken-vis (Dutch East Indies).

D. 3/27; A. 24-25. Colour greyish or light olive-green, with light-yellow spots over head, body, and caudal, those on belly being largest; 3 large whitish blotches usually present on back; on soft dorsal and anal the spots are more olive-green in colour and are regularly set so as to form longitudinal rows; pectorals yellow; sometimes a blue line is present behind the lips. Young examples have irregular blue lines between the pectoral and first dorsal and also on the head and tail.

A common fish, very variable in colour. It is found along the whole Queensland coast and occurs also in Western Australia. Wide-ranging. Grows to 24 inches.

Balistapus

Separated from *Balistes* mainly by the absence of a groove in front of the eyes.

Small, brightly coloured balistids, common in the tropical waters of the Indian and Pacific oceans. Three species are found in Queensland waters.

KEY TO SPECIES IN QUEENSLAND

A. Body covered from snout to tail with narrow diagonal, often undulating, orange or reddish stripes; black patch on caudal peduncle circular.   *undulatus*

AA. Body without numerous diagonal stripes, though some much shortened ones may be present on lower half of body posteriorly.

b. A dark interorbital band becoming blackish below the eye and widening as it progresses, passes downward to the pectoral and backward to the anus and anterior three-fourths of anal fin; a black wedge-shaped band on caudal peduncle. *rectangulus*

bb. Sides of body with 4-5 oblique blue stripes posteriorly; body greenish above, white below; an orange band from snout to pectoral base; caudal spines in an elongate black patch, surrounded by pale blue. *aculeatus*

461. RED-LINED TRIGGER-FISH *Balistapus undulatus* Park [Colour-plate 66]

Balistapus undulatus Park, Trans. Linn. Soc. Lond., 3, 1797, p. 37.
Illustration by G. Coates.

Mol-kotah or Rice-pounder (Ceylon); Sumu uli (Samoa).

D. 3/24-26; A. 23-24. Colour very variable; ground colour may be dark bottle green or light green with sometimes the back bright blue; head and body covered with undulating lines of red, orange, or yellow, which run diagonally downward and backward; these are most crowded on the head; those which run from the mouth, extending back to below the pectoral, are usually more reddish; on the trunk they run from the dorsal to the anal and caudal; membranes of soft dorsal and anal hyaline, the rays bright orange; caudal with the outer rays bright red, the inner ones orange, and with the membranes hyaline; spines on caudal peduncle in a circular black patch. All these colours vary greatly in different specimens, but the general pattern remains much the same in all.

This beautiful fish is common on the coral reefs of North Queensland and also on those of Samoa and many other South Sea islands. It ranges through the Indo-Pacific to Africa and the Red Sea. Grows to 14 inches.

OTHER SPECIES

Black-banded Trigger-fish, *B. rectangulus*. A common Indo-Pacific species found also in Africa and the Red Sea. In Australian waters it has been recorded from North Queensland and Western Australia. Grows to 12 inches.

Black-barred Trigger-fish, *B. aculeatus*. A handsome fish commonly found on the coral reefs of North Queensland. It is wide-ranging and is known from numerous localities in the Indo-Pacific region, and also from Africa and the Red Sea. Grows to 10 inches.

Canthidermis

No enlarged plates behind gill-opening. Groove before eye. Soft dorsal and anal elevated in front. Third dorsal spine well developed.

Species of trigger-fishes inhabiting the East and West Indies. One in Queensland.

462. SPOTTED TRIGGER-FISH *Canthidermis rotundatus* (Procé) [Colour-plate 66]

Balistes rotundatus Procé, Bull. Soc. Philom., 1822, p. 130.
Illustration by G. Coates.

Ami-mongara (Japan).

D. 3, 1/25-26; A. 1/23-24. Colour bluish-black, young examples having numerous light-blue spots or blotches over head and body, being less numerous and larger in adults; dorsal spine black.

This species has been recorded from Torres Strait, North Queensland, and the Brisbane River, South Queensland, both examples being juveniles. It ranges through Melanesia, the East Indies, Hawaii, and Japan. Grows to at least 16 inches.

Family **Anacanthidae**

Fishes with narrow and very much elongated bodies and with an attenuated head. A long fleshy and wide barbel on the chin. First dorsal reduced to a very small flexible spine situated over the hind margin of the eye. A family with one genus and a single species.

463. BEARDIE or TAPE-FISH *Anacanthus barbatus* (Gray) [Colour-plate 67]

Balistes (Anacanthus) barbatus Grey, Illust. Ind. Zool., 1, 1830-6, pl. 84, fig. 2.
Illustration by G. Coates.

D. 1/49; A. 57. Colour dull brownish or greyish, the fins, including caudal, yellow, the latter with about 6 narrow vertical or angular dark bands, sometimes broken into spots. In the males there is a skinny prolongation from the throat, continued almost to the anal fin.

This curious fish is found along the whole of the Queensland coastline, both on coral reefs and along mangrove-lined shores and mudbanks. When captured and laid upon a beach it is said to be able to throw itself a height of a foot into the air. The Beardie is also found in the waters of North Australia and the East Indies, and also in India where it is very common. Grows to 12½ inches.

Family **Monacanthidae: File-fishes and Leather-jackets**

Herbivorous shore-fishes of most warm seas, mainly of small or moderate size though two genera contain species which grow to a rather large size. They are closely related to the Balistidae but differ mainly in having the body covered with very small and spinigerous scales forming a smooth, velvety, or rough surface. The first dorsal fin is reduced to a single spine, behind which is sometimes a rudimentary one. In some species the sexes are quite different in appearance, the adult males sometimes having patches of slender or stout spines on the caudal peduncle.

The flesh of almost all the species is not only bitter and disagreeable to the taste but usnally possesses poisonous properties, and when eaten causes **ciguatera** and often death. Four genera are found in Queensland waters.

KEY TO GENERA IN QUEENSLAND

A. Snout not greatly elongated, without tubular tip.

    b. Pelvic spine movable.

      c. Body and dorsal spine with large cutaneous filaments.   *Chaetoderma*

      cc. Body and dorsal spine without or with only small cutaneous filaments.   *Monacanthus*

    bb. Pelvic spine immovable.   *Cantherines*

AA. Snout greatly elongated, with tubular tip.   *Oxymonacanthus*

Chaetoderma

Dermal filaments greatly developed. Scales relatively large and coarse, those on anterior half of body arranged transversely, those on posterior parts longitudinally. Species few, one in Queensland.

464. PRICKLY LEATHER-JACKET *Chaetoderma penicilligera* (Cuvier)
[Colour-plate 67]

Monacanthus penicilligerus Cuvier, Règne Anim., 4, 1817, p. 185 (ex Peron MS., *fide* Sherborn). Illustration by G. Coates.

D. 26; A. 24. Colour brownish, irregularly marked with darker brown; a round black spot in the middle of the side; some straight black lines along the body and tail; vertical fins with numerous black dots.

A fairly common species on the Queensland coast from north to south, though more frequently met with in the far north. In Australian waters it has also been recorded from Western Australia. Found also in New Guinea, Samoa, and the East Indies. Grows to 10 inches.

Monacanthus

Body short, deep, strongly compressed, covered with rough scales, often reduced to shagreen-like prickles. Snout longer than head. Mouth small. Gill-opening a small slit directly beneath eye, its lower end just anterior to upper edge of pectoral fin. Dorsal fin is a single strong spine, armed with stout hooked downward-directed barbs in rows at the rear and sometimes with similar, but closely set, smaller ones in front. Ventral spine movable, connected to abdomen by a very large, wide, movable flap or "dewlap", which extends far beyond the body-line. Spines often present on sides of caudal peduncle, especially in males.

Small or medium-sized fishes inhabiting temperate and tropical seas, usually in shallow water. The flesh is bitter and quite unfit for food. Species numerous, six in Queensland.

KEY TO SPECIES IN QUEENSLAND

A. Ventral cutaneous expansion large, extending beyond the pelvic spine in adults.   *chinensis*

AA. Ventral cutaneous expansion smaller, not extending beyond the pelvic spine.

  b. More than 30 anal rays.

   c. D. 35; A. 37. Colour brownish, with darker spots; a black spot below anterior third of dorsal fin. Upper caudal rays forming a point.   *filicauda*

   cc. D. 30; A. 32. First and fifth branched caudal rays produced.   *oblongus otisensis*

  bb. Less than 30 anal rays.

   d. Body oblong, its depth 2-2½ in the length to hypural joint; dorsal and anal fins conspicuously elevated in front.   *oblongus*

   dd. Body elevated, its depth less than 2 in the length to hypural joint; dorsal and anal fins not elevated in front.

    e. D. 27-29: A. 25-27. Colour light green with black dots; a broad whitish band from gill-slit to below soft dorsal origin and a dusky blotch above and below.   *tomentosus*

    ee. D. 31-32; A. 26-28. Colour blackish-green, with blackish bar from eye to pectoral base; head black; caudal bright orange with checkered band.   *melanocephalus*

465. FAN-BELLIED LEATHER-JACKET *Monacanthus chinensis* (Osbeck)
[Colour-plate 68]

Balistes chinensis Osbeck, Reise Ost. Ind. China, 1765, p. 147.
Illustration by G. Coates.

Morokoshi-hagi (Japan).

D. 1/29; A. 29. Colour grape-green all over, with an obscure network of whitish-green; throat and belly a little paler; spinous dorsal olive-green; soft dorsal and anal membranes hyaline, the rays reddish-pink; pectorals similar; "dewlap" or ventral fin same as body but with several pale-blue spots; caudal with the rays green, the membranes reddish-pink; 2 dusky transverse wavy bars and 1 or 2 narrow blue pencil lines across caudal from top to bottom.

An extremely common little leather-jacket which is met with in most localities in Australian waters with the exception of Victoria and South Australia. Also found in Polynesia, the East Indies, and China. Grows to 11 inches.

OTHER SPECIES

Thread-tailed Leather-jacket, *M. filicauda*. Originally taken south of New Guinea in 28 fathoms, this has now been recorded from the Queensland coast where it has been trawled in depths of 19 to 26 fathoms.

Horse-face Leather-jacket, *M. oblongus otisensis*. Commonly trawled all along the Queensland coastline. This sub-species differs mainly from *M. oblongus* in having a deeper body, a greater number of fin-rays, and less-defined scales. Grows to at least 5 inches. The typical *M. oblongus* is a small Japanese species which has been trawled along the Queensland coast at various points. It is subject to great variation, both in form and colour. Grows to 5 inches.

Banded Leather-jacket, *M. tomentosus*. Occasionally met with in Queensland and New South Wales waters. Occurs also in the East Indies and China. Grows to 5 inches.

Black-headed Leather-jacket, *M. melanocephalus*. This species is very uncommon in Queensland; it is occasionally found stranded on the ocean beaches of New South Wales and also occurs at Lord Howe Island and in Melanesia, Polynesia, and the East Indies. Readily recognized by the checkered band at the end of the caudal fin. Grows to 5 inches.

Cantherines

Closely resembling *Monacanthus* but differing mainly in having the ventral spine fastened immovably to the pelvic bone. The dorsal also varies: in some species it may be simply roughened whilst in others it bears rows of more or less well-developed barbs. Species many, six in Queensland.

A. Body more or less variously spotted, banded, or lined.

   b. Sides of body with 2-4 longitudinal bands.

      c. Yellowish-brown, fins bright yellow; young ex-
         amples with 2-4 pale-yellow longitudinal bands.   *ayraudi*

      cc. Dark greenish-brown or olive-green, with 3 darker
         longitudinal bands; several narrow, undulated,
         branched, black lines on middle of sides.   *trachylepis*

   bb. No longitudinal bands on body, but with spots or
      blotches.

      d. Head and body pale olive, with obscure blotches
         of brown and thickly covered with small brown
         spots.   *maynardi*

      dd. Dark brown, with polygonal or hexagonal pale
         network over body.   *pardalis*

      ddd. Brownish-grey, marbled darker; 2 large dark
         spots on belly at anal base.   *granulatus*

AA. Body uniform, no markings.

   e. Brownish or greenish, sometimes with dark cross-
      bands on caudal.   *brunneus*

466. CHINAMAN LEATHER-JACKET *Cantherines ayraudi* (Quoy and Gaimard)

[Plate 62]

Balistes ayraudi Quoy and Gaimard, Voy. Uranie Physic., Zool., 1824, p. 216.
Pseudomonacanthus ayraudi Roughley, Fish. Austr., 1916, p. 188, pl. 66.

Yellow Leather-jacket (South Australia and New South Wales); Leather-johnnie (New South Wales).

D. 1/32; A. 31. Colour "Back yellowish-brown, head tinged with blue; sides and abdominal region pale yellowish-brown; all the fins bright yellow; young specimens invariably possess two to four longitudinal bands of a pale yellow colour, which may be persistent more or less in the adult; irides golden, clouded with green." (Roughley.)

This large leather-jacket is a straggler into the waters of Moreton Bay from New South Wales, in which State it is extremely common. T. C. Roughley (loc. cit.) gave the following excellent notes upon the species: "The Yellow Leather-jacket frequents rocky and sandy situations along the coast, and in the estuaries. It is particularly abundant on submerged reefs and similar localities, the recognised haunts of the Snapper, and it causes the line fishermen seeking this latter species considerable aggravation, not only because it is less highly esteemed as food and game, but because it frequently severs the line with its sharp, strong teeth. Specimens captured off shore are usually much larger than those taken in the inlets, where they are, as a rule, immature. . . . Although generally looked upon with detestation by both net and line fishermen—the former on account of the trouble caused by its dorsal spine becoming entangled in the net, the latter because of its inferior sporting qualities—it is actually a very valuable fish food. Its leathery skin accounts for much of the disrespect with which it has been regarded, an impression frequently held being that only fish with scales, which will detach by scraping lightly with a knife, are fit to eat. This, of course, is an entirely erroneous idea, and if the Leatherjacket be skinned before cooking, the flesh will be found to be white, firm and tasty. Moreover, the bones adhering well together, the flesh is more easily removed than obtains in the case of most fish."

The Chinaman Leather-jacket is also found in South Australia and Western Australia. It grows to 20 inches.

OTHER SPECIES

Yellow-finned Leather-jacket, *C. trachylepis*. A southern fish which commonly enters the waters of South Queensland from New South Wales. Also found in Victoria and Tasmania. Grows to 16 inches.

Brown-spotted Leather-jacket, *C. maynardi*. Not commonly met with in Queensland waters but probably plentiful in the deeper waters offshore, several examples having been trawled off Gladstone and also Hervey Bay. Grows to 13 inches.

Leopard Leather-jacket, *C. pardalis*. A wide-ranging fish, being found in Australian waters on the coasts of Queensland and Western Australia. It ranges through Melanesia, Polynesia, and Micronesia, and through the East Indies to the Red Sea. Grows to 7 inches.

Rough Leather-jacket, *C. granulatus*. Occasionally enters the waters of South Queensland. Common in the inlets along the coast of New South Wales and is also found in Victoria and South Australia. Grows to 9 inches.

Brown Leather-jacket, *C. brunneus*. An uncommon little species known only from the waters of North Queensland, where it has been captured in shallow tidal rock-pools. Grows to $3\frac{1}{2}$ inches.

Oxymonacanthus

Comprises a single species, gaudily coloured and characterized by having an elongate form and a very long, narrow, sharp-pointed snout. Confined to the tropical waters of the Indian and Pacific oceans.

467. BEAKED LEATHER-JACKET *Oxymonacanthus longirostris*
(Bloch and Schneider) [Colour-plate 68]

Balistes hispidus var. *longirostris* Bloch and Schneider, Syst. Ichth., 1801, p. 464.
Illustration by G. Coates.

D. 1/31-33; A. 29-31. Colour bright green or greenish-blue on body above and below, darkest on upper part of head; about 6 longitudinal rows of elongated orange spots, those on head slightly larger and more elongate and converging towards the snout; snout orange, with the green of the body extending down from above the eye and along the snout in the form of a narrow stripe which terminates almost on the throat; soft dorsal and anal pale yellow, tinged pinkish at the edges; ventral membrane black basally, orange on outer half, the whole with small green spots; caudal pale green, with a few large lemon-yellow spots and 2 to 3 black ones of similar size subterminally on the lower half.

This small brightly coloured leather-jacket is to be observed swimming amongst the living corals at the edges of the reefs adjacent to the deeper waters on the Great Barrier Reef. It ranges through Melanesia, Polynesia, and Micronesia, the East Indies, and is also found in Mauritius. Grows to 3¼ inches.

Family **Aluteridae**

Body elongate, compressed, covered with velvety skin, no visible scales. Pelvic spine rudimentary or absent. A single slender dorsal spine present above or in advance of the eye becomes sometimes absent with age. A second rudimentary spine is present close behind the base of the first. A knob at the front of the base of this second spine fits under the base of the first and locks it in an erect position.

Widely distributed fishes found in all warm seas. Genera few, two in Queensland.

KEY TO GENERA IN QUEENSLAND

A. Caudal fin shorter than head. Snout profile concave in young, becoming convex with age. *Aluterus*

AA. Caudal fin longer than head. Snout profile always concave. *Osbeckia*

Aluterus

Body compressed, somewhat deep at the breast. Caudal fin shorter than head. A single species.

468. UNICORN LEATHER-JACKET *Aluterus monoceros* (Linnaeus) [Plate 62]

Balistes monoceros Linnaeus, Syst. Nat., 10th ed., 1st Jan. 1758, p. 327 (based on Mus. Ad. Fr. 2; *Balistes monoceros* Osb. iter., 110).
Monacanthus monoceros Day, Fish. India, 1878, p. 693, pl. 179, fig. 2.

D. 1/50; A. 48-53. Colour brownish or blackish, the fins yellow.

A rare fish on the Queensland coast, its inclusion in the State's fauna being based on a specimen taken off Caloundra, South Queensland in March 1951 by Captain J. McIntosh. The species inhabits all warm seas and is said to reach a length of 30 inches.

Osbeckia

Body elongate, somewhat compressed. Profile of snout always concave. Caudal fin longer than head.

Large leather-jackets widely distributed in all tropical and subtropical seas.

469. FIGURED LEATHER-JACKET *Osbeckia scripta* (Forster)
[Colour-plate 69]

Balistes scriptus Forster, Voy. China (Osbeck) 2, 1771, Faunula Sinensis p. 331 (based on Osbeck Chin., p. 144).
Illustration by G. Coates.

D. 1/45-48; A. 50-51. Colour yellow or olivaceous; head and body with numerous irregular marks or lines and spots of sky-blue, the lines or marks being more numerous on head and near bases of dorsal and anal fins, and the spots more numerous on middle of sides and head; between these blue spots and lines are smaller brown spots; dorsal and anal fins pale yellow; caudal dark mustard-yellow, paler towards tip; lips black.

This large and handsome species has so far (1955) been recorded in Queensland only from the waters north of Townsville. It is a circumtropical species occurring in all warm seas. Various authorities warn that it is a dangerous fish to eat because its flesh is very poisonous. Grows to 36 inches.

Sub-order OSTRACIONTOIDEA: BOX-FISHES, COW-FISHES, and TURRET-FISHES

A small group which contains only two families, the members of which have their bodies encased in a series of six-sided bony plates, fused marginally to form a solid box, so that only the jaws, fins, and tail are movable. The spinous dorsal and ventral fins are absent, and the pectorals, soft dorsal, and anal are all small. The mouth is small, with a single row of long, narrow teeth in the jaws. The body is short and may be three-, four-, or five-sided. Gill-opening reduced to an almost vertical slit below and behind the eye.

Fishes widely distributed in all warm seas, living mainly in shallow waters. Most are considered poor swimmers, though some, such as the Cow-fishes (*Lactoria*) and Box-fishes (*Ostracion*), are capable of fast movement. Although some species are said to be good eating, many of them have poisonous flesh.

KEY TO FAMILIES

A.   Carapace open behind dorsal and anal fins. Ventral ridge more or less developed. ARACANIDAE

AA. Carapace closed, at least behind anal fin. Ventral ridge wanting. OSTRACIONTIDAE

Family **Aracanidae**

Dorsal and anal fins not enclosed in the main armour but with either a complete or incomplete ring of small bony plates posteriorly on the caudal peduncle. Ventral ridge more or less developed.

Marine fishes of tropical waters. Genera and species numerous. The family is represented in Queensland by a single genus and species.

470. ROBUST BOX-FISH *Strophiurichthys robustus* Fraser-Brunner [Plate 62]

Strophiurichthys robustus Fraser-Brunner, Ann. Mag. Nat. Hist. (ser. 11), Oct. 1941, p. 310, fig. 2B.

D. 10; A. 10; P. 12. Colour yellowish-brown, with large dark spots on back and upper sides.

Inhabits the waters of Australia and the tropical Pacific at depths down to 150 fathoms. Grows to 10 inches. Fairly commonly taken in the nets of the prawn-trawlers at Coolangatta, South Queensland.

Family **Ostraciontidae**

Carapace closed, at least behind the anal fin. No ventral ridge.

Marine fishes of the tropics. About seven genera, five in Queensland.

KEY TO GENERA IN QUEENSLAND

Based on Fraser-Brunner[77]

A.   Carapace closed behind both dorsal and anal fins.

  b. Lateral ridges prominent.
  c. No preocular or pelvic spines.
    d. Dorsal ridge low. Back flat or slightly concave. Lateral and pelvic ridges sharp. Snout projecting beyond mouth. *Rhynchostracion*

[77] *Ann. Mag. Nat. Hist.* (ser. 10), 16, p. 316.

dd. Dorsal ridge obsolete. Back convex. Lateral and
 pelvic ridges rounded. Snout not projecting. *Ostracion*

cc. Preocular and pelvic spines present. Dorsal ridge
 low, sometimes with a spine. Back flat or concave.
 Lateral and pelvic ridges rounded. *Lactoria*

bb. Lateral ridges scarcely evident or obsolete. Dorsal
 and pelvic ridges prominent.

e. No preocular spines. *Rhinesomus*

ee. Preocular spines present. *Acanthostracion*

Rhynchostracion

Carapace 5-angled, closed to behind both dorsal and anal fins. No ventral ridge; lateral ridges prominent. No preocular or pelvic spines. Dorsal ridge low, back flat or slightly concave; pelvic ridges sharp. Snout projecting beyond mouth. Species few, one in Queensland.

471. LONG-NOSED BOX-FISH *Rhynchostracion nasus* (Bloch) [Colour-plate 69]

Ostracion nasus Bloch, Nat. ausl. Fische, 1, 1785, p. 118, pl. 138.
Illustration by G. Coates.

D. 9; A. 9; C. 8 branched rays. Colour greenish-yellow, with small irregularly scattered black spots; whitish below; black spots on caudal fin. Young examples are bright orange-yellow, with numerous black spots.

This fish is apparently rare on the Queensland coast. It ranges through the Pacific to the Malay Archipelago and the Indian Ocean. Found also in Western Australia. Grows to $8\frac{1}{2}$ inches.

Ostracion

Carapace closed behind both dorsal and anal fins. Lateral ridges prominent. No preocular or pelvic spines. Dorsal ridge obsolete. Back convex. Lateral and pelvic ridges rounded. Snout not projecting. Species numerous, inhabiting the tropical waters of the Indo-Pacific; one in Queensland.

472. BLUE-SPOTTED BOX-FISH *Ostracion tuberculatus* Linnaeus [Colour-plate 69]

Ostracion tuberculatus Linnaeus, Syst. Nat., 10th ed., 1758, p. 331.
Illustration by G. Coates.

General colour when alive dark or light olive-green, becoming dirty fawnish-yellow below; back with light-blue black-edged spots; on the sides the light-blue spots have 2 or 3 black spots against them; those spots on the head and under-surface of the body, however, are plain black; pectorals and dorsal fins orange-yellow; caudal olive-yellow, with black spots on the caudal peduncle.

An extremely common fish in the reef-waters of Queensland from north to south as far as and including the Capricorn and Bunker groups. Said to attain a length of 18 inches. Wide-ranging through the East Indies to Japan and the Philippines, and across to Africa and the Red Sea.

Lactoria

Body 5-angled, a distinct dorsal ridge present, mostly with a spine in the very juvenile forms, sometimes diminishing with age. One or two spines before the eye. Pelvic spines present. Lateral and pelvic ridges prominent.

Species few, inhabiting the Indo-Pacific region, two in Queensland.

KEY TO SPECIES IN QUEENSLAND

A. A long conical spine above each orbit and a similar long
    spine posteriorly at ventral ridge; dorsal ridge with a
    slight keel in middle, but not developed into a spine.   *cornutus*

AA. A short divergent spine above each orbit; ventral ridge
    terminating behind in a strong flat spine and frequently
    with 2 smaller spines on the side; a triangular, com-
    pressed spine in the middle of the back.   *diaphana*

473. COW-FISH *Lactoria cornutus* (Linnaeus) [Colour-plate 70]

Ostracion cornutus Linnaeus, Syst. Nat., 10th ed., 1758, p. 331; 12th ed., 1766, p. 409.
Illustration by G. Coates.

Kongofuga or Adamant Puffer (Japan); Oskop, Cow-fish, and Box-fish (South Africa).

D. 9; A. 9. Caudal moderate in young, elongated with age. Colour pale greenish-yellow, a bluish or whitish spot on each scale, except on belly, which is plain yellowish; lips yellowish, with a broad blackish line between them; caudal pale yellow, with blue spots, the upper and lower edges dusky; other fins hyaline.

The curious Cow-fish is extremely common everywhere along the Great Barrier Reef of Queensland as well as other localities along the coastline. When the fish is quietly cruising in the shallow coral-pools its greatly elongated tail is kept more or less folded. When it is frightened the tail is fully expanded and the fish makes off with a good burst of speed, away from the danger zone.

The species is readily recognized by the 2 pairs of horns, one pair anterior and pointing forward, the other pair posterior and pointing backward. The Cow-fish is also found in New South Wales, the Northern Territory, north-western Australia, Lord Howe Island, New Guinea, the western Pacific, the East Indies, Japan and South Africa. Grows to 20 inches.

OTHER SPECIES

Diaphanous Box-fish, *L. diaphana*. In this species the ventral portion of the carapace is translucent, with zigzag dusky bars along the rim. A tropical Indo-Pacific fish known from Queensland waters by a single specimen 5 inches in length picked up on the beach at Burleigh Heads, South Queensland, in May 1952 by W. E. Norway. Grows to 10 inches.

Rhinesomus

Body elevated. Lateral ridges scarcely evident or obsolete; dorsal and pelvic ridges prominent, with spines, usually diminishing with age. No preocular spines. Species few, two in Queensland.

KEY TO SPECIES IN QUEENSLAND

A. Dorsal ridge angular, surmounted by a single large flattened spine which diminishes only with great age; carapace ventrally somewhat circular.   *gibbosus*

AA. Dorsal ridge more evenly rounded and bearing 2 small spines which become lost with age; carapace somewhat oval ventrally.   *reipublicae*

474. TURRET-FISH *Rhinesomus reipublicae* (Ogilby)   [Plate 62]

Lactophrys reipublicae Ogilby, Mem. Qld Mus., 2, 10th Dec. 1913, p. 92.
Triorus reipublicae Whitley, Mem. Qld Mus., 10, pt 1, 28th Aug. 1930, p. 27, pl. 1, fig. 2.

D. 9; A. 9; P. 1/10; caudal with 8 branched rays. Scattered dark spots (milky-blue in life) are present on head, body, and caudal peduncle, and there are usually dark blotches on back and sides. Sometimes there are some horizontal dark stripes on the cheek. The 2 small compressed spines on the dorsal ridge as well as those on the orbital edge and ventral ridges become less prominent with age, and in a specimen 8 inches or so in length they are absent altogether.

A pelagic fish which is seen only when cast up on South Queensland beaches after heavy weather or when captured in the nets of the prawn-trawlers operating along the South Queensland coast and the coast of New South Wales. Grows to at least 9 inches and ranges from New Guinea and Queensland to New South Wales and Lord Howe Island.

OTHER SPECIES

Black-blotched Turret-fish, *R. gibbosus*. Ranges the Indo-Pacific from the Red Sea, Aden, and Zanzibar to the East Indies, Australia, and the Philippines, north to Japan. Its occurrence in Queensland is based upon a single specimen taken by H. Cook in Moreton Bay in July 1953. Grows to at least 12 inches.

Acanthostracion

Body elevated. Lateral ridges scarcely evident or obsolete, virtually 3-angled. A large preocular spine present. Species few, one in Queensland.

475. SPINY-BACKED COW-FISH *Acanthostracion pentacanthus* (Bleeker)
[Plate 62]

Ostracion pentacanthus Bleeker, Act. Soc. Sci. Ind. Neerl., 2, 1857, p. 98.
Ostracion (Acanthostracion) fornasini Bleeker, Atlas Ichth., 5, 1865, p. 34, pl. 203, fig. 4 (not *O. fornacini* Bianconi).

Body with some irregular bluish and blackish markings. A tropical species recorded from Australia on a single example taken many years ago at Southport, South Queensland. Not seen since. Grows to 6 inches.

Sub-order TETRAODONTOIDEA:
PUFFERS or TOADOS, PORCUPINE-FISHES, and SUNFISHES

Body oblong or short, in all but the Molidae the belly more or less inflatable. Skin naked, or covered with small or large spines, bristles, or small plates, bases root-like. Jaws with an enamel-like covering which forms a powerful parrot-like beak; no distinct teeth. No pelvic fins. No fin-spines. Caudal sometimes absent.

A dangerous group of fishes inhabiting all warm seas and in which the development of poisonous alkaloids in the flesh has reached a very high degree, thus rendering the flesh fatal as food. Their poisonous flesh, plus the powers of inflation and armature of spines and prickles in most species, render them immune from attack. Many species are able to inflate the belly with air or water until they become circular, floating helpless at the surface, belly upwards. With danger passed they rapidly deflate and swim away. Almost all are poor swimmers and drift with the ocean currents. Families few, four in Queensland.

KEY TO FAMILIES REPRESENTED IN QUEENSLAND

A. Caudal fin normal, with a distinct caudal peduncle.
    b. Upper and lower jaws each divided by a median suture.
       c. Head broad; nostrils various. Back broad, rounded, little compressed. TETRAODONTIDAE
       cc. Head narrower, with snout sharp and longer. Back more or less sharply ridged. Nostrils obsolete or very small. CANTHIGASTERIDAE
    bb. Upper and lower jaws undivided. Body covered with stout or slender rooted spines. DIODONTIDAE
AA. Caudal region aborted, without caudal peduncle. Body truncated behind dorsal and anal. Jaws undivided. MOLIDAE

Family **Tetraodontidae: Toados**

Body oblong or long, usually but slightly compressed, sometimes very broad, and belly capable of great inflation. Skin scaleless, more or less prickly, the spines usually weak and movable; rarely the skin is armed with bony scutes; head and snout wide; lips full, the jaws forming a broad prominent bony beak, each divided by a median suture; nostrils various; gill-opening small, close before pectorals; fins composed of soft rays only, no spines; dorsal fin posterior, opposite the similar anal; caudal distinct, well developed; pelvic bones undeveloped; ventral fins absent; no ribs; pectorals short, wide.

Fishes of sluggish habit, common in all warm seas. Not used as food (except sometimes by native peoples) on account of the poisonous flesh. In writing of the toados in the Philippine Islands, where they are known by the local names of Botiti or Bolete in Filipino languages, Herre[78] says: "Although most people are more or less aware of the poisonous properties of the flesh, it is eaten in practically every Philippine fishing village and not a year goes by without several deaths from this cause. A Japanese investigator has studied carefully the alkaloid present in the flesh of the *Tetraodontidae* and finds it to be very near muscarine, the active poisonous principle of *Amanita muscaria* and other fungi. It is a tasteless, odorless, and very poisonous crystalline alkaloid. The dangerous alkaloid seems to be most abundant and virulent in the eggs or roe and sperm or milt; it is claimed by the fishermen that the gall bladder is also very poisonous. Many Filipinos believe that if the entrails and skin are removed from *botiti* the flesh is wholesome. While this may be more or less true, especially when the breeding season is not near, it is nevertheless very dangerous to eat the flesh of botiti, and their sale and use should be forbidden."

Three genera of these poisonous fishes are found in Queensland waters.

KEY TO GENERA IN QUEENSLAND

A. Nostril on each side with two distinct openings, usually in a low tube or papilla. *Spheroides*

AA. Nostrils without openings.

    b. Nostril on each side with a bifid tentacle without a distinct opening. *Tetraodon*

    bb. Nostril a simple unperforated cavity having 2 marginal flaps or fringed margin. *Chelonodon*

Spheroides

Body oblong or elongate, covered more or less by fine spines or prickles. A short and simple nasal tube on each side, with two distinct large openings near its tip, or sometimes the tube is reduced to a low rim. Abdomen capable

[78] *Phil. Journ. Sci.*, 25, no. 4, 1924, p. 479.

of great inflation. Some species with a distinct fold of skin on the lower surface of the tail.

A large genus of fishes with many species, inhabiting chiefly tropical waters, some growing to a large size. Nine species are found in Queensland.

A. Colour uniform above, without spots, speckles, or bands.

    b. D. 12; A. 11-12. Colour uniform greenish above, silvery on sides. Caudal forked in adults, subtruncate in half-grown.   *laevigatus*

AA. Spotted, banded, speckled, or lined above and on sides.

    c. Spots, bands, speckles, or lines chiefly confined to back and upper sides.

      d. A dark median horizontal line separating the dark colour of the back from the lighter sides.

        e. A series of unarmed squamiform processes on the low ridge on either side of the lateral line posteriorly. Sides of head without dark vertical bars.   *squamicauda*

        ee. No squamiform processes on the low ridge below lateral line. Sides of head with several dark vertical bars.   *pleurogramma*

      dd. No dark line between the dark back colour and the lighter sides.

        f. Head and body with numerous close-set parallel narrow oblique lines and spots.   *multistriatus*

        ff. No such oblique lines; back and sides with spots and few bands.

          g. Upper surface with about 4 wide blackish cross-bands; usually without spots or only a few in the young, mainly on the bands. D. 10.   *pleurostictus*

          gg. Upper surface with numerous light or dark spots; no distinct bands (except in the young).

            h. Back with numerous dark spots and with dark vertical bars on sides. D. 9.   *hamiltoni*

            hh. Back with numerous small dark spots on darker background which is sharply defined from the lighter sides. D. 12.   *sceleratus*

            hhh. Back with light or dark scattered spots, between which are darker "tickings", spots dark on sides. D. 9-10.

              i. Outer anterior edge of gill-opening with several short fleshy tubercles.   *tuberculiferus*

              ii. Outer anterior edge of gill-opening smooth, without fleshy tubercles.   *whitleyi*

476. WEEPING TOADO *Spheroides pleurogramma* (Regan)   [Plate 62]

Tetrodon pleurogramma Regan, Proc. Zool. Soc. Lond., 1902 (April 1903), pt 2, p. 300, pl. 24, fig. 2.

D. 9-11; A. 8-10. Colour greyish or greenish above, with dark-brown reticulations which form spots; four broad dark bands across back, one behind eye, second by pectoral, third at base of dorsal, and the last on caudal peduncle; these bars descend to a dark horizontal stripe along middle of each side and separate the colouring of the back from the light under-surface; numerous black bars descend across the cheeks, thinning out below.

A species which is not commonly found here but is occasionally captured by the prawn-trawlers in South Queensland. Found also in New South Wales, South Australia, and Lord Howe Island. Grows to 7 inches.

477. BANDED TOADO *Spheroides pleurostictus* (Günther)

[Colour-plate 70]

Tetrodon pleurostictus Günther, Proc. Zool. Soc. Lond., 1871 (2nd May 1872), p. 674, pl. 69, fig. a. Illustration by G. Coates.

D. 12; A. 8. Colour olive-greyish above, lighter on sides, passing into white below; 4 broad olive-blackish "saddles" or cross-bands above, fading out on the lower sides to the white of the belly; fins pale or bright yellow or orange, more or less tinged with pink; a few blackish spots on the sides posteriorly; eye black, surrounded with bright golden-brown or scarlet-red.

A common fish in the estuaries of northern New South Wales, Queensland, and the Northern Territory. Grows to 6 inches.

478. COMMON TOADO *Spheroides hamiltoni* (Gray and Richardson)

[Plate 62]

Tetraodon hamiltoni Gray and Richardson, Trav. in New Zeal. (Diffenbach); 2, Jan. 1843, p. 226.
Tetrodon hamiltoni Richardson, Zool. Voy. Erebus and Terror, Fish., 1846, p. 63, pl. 39, figs. 10-11.

D. 9; A. 6. Colour: Upper parts brownish, with numerous close-set round black spots; cheeks with some brown vertical bands and spots; some large dark blotches on sides; an indistinct dark band sometimes present across the back; lower surface white.

This little species is extremely common all along the coasts of South Queensland and New South Wales. It also occurs in South Australia, Western Australia, Melanesia, Polynesia, and New Zealand. It is easily the most common little fish at the seaside resorts in Queensland, where it may be seen swimming leisurely at the extreme edge of the water. Small boys with little feeling throw the fish on the beach and roll it vigorously beneath the bare foot until it is fully inflated with air, then explode it by a sharp downward stamp of the foot. Grows to 5½ inches.

OTHER SPECIES

Silver Toado, *S. laevigatus*. Found from Australia through the Indo-Australian Archipelago to China and Japan and tropical parts of the Indian Ocean. Grows to about 20 inches.

Scaly-tailed Toado, *S. squamicauda*. A small distinctively coloured toado known only from Queensland. Characterized by the presence of squamiform processes on the low ridge below the lateral line posteriorly. Grows to 4½ inches.

Striped Toado, *S. multistriatus*. Known by its elaborate pattern of brown stripes and spots on an olive-green background. Ranges from Queensland to the South-west Pacific. Not commonly seen in Queensland, those taken mostly being in the north. Grows to at least 22 inches.

Giant Toado, *S. sceleratus*. A widely distributed fish in the tropical Indo-Pacific. In Australian waters it is found in all States except South Australia. Grows to at least 30 inches.

Fringe-gilled Toado, *S. tuberculiferus*. May be recognized by the presence of several short fleshy tubercles on the outer anterior edge of the gill-opening. A species known only from Queensland and Western Australia. In the former State it has been trawled at depths ranging from 14 to 29 fathoms. Grows to 9 inches.

Whitley's Toado, *S. whitleyi*. A species from Queensland and the Northern Territory. Commonly taken in Queensland by the prawn-trawlers. Grows to at least 8 inches.

Tetraodon

Nostril on each side with a bifid tentacle without a distinct opening. Body robust, covered with more or less prickly or bristle-like spines which are capable of retraction below the skin.

Widely distributed dangerous fishes, their flesh being extremely poisonous and causing death when eaten. Many species are known from the warm seas of the world, eight being found in Queensland. Most are very variable in colour.

KEY TO SPECIES IN QUEENSLAND

Adapted from He re[79]

A. Upper and lower margins of caudal always black; no spots on body, which may be uniform olive or brown above, or with longitudinal parallel lines over whole body or on back.

    b. Body without spots or bands.   *immaculata*

    bb. Body with 6-12 parallel greyish (blackish in death) lines on each side.   *immaculata* var. *virgatus*

---

[79] *Phil. Journ. Sci.*, 25, no. 4, 1924, p. 488.

496

AA. Margins of caudal not black; body always spotted.

 c. Spots white; anus not in a dark spot.
  d. No large irregular black spots on sides.
   e. Entire head and body to base of caudal covered with ovate white spots.   *firmamentum*
   ee. Small or large white spots on upper half of body only; curved or longitudinal lines on sides and belly or belly uniform whitish.
    f. Back dark, with small white spots or lines; curved or longitudinal lines on sides and belly; white lines curving upwards around gill-openings; caudal spotted to its tip.   *reticularis*
    ff. Large circular white spots on upper half of body and anterior part of caudal; belly uniform white or with narrow stripes.   *hispidus*
  dd. Several large irregular black spots on sides below pectorals; upper half with long wavy irregular dark-brown lines enclosing circular white spots; lines on side of head vertical or radiating from eye.   *mappa*
 cc. Spots dark; anus in a black spot.
  g. Spines black; dorsal region covered with circular spots or else pure black; caudal black-spotted.   *stellatus*
  gg. Spines white; belly with a few large irregular black spots; caudal not spotted.   *nigropunctatus*

479. STARS AND STRIPES TOADO *Tetraodon hispidus* Linnaeus
[Colour-plate 70]

Tetraodon hispidus Linnaeus, Syst. Nat., 10th ed., 1758, p. 333; 12th ed., 1766, p. 411.
Illustration by G. Coates.

 Colour very dark or light olive-green above on head, body, and caudal, somewhat paler below; whole of head, back, upper sides of body and caudal, with small bluish-white spots, smallest on caudal; belly with longitudinal white or light olive-yellow stripes, and several obscure oblique blotches posteriorly to them; dorsal and anal olive-green; pectorals olive-yellow; eye surrounded yellow.

 A widely distributed toado; its range extends from Australia to the east coast of Africa and the Red Sea and it is also found in Samoa and the Hawaiian Islands, China, and Japan. In Australian waters it is found in Queensland, New South Wales, and New Guinea. A tropical species which grows to at least 20 inches.

480. A TOADO *Tetraodon stellatus* (Bloch and Schneider) [Colour-plate 71]

Tetrodon lagocephalus var. *stellatus* Bloch and Schneider, Syst. Ichth., 1801, p. 503.
Illustration by G. Coates.

Very variable in colour. Upper parts with black or brown dots which are confluent into parallel stripes in the very young. Some black spots round the root of the pectoral. Old examples are without the lateral or abdominal bands or large spots. In some others the black abdominal bands are very oblique.

A toado from the tropical waters of the Indo-Pacific, from the Red Sea to Japan, Micronesia, Melanesia, Polynesia, and Australia. In Australian waters it is known only from Queensland and New South Wales. Grows to about 24 inches.

OTHER SPECIES

Plain Toado, *T. immaculata*. This species is extremely variable in colour and pattern, the adults being usually uniform and without spots and bands. In the variety *virgatus* there are six to twelve parallel lines on each side of the body. The Plain Toado frequents the waters of Queensland, New South Wales, the Northern Territory, and New Guinea to the western tropical Pacific, the East Indies, South Africa and the Red Sea. Grows to at least 12 inches.

Starry Toado, *T. firmamentum*. A handsome, well-marked species found very uncommonly in Queensland, New South Wales, and Victoria. Also occurs in New Zealand and Japan. Inhabits the deeper waters. Grows to 16 inches.

Lined Toado, *T. reticularis*. Known by the black lower margin to the caudal fin and the dark brownish-yellow lines on back, sides, and belly. Found from Queensland and New Guinea to New Britain, Guam, the East Indies, and India. Grows to at least 22 inches.

Map Toado, *T. mappa*. A well-marked toado which has been recorded from Australia on a large specimen taken at Lindeman Island, Whitsunday Passage, Queensland, in 1936. It occurs in the tropical Indo-Pacific to Australia, New Guinea, and the Society Islands. Grows to at least 21 inches.

Black-spotted Toado, *T. nigropunctatus*. Not commonly met with on the coasts of Queensland and New South Wales. Found also in New Guinea through the tropical Indo-Pacific to Japan and across to the Red Sea. Grows to 10 inches.

Chelonodon

Distinguished from other Tetraodontidae by the nostrils, which are single on each side and in the form of a simple unperforated cavity with a raised and very short tube which is extended into 2 or more flaps or a fringe-like margin. The upper lateral line joins the lower above the anal.

Only three species, one being found in Queensland.

R

498

481. MARBLED TOADO *Chelonodon patoca* (Hamilton Buchanan)

[Colour-plate 71]

Tetrodon patoca Hamilton Buchanan, Fish. Ganges, 1822, pp. 7, 363.
Illustration by G. Coates.

Colour: Back of head and body greenish or greyish overlaid with a reddish-brown network, forming greenish spots about the size of pupil of the eye and extending on to the upper sides to a line with the eye, where they are a pale blue in colour; 3 broad dusky "saddles" on back; belly clean white; sides silvery-fawn, separated from the white belly by a bright-yellow band from chin to caudal base, its edges diffused, broadest and brightest beneath the pectoral fin, which is very pale green, almost hyaline; dorsal yellowish; anal straw-yellow; caudal yellowish basally, passing into black terminally; eye, pupil black, surrounded straw-yellow and with a scarlet stripe above and below; lips rose-pink; the spines of the belly canary-yellow.

In Australia this fish is found in Queensland and the Northern Territory. Its range extends throughout the tropical parts of the Indo-Pacific. Grows to at least 15 inches.

Family **Canthigasteridae**

A group of small toados which differ from the Tetraodontidae in having their bodies more or less compressed and ridged along the back and also in having a sharp or pointed snout. The nostrils are single, feebly developed or absent.

The family consists of a single genus, *Canthigaster*, with about fifteen species, three being found in Queensland. They are brilliantly coloured and well-marked little fishes of the tropical shallow waters of the Indo-Pacific.

KEY TO SPECIES IN QUEENSLAND

A. Body without longitudinal stripes; caudal fin quite plain or almost so.

  b. Body with 3-4 dark cross-bands. — *cinctus*
  bb. Body without distinct cross-bands; a dark ocellus below dorsal region, faded in large examples. — *bennetti*

AA. Body with 1, sometimes 2, dark longitudinal bands from snout to tail, extending along both margins of that fin.

  c. Back and snout closely covered with dark spots and lines; many blue spots on the lower sides. — *callisternus*

482. STRIPED TOBY *Canthigaster cinctus* (Richardson) [Plate 62]

Tetrodon cinctus Richardson, Zool. Voy. Samarang, Fish, 1848, pp. 19-20.
Canthigaster cinctus McCulloch, Mem. Qld Mus., 7, pt 4, 19th Dec. 1922, p. 245, pl. 14, fig. 1.

D. 10. Colour: Back with 3 to 4 blackish-brown cross-bands, the first (when present) between hind portion of eyes; a second and broader one above pectorals descending over their bases in a narrow bar and extending diagonally backward on to abdomen; a third band in front of dorsal descends almost to middle of belly; the fourth band is a broad saddle on caudal peduncle which extends back along upper edge of caudal fin; a dark blotch at base of lower caudal margin and another dusky patch at anus; body with many large orange or brown ocelli between the bands, becoming smaller where they extend on to the head and ventral surface; zebra-like stripes round the eye and on the cheeks; faint lines transversely across snout; breast with pale transverse bands.

A pretty little fish commonly met with only on the coral reefs of Queensland, where it may be observed swimming leisurely in the shallows. It ranges from Queensland and New Guinea through the East Indies to Africa, the Philippines, Japan, Tahiti, and Hawaii. Grows to 5 inches.

OTHER SPECIES

Bennett's Toby, *C. bennetti*. Found also in Queensland, mainly in the far north, this extends its range to the South Seas, the East Indies, and across to Africa. Grows to 4 inches.

Another toby, *C. callisternus*, occurs in Queensland and at Lord Howe Island. In both localities it is rare and little is known of it.

Family **Diodontidae: Porcupine-fishes**

Teeth fused into a parrot-like beak, without median suture. Body covered with spines, short and stout, or long and movable. Belly inflatable, but not so strongly as in the Tetraodontidae. Air-bladder present.

Spiny fishes, widely distributed in all warm seas, where they mainly frequent shallow waters. Some species, however, have been dredged in Australian waters at depths ranging from 70 to 100 fathoms. The flesh of these fishes is highly poisonous. Genera few, three in Queensland. The names Balloon-fishes, Globe-fishes, and Burr-fishes are also applied.

KEY TO GENERA IN QUEENSLAND

A. Nostrils separate, in a tubular papilla.

    b. Most of the spines 3-rooted, immovable.

      c. Spines 2-rooted, movable, only behind pectoral fin.   *Tragulichthys*

    bb. All the spines 2-rooted, erectile.   *Diodon*

AA. Nostrils confluent, each nasal organ appearing as a
bifid tentacle. Some or all of the dermal spines 2-rooted,
erectile. *Dicotylichthys*

Tragulichthys

Each nostril in the form of a raised flap, with an opening anteriorly and
posteriorly. All spines 3-rooted and fixed, except 2 long ones behind each
pectoral, which are movable. Spines on posterior half of sides much longer
and stronger than those on the anterior half. A spine beside each nostril.
Species few, one in Queensland.

483. PORCUPINE-FISH *Tragulichthys jaculiferus* (Cuvier) [Colour-plate 71]

Diodon jaculiferus Cuvier, Mem. Mus. d'Hist. Nat. Paris, 4, 1818, p. 130.
Illustration by G. Coates.

D. 12; A. 12; P. 21. Colour very pale greenish-yellow above, passing into
whitish on lower sides and below; a large black spot above pectoral base,
two others on side, just behind end of pectoral, and another midway between
bases of dorsal and anal fins; 2 smaller black spots are present about midway
between hind border of eye and pectoral base, below eye-level; another small
black spot on cheek, below eye; eye with the black pupil surrounded with
pinkish on which are about 9 squarish maroon-red spots; fins and tail pale
hyaline-greenish-grey.

An extremely common fish in Moreton Bay during the cooler months,
when dozens are caught in the nets of the fishermen. Found also along the
whole coastline of Queensland and in the waters of New South Wales, Western
Australia, and the Arafura Sea. Grows to 10 inches.

Diodon

Spines stout, stiff, and very sharp, mostly 2-rooted and erectile. Nostrils in
a simple tube with 2 lateral openings.

Widely distributed fishes, mainly of the shallow waters of tropical and
temperate seas. Species few, one in Queensland.

484. LONG-SPINED PCRCUPINE-FISH *Diodon holocanthus* Linnaeus
[Plate 63]

Diodon holocanthus Linnaeus, Syst. Nat., 10th ed., 1758, p. 335; 12th ed., 1766, p. 413.
Atopomycterus bocagei Steindachner, Sitzb. Akad. Wiss. Wien, 53, 1866, p. 477, pl. 6, fig. 3.

D. 12; A. 12. Colour brownish above, dirty whitish below, with broad
brown bands and spots, the first, which is between the eyes, being continued
downward on the side to the under-surface; eyes greenish; fins hyaline,
sometimes yellowish.

A widely distributed fish found in all warmer waters of the Atlantic, Pacific, and Indian oceans. Rarely met with in Queensland. Grows to 20 inches.

Dicotylichthys

Spines on head 2-rooted and movable, the rest 3-rooted and immovable. Two species, inhabiting the Indo-Pacific, one being found in Queensland.

485. MYERS' PORCUPINE-FISH *Dicotylichthys myersi* Ogilby   [Plate 63]

Dicotylichthys myersi Ogilby, Proc. Roy. Soc. Qld, 23, 7th Nov. 1910, p. 18.
Illustration by F. Olsen.

D. 12; A. 11; P. 20. Colour: "Uniform olive-brown, shading into lavender or dull white below; lower part of the sides and entire under-surface of the body, with small black spots; a black, vertical band below the eye, a second in front of the gill-opening, and a third below the tip of the appressed pectoral; fins uniform gray." (Ogilby.)

A somewhat uncommon species known only from the waters of southern Queensland and New South Wales, where it frequents the bays and inlets. Grows to 17 inches.

Family **Molidae: Sunfishes or Head-fishes**

Body firm, compressed, oblong or short and deep, truncate behind, the fish appearing to have been bitten off posteriorly, healed over, and leaving only the head. Body non-inflatable. Skin rough, naked, spinous, or tessellated. No caudal fin. Dorsal and anal fins high, confluent posteriorly. No ventrals. Mouth small, terminal, both jaws completely coalesced, without median suture, forming a powerful beak.

Large, grotesque fishes which look to be head only. They are found in almost all warm seas, where they float at the surface or swim idly with the currents, the high dorsal fin projecting above the water. They are quite harmless, their food consisting of plankton and other small marine creatures. The young are quite unlike the adults, being spinous and resembling more an ordinary fish.

Sunfishes are easily identified by shape of body, absence of tail, high dorsal and anal fins, and small mouth. Three genera and a few species only are known. One genus, *Mola*, with its single species is found in Queensland; the other genus, *Ranzania*, is included here as it most probably does frequent Queensland waters and will eventually be recorded.

KEY TO GENERA IN QUEENSLAND

A. Body ovate, not twice as long as deep; skin thick, rough, without hexagonal plates; lips not funnel-like. *Mola*

AA. Body oblong, about twice as long as deep; skin smooth, tessellated, with smooth hexagonal plates; lips produced forward beyond teeth like a funnel, closing as a vertical slit.

Ranzania

Mola

Body ovate, strongly compressed, with thick, rough skin. Gill-rakers concealed in thick skin.

Large sunfishes of most warm seas, some reaching at least 10 feet. Probably only a single species.

486. OCEAN SUNFISH *Mola mola* (Linnaeus) [Plate 63]

Tetrodon mola Linnaeus, Syst. Nat., 10th ed., 1758, pp. 334, 412; 12th ed., 1766, p. 412.
Orthagoriscus mola Schlegel, Fauna Japonica, Pisces, 1850, p. 288, pl. 127.

Skin very coarse and rough, especially in old examples, with patches of bony tubercles.

This giant grotesque fish of the open oceans is found in almost all parts of the world. According to Fraser-Brunner in his excellent paper on the ocean sunfishes[80] the largest record was of a male specimen which measured 10 feet 1 inch in length and 11 feet from tip of dorsal fin to tip of anal fin.

Some authors consider that *M. mola* is replaced in the South Pacific by *M. ramsayi*, a distinct species, but so little is known of these ocean giants and so few and sketchy notes have been made on those found, that until further knowledge is gained it is preferred to recognize only one species.

According to Fraser-Brunner the largest recorded sunfish from the South Pacific, as *M. ramsayi*, was one taken in Poverty Bay, New Zealand, in December 1889. It measured 9 feet 8 inches and was said to have weighed 3½ tons.

Apparently the first record of the sunfish in Queensland waters was in January 1929, when a fairly large one was shot and dragged ashore on Mooloolabah beach. It measured 9 feet in length and 8 feet from dorsal to anal fin-tips.

In November 1932 another specimen, this time a juvenile, was forwarded to the Queensland Museum by W. McHardy. It measured 2½ inches in total length and was disgorged from the stomach of a "King Snapper", probably *Lutjanus sebae*, which was caught forty miles east of Indian Head, Fraser Island, South Queensland, in 65 fathoms.

Although sunfishes are known to feed mainly upon plankton, there have been instances, both in Australian waters and elsewhere in the world, when an odd one has been captured on a baited hook. In California a 7½-pound specimen was taken on a hook baited with a sardine. Yet another was taken

---

[80] *Bull. Brit. Mus. Nat. Hist.* (*Zool.*), 1, no. 6, 1951, pp. 89-121, with text-figs 1-18.

on a hook baited with a live anchovy. In Australia a large sunfish weighing 1,000 pounds was caught on rod and line at Bermagui, New South Wales, in January 1937; the type of bait used was not stated. These occurrences are not unprecedented, however; there are other instances of plankton eaters varying their diet by taking baited hooks, one such being the Australian Devil Ray, *Manta alfredi*.

Ranzania

Form comparatively elongate, compressed. Skin smooth, with small hexagonal plates terminating at bases of dorsal and anal fins and clavus or pseudo-caudal. Lips produced beyond teeth as a funnel, closing as a vertical slit. Gill-rakers free. A single widely distributed pelagic species, not reaching a large size.

487. OBLONG SUNFISH *Ranzania laevis* (Pennant)   [Plate 63]

Ostracion laevis Pennant, Brit. Zool., 4th ed., 1776, 3, p. 129, pl. 19.
Ranzania makua Tanaka, Fish. Japan, 2nd ed., 1935, p. 274, pl. 76.

Apahu, Makua (Hawaii); Kusabi-fugu or Wedge-puffer (Japan).

Skin smooth, velvety. Colour: "Dark blackish-brown above, silvery on sides and belly; sides of head with a number of transverse silver bands, the first three on the snout with black margins, the other 4-6 with small black spots, and black margins only at ventral ends; sides of body with a network of bright silver bands, with small black spots, enclosing oval patches of dull greyish silver; back with irregular dark marks, hind end of body with dull bluish-silver spots, pectoral bluish-silvery; dorsal and anal black, 'tail' pinkish-brown or violaceous." (Barnard.)

Although recorded in Australian waters from Victoria and Western Australia this curious fish has not yet been taken in Queensland. It is included here on the assumption that it will eventually be captured.

A shoal of about fifty of this rarely seen species was cast up and stranded on the beach at Albany, Western Australia, in 1928.

The Oblong Sunfish grows to a length of only about 30 inches. Found in most ocean waters. Specimens secured should be forwarded to the nearest Fisheries Department or to a museum for examination, because little is known of them and they are needed for study.

The young are remarkable for their complete lack of resemblance to the adults, they being complete with tail and resembling much more an ordinary fish in form.

Order **XENOPTERYGII**

This order contains the single family Gobiesocidae, the cling-fishes. They are characterized by the presence of an elaborate sucking-disc on the ventral surface, not derived by modified fins but formed from lobes in the skin and the underlying muscles. The form of the body is somewhat elongate and without scales.

Family **Gobiesocidae: Cling-fishes**

Small, highly specialized, somewhat degenerate fishes, mainly marine, living in shallow coastal waters, often in the intertidal zone among loose stones and coral clinker. Widely distributed in most warm and tropical waters throughout the world.

They are feeble swimmers and spend most of their time firmly attached by the thoracic sucking-disc to various objects such as stones, etc., and withstanding strong currents and wave action. They are able to live for a considerable time out of water. Many genera and species are known, one genus with its single species, being found in Queensland.

Lepadichthys

Form slender, head not broad. A single row of teeth in each jaw. Dorsal and anal fins long, attached to caudal, the former of 9 to 17 rays, the latter of 8 to 15 rays.

There are four known species, inhabiting the waters of the Indian Ocean through the Indo-Pacific to Australia and Japan. One species in Queensland.

488. BRIDLED CLING-FISH *Lepadichthys frenatus* Waite   [Plate 63]

Lepadichthys frenatus Waite, Rec. Austr. Mus., 5, no. 3, 11th March 1904, p. 180, pl. 24, fig. 2.

D. 16 (15-17); A. 14 (12-15). Colour: "When preserved the general colour is pinkish yellow. The edge of the upper lip is bright scarlet, the colour continued as a streak which passes backward through the eye, towards the upper margin of the opercle. Fins colourless." (Waite.)

This curious little cling-fish was first recorded from Queensland in 1910 when J. D. Ogilby found it adhering to the underside of a piece of loose coral on Nor'-West Island, Capricorn Group. Later it was found on Hoskyn Island, Queensland. Found also at Lord Howe Island, South Pacific. It grows to at least 2 inches.

Order **HAPLODOCI**

Head depressed. Body naked or with small concealed scales. Spinous dorsal very short. Caudal fin distinct. Three gill-arches only. One family, widely distributed in tropical and temperate seas.

Family **Batrachoididae**: **Frogfishes**

Voracious carnivorous ground-fishes of small or moderate size inhabiting temperate and tropical seas, sometimes ascending rivers. In form they are robust, with head and anterior part of body more or less broad and depressed. The skin may be naked or with small cycloid scales. The mouth, which is large to moderate, is protractile, the dentition varying from obtusely conical teeth in a single series to narrow bands of small cardiform teeth. Opercles usually armed with strong spines. Three gills. Narrow gill-openings immediately in front of the pectoral fins; gill-membranes broadly united to isthmus.

Two dorsal fins, the first with 2 to 4 spines wholly concealed beneath the skin, detached from the long soft dorsal with its numerous branched rays, enveloped in loose folds of skin. Anal shorter but similar. Caudal usually free. Ventrals jugular, with 1 spine and 2 to 3 branched rays. Pectorals very broad. The young are able to adhere to rocks by means of a ventral disc which soon disappears with growth.

The family Batrachoididae, which is closely related to the Blenniidae, forms a connecting link between those fishes and the highly aberrant Lophiidae in the order Pediculati.

The habits of the frogfishes were remarked upon at some length by Ogilby, who stated:[81] "They may be briefly described as carnivorous ground-fishes of small or moderate size, inhabiting all intertropical and juxtatropical seas. Most of the species show a marked partiality for muddy ground, into which they burrow with great facility when danger threatens. They are for the most part littoral fishes, and even to some extent ascend tidal rivers, but many instances are on record of their capture at depths closely approaching the hundred-fathom line."

Ogilby further stated: "While not disdaining aught else, which chance may put in their way, their principal food consists of crustaceans and mollusks, the hard integuments of which their exceptional strength of jaw enables them to crush with ease. Like all other fishes in which the powers of locomotion are limited, they are compelled to resort to strategy in order to obtain in sufficient quantity even comparatively slow-moving prey; they are, therefore, in the habit of burying themselves in the mud leaving only a part of the head exposed, and possibly using the oral and supraciliary tentacles as lures for the unwary, much in the same manner as the angler-fishes (Antennariidae) employ the rostral tentacle."

Ogilby went on: "When living on ground into which they are unable to burrow, weeds serve the same purpose of concealment, and in either case the normal pattern of their coloration blends so thoroughly with their surroundings that detection is extremely difficult so long as they remain motionless. A very

---

[81] *Ann. Qld Mus.*, 9, 14th Oct. 1908, p. 43.

curious habit is mentioned by Gilbert—than whom no more acute and trust-worthy observer ever lived—when writing on one of our common Queensland species, *Halophryne diemensis*. He states that it 'is an inhabitant of the mud at the head of the harbour of Port Essington, where it may be frequently seen creeping over the surface after the tide has left. It is very difficult to capture, for, on the slightest appearance of danger it plunges down instan-taneously.' (Richardson, Ann. Mag. Nat. Hist., 11, 1843, p. 352.)"

Ogilby concluded by saying: "Though the flesh is firm, white, and to all appearance tempting to the palate, these fishes are rejected as food by all except the very poorest classes; it is probable that their rather repulsive ap-pearance may be to a large extent responsible for this repugnance; personally I have had no opportunity of testing their quality, but I am not aware of any practical reason why they should not be excellent eating. The ova of the frog-fishes are large, round, and few in number; they are probably attached either singly or in bunches to weeds or stones at the bottom, but on this point no definite information is at present available.[82] I have had the opportunity on three occasions of examining females in which the ova were fully matured, and improved the occasion by ascertaining the number and dimensions of the eggs; these are contained in a pair of oval sacs formed of delicate and transparent but strong tough and elastic tissue. In my first specimen (a) a *Batrachomoeus minor*,[83] caught in May, length 186 millim., the left ovary carried 62 eggs measuring from 3.5 to 5 millim. each; in (b), a *Coryzichthys diemensis* of 146 millim. in length, the right ovary contained 45 eggs with a size of from 4.5 to 5 millim. apiece; while the numbers in both ovaries of (c) — same species, length 160 millim. was $35 + 39 = 74$, measuring from 5.5 to 6.5 millim.; unfortunately no record of the date of capture is available in these two latter cases. In all three the enveloping skin was intact, proving that the full complement of ova were still *in situ*. The voracity of these fishes may be conceived from the fact that a specimen of *Batrachomoeus minor* in my possession had swallowed an octopus of so large a size that two of the arms were protruding fully an inch from its mouth, nevertheless this did not deter it from taking a prawn bait, and thereby paying the penalty for its gluttony."

Dr Cantor observed that at Penang "the natives attribute poisonous qualities to these fishes, and reject them even as manure". He also stated that they are capable of living a considerable time out of their element.[84]

Günther observed:[85] "Dr Günther has described a second species of this genus (*Thalassophryne* belonging to this family) *Th. reticulatus* from the Pacific

---

[82] In a note at this point, Ogilby wrote: "Barnard states (Ann. Sth Afr. Mus., 21, 1927, p. 991). 'The eggs are very large and are deposited in a rock crevice or beneath a stone where they are guarded by the male.' "

[83] *Batrachomoeus minor* is a synonym of *B. dubius*.

[84] *Cat. Mal. Fish., Journ. Asia. Soc. Bengal*, vol. 18, pt 2, July-Dec. 1849 (1850), p. 1188.

[85] *Zool. Rec.*, 1864, p. 165.

coast of Panama (Proc. Zool. Soc. 1864, p. 150). On examining this fish, he discovered a most singular apparatus which structurally is as perfect a poison-organ as that of the venomous serpents. Each operculum terminates in a long spine similar to the two dorsal spines; each spine is perforated at the extremity and at the base, and has a canal in its interior. The canal leads to a sac at the base of each spine, in which a considerable quantity of the poisonous substance was found; on the slightest pressure it flowed freely from the opening of the spine. The sacs are not the secretory organs, but merely the reservoirs in which the fluid secreted accumulates. The author believes he has found evidence that the real organ of secretion is the system of muciferous channels, or at least some portion of it."

Captain Dow stated:[86] "The natives seemed quite familiar with the existence of the spines, and of the emission from them of a poison, which, when introduced into a wound, caused fever; but in no case was a wound caused by one of them known to result seriously. The slightest pressure of the finger at the base of the spine caused the poison to jet a foot or more from the opening of the spine." Two genera are found in Queensland waters.

KEY TO GENERA IN QUEENSLAND

A. An axillary pore present. Teeth uniserial, strong, and
    conical.   *Batrachomoeus*
AA. No axillary pore. Teeth in narrow bands, acute and
    cardiform.   *Halophryne*

Batrachomoeus

Spines solid, without poison-sacs. Body scaleless. No canine teeth. Dorsal spines 3. Dorsal rays 18 to 22. Anal rays 15 to 18.

Voracious fishes of small or moderate size living at the bottom and in muddy localities along the coasts of Australia, New Guinea, the Malay Archipelago, and India, some entering the tidal rivers. Two species inhabit Queensland waters.

KEY TO SPECIES IN QUEENSLAND

A. Dorsal rays 19-20; anal rays 16; no frontonasal tentacle;
    supraciliary tentacles small; axillary pore large.   *dubius*
AA. Dorsal rays 21-22; anal rays 18; a frontonasal tentacle;
    supraciliary tentacles large; axillary pore minute.   *broadbenti*

489. FROGFISH *Batrachomoeus dubius* (White)   [Plate 63]

Lophius dubius White, Voy. N.S.Wales, 1790, p. 265, and opp. pl. (ex Shaw MS.).
Pseudobatrachus dubius McCulloch, Rec. West. Austr. Mus., 1, pt 3, 1914, p. 224, fig. 1.

D. 3/19-20; A. 15-16. Colour dark brown above, blotched or marbled with lighter; pale brown below, blotched with bluish-white; branchiostegal region mottled brown and white; dorsal, anal, caudal, and pectoral fins brown, with spots and bars of lighter colour.

---

[86] *Proc. Zool. Soc. Lond.*, 1865, p. 667.

A not uncommon species in the lower reaches of the Brisbane River and the muddy foreshores of Moreton Bay. It also enters fairly deep water and is occasionally taken by hook and line on the offshore snapper banks. Feeds upon shellfish and small crabs. Inhabits the east coast of Australia from northern New South Wales to Cape York in North Queensland, across Torres Strait to New Guinea. Grows to 14 inches.

OTHER SPECIES

Broadbent's Frogfish, *B. broadbenti*. A little-known fish from the east coast of Queensland, where it has been taken at Cardwell and Bundaberg and northwards to Cape York and into the Gulf of Carpentaria. Grows to 10 inches.

Halophryne

Body naked, spines solid, without poison sacs. Three dorsal spines. Two strong opercular spines. No canine teeth. No axillary pore. Dorsal rays 19 to 22. Anal rays 15 to 18.

Small voracious fishes living along the shores of the east coast of Australia and ranging also to New Guinea, Malaysia, and the shores of India. Their weaker dentition suggests that their food is chosen from worms and similar soft organisms, while the more brilliant coloration in some examples shows that they are not averse to dwelling on coral reefs. One species in Queensland.

490. BANDED FROGFISH *Halophryne diemensis* (Le Sueur)   [Plate 63]

Batrachoides diemensis Le Sueur, Journ. Acad. Nat. Sci. Philad., 3, 1823, p. 402.
Batrachus diemensis Richardson, Ichth. Voy. Erebus and Terror, 2, 1845, p. 17, pl. 8, figs 1-2.

Devil-fish (Townsville); Stone-fish (Palm Islands); Nohu (Port Moresby).

D. 19-21; A. 16-17. "Coloration varying from violet to purplish-black above and from pearl-grey to lilac below; tail usually with four broad, more or less connected lighter cross-bands, which are continued on the dorsal and anal fins, where they are inclined respectively forwards and backwards; sometimes the upper half of these bands is scarlet or orange, as also are the spinous dorsal and the cheeks; the bands are usually plentifully sprinkled with darker spots and dots; caudal fin lilac, with more or less conspicuous lighter transverse bars; pectorals and ventrals violaceous grey, with broad basal and median purple bands, or uniform purple." (Ogilby.)

Another colour variety from North Queensland has the throat and abdomen light yellowish-brown, closely mottled with dark brown and the pectorals brown with darker dots. Yet another is brownish, blotched everywhere with clear canary-yellow.

This very common and widely distributed species is found along the whole Queensland coastline from Moreton Bay to Cape York Peninsula and across

509

to the Northern Territory and Western Australia, and also in Torres Strait, New Guinea, and through the Indo-Australian Archipelago to south-western India.

In the Palm Islands, North Queensland, where this fish is extremely common, it is greatly feared by the natives and is known to them and to the white residents as the "Stone-fish". Whitley[87] notes: "Three specimens were caught at Michaelmas Cay, one of which was eating an octopus." Grows to 10½ inches.

Order **PEDICULATI**

Carpal bones notably elongate, forming a kind of arm with elbow-like bend (pseudobranchium) which supports the wide and powerful pectoral. Gill-opening reduced to a large or small foramen in or near pectoral axil, behind or below, rarely before, pectoral base. Ventral fins jugular if present. Spinous dorsal reduced to a few tentacle-like spines, mostly isolated, the anterior ones modified to form some kind of movable lure with tassels or fleshy lobes, or even luminous organs in the case of very deep-water forms. Soft dorsal and anal short. No scales.

Marine fishes, mostly inhabiting deep to very deep water. All are very poor swimmers and obtain their food by stealth and by angling with the dorsal spine and lure. The forms from shallower waters live among masses of floating seaweeds, often drifting long distances, or they may live on weed-covered bottoms. Three families are represented in the waters of Queensland.

KEY TO FAMILIES IN QUEENSLAND

A.   Head very wide, large, and depressed. Body contracted, conical and tapering.

    b. Gill-openings in or behind the lower axil of the pectoral. Mouth large, terminal.   LOPHIIDAE

    bb. Gill-openings in or behind the upper axil of the pectoral. Mouth small, usually inferior.   OGCOCEPHALIDAE

AA. Head elevated and compressed. Body not flattened, more or less compressed.   ANTENNARIIDAE

Family **Lophiidae: Fishing-frogs**

Head very wide, large, and depressed. Mouth very large, terminal, lower jaw projecting, upper jaw protractile; teeth in both jaws very strong, unequal, some canine-like, most of them depressible; vomer and palatines usually with strong teeth. Gill-openings comparatively large, in lower axils of pectorals. No gill-rakers. Skin mostly smooth, naked, with many dermal flaps

---

[87] *Rec. Austr. Mus.*, 16, 1927, p. 31.

about the head. Body contracted, conical, and tapering backward from the shoulders. Stomach enormous. Spinous dorsal in the form of more or less isolated tentacle-like spines on the head and back. Ventrals jugular. Pectoral elements scarcely geniculated, each with 2 actinosts and with elongate pseudo-branchia. Young with the head spinous.

A family of curious fishes living on the bottom of the sea at moderate or even great depths and remarkable for their extremely great voracity. Genera few, one in Queensland.

Lophiomus

Gill-opening not before the pectoral base above. Vertebrae 18 to 19 in number; 6 dorsal spines; 6 to 7 anal rays.

A small genus of fishing-frogs found in the deep waters of the Indo-Pacific regions. Species few, one in Queensland.

491. BROAD-HEADED FISHING-FROG *Lophiomus laticeps* (Ogilby)
[Plate 64]

Chirolophius laticeps Ogilby, New Fish. Qld Coast, 20th Dec. 1910, p. 136 (a suppressed publication).
Chirolophius (?) *laticeps* McCulloch, Biol. Res. Endeavour, 2, pt 3, 1914, pp. 79, 160, pl. 32 and text-fig. 15.

Colour: "Upper surface pale lilaceous brown, the dermal filaments and tentacles darker. Lower surface white. Tongue white with blackish, anasto-mosing lines anteriorly." (McCulloch.)

Only a few examples of this remarkable and apparently rare fish are known. The type, a specimen 184 mm. in standard length, was trawled 36 miles N. 12° E. off Cape Moreton, South Queensland, by the *Endeavour* on 3rd September 1910, in 73 fathoms, on fine sand and mud. A second example was secured by A. Ward in March 1927 when trawling off the Toll Gates a few miles north of Montagu Island, New South Wales, in about 40 fathoms. Grows to at least $7\frac{1}{4}$ inches. A third example was taken by Captain A. Nicolson of Lindeman Island, North Queensland, who picked it up dead upon the beach.

Family Ogcocephalidae: Sea-Bats

Head very broad, depressed, the not very large mouth subterminal or inferior; lower jaw included within upper. Teeth villiform or cardiform. Gill-openings very small, above and behind axils of pectorals. Body short and slender, both it and the head covered with bony tubercles and spines. Spinous dorsal reduced to a small rostral tentacle, which is retractile into a cavity under a prominence on the forehead, sometimes obsolete. Soft dorsal and anal small and short. Pectorals well developed, the bases strongly bent. Ventrals jugular, well developed.

Curious bottom-dwelling fishes, mainly of warm seas, some inhabiting shallow water but many found at considerable depths in the ocean. About eight genera and over thirty-five species are known, most of which are found in American waters. A single genus in Queensland.

Halieutaea

A small genus of anglers inhabiting the waters of the Indo-Pacific. A single species in Queensland.

492. SPINY SEA-BAT *Halieutaea brevicauda* Ogilby   [Plate 64]

Halieutaea brevicauda Ogilby, New Fish. Qld Coast, 1910, p. 138 (a suppressed publication).
Halieutaea brevicauda McCulloch, Biol. Res. Endeavour, 2, pt 3, 1914, p. 163, pl. 33.

Colour: "Upper surface lavender, the tail and edges of the disc shading to gray. Pectoral with a broad violet band crossing the distal half, and there is a similar submarginal band on the dorsal fin." (McCulloch.)

This grotesque angler was first known from a specimen 110 mm. in length which was trawled in 1910 by the *Endeavour* off Cape Moreton, South Queensland, in 73 fathoms. Other examples have since been taken off Wattamolla, New South Wales, in 68 fathoms, and also off Bay of Fires, Tasmania, in 45 fathoms. Grows to 6 inches.

Family **Antennariidae: Angler-fishes**

Fishes with the head and body more or less compressed and with the skin naked, smooth or prickly. Mouth vertical or very oblique, opening upwards; lower jaw projecting; premaxillaries protractile. Gill-openings small, pore-like, in or behind the lower axils of the pectorals. Ventral fins present, jugular, and near together. Spinous dorsal of 1 to 3 separate spines, the first tentacle-like. Soft dorsal long, larger than anal.

Fishes of the tropical seas, most of the members pelagic, rarely descending far below the surface, living on or among masses of floating seaweed or among coral reefs, and by filling their capacious stomachs with air able to remain upon the surface of the water, being therefore widely dispersed by the ocean's currents.

All anglers are fantastic in form, their colours variegated and often brilliant, harmonizing with their surroundings as they lie in wait for their prey, which is secured by means of a fleshy "rod and bait" suspended over their cavernous mouths. The rod and bait is formed by the first dorsal spine being modified into a tentacle-like rod which terminates in a fleshy tip. This lure is brought into play and waved to and fro over the mouth as the fish angles for its unsuspecting prey. The animal's creel is its cavernous stomach, which is able, in some instances, to hold prey much larger than itself. In the British Museum

512

is shown a deep-sea angler which had succeeded in swallowing a fish four times its own length and many times its own weight.

In American waters the name frogfishes is bestowed on these weird creatures, whilst in South Africa they are called toad-fishes.

KEY TO GENERA IN QUEENSLAND

A. Skin smooth and naked.

    b. Dorsal and anal fins separated from the caudal, the peduncle free. Last 2-3 dorsal rays and most anal rays branched.   *Histrio*

    bb. Dorsal and anal fins united with the caudal peduncle and bases of the rays. Dorsal and anal rays simple.   *Histiophryne*

AA. Skin rough, covered with small bristles or spinules, usually forked.

    c. Gill-openings small and pore-like. Anal opposite end of dorsal.   *Antennarius*

    cc. Gill-openings tubular. Anal behind dorsal.   *Tathicarpus*

Histrio

A small genus of wide-ranging fishes characterized by their smooth bodies and by the dorsal and anal fins being separated from the caudal. Species few, one in Queensland.

493. MARBLED ANGLER *Histrio histrio* (Linnaeus)   [Colour-plate 72]

Lophius histrio Linnaeus, Syst. Nat., 10th ed., 1758, p. 237; 12th ed., 1766, p. 403.
Illustration by G. Coates.

Mouse-fish, Frogfish (Americas); Sargassum-fish (America and South Africa).

D. 1 + 1 + 1 + 12-14. Colour: Head, body, and fins rich chestnut-brown or yellowish, variously marbled or banded with dark brown over body and fins; pectorals and ventrals brownish, becoming reddish-yellow terminally. The young are darker and with a few large whitish blotches on the body. Excessively variable in colour.

In this little fish the skin is smooth or granular, but without spines. The skin of the head and body, as well as the dorsal fins, is covered with fleshy appendages or tags, which are sometimes absent in the very young.

A circumtropical pelagic fish which lives in masses of floating seaweed. Known in Australian seas only from Queensland and New South Wales. Grows to 5 inches.

Histiophryne

A genus of anglers found mainly in the waters of South Australia, but occurring also in New South Wales and Queensland. Their chief distinctive character is that the dorsal and anal fins are united by membrane to the caudal peduncle and bases of the rays. Several species, only one in Queensland.

494. SMOOTH ANGLER *Histiophryne bougainvilli* (Cuvier and Valenciennes)
[Plate 64]

Chironectes bougainvilli Cuvier and Valenciennes, Hist. Nat. Poiss., 12, March 1837, p. 431.
Histiophryne bougainvilli McCulloch and Waite, Rec. Sth Austr. Mus., 1, 1918, p. 72, pl. 7, fig. 1.

D. 1 + 1 + 1 + 15; A. 8; C. 9. Colour: "Bright yellow with faint greyish reticulations and a few large and irregular rusty patches on sides and behind pectorals; eye green." (Whitley.)

An Australian species which has been recorded from Queensland, South Australia, and New South Wales. In Queensland it was first known from an example taken at Heron Island, in the Capricorns, by A. A. Cameron. Rarely seen. Grows to about 2 inches.

Antennarius

Skin rough, prickly. Head and body usually with skinny flaps and filaments. Soft dorsal and anal fins not joined to caudal. Pelvics small.

The members of this genus vary greatly in both colour and form and often great difficulty is experienced in determining the species. The variability is so great that scarcely two examples will be found which are exactly alike. This applies not only to the coloration but to the spines and body appendages, which are more developed with age, to the length and flexibility of the second and third dorsal spines, and to the form of the tentacle over the snout.

The genus contains many species found in the warm seas, seven being recorded from Queensland.

KEY TO SPECIES IN QUEENSLAND

A. Body marked with blackish stripes.

    b. Brownish or yellowish, with blackish parallel streaks which radiate from eye and break into spots on belly.   *striatus*

    bb. Yellowish, irregularly or more sparingly spotted or streaked with brown; radiating streaks from eye often absent.   *striatus* var. *pinniceps*

AA. Body not striped.

> c. Caudal with 3 series of transparent black-edged ocelli on the membranes between the rays.
>
> d. Yellow, densely spotted all over with brown; a large yellow patch with a black spot in its centre, about the middle of the base of dorsal. *asper*
>
> cc. No ocelli on caudal, though bands or spots may be present.
>
> e. A black yellow-edged ocellus between seventh and eighth dorsal rays, and another behind and above end of base of pectoral fin. *nummifer*
>
> ee. No ocellus on dorsal fin.
>
> f. Colour usually blackish (sometimes red or yellowish), with blotches of white or rose-colour; pectorals and ventrals usually white-edged. *moluccensis*
>
> ff. Blackish, densely overlaid with irregular lichen-like patches of pink and greyish-brown. *goramensis*
>
> fff. Brownish; a large whitish blotch (yellow in life?) on middle of side above base of pectoral. *stigmaticus*

495. STRIPED ANGLER *Antennarius striatus* (Shaw and Nodder) [Plate 64]

Lophius striatus Shaw and Nodder, Nat. Miscell., 5, 1794, pl. 175.
Antennarius striatus Günther, Fische der Sudsee, 5, 1876, p. 162, pl. 99, fig. B.

Striped Toad-fish (South Africa).

D. 1 + 1 + 1 + 12. First spine divided into 3 flaps. Colour brownish or yellowish, with blackish parallel streaks which radiate from the eye and break up into spots on belly; all fins more or less barred with large black spots.

A very common angler inhabiting the waters of the Indo-Malayan regions and the east coast of Queensland and New South Wales. Though common in South Queensland and New South Wales it is seldom met with in the far north of Queensland. Occurs also in South Africa. Grows to 7 inches.

496. BLACK ANGLER *Antennarius moluccensis* (Bleeker) [Plate 64]

Antennarius moluccensis Bleeker, Nat. Tijds. Ned. Ind., 8, 1885, p. 414.
Antennarius commersonii Bleeker, Atlas Ichth., 5, 1865, p. 20; pl. 197, fig. 3.

D. 1 + 1 + 1 + 13-14. Colour variable; usually dark brown or blackish, almost uniform or with some white or rose-coloured spots; pectoral and ventral fins white-edged. Some varieties are pale brown, red, or yellowish, with spots or blotches of greyish or black.

In this species, as in most of the anglers, the stomach is capable of great distension. A specimen in the Queensland Museum measuring $6\frac{1}{4}$ inches in total length when opened was seen to have in its stomach a silver-belly, *Gerres* sp., $5\frac{3}{4}$ inches long.

A widely distributed fish which, in Australian seas, is known from the Northern Territory, Queensland, New South Wales, and Lord Howe Island. It grows to 12 inches.

OTHER SPECIES

Ticked Angler, *A. striatus* var. *pinniceps*. A colour variety of the former *A. striatus* in which the stripes and spots on the body and fins are not so well developed as in that species. Wide-ranging, and in Australian waters known from South Queensland and from New South Wales. Not commonly seen. Grows to 7 inches.

Argus Angler, *A. asper*. A species known only from Torres Strait, North Queensland. A specimen in the Queensland Museum from Thursday Island measures $5\frac{1}{2}$ inches.

Scarlet Angler, *A. nummifer*. A wide-ranging species which has been recorded from the coasts of Queensland and New South Wales. An example was trawled off Wollongong, New South Wales, in 55 fathoms by the *Thetis* in 1898. In Queensland it is known from a single example taken in Moreton Bay, South Queensland. Grows to $6\frac{1}{2}$ inches.

Baggy Angler, *A. goramensis*. A species found in the seas of Oceania and the East Indies and known in Australian waters from a single example which was vomited from the gullet of a Queensland groper, *E. lanceolatus* as it lay on the deck of a vessel in North Queensland. The groper was caught by line at a depth of 24 fathoms and the Baggy Angler was alive when disgorged. It is very probable that this species is yet another colour variety of *A. commersoni*, which it closely resembles. Grows to 12 inches.

White-spot Angler, *A. stigmaticus*. Known only from the unique type specimen which was captured in Moreton Bay. It measured 98 mm. in length, and from its enormously distended stomach was taken a specimen of *Holocentrus* measuring no less than 108 mm.—that is, 37 mm. more than the body of its captor not including the tail.

Tathicarpus

Skin dotted with small tubercles, each bearing a bifid spinule. Jaws, vomer, and palatines with strong unequal cardiform teeth. Gill-openings tubular. Anal behind the dorsal.

A genus of Australian fishes known only from the waters of Queensland. One species.

497. HARLEQUIN ANGLER *Tathicarpus muscosus* Ogilby [Plate 64]

Tathicarpus muscosus Ogilby, Proc. Roy. Soc. Qld, 20, 2nd Jan. 1907, pp. 20, 22.
Tathicarpus muscosus McCulloch, Proc. Linn. Soc. N.S.Wales, 40, 1915, p. 277, pl. 37, fig. 4.

D. $1 + 1 + 1 + 11$. Colour in life a brilliant orange or brownish, the whole densely spotted and streaked with blackish or greenish spots, bars, or ocelli. Colour very variable. Most examples have an irregular black blotch on the body above the arm-like pectoral fin, which stands out distinct from the other body markings. The first dorsal spine is extremely fine and hair-like and terminates in the usual fleshy "bait".

A curious fish known by its numerous "mossy" filaments. It is fairly common on the coast of Queensland and has also been recorded from Shark Bay, Western Australia, and from north-west Australia. Grows to $4\frac{1}{2}$ inches.

GLOSSARY

GLOSSARY

Abdomen: Belly.

Abdominal: Pertaining to the belly.

Aberrant: Diverging from the normal type.

Actinosts: A series of bones at the bases of the pectoral rays.

Acuminate: Tapering gradually to a point.

Acute: Sharp-pointed.

Adipose: Fleshy or fatty; applied to small rayless fins, and to eyelids.

Adpressed: Pressed against the body.

Air-bladder: A sac filled with gas, lying beneath the backbone.

Anal: Pertaining to the anal fin or area of anus.

Anal fin: The fin on the median line behind the vent.

Anal papilla: A fleshy projection at the vent.

Anastomosing: Interjoining.

Anguilliform: Eel-like.

Ankylosed: Grown firmly together.

Annular: Ring-like.

Anterior: Relating to the front portion.

Antero-median: Forward of the middle.

Antero-supraorbital: Above and before the eye.

Antrorse: Turned forward; usually refers to barbs or spines.

Anus: The external opening of the intestine; the vent.

Appressed: Pressed close to or lying flat against.

Approximate: Placed close together.

Arborescent: Tree-like in growth or appearance.

Asperity: Roughness of surface.

Asymmetrical: Without symmetry.

Attenuated: Drawn out, slender.

Axillary: Pertaining to the axilla or upper angle of the pectoral fin.

Barbel: An elongated fleshy projection, usually about the mouths of fishes.

Basal or basally: Pertaining to the base; at or near the base.

Bicuspid: Having two cusps or points; usually refers to teeth.

Bifid: Cleft in two.

Bifurcate: Forked.

Boss: A protuberance.

Branchiae: Gills; respiratory organs of fishes.

Branchial: Pertaining to the gills.

Branchiostegals: Bony rays supporting the gill-membranes below the opercular bones.

Bristle: A stiff hair-like projection.

Buccal: Referring to the mouth.

Buckler: A bony shield.

Caecum: Blind sac-like appendage connected with the alimentary canal at the posterior end of the stomach.

Canines: Conical teeth which are longer than the others.

Caniniform: In the form of canines.

Caninoid: Like canines.

Carapace: A horny or bony covering encasing the body.

Cardiform: Refers to slender teeth, coarse and sharp like wool cards.
Carinate: Keeled; having a ridge along the middle line.
Carpal: Of the wrist.
Cartilage, cartilaginous: Gristle, gristly.
Caudal: Pertaining to the tail.
Caudal fin: Fin at or on the tail.
Caudal peduncle: Region between anal and caudal, and dorsal and caudal, fins.
Cephalic: Pertaining to the head region.
Cephalic fin: Detached part of pectoral fin on the head of certain rays.
Chin: Space in front of the lower jaw.
Cilia: Eyelashes or similar fringe of hair-like organ on animal and vegetable tissue.
Ciliated: Fringed with eyelash-like projections.
Circuli: Concentric lines on scales.
Cirri: Fringes.
Cirrus: Appendage or fringe.
Claspers: Male reproductive organs attached to the ventral fins of sharks, rays, skates.
Coalesced: Grown together.
Confluent: Joined together.
Conical: Cone-shaped; with a cylindrical base and pointed tip.
Corselet: A scaly covering behind the pectorals of some fishes.
Cranium, cranial: The skull, pertaining to the skull.
Crenulate: Having the edge slightly scalloped.
Ctenoid: Rough-edged; minutely spiny.
Cusped: With a peak or point.
Cuspidate: Of (the nature of) a cusp.
Cutaneous: Pertaining to the skin.
Cycloid: Smooth-edged (refers to scales).

Deciduous: Easily shed; falling off or temporary.
Dendritic: Resembling a tree or shrub.
Dentate, denticulate: With tooth-like projections.
Denticle: A little tooth; having an edge with small projecting teeth.
Dentition: Characteristic arrangement of teeth in animal.
Depressed: Flattened vertically, as in skates and rays.
Depth: Usually refers to vertical diameter of body.
Dermal: Pertaining to the skin.
Dextral: Referring to right-handed flat-fishes. A flat-fish with both eyes on the right side is referred to as dextral.
Disc: The flattened head and body of various fishes, which also commonly includes the pectoral and ventral fins.
Distal: Remote from the point of attachment.
Dorsal: Pertaining to the back.

Edentulous: Without teeth.
Elongate: Extended; drawn out.
Emarginate: With the margin slightly hollowed.
Entire: With a smooth margin.
Erectile: Susceptible of being raised or erected.
Estuarine: Living in estuaries.

Falcate: Sickle-shaped; long, narrow, and curved.
Falciform: Curved like a scythe.

Fasciae: Bands.
Filament: A thread.
Filiform: Thread-like.
Fimbriate: Fringed at the margin.
Fluviatile: Living in rivers.
Foliate: Leaf-like.
Foramen: Orifice, hole, passage.
Forehead: Frontal curve of the head.
Fossa: A pit or depression.
Furcate: Forked.
Fusiform: Spindle-shaped.

Geniculated: Having a knee-like joint.
Gibbous: Convex, protuberant.
Gill-arches: The bony arches to which gills are attached.
Gill-membranes: Membranes covering the gill-openings, attached to the branchiostegals.
Gill-openings: Openings behind the head, leading to the gills.
Gill-rakers: A series of appendages along the anterior edges of the gill-arches.
Gills: Branchiae; organs for breathing the air contained in water.
Glossohyal: The tongue bone.
Granulate: Finely roughened.
Granules: Grains.
Gular plate: A plate covering the upper part of the throat.

Heptagonal: Seven-sided.
Heterocanth: Lying alternately broader and narrower; used in relation to the spines.
Hexagonal: Six-sided.
Humerus, humeral: Bone of the upper arm, and pertaining thereto.
Hyaline: Without colour, clear, glass-like.
Hypocoracoid: The lower of the two bones attached to the clavicle.
Hypural joint: The joint of the caudal fin with the last of the vertebrae.

Imbricate: Overlapping, like shingles on a roof.
Incisiform: In the form of incisors.
Incisors: The front or cutting teeth.
Infraorbitals: Arch of small bones along lower edge of eye.
Interdorsal: Between the dorsal fins.
Intermaxillary: Between the maxillaries.
Interopercle: Membrane bone attached between preopercle and branchiostegals.
Interorbital: The space between the orbits.
Intramarginal: Within the margin.
Isthmus: The fleshy projection of the chest separating the gill-openings.

Jugular: Pertaining to the throat; placed below the throat.
Juxtaposed: Placed side by side.

Labial: Pertaining to the lips.
Laminae: Thin layers or plates of bone, skin, or other tissue.
Lanceolate: Spear-shaped; gradually tapering towards the extremity.
Lateral: At or towards the side.
Lateral line: A series of muciferous tubes forming a raised line along each side of the body.
Lunate: Shaped like a crescent moon.

Mandible: The lower jaw.
Margaritaceous: Pearly.
Marmorated: Mottled.
Maxilla or maxillary: The upper jaw, or pertaining thereto.
Maxillaries: The hindmost bones of the upper jaw, preceded by the premaxillaries.
Median, medially: Pertaining to the middle.
Mediolateral: Between the middle and the sides.
Mesial: Pertaining to the middle.
Mesocoracoid: A bone of the pectoral arch or shoulder girdle.
Milt: Testes; the white "roe".
Molars: Blunt or rounded grinding teeth, usually posterior in the jaws.
Muciferous: Producing or containing mucus or slime.
Multicuspid: With many cusps.

Nape: The part of the neck adjoining the skull.
Nasal: Pertaining to the nostrils.
Nasoral: Between the nostrils and the mouth.
Nictitating membrane: An inner eyelid.
Nuchal: Pertaining to the nape.

Obsolete: Faintly marked or scarcely evident.
Obtuse: Blunt.
Occipital: Pertaining to the occiput or back of the head above.
Occiput: The hind part of the skull.
Ocellate, ocellus: An eye-like spot.
Oesophagus: The gullet.
Opercle or operculum: Gill-cover. The posterior membrane bone of the side of the head.
Orbicular: Circular.
Orbit: The eye-socket.
Osseus: Bony.
Ossified: Turned into bone; hardened.
Ovate: Egg-shaped.
Oviparous: Producing eggs developed after exclusion from the body, as in most fishes.
Ovoviviparous: The young are born alive from the egg hatched within the mother.

Palate: The roof of the mouth.
Palatines: Membrane bones on each side of the palate.
Palmate: Palm-shaped.
Papilla: A small fleshy projection.
Papillose: Covered with papillae.
Parallelepiped: Solid, contained by parallelograms.
Parietal: Bone on each side of the head above.
Pectinate: Shaped like a comb.
Pectoral: Pertaining to the breast.
Pectoral fins: The anterior or uppermost of the paired fins, which correspond to the anterior limbs of the higher vertebrates.
Peduncle: The stalk or basal support of the tail.
Pelagic: Living on or in the open sea.
Pelvic: Pertaining to the hind paired fins or the bony girdle which supports them.
Pelvis: The bones to which the hind limbs or ventral fins are attached.
Penultimate: The last but one.
Pharyngeal bones: Bones behind the gills in the oesophagus or gullet.

Pharynx: The cavity between the mouth and oesophagus.
Pluriserial: Consisting of several rows.
Polygonal: Many-sided.
Posterior: Relating to the hinder portion.
Postocular: Behind the eye.
Postorbital: Behind the eye.
Postventral: Behind the ventral.
Preanal: Before the anal.
Precaudal: Anterior to the tail portion.
Predorsal: Before the dorsal.
Prehensile: Capable of grasping.
Premaxillaries: Two bones forming the front portion of the upper jaw.
Premolars: Small grinders or teeth; between canines and true molars.
Prenuchal: Before the nape.
Preocular: Before the eye.
Preopercle: The membrane bone between the cheek and the gill-cover.
Preoral: Before the mouth.
Preorbital: Usually large membrane bone before the eye.
Procumbent: Directed forward.
Protractile: Capable of being extended.
Proximal: Nearest, usually basal.
Pseudobranchiae: Small gills developed on the inner side of the gill-covers.
Pterygoids: Two lateral bones situated in the upper and rear mouth region.
Pubic bones: Same as pelvic bones.
Pungent: Sharp-pointed.

Quadrangular: Four-sided.

Radial: Arranged like rays.
Radius: Outer bone of forearm.
Ramus: One branch or one half of the jaw.
Ray: A cartilaginous jointed rod which supports the membrane of the fin.
Rectilinear: Formed or bounded by straight lines.
Recurved: Curving upward.
Reticulate: In the form of a network.
Retrorse: Turned backward.
Rhombic: Diamond-shaped.
Roe: Ova or eggs.
Rostral: Pertaining to the snout.
Rostrum: A projecting snout or beak.
Rugose: Rough.

Scapula: Shoulder-blade; a bone of the shoulder-girdle.
Scute: An external horny or bony plate.
Second dorsal: Posterior or soft part of a dorsal fin when the two parts are separated.
Serrate: Notched like a saw.
Setae: Bristles or hairs.
Setiform: In the form of bristles.
Sinistral: Of, on, the left.
Soft dorsal: The posterior part of the dorsal fin which is composed of jointed rays.
Spatulate: Spoon-shaped.
Spine: A sharp projecting point; an unjointed support in the anterior portion of the dorsal and anal fins.

Spinigerous: Spiny.

Spinous, spiniform, spinate: Spine-like or composed of spines.

Spinous dorsal: The anterior part of the dorsal fin supported by spines.

Spinule: A small spine.

Spiracles: Openings behind the eye in sharks and rays.

Squamation: Scales.

Stellate: Star-like or with radiating ridges.

Striae, striated: Stripes; striped or streaked.

Sub- (a prefix): Less than, somewhat, not quite, under, etc.

Subcaudal: Lower lobe of the tail, as in many sharks.

Subfusiform: Somewhat spindle-shaped.

Subopercle: Bone below the opercle, suture of connection hidden by scales.

Suborbital: Below the eye.

Superciliary: Above the orbit; over a brush-like process.

Superior: Above or on the upper surface.

Supralateral: Above the side.

Supramaxillary: A supplemental bone lying along the upper edge of the maxillary.

Suprascapular: A bone uniting the shoulder-girdle with the skull.

Suture: The line of union of two bones or plates.

Swim-bladder: A sac filled with gas and which lies beneath the backbone.

Symmetrical: Similarly arranged on both sides.

Symphysial: Of the junction of the jaws.

Symphysis: Point of junction of two parts of the jaw.

Synonym: A different word having the same or a similar meaning.

Temporal: Pertaining to the temples.

Terminal: At the end.

Tessellated: Marked with checks or squares like a mosaic.

Tetragonal: Four-sided.

Thoracic: Pertaining to the chest.

Transverse: Crosswise.

Trenchant: Compressed to a sharp edge.

Tricuspid: With three cusps or points.

Trilobate: With three lobes.

Truncate: Terminating abruptly, as if cut off square.

Tubercle: A small excrescence, like a pimple.

Tubiform or tubuliform: In the form of, resembling, a tube.

Undulated: Waved.

Undulous: Wavy.

Uniform (as applied to coloration): Of one colour.

Vent: The external opening of the alimentary canal; anus.

Ventral: Pertaining to the abdominal or lower surface.

Ventral fins: Paired fins below or behind the pectorals.

Venules: Small veins.

Vermiculating: Forming a pattern of wavy worm-like lines.

Vertical fins: Fins on the median line of the body; the dorsal, anal, and caudal fins.

Vestigial: As a remnant, rudimentary.

Villi: Minute finger-like processes.

Villiform teeth: Slender and small teeth forming velvety bands.

Viviparous: Bringing forth living young.

Vomer: A bone forming the front part of the roof of the mouth.

INDEX

INDEX OF SCIENTIFIC NAMES

The numbers refer to pages

528

S

INDEX OF VERNACULAR NAMES

The numbers refer to pages

560

566

Cover design by Quinton F. Davis

Photo-litho reproductions by Ralfs and Hermsdorf, Sydney

Colour plates printed by S. and A. Wheeler, Sydney

Text set Monotype in 10 on 12 point Times Roman
and printed on Burnie Special Offset paper by Halstead Press, Sydney

Bound in Sundour and Winterbottom buckram by Halstead Press, Sydney